THE NATURAL BENT

THE
NATURAL
BENT

Lionel Fielden

But a fool must follow his natural bent
(Even as you and I!)
KIPLING - THE VAMPIRE

ANDRE DEUTSCH

FIRST PUBLISHED SEPTEMBER 1960 BY
ANDRE DEUTSCH LIMITED
12-14 CARLISLE STREET SOHO SQUARE
LONDON W I
SECOND IMPRESSION OCTOBER 1960
COPYRIGHT © 1960 BY LIONEL FIELDEN
PRINTED IN HOLLAND BY
DRUKKERIJ HOLLAND N.V., AMSTERDAM

AUTHOR'S NOTE

DIFFIDENCE SUGGESTS some brief explanation of the origin of this very personal book. Throughout my life I have kept a series of irregular but detailed diaries: they died away when my life seemed humdrum, flowered when it appeared interesting: I suppose that they were the result of an itch to write. Once I showed some of them to a publisher, with the result chronicled on page 279. After that, they lay unregarded for twelve years. Then my friend Alan Moorehead, while staying with me in Italy, showed interest in my description of Gallipoli, and read my scribbles about it. As a result, he wrote his admirable book on that campaign, which he dedicated to me. And I, as a result of that, wondered whether, after all, these notes on my life might be of interest to others. I hope that they may be so.

My thanks are due to Lettice Cooper, Lucy Moorehead and Santha Rama Rau, all of whom took immense trouble in reading the MS and indicating how I could best make the immense cuts required by the exigencies and costs of printing. Without their guidance, the task would have baffled me.

Although I have made many personal deductions from personal experience, this is not a moral tale: its intention is to amuse and entertain, and thus, in my own small coinage, repay a tiny part of the debt I owe to English literature.

L. F.

Then how should I begin
To spit out all the butt-ends of my ways and days?

No, I am not Prince Hamlet, nor was meant to be:
Am an attendant lord, one that will do
To swell a progress, start a scene or two . . . .

T. S. ELIOT - THE LOVE SONG OF J. ALFRED PRUFROCK

'It's a funny business,' my father said at last. 'I don't seem to get any
further with it at all. I wonder if we've taken the wrong track - I won-
der if everyone's always been wrong?'

C. P. SNOW - THE SEARCH

Chapter One

'EVERY TIME THAT you are naughty,' said Nannie, pinning together
on the top of her head the tapes which secured the large white
bow under her scraggy chin, 'a jewel falls from your mother's
crown in Heaven.' I heard it fall. I saw it drop. Clearly,
accusingly, leaned out towards me from the blue sky that fearful
dilapidated tiara. My aunt, reading the Bible to me while I
guzzled bread-and-milk in bed, said: 'You see, to be a Minister
of Christ is the highest calling: or even a missionary of His
Gospel.' A missionary, I thought, might do: travel, the cannibal-
istic pot. Grandmamma, incredibly elegant in silk and lace and
diamonds, whispered confidentially: 'You must learn to sit still
and not fidget: and also, that *nothing* matters.' At the age of five
I was commanded to read the first *Times* leader to her every
morning: she told me later that she had found it more intelligible
and amusing, and less ponderous, that way. Mitchell, the head
gardener, an endearing man with a fine black bushy beard, told
me: 'If you stick to gardening, you won't go far wrong in life.'
I did not profit by that sage advice.

'If,' said my stepmother, 'you don't eat this nice boiled cabbage
for luncheon, you will have it again for tea and then for supper,
and, if necessary, for breakfast tomorrow.' Those wet squares of
cabbage haunt me still: I cannot think of food except as a kind
of medicine. 'Why,' asked the headmaster of my private school,
'can't you be like other boys?' I did not know the answer to that
one. He padded around in sneakers, carrying a fives bat, and
hoping to catch someone in a delicious *flagrante delicto*. 'I
intend,' said my father, 'to engage a tutor for your holidays: he
will see that you have a cold bath, and attend the riding school.'
Hot baths and no horses became two of my chief aims in life.
'I shall expel you,' said the Headmaster of Eton, 'if you attempt
to leave the Officers Training Corps.' I passionately believed him
to be wrong, but could not call his bluff. 'If you don't,' said my
father in 1914, 'join the Public Schools Battalion tomorrow, I
shall cut you off with a shilling.' I did not join. But, three weeks
later, white feathers pushed me into the Army.

'This officer,' wrote the General, quite unjustifiably, 'is too young to command a battery.' Demoted to Captain. 'Not the right type for the Diplomatic Service,' noted the Committee at Burlington House. Probably not: still, I had sweated my guts out to pass the Foreign Office examination: many thanks for nothing. 'A brilliant fellow,' wrote Sir Eric Drummond, Secretary-General of the League of Nations, 'but unreliable.' In spite of that, I am invited by the Italian Government to go to Rome and supervise the records of the Genoa Conference: six pounds a day. I throw it over because the Dutch Government asks me to take a staff of translators and interpreters to the Hague: seven pounds a day. But I am bowled over by Fridjof Nansen, who says I may go with him to Greece and Asia Minor to save refugees: nothing a day. I go. Nansen writes warmly: 'Thank you for all that you have done: I am afraid that our organisation will have to pack up for lack of funds.' Thirty-four nations had contributed thirty-two thousand pounds. Pause, while I think I will be a painter, and live gloriously in Italy on twopence a day: no, it doesn't work. 'Really, Mr Fielden,' says Lord Parmoor, Lord President of the Council, 'I shall have to get another secretary if you are so very casual.' Quite right too: I had had enough of Westminster and a Labour Government to last me for two lifetimes. 'A very fertile brain and a charming person,' wrote Sir John Reith to Margot Oxford, 'but, political judgement – I ask you!' Well now, who would you say has had political judgement, I wonder.

The Home Secretary of the Government of India noted: 'Fielden goes to see Gandhi against my express orders: I think that there is a case for declaring him to be of unsound mind.' Gandhi, chuckling on his *charpoy* and consulting a huge turnip watch, remarked: 'You must leave me now, dear child: but remember that there is no place for a milk-and-water liberal in this armed camp: of course, if you wish to have a job by virtue of the guns behind you, that is your affair.' The Viceroy mumbled over a mammoth silver inkpot: 'We ah verah conscious of yourah woahk and sacrahfahcies, but I amah afrahaid we cannotah ... extendah your contract.' With relish I replied: 'If ah haveah doneah anyathing, your Excellencyahcy, it has beenah in the teearth of yourah opposition.' Nevertheless, the King, stammering, draped a CIE over my head.

Freddy Ogilvie, new Director-General of the BBC, murmured: 'I have no option but to accept your resignation.' Perfectly correct: I had had the extraordinary idea that Nation-should-speak-peace-unto-Nation. At the Ministry of Food Lord Woolton growled: 'If you must persist in employing conscientious objectors...' At the Ministry of Aircraft Production Sir Archibald Rowlands was more candid: 'I don't know, Lionel, what you are belly-aching about: you have a good salary and not much to do.' But I had had enough of the factories of death and the lying eulogies of workers in them. Surprisingly, out of the blue, I became Editor-on-trial (a short trial) of the *Observer*. Waldorf Astor, ever kind and courteous, said over lunch at the Holborn Restaurant: 'You write very well, my dear Audax, even Bernard Shaw says so, but I do want you to outwrite Scrutator.' But I could not outwrite Scrutator: war strategy bored me stiff. My thoughts are turning to embusqués chickens in the country when a War Office letter flutters on to my table. Italy. The little King pacing up and down in Brindisi. 'At least I have saved the House of Savoy: but oh! my coins!' Mason MacFarlane grunts at me and I could get on with him if he were not surrounded by so many feckless advisers. Admiral Ellery Stone, U.S.Navy is quite another proposition. 'After this Matthews affair, I shall have to intervene personally with the President to get you replaced.' Okay by me: another fruitless war is over anyhow. Let America reign. Aeroplane from Rome to Cornwall, of all places. My father is dead: and after all I am not cut off with a shilling. A hundred and twenty thousand pounds. Quite something. I am fifty years old: what shall I do now? Not the vaguest idea. Death duties forty thousand, debts twenty-five thousand, legacies twenty thousand, lawyers two thousand – am I really signing all these colossal cheques? Not so much after all. Still, I have never had capital before. Should I go on working? Perhaps I must.

Lord Wright growls angrily: 'If you must resign in this tempestuous manner, you will kindly remember that you are not at liberty to divulge what you have learned in the Allied War Crimes Commission.' What I had learned, I said, was that victorious nations were vindictive. I added, just for fun, that I should publish every detail. 'If you do –' spluttered Lord Wright. But no, I had had enough of bureaucracy. I would go to Italy, home of the irresponsible and the warm-hearted. There, in a lovely house with a lovely garden and an extensive view, I would forget the world. Easier said than done. The world continued to annoy me. I grunted and muttered about it. I was getting old. 'Sour grapes!' said my friends.

Not quite what one had expected, certainly. I have gone wrong. I am out of step. Where did that start? Since my mother died, rather melodramatically, when I was nine months old, my only impressions of her are derived from old photographs, a few facts, and some hearsay. Evidently she was very handsome, according to hearsay she was wildly impulsive, and her musical compositions, some of which are still procurable, suggest a charming talent in the manner of Chaminade. She was certainly very popular. She had no money. To her greatest friend, later my godmother, she confided that she had married my father because he looked like Sir George Alexander: a rather slight foundation for a life partnership. My father may have looked like that: he was in fact more like Mr Jorrocks without the gaiety.

There they were, then, happily wed in the year 1895, and settled, as my father's mania for hunting dictated, in the depths of the country. And they were depths. The house was twenty miles from a railway station, gained only by trit-trot. One January evening, when snow was beginning to fall, my father, returning from hunting, slid from his horse at the drive gates. He was picked up unconscious and carried into the house. Specialists summoned (and they must have taken some time to arrive) declared that he had serious and incurable heart disease. He would never be able to walk upstairs, much less ride a horse, again. He was then about thirty years old. He proceeded to hunt every day until he died of cancer in his eightieth year. So much for specialists.

My mother, nursing devotedly (but I should guess scattily), had called in a sister-in-law to help her. One day she said: 'I have a frightful pain, and I think I am going to die.' She was right. Specialists summoned again made a hideously wrong diagnosis, operated there and then (under conditions which one flinches to think about), and killed her. My father, still half-conscious, was dragged to her bed to say goodbye. No one expected him to survive. My mother's brother, an unattractive gadfly who later became Mayor of Tunbridge Wells, had been sent for, and sat by her bedside recording her last words. I still have those strange yellowing pages. Perhaps death makes us all altruistic: perhaps my mother really was so. Most of her remarks are concerned with people in the village, to whom soup or bandages or medicines should continue to be sent: there is a passage, not ironic, 'thanking the doctors for all that they had done': there is a wish that I should be brought up by a specified aunt: and a direction that her dowry of twenty-five thousand pounds should go to her brother, where indeed it went and disappeared. The concluding phrase, 'I am quite comfortable now', gives me an optimistic feeling about death.

As the upshot of all this, my father disappeared for seven years, and I was sent to live with my grandmother and three maiden aunts in an enormous house in Surrey.

I have a persistent belief that my grandmother was a remarkable woman. However, I am wary about this, as I know that grandmothers are apt to become legendary. Nevertheless, her pictures prove beyond doubt that she had unusual beauty and unusual serenity, qualities which she never lost even when, in her hundredth year, sitting upright in a chair and looking exquisite, she imperceptibly breathed her last. I knew her daily and hourly for the first seven years of my life, and for the ensuing twenty-five of hers saw her as often as I could. No other human being has ever made on me the same impression of unruffled dignity and complete unselfishness. I never saw her show a trace of anger or exasperation. Her favourite phrase was: 'It doesn't signify.' But she was not indifferent to people or things: far from it.

She was no intellectual, but attracted them as a flower bees. There was always a steady trickle of celebrities from the worlds of science, medicine, and literature. Manuscripts and missals were brought for her delight, and she was not above placing on them a large indiarubber facsimile of an ink-blot, and feigning a horrid alarm, vividly shared by the curator. She had a fertile imagination, and on one Christmas Eve, when many of the family children were gathered round the table, chafing to get at the presents, she caused the butler to present her with a huge scarlet envelope carrying a dangling seal. Opening it very slowly and peering at the contents, she announced with a little squeak of surprise: 'Gracious! Father Christmas has called, and tells me that you may open your presents tonight! Run, children, *run*, you may see the sledge and the reindeer!' We ran, and could almost swear that we saw it, or at least heard its bells, tinkling away down the drive.

'When I married your grandfather in 1847,' she told me, 'we went to Bath for the weekend before starting on the Grand Tour. It was what people did then. After supper, your grandfather took me to walk in the churchyard, and spoke of the life hereafter, and I thought it rather funny, but didn't like to say so.'

11

Grandfather was a handful, no doubt: he came of a line of Quakers but had made himself a Unitarian. His oleograph shows him handsome and bad-tempered. When, as a child, one of my aunts bit her small brother, he told her: 'True, if you do that again, I shall bite *you!*' She did it again and heard his heavy footstep approach. Slowly he raised her and bit her arm to the bone. He fussed about his health, and kept a large steam yacht, a thousand tonner, in which he sailed the Mediterranean every winter. He 'gave' my grandmother fourteen children, a chore which kept her busy from her seventeenth to her thirty-third year. They were raised by an army of nurses and tutors, presided over by Dorsay, the old nurse: an endearing product of Lancashire who stood no nonsense from anybody. The children in their holidays were sent overland to join the yacht in Lisbon or Barcelona or Venice or Athens. My grandmother detested the yacht, and got off it whenever possible. From Lisbon she would drive with postillions to Barcelona, and from Genoa to Venice, making water-colour sketches and writing a witty diary. Small wonder that in later years she seldom knew her children apart. 'Was that,' she would whisper to me, 'Beatrice? It was *Katie?* Of course: how stupid of me!'

Nutfield Priory, which my grandfather had built when he married, was (and is) a house of extreme hideosity. My reason tells me this, though my emotions do not. Mr Gibson, the architect, had to keep to grandfather's command that no wall should be less than three feet thick. Apart from that, he was allowed to spread himself in neo-Gothic abandon. There were two crenellated towers, a vaulted cloister, thirty bedrooms, a Great Hall with (needless to say) an organ and a minstrel's gallery, as well as a stained glass window as large as that of York Minster, in which, in fearful colours, the joys of the Lancashire cotton operatives at the passing of the Ten Hours Bill (which my greatgrandfather had pushed through the House) were appallingly celebrated. The fenestration was a riot of pierced stone: gargoyles sprouted everywhere. The clou of the house was, quite by chance I think, the grand staircase. This, seen through a high Gothic arch, flowed down to the Great Hall like a smooth river. It was an IQ test of the first order. The rule (obvious to those who lived in the house) was that you must come straight down the middle of it, head erect and back straight, never stumbling or wavering. Grandmamma, of course, got first prize: she floated down. Aunt Una, plump and practical, managed it with dignity if not with grace, and kept a straight line. Aunt True, whose hair had gone white at twenty-five, and who was pretty and a bit daft, wavered about and glanced upwards and downwards, left and right. Aunt Sarah, to whose especial care I had been committed, was mannish in stiff collars and uncompromising shoes: she crushed the staircase but kept a steady line. The guests often provided a comic turn, tacking wildly between wall and bannister. Those stairs gave me a habit of watching people's movements and deducing – rightly or wrongly – their character therefrom. I would still make considerable bets about that deduction.

I was very fortunate – or my mother was very wise – in the matter of Aunt Sarah. She was a duck and a darling. She was the only woman I have ever known who had no trace of vanity. Although very handsome, she never looked into a mirror if she could help it: the absence of mirrors was a feature of all her dwellings. She parted her hair in the middle and drew it back into a tight bun. She never used cosmetics or powder. Her clothes were severe and she disdained hats whenever possible: at home, she would cram on an old cloth cap in inclement weather. She was a fearless horsewoman, an exceptionally good swimmer and diver, a gifted gardener, and a true Christian. And she was the soul of fun. Given me to play with for seven years, she was desolated when my father removed me, and fell into a nervous breakdown which lasted for two years. Then she took a house in Percy Street and devoted herself to rescuing prostitutes. It was not a great success, and she married an attractive clergyman, and at forty-two produced a son. From then on her life ran smoothly, with an increasing and charming family. My life took me further and further away from her, but, when she died at the age of ninety-four, I still loved her more than I have ever loved any human being. Once she left me in a toyshop, saying, 'You can pick what you like: I will be back in an hour.' She came back to find me red and flustered, saying 'Difficult, difficult, difficult!' So she took me away, saying: 'Now you get nothing, as the result of feebleness.' That summed me up.

If Nutfield is ugly, its setting is superb. Situated on the spur of a hill seventeen miles south of London, it is (or was) as lonely as Devon or Wales. Behind the house, thick woods of beech and rhododendron rise steeply: from the terrace on the south, the ground drops away in a smooth green robe to the lake below, and rises again to other woods. Beyond them stretches an immense view: on clear days the sea sparkles on the horizon. The gardens wander for a mile along abrupt slopes, and here my grandfather planted every rare tree that he could find. Even if today it is the Headquarters of NAAFI, dotted with hideous huts, it was once a Paradise, and a private one. I am all for Paradise being private.

Life at Nutfield was held firmly in a framework of habit and ceremony. As the hands of the grandfather clock which stood beside the organ moved towards eight in the morning, doors would softly open upstairs, the sound, followed by that of rustling skirts, percolating through the gallery to the Great Hall. The descent of the staircase would be made by the family and guests. Arrived in the Hall, they stood: no one said good morning, no one spoke. As the clock struck eight, my grandmother's door, in the centre of the gallery, opened: and presently she floated down to us. She smiled but did not speak, continuing past us through the Gothic arch beyond the organ, and entering the morning-room. We followed, and arranged ourselves on small gilt chairs round the walls. Then the servants, who had been waiting at the green baize door in strict order of precedence, headed by the cook and butler, filed in. I suppose there were about twenty of them. Grandmamma read prayers – brief – from a book which she had printed for these occasions. Then she rose, and wished the servants good morning: they filed out. She would then make some optimistic remark about the weather, and we went into the dining-room, where breakfast was set at a huge circular table in the window-embrasure, overlooking the immense view.

And what a breakfast it was! A feast far different from the mingy hurried breakfasts of today. There were always six or seven silver dishes sizzling above spirit lamps: kidneys, sausages, eggs in various form, kippers, haddock, devilled chicken, kedgeree, and of course porridge and cream and brown sugar. On the opposite sideboard were the cold dishes: peach-fed York ham, glistening tongue, cold turkey, grouse, partridge, pheasant, guinea-fowl, and home-made brawn. And, naturally, fresh warm home-made cottage loaves and scones, and butter from the dairy, salted and yellow as a buttercup. A delicious profusion. No doubt people were starving all over the world, as they are today. That melancholy fact no more affected the splendour of those breakfasts than a million bad painters affect the beauty of a Rembrandt. Life is unfair, and will be.

After breakfast I read *The Times* to Grandmamma, and she

talked to me about the estate and the people on it, the political scene, and the latest literary developments. She treated me always as an adult. She then attended to her correspondence, which was voluminous. Apart from anything else fourteen children and their descendants, however vague she was about them, made considerable claims. I, meanwhile, stretched myself on the carpet underneath the ebony and ivory desk which was so like her, and gave myself up to the fairy tales with which she provided me lushly. The brothers Grimm, Hans Andersen, Andrew Lang, *The Phantastes* of George MacDonald, *Alice in Wonderland, Prince Perrypets,* and so many more: I was soon lost in a world of dreams. Towards eleven o'clock, Grandmamma took her pony and trap and did a round of the estate. This was a business which she took very seriously: she was aware not only of the health or illness, but also of the character and temperament, of every man, woman, and child on it. She was immensely popular, and indeed respected for many miles around: had she stood for Parliament she would have had a thumping majority. She was not, of course, alone in that: plenty of landlords felt their responsibilities keenly. It was only after 1918 that the absentee landlord came to dwell in London and rejoice in *Tatler* photographs.

Meanwhile I was free to wander, and wander I did. Filled with ideas of gnomes and elves and fairies, I saw them all. I spoke confidentially to the great redwoods, snuffling against their soft bark: and they answered me. I sat under the weeping acacia, knowing that she was dangerous and might at any moment enfold me. I was well aware that the oak and the beech could be trusted, but that the ash and the birch were false and could catch me in their long fingers. I had my special garden, up the hill through a tangle of rhododendrons, where a tame toad came to my whistle. It was understood that nobody else came, except at my invitation. There stood the great tree known for miles around as the High Beech, of colossal mossy girth and sprawling roots: to her I confided my innermost secrets. Forty years later I made my way through an increased tangle to sit again beneath that smooth trunk: and I kissed it, and knew the strange joy of animism.

Children, except on festive occasions, seldom came to the house; the exception was my cousin Noel Stone, for whom I cherished a hero-worship which was amply justified. He was charming, gentle, wise: he was the nearest thing I had to an elder brother: to my everlasting loss, he was killed in France in 1918. I never went to parties. There I was, a precocious, elderly little boy: a prig: and very vulnerable. I had had a magic childhood, which suited me to perfection. It was not a preparation for the turbulence to come. I did not learn to be a good mixer, I did not learn ambition, but I did learn to be on excellent terms with solitude. And since, whatever we may say, we are all solitary throughout life, I am humbly grateful for those seven gentle years.

Presently there appeared at Nutfield a dazzling being whom I knew as Dodo. Dodo was something quite new. I did not find her beautiful, possibly because she conformed to Edwardian standards with which I was unfamiliar: thin lips, dogged chin, a statuesque lack of warmth (Queen Alexandra, I suppose, was the model). But she exuded an atmosphere of wealth and luxury. My grandmother and aunts, though dressed by Mr Worth, were, if not exactly dowdy, very sober in dress. But Dodo was superbly elegant. Her constantly changed gowns and furs and rings glittered and glowed. She condescended to play with me, and although in some recess of my mind I knew that she was illiterate about fairies and trees, I was flattered by the chinchilla and Parma violets. I knew obscurely that there was a great gap between her and my grandmother and my aunts: they were extremely courteous, but conversation did not flow.

I did not of course know that she was engaged to my father: and had I known it would have meant nothing. She was the daughter of Thomas Ismay, who had founded the White Star Line and was wealthy far beyond the Fieldens. Neither family could claim aristocracy, but the Fieldens had a three-generation start on the road to gentility. Dodo, already an Edwardian, was a trifle vulgar by Victorian standards. She had been brought up to social climbing by way of titled guests, bridge, racing, cosmetics, scent, and other social quirks which Nutfield deplored. On her side she deplored intellectuals, art, and dowdiness. The chasm which opened between her and Nutfield was wider and deeper than any that existed between, say, my grandmother and her servants and tenants.

I was taken to London, and at St George's, Hanover Square, dressed in a white sailor suit, I distributed 'favours', walking up and down the aisle and handing lilies of the valley, wrapped in silver paper, to ladies in feathered hats whose frothing skirts filled the pews. 'Isn't he sweet? The stepson, you know,' they whispered. It was all a mystery to me. There was a reception, with a red carpet and an awning, in Cadogan Square. I was led down, and my head poked into the waiting brougham, where my father and Dodo strangely sat. I knew that they were going 'abroad', which seemed exciting. But my father, whom I scarcely knew, frightened me with his long face.

I said: 'Good-bye, Dodo!' My father said: 'In future you will call her Mother.' Black rage filled me: I saw the now empty tiara in Heaven. I screamed: *'Never! Never! Never!'* and was removed, a hideous blot on the festivities.

So, a new life began.

My father, it seems to me, was an unusual man. But I may be wrong about that. Perhaps men with limited minds are far more usual than we care to allow. Certainly my father went through life in blinkers of his own making. What he did not like he did not choose to see. What he liked were horses, hounds, and foxes: and very little else. Connected with those came the inevitable accoutrements: saddles, bridles, scarlet coats, white breeches, top boots, velvet caps, and stables of staggering expense. He kept fifty horses, and half as many grooms to look after them. He hunted on five days every week, on the sixth he did his accounts and attended to any business which a mastership of foxhounds involved, on the seventh he went to church (not attending to it, but for example), and afterwards conducted guests round the stables and kennels. That was his life. His philosophy was based on it. Until his death in 1944, he would stoutly maintain that no war could be won without cavalry. He saw the world like that, and nothing would change him. He was a perfectly sincere man. He never, as far as I can make out, had the smallest doubt about his aims in life. Furiously opposed by his father, he refused to go to any University, and went to a veterinary college instead. Fortunately for him, his father died when he was twenty and left him a couple of hundred thousand pounds. From then on, he could please himself.

No one can plumb the depths of the human heart, but I think that my father was largely indifferent to houses, family, food, heat and comfort. He had a cold bath every morning, breaking the ice in winter, until the end of his life: a hot bath, he once told me, made him feel ill. He detested all 'made-up' dishes, and frequently sent them away, demanding cold beef, which I think he would have preferred for every meal. He had no interest in clothes except as a convention: he wore stiff choker collars in summer and winter, and ordered the same dark suits every year. He recognized the need of a wife, but his ideas were oriental on that subject: the female must be there, she must run the house and bear children, and she had no right to absent herself. (My stepmother took this well, and rather liked it.) He never went out to a meal, never stayed away in a strange house, and never (it is hardly necessary to add) went willingly to that fearful 'abroad'. (My stepmother once took him to Oberammergau: two cars were necessary, one to take them and one to follow with stores of bacon, marmalade and cold beef: it was a frightful failure.) All in all, I don't think that my father would have cared one jot if he had had to live in a wigwam in direst poverty, provided that he could hunt the fox.

My father's views on Art will now, I trust, be fairly obvious. His reading was confined to Surtees and Whyte-Melville, on the rare occasions when he was ill. He never visited a picture gallery, never went to a concert (any such idea would have been daft), had no interest in architecture or sculpture. He must have had some vague ideas about great painters, but I think he pushed them out of his mind. (The only comment I ever heard him make about the lovely Canalettos in his dining-room was 'Well, so that old tower's fallen down at last'.) He thought in all sincerity that painting and music were occupations for ladies. That a man should paint or play the piano was, to him, a decadent horror. He refused, naturally, to allow me to have drawing lessons, and kept the piano locked against me. He wanted me - and quite rightly, from his point of view - to be a Master of Foxhounds. I was a terrible, a shattering, disappointment. Under his frightful tuition I learned - partly thanks to my long legs - to have a good seat on a horse, and to control it: I also learned to hate horses. I also learned to hate him. It was an unreasonable hatred, because my father was a just and not unkindly man: but no hatred is more stubborn than the hatred of those who confer obligations which we cannot fulfil.

It did not, obviously, occur to my father, after his marriage to Dodo, that my removal from Nutfield would produce a confusion of thought - now called schizophrenia - from which I should never recover. For seven years he had allowed me to be submitted to one code of behaviour: now for another ten he gave me another, diametrically opposed. My grandmother had taught

18

me that gentleness, repose, tolerance, self-effacement and solitude were life's best prizes: my stepmother insisted that ambition, ruthlessness, gregariousness and success were the essentials: my father did not worry himself about ethics or behaviour, so long as I 'went well to hounds'. Thus I became and have remained tolerant and intolerant, gentle and ruthless, ambitious and timid, worldly and yet solitary: a walking contradiction in terms, to be summed up by various people, according to their tastes, as unreliable or unpredictable, unstable, disloyal, or plain eccentric. In these days, when so many complaints are heard about young delinquents, and education – or psychiatric brain-washing – is skied up as a cure-all, I sometimes wonder whether parents, rather than their children, are in need of reform. It seems curious, to say the least, that degrees and examinations are required for teachers, but no sort of test is demanded for prospective parents, who are responsible beyond all others for the behaviour of each younger generation.

Returning from their honeymoon in Germany, my father and Dodo took themselves, and me, to Foston Hall near Derby. Nutfield was certainly no gem of architecture, but it was at least built of grey stone and set in a superb situation. Foston was mauve Victorian brick and slate in a dull landscape. Here began the squares of cabbage, the tutors, the cold baths, and the horses (or, rather, the ponies). I was utterly lost in a strange land. My father and Dodo were remote and frightening people. My grandmother and aunts had treated me as a loved equal: at Foston I was an unwanted child. Nature, which had seemed so great a friend at Nutfield, retreated at Foston: the Derbyshire trees had nothing to say to me, nor I to them. Foston was then a very isolated place: an hour and a half in the brougham to Derby, and nothing nearer than that. I do not remember that any children ever came to that house. Visitors were grown-ups of the hunting and racing clans. I was unhappy with the deathly hopeless unhappiness of unloved childhood. I was so unhappy that I became ill. I don't know what ailed me, but I remember being wheeled around the garden on a kind of bier, upon which I had to lie flat. I wanted nothing but to run back to Nutfield. My stepmother's natural exasperation with me must have begun at about this time.

In spite of all that, I wrote a novel. I suppose it was prompted partly by loneliness and partly by the Nutfield addiction to literature and its lack at Foston. It started, God knows why, with the 'rescue' of a 'forlorn maiden' on a 'deserted beach', and went on to improbable Hans Andersen adventures in improbable parts of the world. I wrote it all out carefully in copperplate, and illustrated it with full-page pen-and-ink drawings: it was also bound in green ribbon. Proudly one evening I handed it to Dodo, who was writing letters at her desk. She riffled through the pages, said, 'What a funny child you are,' and handed it back to me. I never tried that again, and it was not until fifteen years later that I began, owing to the kindness and encouragement of Kingsley Martin, editor of the *New Statesman,* to write for publication. Not that that calls for any self-pity: had I been a born writer, my stepmother's indifference would not have discouraged me. I was not a born writer, or at least had not the necessary perseverance, and so I was deflected. Probably the world was spared a lot of rubbish.

The mauve episode of Foston was fortunately brief, and ended when my father and Dodo moved to London to await the arrival of my half-sister. I was despatched to Nutfield, where I recovered instantly. But, as soon as my sister was safely born, I was sent to the house leased for the occasion, 20 Hertford Street, Park Lane. That then luxurious mansion (I believe it is now a block of flats) had an automatic lift, a marvel in 1903. I took myself up and down in it continually, until Nannie recounted a grisly tale of two charwomen in an adjacent house, who had got stuck between floors while the owners were abroad, and were discovered, grinning skelingtons (that was how she told it), six weeks later. After that I gave the lift a miss, and have never since been quite at ease in automatic lifts.

Life in London was planned for me to the last detail and minute. I had a governess, an incoming teacher of French, another of mathematics, another of Latin. I attended a gymnasium called MacPherson's, a dancing school, a fencing master, a riding school (of course), and a swimming bath. The fencing was splendid fun: I found myself quite good: but that was my only experience of it. The dancing school was repulsive: I was quite ready to dance, but my ear was offended by the banged piano, and my nose by the sweaty little girls I had to partner. Riding in the Row was easy after the country, though fraught with some terrors: what would happen if the pony bolted into Knightsbridge? But the swimming bath was nightmare: here I encountered for the first time my step-cousin Charles, of the Ismay clan, destined to be a thorn in my side, and held up as an example, for the next ten years. He was everything that I was not: beefy, tough, active, talkative, extrovert. My father and step-uncle attended the swimming bath and said: 'Jump in!' Charles jumped: I didn't. Pushed, I sank to the bottom and remained there until rescued. It was idiotic: I learned later that I was by nature a much better swimmer than Charles and liked water far more: but my father paralysed me. The gymnasium was worst of all: some forty children attended, and all herds arouse my obstinacy. I did not in the least desire to vault and climb and box and wrestle and pant over press-ups. For some strange reason I was placed in the front row when we gave a demonstration before assembled parents. Instantly I peed in my trousers, and was led away from the shaming pool.

On Sunday afternoons, as a duty (I did not see him otherwise, except at the swimming-pool), my father 'took me out'. A hansom was called at two thirty, and when we were seated in it my father would say, 'Which is it to be? The Houses of Parliament, the Zoo, or Earls Court?' I knew that the proper answer was not the last: but the water-chute, the side-shows, the coloured fountains, the switchback and the flip-flap were of infinitely greater attraction than Regent's Park or Westminster. Sometimes I dared it but soon discovered that, alone with my solemn father (in top hat, of course), it was not much fun. Once our horse fell down in Hay Hill, and that was the best outing of all. Hansoms were exciting, and I wonder if any more engaging vehicle has ever been invented: one had a splendid view, with the apron doors cosily over one's knees: the cabby's bent head was mysteriously outlined against the sky when one spoke to him through the overhead hatch, pushed open with an umbrella: when it rained, down came the fascinating folding window.

Presently my parents moved to Farnborough Hall near Banbury. On the first evening my stepmother had a fit of hysterics in the hall, and vowed she couldn't live there. I watched, entranced but unmoved. It was not very surprising. The house was arctic and uncomfortable: I suppose my father had taken it with nothing but hunting in mind. It had twenty bedrooms and one prehistoric bath. But architecturally it was of great beauty. It possessed a superb carved staircase and a unique diningroom, in which half-a-dozen exquisite Canalettos had been let in to the walls, and a charming frieze of plaster-work arranged round them. It also had three large natural lakes, and a strange garden feature called The Terrace, which flowed for a mile in a thirty-yard-wide carpet of mown grass along the hill, and ended in an obelisk which commemorated something or somebody. It was and is a beautiful place. It is now in the hands of the National Trust.

Here I happened on my first experience of sex, though I should not, of course, have recognized it as such. My cousin Evelyn, aged six to my eight, arrived for a visit. She was a charming little person and we got on very well. It was the first time that I had been friendly with a small girl. One day, playing in the shrubbery, I was seized with a desire to know why she was in some strange way different from me. I asked her to take off her clothes, which she did at once, and I did the same. Greatly puzzled, we examined our different bodies. We could make little of it. We came to the conclusion that one of us – but which? – must be deformed. The shrubbery was overlooked by the stables, and a groom carried the news to my father. There followed an almighty row. We were both beaten into bruises and tears. We had not the faintest clue as to what we had done that was wrong. We were only called 'disgusting'. I never dared to speak of it to Evelyn again. I imagine that we both continued to think that one of us – but which? – had a deformity which must be conceal-ed at all costs. I don't know what this did to our sex lives: per-haps quite a lot. But perhaps nothing. I don't know how parents should deal with such a situation. The only deduction I can draw is that the so-called 'facts of life' should somehow be made familiar and ordinary at a very early age.

Soon after this I was packed off to a preparatory school at Broadstairs. This was a new blow, a veritable nadir. Stone House was, no doubt, good as preparatory schools went: from the moment when the four-wheeler containing myself and my silent father turned the corner under the dripping wall, I knew that I was going to prison. Most small boys of eight are probably not happy about going to school for the first time, but I was and am more allergic than most to human nature in the herd. My dislike of all places – schools, cinemas, theatres, football matches, rail-way trains, aeroplanes, restaurants, public meetings, crowds, and cocktail parties – where human beings are massed, amounts to agoraphobia and claustrophobia combined. Even in cities I am ill at ease. Human beings packed together are turned, as by Circe, into swine. That is why I would rather die than submit to com-munism or socialism or any other ism which seeks, in a dotty dream of non-existent equality, to have a merry ghastly get-together of all. Human beings are only tolerable as individuals.

The presiding deity of Stone House was the Reverend W.H. Churchill. He had a drooping grey mustache, a large red nose, and an immense sapphire ring. He wore rubber shoes, and prowled around silently carrying a fives bat, with which he clearly derived much satisfaction in beating tender young bottoms. He had a ham sense of theatre, and the chapel – rather a pretty one – was hung with embroidered silk flags of various colours on silver standards. What they represented I cannot imagine. When he preached on Sunday evenings, the lights were lowered, leaving only two altar candles to halo his face. On one occasion he went so far as to tell us: 'Ah! my friends! When sin becomes a bore, there is the real tragedy.' We drew some nasty conclusions about that.

The chapel was, however, for me about the most exciting thing at Stone House. True, it was a herd, but a controlled and quiet herd. I had by chance an unusually true and strong treble voice, and I was therefore picked to sing solos in anthems. This was fun and, in spite of my father, gave me the beginnings of a knowledge of music. Again, it was exciting when relatives came, and were seen for the first time in the visitors enclosure at the back of the chapel: and one knew (while singing *The Wings of a Dove*) that one was going out to a delicious lunch at the Granville Hotel at Ramsgate. Then came the tragic (but rather succulent) moment when, at the evening service, one saw the relatives for the last time, and sang (with fought-back tears) *The Day Thou gavest Lord is Ended*. I need not say that my father and stepmother were not among the relatives: they did not approve of such visits.

I can't leave the chapel without one other memory, which remains astonishingly vivid. The father of one boy, Dames-Longworth, died suddenly: he was found dead in a wood. The mother was a well-known Irish beauty. She came down to the school shortly afterwards, and by special concession was escorted to a front pew usually reserved for Mrs Churchill. She was dressed with stunning elegance and, as was the fashion in those days, swathed in long black veils which swirled from her black ostrich-feather hat. It was an occasion, and the eyes of the school were upon her. Slowly she drew off her long black gloves, and, raising white hands covered with diamond rings, put back her veils. The sun glittered on the diamonds, and on the beautiful pale face. We were enraptured: she was a goddess.

Mr Churchill was a mean man: the food was nearly uneatable, and although we did not quite freeze I remember few occasions so continuously cold as those Thanet winters, with the fog-horns blaring out at sea. The masters, probably underpaid, were an uninspiring lot. That did not matter: we were only required to achieve a pass into a public school. I suppose we gathered a smattering of English, mathematics, and Latin. Games were held to be much more important than work, and in these, I need hardly say, I lamentably failed to distinguish myself.

Thus five years passed away. There was not a great deal to choose between holidays and school. Farnborough had its advantages: it was more comfortable, the food was much better, there was some privacy: but there were also the tutors, the cold baths, the riding school, and, worst of all, the parties. To these last my stepmother (and quite rightly, poor dear, according to her views) insisted that I must go. Cricket matches, pony shows, dances – they were all undiluted hell to me. I set up a hideous and irrational fuss about them. I was pushed into the brougham (two hours each way) and, once arrived, stood in a corner with tears pouring down my cheeks, or in some such way disgraced myself, until removed. I screamed at the idea of going to stay in strange houses: forcibly taken, I not only wetted my bed but also soiled it: I would not visit strange lavatories. Small wonder that my stepmother was infuriated and ashamed: in her place I would have strangled me: I was a torture to myself and everyone else.

Memory paints these years dead black: but of course nothing is ever quite that. I had a stately home, a good school, wealthy parents, a privileged position. I was, best of all gifts, young. I adored my small half-sister. Occasionally I escaped to Nutfield. Even at Farnborough, there was a boat on the lake, collections of bird's eggs and butterflies and stamps, outings now and then, and the fearful excitement of a mammoth Daimler car in that carless age. I must have enjoyed quite a lot of it. Yet I remember that I regarded tramps and crossing-sweepers with envy, and wished that I could change places with them. Whatever my privileges, my sort of freedom, the freedom to be private and to *do nothing,* a freedom to which I still cling in spite of all the slogans and interferences, was not among them.

Now came Eton. I was by this time inured, at least on the surface, to going to school. Before I left for my first term at Eton, my father called me into his study. 'Sit down, please,' he said.

I felt that something dreadful was coming. 'I suppose,' he said sternly, 'you have heard of sodomy?' I gasped, 'Yes, father.' I had not the faintest idea what he was talking about. 'You can,' said my father, 'get nine years penal servitude for it.' I said, 'Yes, father.' I sat in the Daimler and wondered. I asked Irwin, the chauffeur, if he could please drive me at sixty miles an hour. He was a nice man, and did so: it was thrilling, I could brag about it. *What* had my father said? Follow me? Roddery? Goddamy? Something to do with religion? Nine years penal servitude? All very puzzling.

After Stone House, Eton offered expanding horizons. It is not a bad prison, as prisons go. It had, for me, three great advantages: a room of one's own, leisure to read, and the possibility, on half-holidays, of slouching idly around the streets of Windsor or the countryside. There were of course other prizes: election to 'Pop', Captain of the Boats, and so on. I did not aspire to such. I should have been uncomfortable in a fancy waistcoat and a buttonhole, and sport was, as it is, a closed book to me. I marvel at the pursuit of balls by adults. I suppose that, if there had been a rush to elect me to Pop, or to make me Captain of the Cricket Eleven, I should have swelled with pride: I don't know: I cannot remember ever lusting after such things. When my father died I found in his safe some old Eton reports on me: one of them, by Headlam, my classical tutor, read: 'This boy has a strange and puzzling character: he could be brilliant but he does not wish to excel. Nor does he wish to fail. As far as I understand him, he wishes to avoid any limelight.'

Education is an elusive and debatable affair. The human race certainly has made a muddle of it, so far. Perhaps it can be divided under four heads – character, erudition, arts, and technology. I don't think anything falls outside these four. They are all quite different, and all to some extent necessary. If they could be combined exactly to fit the limitations of personality and ability, a perfect education might result. They never are and never can be, because inspired teachers are as rare as dodos, and human scholars learn at different paces and with different tastes. No legislation can ever solve that problem. History shows clearly that education, by itself, never produced outstanding men. Heredity, environment, circumstance, natural talent, may do that: not education. Nor do we really believe that it can do so: children are sent to school not to be educated but to get them out of the way at an awkward age.

The value of Eton (at least in my day) was perhaps precisely the dismissal, by long tradition, of education *per se*. Scholarship was regarded as eccentric, the arts were non-existent, technology was a matter for 'saps', and even athletics, though prized, were not insisted on. You were, so to speak, left to fight it out for yourself. The *beau idéal*, almost the idol, was the member of Pop, who was – in so far as he could be defined at all – a mixture of glamour, good manners, and self-confidence. It was not a bad star to follow. Tradition was ferocious: it stretched from definable things, such as leaving the bottom button of one's waistcoat undone, having the trousers turned up, and the top hat not too shiny and yet not too disgustingly buffed, to matters undefinable such as a stop on all reference to wealth or family, an avoidance of both scruffiness and smartness, and a refusal to sneak or whimper when – a usual and terrifying occurrence – one was shut up for an hour inside an 'ottoman', with a lot of boys sitting on top. Eton could not make silk purses out of sow's ears, but it could veneer them to look very much like silk for some considerable time.

Since grandmamma, or my natural bent, had taught me to read, I read voraciously during my five years at Eton, and undoubtedly I found my happiest hours with a book on my window-sill, or beside the fire, or discovering new treasures in the Windsor bookshops. Nobody guided me, and my reading was scatty. I plunged through Dickens, Thackeray, Reade, Austen, Trollope, the Brontës: I also wallowed in Rider Haggard, and the delicious forbidden fruits of Marie Corelli, Hall Caine, Elinor Glyn, and Mrs Henry Wood. Half-way through the five years, I discovered poetry by chance.

Whatever it may be now, the teaching at Eton then was of a very low standard. Few 'beaks' had any gift of inspiration. Or possibly we did not look for it. Among the classicists was Booker, who taught Greek. When we were unable to remember a word like, say, KEKAUKA, he would bark at us: 'What are *you*? What *are* you? Tell me what you are!' And we knew the answer. 'A corker, Sir!' 'Yes, a corker, an ignorant corker, you great big floundering jackass!' He had a gold repeater watch, and would draw it out and make it strike while we were writing an essay. If we looked up, he would make a ferocious face and demand: 'What are you gaping at, you great booby?' It was a bit music-hall, but he was popular and made some Greek stick. Later he had a murder in his house, which much increased his glamour.

There was Ramsay, who taught Latin, and made it obligatory to speak nothing else in school. For those who suddenly wanted to pee or vomit, as boys not infrequently do, this was difficult: to explain why one had whispered to one's neighbour, and what, was sheer stalemate. It was a good idea, but it needed a greater sense of humour than Ramsay's to make it work. French classes were a riot of insubordination, and nobody learnt anything (why learn frogs lingo anyway?). Mathematics were a long yawn. The final absurdity was reached with Broadbent in the Upper Fifth. He was a half-paralysed man in his eighties and his sight and hearing were seriously affected. He never entered school without water or cabbages or confetti falling on his bald pate: mice, snakes, and frogs were let out and chased: all translations were read directly from a crib, so that we must all have had full marks every time. I suppose the poor old man gave us excellent reports. Education!

Of Eton three things stand out in memory, and a fourth merits a digression. First of the three was a classical 'beak', Bevan, who one day departed from tradition by saying: 'Before we begin, I think I must read you a poem from *The Spectator*.' (I think it was *The Spectator*: I know it was not a good poem.) He read it, and I was spellbound. Not only did I learn it and still remember it: it opened the gates of poetry to me. It was an example of the spark which a teacher can sometimes convey, perhaps altering a whole life. Maybe I should have discovered poetry in any case: I am not sure about that, and I salute Bevan. Second was the fainting of a boy next to me in chapel. He was carried out and I thought him dead. I was instantly convinced that the same fate lay in store for me. The chapel swam before my eyes, sweat beaded my forehead, I gripped the pew with wet hands. Soon I could think of nothing else. By day and by night I trembled at the thought of chapel. I lost weight: I could not eat. My house tutor, a kindly man, wrote to my father saying that I had a bad nerve-storm, and recommending a term's vacation. My father replied that he did not believe in nerves. I became allergic to churches.

The third matter was more serious. The Officers Training Corps at Eton was, like all military or semi-military bodies before 1914, a strictly 'voluntary' affair. The idea of any forced militarism was highly unpopular. Doubtless the sons of soldiers and sailors were subjected to a steady, if half-unconscious, pressure, to follow in their father's footsteps. In much the same way, although every regulation clearly stated that a boy could choose to join or not to join, to leave or not to leave the OTC, Eton tradition decreed that everyone must join and stay. Like others, I joined. I did not like the weekly parades and drill, but they were brief and could be suffered. I disliked more violently the field days, when we were required to throw ourselves down in mud, stagger across wet ploughed fields and throw ourselves in mud again, for no purpose that I could discover: and then to sit, huddled like sardines, on long train journeys filled with bawdy songs and bullying. But these were trifles compared with Camp. Camp was ten days at Tidworth in pouring rain: ten to a tent, vicious homosexuality, greasy food cooked in dirty dixies, latrines made of a pole over a ditch, and all foulest instincts encouraged. Jolly good for the chaps, no doubt.

I made up my mind that I would never go to camp again. On my return to Eton in the autumn of 1913, I explained this to my tutor, M.D. Hill. He pooh-poohed it. He said, not without reason, that ten days of discomfort was of small importance: he added, less reasonably, that if I 'shirked' camp I should be excluded from all respectable careers – the Army, the Navy, Diplomacy, the Civil Service, and so on. In vain I protested that I wanted none of them. He would not help me: I had to help myself.

I therefore read the Training Manual with care, and found that, if a member of the OTC missed three parades in succession, he was sacked. I missed two, and then, as I had anticipated, was sent for by the Headmaster. I had prepared a careful brief for this eventuality, pointing out that I had the right to resign. Edward Lyttleton cut me short. 'I don't want,' he said, 'to hear anything about your strange attitude. If you do not go on parade on Monday, I shall expel you.' I retired: no boy of seventeen could call such a bluff. But bluff it was. In the then climate of opinion, an expulsion for failing to stay with the OTC would have brought down the Headmaster, not me. He knew it. But he counted, like Hitler, on fear, and he counted right. It made no difference, except to my rage against Lyttleton and against all things military. When camp came round again, I did not go. How happy should I have been if that had banned me from the Army! Not at all: Kitchener pointed his accusing finger at me, and I was cannon-fodder.

Last comes a small, but I think necessary, digression. When I was at Eton, homosexuality was not only common, it was a general rule. I am tickled by the protestations of elderly gentle-men in the House of Lords or on the Bench, that they never knew or heard of anything of the kind. I almost think that they believe it themselves. It is the sheerest hypocrisy to imagine that, if you shut boys up with one another between the ages of thir-teen and eighteen, when sex begins to stir, and deny them access to the opposite sex, they will refrain, like saints, from experi-menting with each other's bodies. For some obscure reason – per-haps it was my mother's tiara – I was terrified of sex. I repulsed advances but regretted it. I emerged from Eton virginal, but cursed my virginity. The point I wish to make here – and I think it is a very valid point – is that, although I was and am by nature homosexual, Eton never corrupted me. I resent the silly old men who prate about the 'corruption' of youth. Sexual corruption is only possible among those who wish to be corrupted. The strange belief (if we are to believe Mr Butler in the House of Commons) that circumstances can change a heterosexual into a homosexual, or vice versa, is one of the silliest fantasies of our times.

Let me pause here. I have cantered over what may be a mono-tonous tract of country, noting points which have stuck in memory: a dark forest, a sunlit glade, a tangle of briars, an un-expected ditch. There remains the climate: the climate of opinion. Climates of opinion are not 'facts', and in this century we love 'facts'. Yet all history is meaningless without its climates of opinion. We cannot begin to understand historical events (as Gibbon so clearly saw) without placing ourselves under the in-fluence of the opinions then current. Our own opinions will not do. We may think today that there should be equal opportunity for all, that medicine should be free, that imperialism is a bad thing, that wars should stop, that we should travel to the moon: these are today's ideas, which were not those of yesterday and may not be those of tomorrow: they are not eternal truths, though each generation may think its own truth eternal.

I speak here only of the climate of opinion in a relatively wealthy, rural community such as Nutfield at the turn of the century: I do not refer to climates of opinion in, say, factories or large cities or gatherings of politicians or revolutionaries. Those climates were different. But, at the turn of the century, 'Nutfields' were common in England: isolated islands of respect-able feudalism, they preserved a climate which deeply affected those who dwelt in them. That climate now seems so remote, so unreal, so almost unbelievable, that it is hard to recapture even by those who knew it, and nearly unimaginable by those who did not.

First, there was security. Nobody since 1918 has known that kind of security. And let me assure my socialist friends that it was a security which applied not only to the wealthy, but also to their dependants. People as old as my grandmother had known from afar the Crimean, Franco-Prussian, and Boer wars: the last had been somewhat shocking, but had ended as it should. Wars were the business of the Army and the Army alone, just as order was the business of the police. Wars were won as a matter of course, and they were localised and distant. Civilian families were not affected, except by the rather rare, but glorious fall of a member on the field of battle. England had been divinely appointed to keep order in the world, and keep it she would. It was not only a conviction, it was an absolute and unquestioned certainty, that Britannia would rule the seas for ever and ever, that the pound sterling would always buy two hundred loaves of bread, home-brewed beer be a penny a pint, and that the person of an Englishman could not be touched, except at extreme peril, in any part of the globe. It followed (in the then climate of opinion) that life as lived in England was the best kind of life that could be imagined. It was not thought that poor and un-educated people needed more than a bare living standard for happiness, and in any case it was not supposed that natural laws would permit anything else. *Hubris*, it may be said. *Hubris* no doubt. But you cannot, simply because you live in the context of today, regard it as unjust or unfeeling: that particular form of sentimentality did not exist. God was seated somewhere just above London: He liked it there, and He had ordained the English hierarchy.

This sense of security, of Time stopped, as it were, by the Pax Britannica, of living in the best country in the world, produced a feeling of placidity. Wealth was not coveted and hated as it is now, if only because there was not nearly so much to buy. My grandmother, though wealthy, was not rich as riches went then: she had a life interest of £6,000 per annum: her sons had each inherited about £200,000 and her daughters £30,000. Thus the wolf was a good long way from the door, and since income tax was a shilling in the pound, and servants could be had for ten shillings a week, there was not a great deal to spend money on. Ostentation was frowned upon: parties were rare: alcohol (except for port, which was cheap) seldom appeared. In the homes of Mitchell the head gardener, Burgess the coachman, Terris the bailiff, Pound the butler, Hawkins the lodge-keeper, Dorsay the old nurse – to one or other of whom Grandmamma sent me on most days for tea – the standard of food, comfort and cleanliness seemed no different from that of the Priory. Central heating did not exist, and Victorian furniture was mostly hard. My host did not scruple to bat me over the head if I fidgeted or misbehaved. I was the son of the big house, so to speak, and there was, I suppose, a class distinction: but I was certainly unaware of it, and it carried no trace of servility or envy. My grandmother felt it her duty to look after the health, education, and well-being of her dependants and their children: it was understood that sons, if they wished, would succeed their fathers. The tight little community was geared to human life eternal.

Then, there was the absence of noise and gadgets. No motor cars, no motor buses, no aeroplanes, no pneumatic drills, no lorries: and no radios, no gramophones, no television sets, no cinemas, no dance-halls. Amenities (if they are) such as these were not missed, because they were not known. Advertisement had not got into its giant stride: apart from patent medicines, people were not urged to buy what they did not require. The wealthy could buy more and better clothes and furniture, collect pictures or china or silver, drive out in spanking carriages, eat rare food, and live a leisured life. But I doubt if these material advantages – except perhaps the last one – contributed greatly to happiness. Since food was cheap, and distractions few, life in a community such as Nutfield, though dull by modern standards, was neither uncomfortable nor insecure.

There was, of course, London. My grandmother went there – to Browns Hotel – twice a year: once to buy Christmas presents, once to buy clothes. My aunts went a little more often. Clippety-clop for three quarters of an hour to the station: chug-chug in the train (reserved compartment) for an hour over seventeen miles. Exhausting! And then London! Such clatter of hooves and hard wheels over the cobbles – did not anyone of consequence have straw laid down in the road in case of illness? The noise would have been fatal. One could only bear it occasionally. No wonder that, of my grandmother's fourteen children, seven lived into the late seventies, four into the nineties, while Grandmamma and her eldest daughter reached their hundred. People lived then, because noise and worry did not tear their lives to pieces: now-

31

adays we are told that they have a better expectation of life because, although torn to pieces, they are pepped up by medicine.

Then again there was a rather pleasing (I think) dichotomy of thought between respectability and duty on the one hand and the gay life on the other. Queen Victoria had placed her black German bonnet on England's head, and insisted on severity of morals. But Edward VII was coming along, and in spite of divorce courts and Tranby Crofts, represented a reaction against too much solemnity. The well-to-do, following Victorian or Quaker (or even, one might say, communist) principles, were expected to make some sacrifice and set some example. My aunts all belonged to the Charity Organisation Society or some such body and did their stints as required: my grandmother kept at Nutfield what was called a 'Fresh Air Home' – a roomy farmhouse in which thirty children from the slums were kept, month by month, throughout the year. At the same time a more indulgent eye was turned on Mrs Langtry and Mrs Keppel than posterity, more narrow-minded, found it possible, later, to turn on Mrs Simpson.

So life went on at Nutfield: very slowly, very gently, very serenely. My grandmother drew her wealth, at a remove, from the sweated industrial slaves of Lancashire: but that fact, in the then climate of opinion, did not register. The poor were poor, and the rich rich. Had not my grandfather infuriated his contemporaries by pushing the Ten Hours Bill, which saved the children from fourteen hours work? Could more be expected? In the context of the times it was a realistic view. My grandmother would have been prostrated with grief if anyone had even sought to convince her that her wealth flowed from misery. No one did anything of the kind, since no such views were current. You were wealthy and you lived accordingly. Today equality is the slogan, but there is no equality in nature. The Welfare State is an admirable project, but so long as it is national and not international it is only an extension of the same disparity between wealth and poverty. Fifty years ago individuals were rich or poor: today nations are rich or poor. The division of wealth and poverty becomes vertical instead of horizontal: at one time it is between rich and poor in all countries, at another, between rich countries and poor countries. The manual worker who draws his twenty pounds a week is exactly as innocent or guilty as my grandmother was innocent or guilty: he does not think of the coolie or the ryot any more than my grandmother thought of Lancashire.

But human beings continue to live off one another, and in the process somebody must lose. Just as my grandmother and her class were taxed out of existence to benefit the English working classes, so the English working classes will be overtaken by the millions of Africans and Indians and Chinese who are still compelled to live at a lower level. Once you start equalization, the wheel runs on until, at some point, you revert again to natural inequality.

Old men, such as I am, doubtless always look wistfully towards the good old days, and angry young men curse them. The process is repeated in every generation, and always greeted as something quite new. In my young days there was a tag (now thought repulsive) about 'knowing one's place'. It's not a bad thing to know. If you know your place and stay there you may be fairly happy. If the only place that anyone knows is the front seat of a Rolls Royce with a mink coat and a television set and a large income, the rat-race is bound to be ferocious. So I shall continue, unrepentantly, to think that, all in all, Nutfield was a happier human community than any I see in England now.

However, I have attempted to describe only a comparatively wealthy community in a time of prosperity. Had I been born in the slums of Manchester, I should undoubtedly think that life had greatly improved today. We are all victims of circumstance: and until civilization reaches a point at which every child born on earth is assured of food, warmth, and shelter from the cradle to the grave, all thinking about wealth and poverty, justice and injustice, privilege and equality, will be muddled thinking. I am biased by my experience, but then, so is everyone else.

Chapter Two

What did you do in the Great War, Daddy?
RECRUITING PLACARD 1914

HAVE NO FEAR: this is not a book of war. The war of 1914 has been described with great eloquence by gifted writers and poets: in that it differs from the war of 1939, which has been chronicled at great length by soldiers and statesmen. The 1914 war flamed up suddenly into a crusading fire for a peaceful but still adventurous generation: the 1939 war was a thunderstorm already expected by people depressed by clouds. I cannot exclude 1914, because my life, like that of many, was completely changed by it.

Harried by white feathers, patriotic songs, and candid friends, I joined the Artists Rifles. I did not do so because I thought that they were artists, but because their headquarters happened to be round the corner, and also because I hoped that the name would annoy my father. It was in fact a good deal rougher than anything I had anticipated. I was five foot five inches when I left Eton. In the ensuing year I grew to six foot two. I was therefore a gangling youth, with small physical reserves: the long route marches every day, with a heavy pack and a rifle which seemed to bore into my thin shoulder blades, were exhausting: I found it difficult to keep awake on guard duty at night.

In July 1914, 'shirking' camp, I had escaped to Nutfield. There, at breakfast at the round table, I heard of the declaration of war. It did not then seem to have anything to do with me: another war for the Army. My grandmother said something like 'Dear, dear!' or 'It doesn't signify'; Aunt Una remarked that probably Anthony would have to go to France. We were only three: Aunt Sarah was married to her clergyman: Aunt Gertrude had gone off to found a Rest Home for Nurses at Eastbourne. Nutfield was very peaceful. All my thoughts were on the coming glories of Oxford, where I should become a Fellow of All Souls, and live a quiet life for ever. Destiny had other plans.

After a week or so, I had to return to my parents' house at Kineton, a singularly unattractive mansion which my father had bought in order to be near the kennels of the Warwickshire Hunt. It was in fact so near that the stink of them was ever-present. Here the pressure grew apace. Every post brought me letters from Eton friends who had joined this or that crack regiment, and invited me to do the same. Conversation seemed to centre exclusively on the necessity that all 'able-bodied' young men should join up. (How I wished to be a cripple!) My uncle commanded the Brigade of Guards and offered a commission. Since I remained mutinous, even Aunt Sarah was called from her rectory. To my surprise and horror, she added herself to the pressures. 'You must join up for the sake of England.' I remained obstinate: was life to be just a return to an eternal OTC?

One evening my father said, 'You will be in the hall at eight o'clock tomorrow morning, and I shall take you to Epsom, where you will join the Public Schools Battalion.' I said, 'No.' My father repeated: 'You will be in the hall at eight o'clock to-morrow morning.' I was in the hall at eight o'clock tomorrow morning. In the train, after an interval (reserved first-class carriage) my father said, 'If you join up today, I will see that after the war you lack for nothing: I will engage myself to pay you £2,000 a year, and you can do what you like.' I said miserably, 'And if I don't?' 'If you don't,' replied my father, 'I shall put you into a third-class business house and cut you off with a shilling.' I wondered what he meant by a third-class business house: did he know himself? Better than soldiering, perhaps. I was too young to think about the shilling. The £2,000 a year had no attractions: I was sure that, if I became a soldier, I should be killed.

At Epsom I was measured, weighed, medically examined, asked questions and then invited to sign a form. I refused. There was a shameful pause. My poor father (it makes me sad to think of it) pulled himself together and said, 'Well, if he won't, he won't: we all have our different views.' We travelled back in silence. The next day I ran away to London, where a more or less pacifist aunt gave me an attic to sleep in. But it was no use: the climate of opinion had me gripped.

The staggering losses in France soon made the Artists Rifles, like other such bodies, a source of potential officers. Early in December 1914, I found myself a second lieutenant in the gunners. This seemed at least out of the fire into the frying-pan: I thought that an officer's life would be smoother, and gunnery perhaps interesting. I was sent for training to Harwich and then

Lydd. It was a cold winter: neither resort was exactly gay. At Harwich we were placed under Major Hammersley, a Kitchener-like figure with no conversation and much wrath. He had us up at 6 a.m. to service the guns. This meant, among other things, picking up a hundred-pound shell, icy, slippery, and covered with mud, balancing it on the left forearm, and thrusting into the breech, getting one's hand away before, as Major Hammersley grimly said, he took off the back of it with his ramrod. I need hardly say that I dropped the shells on my frozen toes, on the floor, on the gun, anywhere but in the breech, and had my blue hands skinned. We did regular night watches, eight to twelve, twelve to four, four to eight: sad solitary stints, with the gun-crews calling through the cold night: 'Tide, four foot fall, falling.' Hammersley made us stand at opposite corners of a huge field, and bawl commands: the silly man had no idea of voice production, and thought (like so many military gentlemen) that shouting meant strength. All our voices became whispers, and I lost mine for good and all: I could never again sing a note in tune: and for that I curse Hammersley and all his stupid clan. He robbed me of a great pleasure in life through sheer ignorance.

Lydd, though a waste of frozen shingle, was a little better. Here we were allowed to play with what were then monster guns, running on rails: and some ballistic science was forced into our brains (though never much into mine). To my unspeakable fury, I was then sent back to Landguard Fort, on the other side of the Harwich estuary. I don't know what I had expected, but not that. It was just dreary. One evening a sergeant poked his head into the mess, where some majors and colonels were snoring, while a few subalterns knocked billiard balls about, and said: 'Volunteers wanted for Eastern Mediterranean.' No one took any notice. I did not dare to speak. Mediterranean? If I was to be killed, I might at least see that. I sidled out, and caught up with the sergeant on the rainy catwalk. 'What did you say?' He repeated it gruffly. I said, 'Put me down.' He said, 'Better come into the office.' I followed him. 'It may be rough,' he suggested. I did not know if he was referring to the sea. I repeated: 'Put me down.'

My orders arrived almost instantly. I was to sail from Wharf Number So-and-So from Liverpool on such-and-such date. Secrecy was not such as it became in the next war. I could get to Liverpool as I liked. I had forty-eight hours. My father and stepmother (it seems queer now) decided to accompany me. There was a great crowd at Euston station, cheering and waving flags. At Rugby my small stepsister met me to say goodbye. I was sure that I was off to my death, but it was all very exciting. I presumed that I should travel on a cattle-boat in great discomfort, but even that did not matter. My parents were pleased: they were 'giving their only son': the right thing to do. In the dusk I slipped through the dock gates at Liverpool.

A great surprise awaited me. I found myself gazing up at the iron cliffs of the largest ship I had ever seen. It was the *Olympic*, and on her I was to travel. It was a thousand times more exciting than anything I had dreamed of. I was delighted: all regrets vanished. I joined the long queue going up the gangways, and, after a long shuffle, reached the Embarkation Officer's desk. He riffled through his papers and said, 'I can't find any trace of your name: come back in three hours.' (This always happens to me: I am never on any list.) I milled around, and noted that there was a huge number of troops on board: I believe it was seven thousand. I realized that, after all, it might be very uncomfortable. But, I said to myself, this is the *Olympic* and she is White Star Line. I went down the gangway and into the White Star Offices opposite. They knew all about me there: I guess my stepmother had seen to that. Without any fuss they gave me a cabin ticket: B 47. Privilege, how nice. I went on board again and was ushered into a Louis XV suite with bath. It was a bit too much. I noticed that the adjacent doors were labelled with the names of generals. I wondered if I could get away with it, and feared not. I made my way to the bar, and there, after a careful reconnaissance, discovered a colonel who seemed pleasant. His name was Maurice Holmes. After a drink or two, I asked him what sort of accommodation he had. 'Lousy!' he replied. I said, 'I find myself, by some mistake I suppose, in . . .' I took him to B 47. He was delighted and had his baggage moved in immediately. 'Don't worry, it'll be quite all right,' he assured me. And it was. We travelled in millionaire comfort.

My spirits soared sky-high. I was away from Father, away from the dreary routines of Harwich and Lydd, going south. Nothing mattered. Maurice Holmes was a perfect companion, witty and intelligent, with what seemed to me a vast experience of life. He was a great raconteur and I listened enthralled to his stories. He threw middle-aged cold water on my enthusiasms, but I did not mind. 'I suppose you know,' he said, 'that you'll have a hell of a time on Gallipoli.' I said that I didn't care: it would be better than England. 'Shall I tell you,' he said, '*why* you don't care?' I said, 'Tell away!' He said, 'Because you think you'll be able to tell the waitress in the ABC shop all about it when you get back – *if* you do!' I thought this was a bit unfair, but wondered if there were a germ of truth in it.

We passed Gibraltar and I took photographs. In those days there was nothing against that. We sailed on under cloudless skies. The isles of Greece! And then suddenly we were at anchor in Mudros, and everything was terrible. Mudros was bare and hot and hideous. Maurice Holmes disembarked, fortunate fellow, for Egypt. I saw him down the gangway and felt alone. With a herd of others I was rowed in a caique to the *Arcadian*, the headquarters ship which was popularly supposed to be aground on empty champagne bottles. I was handed a ticket (which I still by some marvel possess) '2nd Lieut. Fielden, to embark this evening for Cape Helles'. Suddenly, I was for it. I cast about madly for means to evade my fate. A soldier on the *Olympic* had attempted to cut his throat with an army razor, but had fumbled it. When I asked him why, he said: 'I signed on for Home service only, and I ain't going to Gallipoli.' Should I do something of the kind? (He got seven years penal servitude.) But there was no time. Soon I was chugging in a tug through the dusk.

It was very quiet and very dark. We were instructed not to smoke, not to show a light, and not to talk. The tug glided on over the oily water. Indian sepoys stifled hacking coughs. Once we bumped and slid over something. 'The wreck of the *Majestic*,' said the skipper. Turkish searchlights from Chanak began to sweep across our path. Presently we were wading ashore in darkness. Baggage was somehow sorted out. There were gun flashes from the north east and from the south: Troy. We were piled into a dugout with our sleeping-bags. I suppose we slept.

In the morning a staff-captain said: 'You to So-and-So, you to Such-and-Such: Fielden to Eighth Corps Trench Mortars.' I broke into a cold sweat: this was much worse than anything I had anticipated. Trench mortars, of which I knew nothing, were called 'The Suicide Club'. Surely this could not happen to me! 'There'll be somebody coming down to fetch you,' said the Staff-Captain. 'You can ride, I suppose?' I said that I could ride. I sat on the beach and waited. Out at sea there was a hospital ship. I wondered whether, if I swam out to her and arrived exhausted, I should be taken away to somewhere else. Probably not. With great inexactitude I visualized, behind the small hills behind me, a sort of OTC camp. And a very dangerous one.

After what seemed an interminable wait, a man cantered up, leading a second horse. This was Douglas, a grand fellow who was to be with me for a long time. I mounted, and off we went. Douglas said, 'I'd better lead, sir, it's a bit tricky.' It was. He went swiftly ahead in a cloud of dust, and I followed. Suddenly he shouted back at me, 'Have to gallop here, sir, Asiatic Annie's got this taped.' We galloped. Then he turned right and disappeared. My horse followed. I found myself in a small gully. To right and left, there were men and horses in dug-out bays: in front, astonishingly, was a little low house built of stone with a sandbagged roof, thrust into and level with a slight rise in the land. Three officers, standing outside it, gave me a friendly welcome. Calvert, who commanded the unit, was spare, quiet, nervous: Williams was round-faced, chubby, gay: Peake was grizzled and grandfatherly, a ranker officer who was a sort of nannie to everyone. Both Peake and Williams were shortly to be killed.

I was handed a whisky-and-soda. In those days, whatever else went short, a whisky-and-soda was de rigueur in every officer's mess. You offered it to every guest and you drank it with every guest whether you liked it or not. We went into the little house, where there was just room for the four of us to sit round a table made from crates. Bully beef, slightly curried, and army biscuits, were put before us. This was the staple Gallipoli fare, which hardly ever changed. The difficulty of landing stores was so great that fresh food seldom got as far as the trenches, and none of us, during my time at least, ever received a parcel or a letter. Personally I found the bully beef and biscuits excellent. I was delighted: it was not, after all, anything like an OTC camp.

While we were eating, a 5.9 howitzer shell whined over us and burst with a shattering explosion just outside the hut. We were protected by the stone walls, and the men in the unit, in their dug-out bays, were untouched. But eight men of a Scottish infantry regiment, who were drawing water from a pipe, had a direct hit: and all were killed. We ran out: in the swirling smoke was a heap of bodies. And they were screaming. The scream of a human male, when you hear it for the first time, is a devastating sound. Williams and I picked up a man who was waving his arms: he came up like a feather: both his legs had been severed. I staggered back. Williams glanced at me and said, 'Go into the hut: you aren't used to this kind of thing yet.' I did not go in: but I was useless. A man was laid down at my feet: he had had his liver blown away. Into the bloody mess Borg. the Maltese cook, poured a bottle of iodine. The man kept repeating, 'Och! they've done for me this time.' My hair rose on my scalp. Yet, a few days later, that became a joke in the unit, and at every whine of shell or bullet, we would say, 'Och! they've done for me this time.' One soon becomes inured to death.

Trench mortars were unpleasant and unpopular. We used in the main what was known as the 'Japanese Bomb Howitzer'. It was a glorified mechanical catapult. Shaky and imprecise, it sent up from the bottom of a trench, a fat 100 lb bomb, generally known as a 'flying pig', which soared slowly into the air and fell down within a very short range. The idea was that with such a high trajectory it spelt blue murder if it fell into an enemy trench. And so it did. The only trouble was that it was quite apt to fall back into one's own. From the first shot it was obvious to everyone, and instantly attracted an enemy barrage. Therefore the infantry groaned when we appeared.

Like everyone else on Gallipoli, I got dysentery. Dysentery in Gallipoli provided a curious example of human adaptability. Since almost everyone had it, and almost everyone could not, obviously, go to hospital, it had perforce to be played down. One fainted on the way to the latrine, was picked up by one's batman, put on the stool, and fainted again after shooting out blood and pus: then, after an hour or so, one resumed duty. There was a plentiful supply of chlorodyne which one swallowed thankfully. There was no heroism about it: it became a nuisance like the common cold in England, or malaria in India. Occasionally someone died, as they may die from malaria or pneumonia, but mostly we recovered and relapsed and recovered again. But we were not exactly the better for it. I have often wondered how far dysentery alone was responsible for our failure in Gallipoli. It certainly sapped vitality.

Nobody, I think, hoped or expected that we should ever 'take' Achi Baba, the low hill held by the Turks some four miles from the beach. The classic stalemate in France had set the pattern of war. You held your own trenches if you could, and occasionally made an advance of a hundred yards: that was about all. The distant goal of Constantinople had become a farcical idea. You did your job and saved your skin, if you could.

The days passed, and eventually one of them brought the

41

news that Anzac and Suvla had been evacuated. Hope flared up: surely we must go too. But very soon a document arrived. I always wish that I had kept a copy of it: so far as I know, it has never been published. It was a grandiloquent effusion, of which I now only remember a few words. 'The positions at Anzac and Suvla Bay have now been successfully evacuated ... but that at Cape Helles will not only be maintained, but strengthened by strong reinforcements from the Ninth Army ... battalion after battalion of the Turkish Army has been mown down before you, and Cape Helles has become known to the Turks as the "Slaughter House" ... we will go on ...' I suppose that this document was issued in order that it should fall into Turkish hands and mask our evacuation. Strangely enough, we believed it. We believed it all the more because units of the Ninth Army did arrive, and passed through our gully. Our spirits sank to zero: we were on Gallipoli for ever. It must have been a very successful piece of propaganda.

Soon, however, we were ordered to 'report to the beach for fatigues'. More significantly, we were instructed to 'burn all papers'. (Even then, though we began to hope that *we* were destined to leave, we did not yet believe in a full-scale evacuation.) The burning of papers was not an easy job. Smoke (except by night), and glow (except by day), had to be avoided. Calvert and I, the only two remaining officers, crouched over a brazier which was constantly dowsed with water. Calvert was now in a profound state of depression, because his wife, whom he adored, was expecting a first child and he had no news. This made him largely indifferent to what went on.

The men of the unit were, without exception, old soldiers of some ten years service. They were tough. Curiously enough, and to my own great surprise, I got on well with them. They thought me a comic sort of baby, but the queer feeling that I was a gent carried enormous weight. Was it a bad feeling? I don't know now. I only know that they never let me down, and always, while I was with them for the years of the war, they nursed me through every crisis and never failed in their loyalty. I owed them an enormous debt, and I salute any of them who may read this.

The evacuation of Cape Helles was the most dramatic event that I shall ever know. Only very slowly did we get around to the idea that the whole Army was leaving. And with that knowledge came terrors, elastic stretching of the nerves. The beaches were enfiladed by the Turkish guns in Troy, and every five minutes or so a salvo would explode. It was known now that the front line was held more and more thinly, and that the Turks could quite easily descend on the beaches. It was said, perhaps intentionally, that the Turks castrated and tortured prisoners. A horrid fear was engendered: a horrid fear that one might get left. On one occasion I was sent up to a distant gully to fetch something: I remember my sweaty panic: I should be wounded by some stray shell, at the mercy of the Turks.

At nights we worked on the loading of guns and ammunition. The sea, at first calm, began to be rough. It became difficult to load heavy stuff on to lighters in the surf. On one unforgettable night, the Navy sent all our lighters back from Tenedos, saying that the sea was too rough to unload them. The remarks about the Navy were unprintable, and I cherish an anger to this day. They could have taken the lighters somewhere: the last thing was to send them back to the beaches. We had to unload them and push the stuff into the cliff caves again.

Our last night arrived. We were instructed to stand by for embarkation. We sat on W beach. We now knew that there was no one in the front line and that the plop-plop of rifles, dimly heard, was caused by their automatic discharge through sand-weighting of the triggers. There was nobody at all between us and the Turkish Army. The men were nervous. Calvert had retreated into a melancholy of his own, walking up and down and muttering. On our left were the ruins of the fort of Sedd-ul-Bahr, and on them a French *poilu* was perched, giving a shrill trumpet-blast every time that he saw the flash of the guns in Asia. Eighteen seconds elapsed before the shells arrived. Eighteen seconds one counted. Then there would be a flash and a roar: and a scuttering of men and mules. In front of us was the beached steamer, the *River Clyde*: with a bridge of boats connecting her with the shore. Every now and then a voice called through the darkness 'Unit 304, down to the boats'. Men ran: the trumpet shrilled: the shells exploded. Out at sea, red lights moved. At 4 a.m. our turn came. We ran down, and across the bridge of boats. As we were running, the trumpet shrilled. The shells fell on either side of the bridge, deluging us. Then we were running through the *Clyde*, were on the tug, were putting out to sea. Calvert, hysterical, stood on the bridge and laughed: 'There they go, and we are *off*!!' Soon we were on a deck crowded with sleeping figures. Happy, I slept.

Interlude in Egypt. This is fine. The retreat from Gallipoli is as disorganised, though in a different and less critical way, as the retreat from Dunkirk twenty-five years later. The Gallipoli army, flung on to the beaches of Alexandria, stays there, for the most part, for six months. Perhaps Authority is uncertain about redeployment - Salonika, Alexandretta (there are rumours of another landing there), Palestine, Mesopotamia, Italy, France, India? Or perhaps transport and equipment is lacking. A small unimportant unit like ours was forgotten altogether. We had no orders and Calvert was indifferent: the men were free to amuse themselves in Alexandria, which swiftly became a very gay city. My uncle by marriage, Dr William Hunter, had arrived in Cairo after dealing with typhus in Serbia: and my very enchanting aunt had joined him there. Moodily Calvert agreed that I could go. I found myself in a luxury suite at Shepheards Hotel. Beatrice Hunter was pretty, amusing, intelligent, and a keen Egyptologist: she was a friend of Quibell, the Curator of the Museum. She took me in hand and whisked me through museums, bazaars, mosques, and down to Luxor. Suddenly, as one who awakes, my eyes were opened to man-made beauty. The sleek regal cats, the tragic handsome Pharaohs, the great lotus columns of the temples, the iridescent tear-bottles, the scarabs, the jewels, the mummies in their painted coffins, filled me with a new delight. And Shepheards was gay: full of laughing people: nobody seemed a whit depressed by the Gallipoli fiasco. The sun poured down: every moment was a new experience: I was alive: I was nineteen, and life was grand.

After a month, Calvert recalled me. He was departing, and the unit was to be merged in a new siege battery under a Major Burrows. Our first chore was to dig gun replacements for coast defence. It was an easy, undemanding job: nobody worked very hard: there was a limpid sea to bathe in, and we unearthed a beautiful Roman pavement. Burrows was a Theosophist and introduced me to the works of Madame Blavatsky and Mrs Annie Besant. Having been close to sudden death, I had had some thoughts about an after-life: and I found Theosophy thrilling. (For two years, despite Army fare, I lived on a vegetarian diet and wrote down all my nightly experiences on the Astral Plane. Then I forgot all about it). I cannot say that my contribution to winning the war was very great at this time: indeed I never thought about the war at all. In the 1914 war, as in others before it, that was a possible thing to do.

Along with many others of my generation and immediate experience, I was, not perhaps surprisingly, in a mood of rather exalted romanticism. Like a curtain falling on the first act of a play, the Gallipoli adventure, brief, vivid, abrupt, had cut me off from the sheltered life of parents, teachers and humdrum development. I had commanded men, escaped death, gained confidence, and discovered an entirely new world. I was young, tall, slim, and, as far as I could gather, not ugly. I had never had sexual relations with anyone, and my virginity teased me: partly, perhaps, because there was a good deal of bragging about sexual prowess among the troops in Egypt then. But at nineteen (at any rate in my case) thoughts about sex are apt to soar into cloud-cuckoo-land, and physical facts are misted over by romance.

In the evenings in Alexandria, I used to sit alone (the habit of solitude being always with me) on the balcony of the Mohammed Ali Club, a luxurious institution to which all officers could belong. It was a splendid place for one who preferred the stalls to the stage: from it one looked directly down the Bond Street of Alexandria, the rue Cherif Pasha. Egypt was then at the height of its exotic dazzle as a meetingplace of East and West, and the street was one of the most colourful places in the world. Soldiers, mostly young, were everywhere – British, French, Italian, Senegalese, Indian, Gurkha, Australian. Greek, Italian and Egyptian civilians, moneyed by army pickings, swept past in what then seemed sleek cars or sparkling carriages. Even poverty, in the guise of street-vendors or beggars or dragomen, dressed in gaudy rags, appeared glamorous and gay. The slanting sun touched the crowd with a red glitter. It was my first view of the East. I did not come to it, like the hero of Conrad's *Youth*, from a devastating shipwreck, but I did come from the beaches of Gallipoli, and its brilliance enfevered me. I felt as if I had been transported on a magic carpet into an Arabian Nights Entertainment. Adventure, surely, must await me.

Through the glitter and movement of the street there came, every evening at the same hour, like some royal barge cleaving through a crowded waterway, an equipage which outshone all others. It was a victoria drawn by grey horses, and it seemed to me the perfection of elegance. From spokes to shafts it was so polished that it might have been of ebony: silver bridles, silver lamps, silver hubs, shimmered against the black. In it, alone, sat a woman who to my innocent eyes appeared the most dazzling creature in creation. (And so potent was the spell that, across

45

nearly fifty years, I feel its thrill.) The lady was dressed, always differently, with a sumptuousness which fell just short, but not very far short, of vulgarity. Diamonds glittered under a low-swept hat from which ospreys or ostrich feathers curled. I thought her a mixture of Lady Deadlock, La Dame aux Camelias, and Rider Haggard's She. I also thought her remote as the stars: I was worshipping a goddess from afar. But my heart leapt up to the victoria more than it would have done to any daffodil. Each evening I was bewitched.

Suddenly the eyes of the goddess flashed in my direction. I turned round to see at what or whom they might be flashing: I could see nothing. I moved my chair so that I was alone, next day, in a corner of the balcony. This time, unmistakably, there was a smile. I could not believe it. She has, I thought, mistaken me for some acquaintance. Nevertheless my legs, one evening, carried me down the steps and set me walking after the victoria. Did it stop? It did. And, as I came up to it, the goddess leaned out and extending a small gloved hand, said (what an anticlimax) *'Bonsoir, mon ami'*. And in a flurry of silk and lace she descended, and walked into a teashop. I, innocent idiot, walked on. Doubtless there was a cackle of laughter from Olympus.

Why did I walk away? Shyness, ignorance, innocence? Or did I not really wish to meet the goddess face to face? At this distance I cannot tell. But the result was to arouse her attention – and resentment. Next day and on days following, as I walked to or from the club, the victoria drew in to the curb beside me, and the greys, slow-stepping, walked at my pace. I looked away. To become the pursued rather than the pursuer was, to my young mind, something of an affront.

Clearly it could not stop there. With infinite caution (so I imagined) I sat at the bar of the Mohammed Ali club and chatted with the barman. He, like all his species, knew about everything and everybody in social-sexual circles. With great tact (so I supposed) I got around to the victoria. He laughed. 'You mean that trollop Marica? A good bint, but she's married to a Turk and kept by old Achmed Bey: anyway, she's slept with everyone in Alex. Better watch your step.' I was dismayed but not convinced. Barman's gossip, I thought. It did not match my vision: I would not believe it. A few days later the victoria passed me, and in it, with Marica, sat Gourlay. Gourlay was fat and florid and vulgar: the most repulsive subaltern in Egypt. It seemed

46

incredible that he should sit beside the goddess. He had, by some chance, I said to myself, been introduced to her, and she was graciously giving him a lift. A day or two later I cornered him, and – with a brash stupidity – said, 'Did you have a nice drive with Marica?' He looked at me with contempt. 'A naice drive,' he mimicked me. 'I had a jolly good grind, if that's what you mean.' With those words a goddess fell with an almighty thud into limbo. Suddenly I was in a mad rage, not only with Marica and all her sex, but also with my own stupidity, ignorance, and failure. I rushed into the brothels of Alexandria. They were legion, and (in the absence then of cinema and radio) the most usual form of distraction for the troops. I wanted, I suppose, to revenge myself on Marica and on all women. Like a dipsomaniac who is weaned from alcohol by overwhelming and sickening doses, I procured a satiety which revolted me. Women, I decided, had nothing to do with romantic love.

This partly romantic, partly squalid, episode is germane to my story for two reasons. In the first place it is true, and strange, and still vivid: in the second, it may have considerably deflected my life. I do not know – nor does anyone else – when and why homosexuality occurs: perhaps the Marica muddle was a symptom rather than a cause. Freud says that you can never make a homosexual into a heterosexual, and vice versa: that the pattern is fixed at birth. But sometimes, when I hear people talking about the dangers of the 'corruption' of the young by homosexuals, I wonder how far the heterosexual young may also be 'corrupted' by the wrong kind of woman. Heterosexuality also has its perversions. Had I had a romantic affair with Marica at that romantic moment of youth, my attitude to women might have been a different one: as it was, I was romantically bruised about women in general, and the two years of all-male society, then a part of war, which followed, did not help to correct my estrangement.

While this was going on, I had embarked on another and different activity. Hugh Buckler – perhaps that was his name, I cannot now be sure – was an Australian actor-manager who had a perfectly correct idea that, in the absence of other diversions, the largest theatre in Alexandria could be filled to capacity by almost any tripe. I became, God knows why, a member of his repertory company. We staggered through a mass of plays, *The School for Scandal, The Second Mrs Tanqueray, The Rivals, His House in Order, The Truth, The Gay Lord Quex.* We must have been frightful. It did not matter: the house was always full: we got tumultous applause: we even got flattering notices in the local press. Hugh was a good producer and a bully. He would keep us up all night, sitting away at the top of the gallery and shouting 'What's this? A funeral? Start the scene again!' or 'Not a single word have I heard: start again!' or 'Can't you use your legs? Are you paralysed? Walk straight down stage!' or 'Put your voice up, up, up! Hey, come out to the front and put your voice UP!' He frightened me so much that I scarcely knew what I was doing when on stage, but he did give me back the use of my speaking, though not my singing, voice.

All this came to an abrupt end when I was ordered to Sollum. It was just as well that I was. I was very nearly on the mat with Major Edwards, who had succeeded Burrows. He thought that I did not work, and his thought was right. I did not deserve Sollum, but it fell into my lap. Sollum had been the scene of a dashing little exploit by the Duke of Westminster – at least he figured as the hero – against the Senussi, and a holding operation, known as the Western Frontier Force, was put in there. I was promoted to captain, and put in charge of a half-battery of captured German howitzers. With me (I cannot now think why) came the men of the trench mortar unit. I had one subaltern under me. I also had a pair of horses. I was, more or less, on my own. As often happens – perhaps as always happens – responsibility made me a much better man.

Sollum was altogether a lucky dip for me. Many people might have been bored by it, but, if you like deserts, as I do, Sollum is (or was) a Paradise. The bay, twenty-five miles across, sweeps round in a scimitar curve of silver sand, and from it red cliffs rush up eight hundred feet to flat desert above. In the little port the water, emerald green, is so clear that you can see a rusty anchor two hundred feet below. I had little to do save for keeping the guns in trim and organising practise shoots round the perimeter. For the first time I enjoyed riding: there was nobody to tell me what to do and I was quite at home in the saddle. I used to gallop by myself over the desert which never changed, except for the mirages, unbelievably complete with palms and minarets and gleaming water, shifting into nothing as one approached them. I found the strange old Roman wells, dry vaulted caverns which must once have collected water, and, with the aid of our instruments, plotted maps of the area. I played water-polo with the men in the translucent sea, and got much

48

ducked for my pains: but I had become a good swimmer. With my subaltern, Caldwell, who was a Roman Catholic, I argued much about religion with no result. I went out on a minesweeper, and for the first time heard that extraordinary thing, Marconi's wireless – a voice actually speaking over the water at a distance of a mile! And I fell in love with a blond young man called Steed, who seemed to me Sir Galahad. I would no more have declared my love than I would have screamed in church: and I don't suppose I saw Steed more than a dozen times, and always on formal occasions – a meal in an officer's mess, a military exercise, a foray with the Camel Corps, a walk with the tame gazelles which he kept. And I never saw him again. But I needed to love, not to be loved: and my love gave a shimmer to Sollum.

It did not last, of course: I should have liked it to last for the duration of the war. After six months, I was ordered, with my men, to join a battery in Palestine. The move was not only unpleasant: it was also, for me, terrifying. I was well aware that it was one thing to command a small unit in the back of befuff, and quite another to be a captain in a battery of the front line. I did not think I could do it: and therefore I couldn't. I swiftly became the worst captain in the British Army. Not only was I an abject physical coward, throwing myself into a dugout or slit-trench whenever we were bombarded, and telling a subaltern to take over: I was also grossly incompetent in all my duties. The captain of a battery was then (I don't know what he is now) the pivot of the unit: the major commanding was usually taken up with administrative duties, visits to headquarters, plotting of future moves, discussions of range and barrage with infantry commanders, and so on. The subalterns were controlled by the captain. I controlled nothing: I was a figure of fun. I deserved to be shot out with ignominy: but Major Bagnall, who commanded the battery, was a man of extraordinary patience and kindness, and he was not going to let down his captain, however bad. His tolerance made me the more ashamed, and perhaps worse. Shielded by him, I did less and less. I was about the worst soldier in the world.

Then, suddenly, things changed. Bagnall was given red tabs and taken to headquarters. In his place came a Major who was – and it is saying quite a lot – even worse than I was. He was, I think, a sick man: a pale little squirt, with no authority and no decision. He was terrified of everybody and everything. Perhaps Bagnall had subtly educated me: perhaps I felt a surge of responsibility. Almost overnight I changed. My cowardice fell away like the Albatross: I felt perfectly capable of running the battery. Quite quickly I became an efficient officer. And then the Major was wounded or fell sick: I don't now remember which. He disappeared, and, *faute de mieux* I suppose, I became CO, and presently was exalted to temporary major. I began to enjoy the war. The battery was my pride, and I took great pleasure in seeing that it was efficient. But I had reckoned without the Brigade Commander, Colonel Moore. He – probably for good reasons – detested me, and wished to get me out. Through the grapevine of my still loyal trench mortar men, I came to know that he wished to replace me by a protegé named Burns. And I was now subjected to a sort of witch hunt. Moore would descend on the battery at all hours, ply me with questions, examine my reports and returns, be present when the battery moved, watching me. Presently he sent a complaint to headquarters, saying that my ammunition returns were inaccurate. (So they were: you cannot keep on firing shells and at the same time have your ammunition returns up-to-date.) I was summoned to headquarters. There was an odd parallel with my summons by Lyttleton at Eton. I had prepared – oh fool! – a brief to show that the battery had been efficient under my command. The General, like Lyttleton, cut me short. 'I think,' he said, 'you are a little young to command a battery: so I shall transfer you.' I walked across the yard of the farm with the Staff Captain, and had difficulty in controlling my tears. He slapped me on the back. 'Come. I'll give you a drink,' he suggested, 'these things happen to everybody.' Gratefully I swallowed the whisky, but I was humiliated, ashamed, and enraged. I had come to love the battery and the men: at one fell unjustified swoop, I was treated as a criminal. From that moment, perhaps, began in me a pathological hatred of all Little Men in Authority. In later years, I had it out with the General. He said, 'What could I do? Go against my Brigadier? And where would that have ended? What did it matter to me?'

Demoted again to captain, I was sent to a 'Derby' battery on the coast. 'Derby' men were then regarded as conscripts, and thought poorly of. I was of the same opinion. I loathed the battery and its officers and men. I was desperately unhappy. But my unhappiness – or my experience – had cancelled out both cowardice and laziness. With no pleasure, I did my job with efficiency. I had learned the rigmarole and could carry it out.

I was a quite good captain, but in my heart I wanted to howl. One day I was called to the telephone by HQ. Bagnall was on the line. He said, 'The General wants to know how you are getting on?' I said, ungraciously, 'You must know perfectly well that I'm not getting on at all.' He said 'Happy?'. I said: 'No, sir.' After a pause, he asked: 'Would you care to come to Headquarters, the General says?' Ungratefully I replied, 'Anything better than this.'

I found myself working under a Major Armstrong, who was called Counter Battery Staff Officer. Counter battery work of those days would in these seem ridiculous. Nevertheless it was the greatest fun, and admirably suited my capacities. The aim of it was to find and silence enemy batteries. For this purpose we had ten telephones, a huge map, and the power to ask the Royal Air Force to take photographs. The ten telephones, at which one or other of us were in attendance night and day, were connected with various points in the front line: if *one* enemy battery opened fire, the observer would give us, as best he could, a rough bearing by ear. When several of these bearings came in, we crisscrossed the strings on our map (each leading from an observer's post) and guessed the position of the battery. Then we would ask the RAF to photograph the map square. With a jewellers' lens we studied the photographs. It was a Heath Robinson procedure by the standards of today: yet long practise soon made us expert in it. Armstrong went away and I took his place. I had become so accustomed to the job that I had a quite accurate (I was later able to check it) idea of where the enemy batteries were. I developed almost a sixth sense about it. In the back of my mind, I knew that some enemy battery had not fired for some time and must have moved. A couple of bearings would tell me that that was the six-inch in AQ 5 – 17; and quite often, turning one of our own batteries on to it – could silence it.

For the first, and last, time in my army career I had a sense of achievement. I had an idea that I was doing something which fitted me, and which I could do well. Perhaps this was partly due to the fact that I was comparatively safe (for, although I had learnt not to flinch disgracefully from high explosive, I did not care for it), and partly to the freedom from commanding men, a chore which has never appealed to me. I am often surprised by the apparent desire of many human beings to have authority over others: I dislike it quite as much as I dislike the authority of others over me. Then again – since I was pacifist-minded – I pleased myself with the notion that I was engaged in defence and not offence: I was protecting, as far as I could, our men from enemy gunfire. This is the classic rationalization of aggression as a means of defence: and, of course, nonsense. I did not stop to think that I was helping to kill enemy gunners: had I done so, I should, I suppose, have fallen back on the hoary old argument, 'Well, they started it.'

About a year before this, in my first and very unhappy days in Palestine, the poets had begun to invade my mind. I discovered by chance that the more difficult poems of Browning, *Sordello, Paracelsus, The Ring and the Book,* could banish my trembling fear under gunfire: and I gradually began to accumulate volumes. Bit by bit, mostly through periodicals, I came to know the then modern poets, Brooke, Blunden, Owen, Sassoon, Sorley: and they made me rejoice. Somebody somewhere was clothing in words my own detestation of war. The habit of reading poetry grew on me and added a new dimension to my life. I wished that I could write it but knew that I had no talent. I also began, when I had a chance, to sketch and paint. I still have a few pictures done in Palestine: much better, alas, than anything I ever achieved later, when I had been to the Slade School. Under the influence of a congenial job, my mind began to wake up.

Since at this time of my life (and perhaps always) I had to have a hero to worship, I found one in Atkinson, the Staff Captain. He was a dour north-countryman: an admirable soldier of indomitable courage. It was the attraction of opposites, perhaps. It started when, one day, we were both in the front line, and I was trying, with the donkey's ears (double periscopes), to spot an enemy sniper. A German howitzer shell landed about three yards in front of me: the donkey's ears were blown away and I was buried in rubble. Emerging, I found Atkinson looking at me with distaste. 'Do you know,' he asked me, 'that you've gone quite pale? It's a very bad example to the men.' 'Well, damn it,' I spluttered, 'and so would you.' 'No,' he said. 'You must learn to control yourself.' A little later we were walking over an open stretch of ground between the reserve trenches and headquarters when a Turkish 'pipsqueak' battery spotted us, and thought it would have some fun with us. The three-pounder shells were small but noisy: one burst ahead of us, and then one behind. 'They've got us bracketed,' I said to Atkinson. 'Shouldn't we run?' My legs were trembling. Atkinson sat down on the ground, and slowly unrolled one of his puttees. 'Do what you like,' he said. 'No Turkish pipsqueak is going to make me run.' For a moment I balanced precariously between my fear and his esteem. His esteem just won. And no more shells came. From that time Atkinson took a fatherly interest in me: he hoped to improve me, I think, and perhaps he did: but nothing could make me a good soldier.

Presently we began to prepare for the offensive of September 1918. This was enthralling, partly because it was a beautiful operation, partly because we were entrusted with what was a very well-kept secret. I had by now an almost unique knowledge of the enemy guns in our sector, and could see how they could be neutralized. We drew beautiful maps of the planned forward movements of our batteries and their subsequent ranges. I suppose that Allenby had an overwhelming superiority of men and guns and aeroplanes, and was bound to win his battle: perhaps that happens with almost all generals. But the feint with a thinly held line in Jordan, the secret movement of nearly the whole army to the coast, the sudden thrust and the wheeling movement which nearly – though not quite – trapped the whole Turkish Army, formed a very pretty piece of strategy. For a few weeks I enjoyed war.

On the evening before zero day, Atkinson and I thought – since our part of the work was finished – that we might pay a last visit to our respective batteries. The general, somewhat reluctantly, allowed us a car. We drove through the darkness up the new road which had been made, in preparation for the offensive, up to the front line. Missing our way, we drove straight in to the front line trench. We were thrown on to the parapet, and the car, with its engine nicely telescoped, stood straight on end. The infantry laughed a good deal. The car, ruined, was put under some brushwood, and we walked the six miles home. The general was not pleased. 'In future,' he said, 'you two will not go out together.' The next day, however, the army had moved far ahead, and I was filled with an overwhelming desire to see the country, now cleared, which I had long been studying from photographs. I asked the general if I might have a horse. With a not very good grace he assented, warning me to be careful of snipers. I trotted along in the glorious weather, very pleased with myself and life. One by one I found the battery sites which I had studied: sometimes without their guns, sometimes with: in two cases I discovered dummy wooden guns which had completely foxed me.

Towards evening I approached the site where I knew my old battery should be, saw it in the distance and waved: and at that moment the horse and myself fell into a deep Turkish dugout. We disappeared. The horse was staked and had to be shot: I got a slashing cut on the leg. When I got back to headquarters, the general was less angry than I had feared: he grunted and said, 'I suppose boys will be boys.'

Almost immediately we were asked to 'volunteer' for France. I do not know now whether this was a kind of overspill of panic from March, or whether, even in September 1918, the situation in France was still bad. It was obvious that we all had to 'volunteer', though I for one greatly regretted the glittering possibilities of Constantinople. Soon we were sailing from Alexandria for a destination unknown: and with T. E. Lawrence on board, a strange and very unsympathetic figure, wrapped in anger, about whom we had heard vague rumours, but whose acquaintance it did not seem worth cultivating. If we tried to speak to him, he was rude and boorish: so we left him alone. At that time, oddly enough, it did not occur to us that the war was coming to an end: we thought that we were going to spend years in France.

At Taranto we were put on to a train. There were four hundred of us, four to a third-class carriage of incredible filth, which meant that two slept on the seats and two on the floor. I was on the floor, of course. The journey actually lasted nine days. It was so rough that a hundred and fifty officers fell out on the way, stricken by various diseases. The rest of us arrived, somewhat battered, at Cherbourg. Here we were told that we were going to England, that our train would arrive at Waterloo at such-and-such time, and that we could send telegrams to our families announcing our arrival. This we did.

It was very strange, after three-and-a-half years, to see the English countryside again. I had mixed feelings about it. I had got used to sunshine, and England was drab and wet. At Waterloo there was a great crowd, and an orgy of kissing. Suddenly I found myself alone on the platform with another officer whom I knew slightly. Nobody had come to meet us. We sat on our valises, and talked. At first we said, 'They'll come presently.' Then we knew they wouldn't. We began to talk of the possibilities of taking an orange farm in Palestine: a nice country, we thought, and oranges seemed to grow easily: a little ploughing and manuring, and one picked them off the trees, crated them, and made a decent living. Presently, as the fog became thicker,

we felt that we had better go. I remembered an astringent spinster aunt who lived in Hill Street, was wealthy and not given to
emotion: and thither I went. Charlotte Ismay received me perfectly, showing no surprise and giving me a hot bath (which I
greatly needed) and an excellent dinner. After it, I told her that,
since my parents had not bothered to meet me, I should not go
to Kineton and I should not see them again: I felt quite confident that I could make my own way in the world. I was not
upset: I simply felt that my family no longer existed. Aunt Dot
pooh-poohed this attitude and said that I was being melodrama-
tic, and that my parents never had met anyone at stations, which
was true. She picked up the telephone, rang them up, and told
them that I should be down at such-and-such a time and they
must meet me, or else ...

I went down, and was met. Everyone was embarrassed. The
house was a hospital, and twenty girls whom I had known in my
teens sat round the dinner table, disguised in VAD uniforms.
They seemed to me unattractive, clumsy, and dull. My father
presented me with a cheque for £300, for my past twenty-first
birthday, and said he would now give me an allowance of £300
a year. I had a gratuity, and quite a lot of back pay which I had
not been able to spend in Palestine. It seemed to me that I was
staggeringly rich. Since it was still supposed that, after ten days
leave, I was going to France, I was able to persuade my stepmother to allow me to take my stepsister and her governess,
Stella Phillips – the two people I really loved – to London. I took
a suite at Claridge's, and asked everyone I knew to lunch, dinner,
supper and the theatre. I made Atkinson come down from Dur-
ham. On his first day there, my stepmother also came to lunch:
there were about ten of us. I noticed that Atkinson seemed
strangely ill-at-ease, and that there was sweat on his forehead.
I thought perhaps the room was too hot. After lunch my stepmother, as we sat on the sofa on the right of the entrance to the
lounge (that moment is very clear), said: 'Did you know that
your friend Atkinson was a *trooper*?' I said no, I hadn't known
it, but in any case I had been a private. 'That's different,' said
my stepmother. 'You make strange friends.' The next day Atkinson told me that he must go. I was too much buried in enjoyment
to care. He went. He wrote me a charming, heart-breaking letter
saying that he had enjoyed our friendship, but that 'we moved in
different circles'. Pest and fiend that I was, I did not bother to

answer. I never saw him again. In the whole of my life, I regret nothing so much.

One morning, while my sister was trying shoes at Pinet's shop in Bond Street, the maroons blared. Across this distance of time, I cannot imagine why we were not prepared for that moment: on tiptoe, so to speak, for it. But we were not. Scurrying out, we secured a taxi by great good luck, and, with a sort of conditioned reflex like that of everyone else, said: 'Buckingham Palace!' There followed an hour during which London was bewitched as never since, and, I should guess, never before. 1945 was a damp dull squib compared to it, and I doubt whether Mafeking night saw such a release from tension. By the time we reached Trafalgar Square (and I cannot think why we went that way: perhaps St James's Street was blocked) people were pouring out of the houses like ants, flushed, crying, laughing, shouting, throwing hats and shoes and scarves into the air, clambering on to every cab, every taxi, every bus, every delivery wagon, every bicycle. I see now, in front of us, a lorry filled with sacks, on to which a whole lot of girls had clambered, tears streaming down their cheeks, laughing and weeping. All traffic control was gone: the mass of vehicles, heavy with cheering people, moved up the Mall. Through the trees, below Carlton House Terrace, an officer perched on a milk waggon drove his horse at a gallop, the milk-pails rattling behind him. The war was over. And an epoch, though we did not realize it, was ended.

I was now a person very different from the young man who nervously slipped through the dock gates of Liverpool in 1915. Whether the change was good or bad, whether I was better or worse equipped for life, are questions answerable only if we lived our lives twice over. Undoubtedly I was more self-reliant, more decisive, and more adventurous, than I should have been had I spent those four years at Oxford. On the other hand I was more restless and more confused. Had I been at Oxford, I should perhaps have seen a straight dull road of life stretching ahead and taken it. Now I saw too many possible roads. Like all young people – or at any rate most – I was divided in mind between practical possibilities, vague desires, and conventional associations. I had been an undistinguished soldier and an undistinguished schoolboy, and I had (though this came later) few illusions about my talents. If I thought about the future, which I did not do very much, it was with a sense of alarm: I was trained for nothing and I seemed to myself already old. I had a vague desire to live somewhere on the borderland of the arts, but since I had never met a single musician, painter, architect, journalist, writer, poet, actor, producer or publisher, I had no idea how such a borderland could be reached. I also had a vague desire to get away from people, and to live a life apart from cities, societies, and institutions. Again, I had no idea how such a thing could be accomplished. My conventional associations decreed that Work was a different thing from Pleasure – as it ought not to be. I was aware that my father might take a strong and unpleasant attitude if I did not follow approved lines, and the approved lines were few. The Army, the Navy, the Air Force, the Foreign Office, the Civil Service – these would pass: to become a lawyer, a doctor, or an architect might have been just possible if (as I thought) I had been younger, but at twenty-two I was too old for long studies, and there was a host of much younger people coming up. I should, I felt, be instantly condemned – and deprived of money – if I attempted to become a painter or a writer or a musician: in any case I had small faith in my abilities. I can see now that I was timid and silly: but most young people are: and the early twenties of 1918, thrown back into the world with a half-completed education, were curiously unwanted by society. Older people shook their heads and thought that we had better stay in the Army: younger people were irritated by our tales of war, and wanted us out of the way. Except for those of undoubted talents and decisive aims, the situation was uncomfortable. Among a mass of confused feelings I had one sure wish – that I did not want to live in England. The spacious days of Nutfield still held my affection, and I did not doubt that the English should govern the world: but the grey wet climate and the conventional masks held no charm for me.

I now entered upon a decade of glorious life. I was stiff in opinions, always in the wrong, everything by starts, and nothing long: I was unstable as water and I did not excel: nevertheless, I enjoyed life to the full. The way that I chose – or that circumstances chose for me – was disorderly, aimless, and often plain mad: but, as I now see, it was the pattern which fitted my character, and which, lamentably, through economic necessity and convention, I failed to maintain. My character was allergic to all respectability, routine and repetition: steady jobs, long service, 'loyalty' and patient effort seemed to me then, as they seem to me now, denials of life. Man is born to skim every possible experience and enjoy them all: not to spend his whole waking hours – Good God! – in an office or a factory, with the carrot of an old-age pension dangling at the end of it. In this matter our age has made its most dreadful error, and that will be the verdict of posterity: and worst of all creeds is the famous communist delusion which seeks to dragoon men, like ants, into 'usefulness'. A pox on usefulness! There they go, the useful scientists who help to destroy humanity, the useful politicians who muddle the world, the useful business men who pick pockets and create anxiety, the useful civil servants binding men with rules: there they go, tumbling into the dark, forgotten: and, as Matthew Arnold said, 'unfreed, having seen nothing, still unblest'. True, Matthew Arnold also had hard things to say about the wide ocean: but for me, at any rate, it seems preferable to be struck by the tempest than to live in a brazen prison. My trouble was that, instead of exposing myself to tempests, I was apt to run for shelter.

Demobilization in 1918 was a long and frustrating business. It was indeed such an infuriating process that in 1945 the War Office, under my friend Sir James Grigg, took efficient steps to see that it was not repeated. I was sent to Catterick Camp, a dreary place where for four useless months I carried out useless army duties – long fussy drills, spit and polish, ceremonial parades. I was bored (as most of us were) by this aimless prison life. In the evenings, for want of anything better to do, I went to the Officers' Club and had dancing lessons. But I could not dance. I could learn steps, and dance by myself: I could not dance *with* someone. This was not due to anti-feminism: in later years at 'queer' parties I tried dancing with men, and that was worse: it was due to some strange lack of response to another human body. I am oddly and unreasonably revolted by physical intimacy. I am astonished by the desire of many human beings to share a bed with another, even for one night, or, God save us, sometimes for a whole lifetime: to me the idea seems repulsive. The Western idea of kissing is something that I could do without: and as for what the Americans have aptly termed 'necking', I find it a hideous bore. I fail to understand why human beings should feel compelled to stand or sit or lie, sucking at each other's flesh. The good or wicked fairies at my birth left these pleasures out of my composition. When people pat me on the back or ruffle my hair, my immediate reaction is to strike them.

So, although I loved music and movement, I could not dance. One day I happened to attend a lecture given by Alec Waugh. He extolled the delights of a university, and the value of them as a part of experience. I was carried away. For a shining moment the four-year-dead dazzlement of Oxford was revived. Impulsively I decided that I must go. And this decision was convenient, because demobilization was made easier for accepted students. But to arrive in Oxford was far less easy than I had imagined. In 1914 I had matriculated and been accepted by the House: but now the House would have nothing to do with me, at least for a couple of years: it was full of younger men, and also those from the Army who were more distinguished, or showed more promise, than I. I therefore had to accept Brasenose, and thereby, I suspect, cooked my goose. BNC was then a college curiously divorced from Oxford's intellectual life: it was the habitation of 'hearties', intent on sport and rowing: and I was a fish out of water. My splendid visions of warm friendships, enthralling studies, and brilliant honours rapidly dissolved. The ever-jangling bells and monastic atmosphere grated on my nerves. When Mr Stallybrass enquired what school I wished to take, I replied 'International Law'. He smiled benevolently and said that no such school existed. I said that it should exist: we had to learn to avoid war. He suggested that I take History, which 'would come to much the same thing'. It did not, although idiotically I agreed. I might have done well in English, and, since I was drifting towards the Foreign Office, modern languages were essential. I was a complete fool at History: those biased national accounts of events have never held my attention. For two terms I sported my oak, and waded through volumes which bored me: then I threw in my hand, and had a splendid time on the river. And I went to see Robert Vansittart at the Foreign Office. He was an old acquaintance, since he had been a friend of Lord Willoughby de Broke, who lived near Kineton. I explained my dilemma to Vansittart, and asked him whether (since I was now more or less committed, by lack of other ideas, to the FO examination) I should stay at Oxford for the three years necessary for a degree. He said that he thought that modern languages, learnt abroad, would be far more valuable. I therefore decided to go to France, Italy, and Germany.

My father was, perhaps not surprisingly, much angered by my behaviour. Not having been to a university himself, he thought that they were a waste of time. However, once I had decided he expected me to stick to my decision, and the idea of 'abroad' was hateful to him. He began to embark on a kind of passive resistance which became a habit: it consisted in forgetting to pay me my quarterly £75, and thus making me write to ask for it, which, as he knew, I did with some distaste and guilt. Indeed I would spin out my money at the end of each quarter until I was stony broke. Later, when I began to earn money, he frequently forgot to pay it altogether: but by then it did not matter. In those early years I could not do without it, because I was superbly unfitted to earn money at anything. And I developed an angry resentment at being dependent, which stayed with me even when, in my fifties, I inherited an unearned income. I am all in favour of unearned incomes for all, but I cannot escape a feeling that such money is not quite real and may disappear. Which of course is possible.

I did not know quite how to go about learning French in France. It was easier planned than done. I asked Vansittart and others of his circle, but the war had created a gap in the tradition of French cramming-houses, and I got no further. I went to Paris and stayed in a series of (necessarily) cheap *pensions,* and took lessons from a charming lady of the Comédie Française who made me stand up and declaim Racine and Molière. It was a moment of acute Anglo-French tension, and the French were full of the idea that we had fought to the last Frenchman, did not care that France was devastated, and were letting them down. The people in my *pensions* carefully shook hands with me at every breakfast, and never ceased being rude about England and the English. I began to feel enveloped in a fog of hatred. A detestation of Paris was born in me, and flourished: even to-day, I cannot go there without feeling stifled. It is the only city which I have steadily disliked. And I felt at odds with the French. Later experience taught me to modify that view: but that couple of months in Paris bred in me an unreasonable kind of idea that Edward VII had been very much mistaken, and that our proper allies were the Germans. And so I think they are: it is, paradoxically, the closeness of our views which makes us jealous of them. England is never really allied with a Latin country.

Presently I heard of a place in Blois. Madame la Marquise de Montarby had, it seemed, accepted pupils before the war and been very successful with them. It sounded grand: I took off for Blois. Nothing could have been worse. The very doubtful 'Marquise' was a yellow old dame dying of cancer in a very small flat: her daughter, poor, sad, sacrificing Marie-Louise, was to take over the teaching, which she was quite incapable of doing. They were desperately poor, and I was the only pupil who had come their way since the war. Marie-Louise and I sat on the floor in the old dame's bedroom, while she read the Lives of the Saints, and occasionally, in a hoarse voice, uttered some comment such as: 'Sa langue était noire! Est-ce que ma langue est noire?' – putting it out. The position was horrid. I knew that they needed my money, I knew that I was wasting time, and I had not enough money to make another move. I bicycled around the countryside, trying to discover other possibilities. One day I found myself at a gate in a long white wall outside St Avertin. I glimpsed what seemed an attractive house and a large garden. There was a barking of many dogs. The gate was opened by a tall, gangling, completely bald man, who regarded me with disfavour. 'Aucune place ici!' I asked if I might come in. With a bad grace he allowed it. There was indeed a charming garden, dipping down into a valley and up a hill beyond. There were several beautiful Alsatian dogs. We sat in a cool hall, and presently some white-and-gold doors were opened, and Carola de Ritter came in. At that moment a bell should have rung in my head. She was a beautiful woman, with deep blue eyes and a strange scar which somehow increased her attraction. She was decisive to the point of rudeness, but there was something dramatic about her. Abruptly she told me that she was full up and could take no more pupils. I said that I was sorry, stood up, and left.

I went back to Blois with my mind made up. I felt sure that Madame de Ritter was the right teacher for me. I sat down and wrote her what must have been a very naïve letter, in which I said that I had liked her dogs and her garden, and that, when she had a vacancy, I should like to come. She wrote back saying that my letter had amused her, that she was glad that the dogs and the garden had passed muster, and that I could come at once if I was un jeune homme sérieux. She added that she had no use for pupils who were not sérieux. I packed my bags and went.

There were four other young Englishmen in the house. Madame de Ritter was a teacher of whirlwind rapidity, quick impatience, and – if you met her half-way – glowing enthusiasm. The gifted teacher is very rare, and I was fortunate. From 7 to 12 a.m., she took each of us for an hour. During that hour, one

was expected to have learnt twenty of the idiomatic phrases –
A qui le dites-vous? Don't I know it? – of which she had accumulated many hundreds: to read an essay in French which she
had set the day before: and to recite by heart a passage from
a French author, dramatist, or poet. Each of us came out from
that hour with perspiration beading our brows: but also with
increased knowledge. In the afternoons the young gentlemen
went off to Tours to amuse themselves, or to play golf: but I
could neither afford, nor did I want, such distractions. On my
first afternoon I rang the bell for tea. The bonne who answered
said that Madame did not give *le gouter*. I leaned out of the
window and saw Madame de Ritter sitting in the garden, reading. I said: 'I want tea.' Without looking up, she replied, 'Go
and get it in Tours, like the others: I don't provide it.' I said,
'On the contrary, I want to stay here and work: and I want tea.'
She looked up laughing and said, *'Foutez-moi le camp.'* I said,
'No, I won't.' 'Very well,' she said, 'come down and have tea
with me.' I went down, and, as I sat under the trees with her,
she suddenly became warm and charming. She told me something
about her life, that she had studied at Oxford and the Sorbonne,
and was a friend of Rénan, with whom she greatly wished to go
and work. She asked me about my past and my plans. *'Si vous
êtes vraiment sérieux,'* she said, 'I think that I might help you not
only in French – that is easy – but also in other subjects. I know
these Foreign Office examinations.' I said that I was *très sérieux*.
Her blue eyes sparkled, and her cheeks were flushed. She had
fallen in love with me. That fortunate event probably enabled
me to pass the Foreign Office Examination.

But, as always, I could not stick to anything for long. One
day, at a tennis party, I was introduced to a distinguished French
General called de Bonneval. He was an enchanting old gentleman and I got on very well with him. He told me that his great
ambition was to learn English. I said, meaning nothing, 'I should
be delighted to teach you.' The next day I received a letter in his
spidery handwriting. He told me that he was Governor of
Constantine in Algeria, and that if I would care to go and stay
with him *au pair* and teach him English, he was sure that his
three daughters would increase my knowledge of French. The
invitation seemed to me exotic and enchanting: I accepted immediately. I had reckoned without Madame de Ritter. Her fury
was blistering. *'Tu n'es pas sérieux!'* She wept; she was distraught. So was I: but I was determined to go. (God knows I

have been punished in later life for my callousness towards the few people who loved me.) I sailed for Algiers. It was a terribly rough crossing: the three men in my cabin were laid out, retching and green in the face. I stayed on deck for the thirty-six hours, thinking that if the boat rolled over I would rather be drowned than caught inside. Fear has always conquered seasickness for me.

Constantine was, I thought, a dream of beauty. It is one of the most dramatic cities of the world. Round three-quarters of it the river rushes in a chasm so deep as to be reminiscent of Kubla Khan. The General lived in a Moorish palace with innumerable courtyards, and I had a suite of dazzling rooms. The de Bonneval family were enchanting, and called me 'Monsieur Pagaie' because I was, as they thought, so untidy. I did my best to teach the General English, but it was not easy. He had studied it with dictionaries, which had told him that 'come' should be pronounced 'keum', and so on and so forth. I could not cure him of these addictions. But his kindness to me was immense. He took me on all his rounds, and treated me as an honoured guest. I came to know quite a lot about Algeria and French colonialism. The great aim of the General was to make me sick. When he took me to lunch with sheikhs, and they handed me, from the couscous, a wet and slippery sheep's eye, he would chuckle, '*Vous aurez mal au coeur!*' I was determined that I wouldn't, and swallowed the sheep's eye as an oyster. He took me to see the Aïssoua, who mutilated themselves every Friday, and when a man stuck a dagger through his belly or thrust his head into flames – '*Vous aurez mal au coeur!*' I didn't. I laughed a great deal and enjoyed myself immensely. But I had yet to learn Italian and it was time for me to leave. I took myself, as a parting gesture, to Biskra, which I had not seen. On the way I read Robert Hichens' *Garden of Allah,* and was caught up in a wave of sentimentality. Biskra seemed incredibly romantic. But all the hotels – it was out of season – were shut, and it was not comfortable. I went to the 'Garden', and asked Smaïn, the gate-keeper, whether I could have my fortune told, as it is told in the *Garden of Allah.* He summoned the fortune-teller, and under the twisted trees on the edge of the desert, he ran the sand through his fingers and spoke of my life. I am no believer in fortune-tellers, but I very nearly believed him. He described my family with uncanny accuracy, said that I was bemused by foreign countries but that my life lay in my own, that I should shortly get a 'brown letter' to recall me (and on my return to Constantine, I got, anticlimatically, a telegram asking me to be best man at a friend's wedding), and that 'what I wanted' were 'bits of paper' which I should get through a relative with a mark like this – he drew it on the sand – on the calf of the left leg. When I described this later, my stepmother cried, 'But I *have* a mark like that!' And so she had. But I don't think I ever got bits of paper or anything else from her.

Suddenly, Isadora Duncan descended on Biskra. The Royal Hotel was opened for her, and I gratefully moved in. Isadora had a pianist in tow called Walter Rummel, whom she spoke of as 'The Archangel Gabriel! Isn't he beautiful?' She included me in her slapdash emotions – we were the only three guests in the hotel – and I was spellbound by her extraordinary personality and beauty. She was one of the strangest human beings I ever knew. You could not say that she had any exceptional talent, or even that she was strikingly intelligent: but she radiated such colossal animal magnetism, combined with an utter disregard of all conventions, that she seemed apart from the human race. I met her again some four years later on the Riviera, just before she died, and, although she had grown fat, she still seemed to possess the same magical attraction.

Italian arrangements were as vague and unsatisfactory as those of France had been. I went to board with a Professor Jalla in Florence. He was an old man with a long white beard, and not quite right in the head. His wife was Swiss, angular, fussy, and nervous. They lived in a small and ugly flat outside the Porta Romana, and apparently knew few people. It was not a promising set-up. Presently the old man developed anthrax, and his wife in tears told me that I must go. I moved to a *pensione* which was not much better. I found Florence enchanting but was stuck in a horrid isolation. One day some English acquaintances, whom I met in an hotel, introduced me to an old Marchese and his nephew, Sandro. Sandro was about my age and we took to one another. I was not (thank God) in love with him, nor he with me: but we were, so to speak, on the same wave-length of ideas, amused and attracted by the same things, and between us was the bond of constant laughter. He became perhaps the best friend I ever made, as snug and comfortable as an old coat. He was a painter, and had a large studio flat in a tower in the via dei Bardi which belonged to his uncle. He invited me to move in, and I did. Not only the learning of Italian, but also life in general, became much easier: Sandro knew a host of people, and also, since he was poor, how to live cheaply. And in those days life in Italy could be dirt cheap. Sandro was, I think, an exceptionally gifted painter, and, like the painters of the Renaissance, did a bit of everything. He was an expert painter, etcher and lithographer: he amused himself by cleaning or faking-up old pictures and furniture which he found in the markets: and he designed for a firm of jewellers. He laughed a great deal over my intention to go into the Foreign Office, and asked me why I had chosen such a dreary career. Faced with his activities, I began to wonder myself: there seemed to be many more interesting things to do. My resolution became so shaky that I took myself off to Rome: after all, to become a painter and be cut off with a shilling wasn't on my list of possibilities, and it was high time I passed some sort of examination. Shutting myself in a small room in the via Gregoriana, I plunged through Dante, Carducci, Leopardi, and *I Promessi Sposi,* and went out for lessons in Italian and also German, of which I hoped to acquire a sufficient smattering to take it as a third language.

I had now spent nearly a year in France and Italy, and it was time to present myself at Burlington House. I paid a flying visit to Naples, which enchanted me: indeed I was in love with Italy, and made a vow, which I have kept, that some day I would live there.

Examinations are an unsatisfactory method of testing human ability. At that conclusion everyone of sensibility, who has been both examiner and examinee, must surely arrive. The young man or girl who is nervous – and who of intelligence is not? – when confronted by a paper or a row of faces, a time-limit and questions which may decide a whole future, may often present a caricature of himself or herself. An examinee, unless of blunted feelings, can never be normal during an examination. An effort is being made which alters character. True it is that facts, dates, sums and arguments can be remembered and written down or even spoken, but it is only memory, not character, that is under examination. An assessment of character is not made, any more than a friend is made, in a few moments or hours. True again, there will be records of character to consult, reports and references to be read: but in most cases they will be prejudiced half-truths - prejudiced, that is to say, by a desire to help or a dislike of condemnation or even plain likes or dislikes. On the other side of the table the examiner, perhaps well-intentioned (but, if the appointment does not concern him personally, likely to be indifferent) fits the puzzle together as best he can, and judges the examinee. He cannot, however, say with any certainty, 'This individual will *not*, within the next month, become a dipsomaniac, murder his mother, burgle a bank, or turn into a lunatic.' Nor can he say, 'This individual will be Prime Minister, or the Head of Scotland Yard, or the Governor of Canada, or the Managing Director of Harridge's.' All that he can say is that the individual has or has not a good memory, and seems in his or her first twenty years to have followed a safe conventional pattern. Delude yourself as you will, this is not a recipe for finding great human beings. And, if you take men who have risen to the top of the human scum and made history, you will scarcely find a single one who has excelled in examinations. The human brain has not devised a substitute for examinations, but it is debatable whether their futility is not the root of all our troubles. Men in authority, in any field, should be, paradoxically, men without ambition.

The approach to Burlington House was frightening. A whole life depended, or seemed to depend, on a week's examinations. I was appalled by the discovery that there were three hundred and eighty candidates. I was even more appalled by their appearance. They all seemed smarter, quicker, more intelligent and more studious than I could ever hope to be. When the first paper was placed before me, I could not even read it. The hall, with all the assembled and busily-writing candidates, swam before me. Absurd as it may seem, I was at the point of fainting. For some twenty minutes I was stuck in this self-inflicted hell: then I answered the questions in a great hurry, with my brain functioning at about twenty per cent of normal. (Do you think that I am going to tell you that I failed in these examinations? Not at all. If you think that, you have misunderstood my arguments.) At lunch-time Sir Adrian Baillie, who was one of the candidates and had been with me for a short time *chez* Madame de Ritter slapped me on the back and said: 'You're looking peaky! I shall take you to Buck's.' He gave me oysters (the first time I had ever swallowed them) and black velvet. I was fortified not only by these, but also, and more effectively, by a notion that Adrian was a complete ass (I knew that his French was lousy) and that I could at least do better than he. In this idea I was quite mistaken.

The examinations concluded, a nerve-twanging period of waiting followed. Then the printed results were circulated. In those days (I do not know what the practice is now) marks were awarded not by numerical figures but by signs – Alpha plus, Alpha minus, Beta plus, Beta minus, Gamma plus, Gamma minus, and so on – under each subject. I presume that this is or was a dodge (and perhaps a wise one) of examiners to avoid claims which concerned only high marks. The Alphas and Betas could always be interpreted in different ways: for instance, that the English paper represented only fifty, the Italian seventy, the French a hundred, and so on. The total could be juggled. However, the hieroglyphs had to mean *something*. Adding them up in various ways, I concluded that I must be, on any count, among the first six. I had of course passed: that is to say I was above the line of those who had failed. I was thus a candidate for the Selection Board, which was held after the examinations. This was quite fair: the Selection Board did not have to concern themselves with a mass of unknown candidates, but only with those who had passed a certain standard of intelligence. As far as I remember, there were about thirty of us.

When the high white-and-gold double doors were opened in front of me, and I walked unsteadily up an enormous room towards a table at which twelve elderly gentlemen were sitting, staring at me, I was, as you may or may not imagine, paralysed by fright. The Chairman asked me to be seated, and I nearly missed the chair. He said:

'Colonel Phillips, I think you might begin.'

There was a pause, during which Colonel Phillips riffled through the papers in front of him, and my nerves rose to concert pitch. Then the Colonel said:

'I see, Mr Fielden, that at the beginning of the war you joined up as a *private*. Now why did you do that, when you knew that England was calling for officers?'

The question was entirely unexpected. My mind fizzled. Had my uncle told Colonel Phillips that I had refused a commission in the Guards? I said haltingly:

'I thought that I ought to learn the job.'

Colonel Phillips said suavely:

'Did you think that officers were not trained?'

I mumbled: 'I don't know.' Colonel Phillips rolled his eyes towards the Chairman. They said plainly: that is enough. My spirits sank to zero. The Chairman said: 'Air Marshal?' The Air Marshal, friendly, leaned towards me:

'It seems that in Palestine you volunteered to be an air obser-

67

ver, and did a course. And then you left it. How was that?'

All my weak points, I thought. I can hardly say that I was in a funk.

'I wasn't very good at it –' I started. The Air Marshall cut in, and said that the reports on me seemed to be excellent. 'But I couldn't,' I said, 'see enemy planes quickly enough, and I wasn't good at ground spotting.' 'Tell me,' said Air Marshal, 'were you frightened?' 'Well, yes, I think I was,' I replied. There was a little laughter. A wave of anger went through me. The Chairman said: 'Mr Reaper?'

'Now,' said Mr Reaper in a hearty voice, looking down at his dossier through gold-rimmed spectacles, 'you went up to Oxford. It seems that you attended very few lectures indeed. Is that so?'

'I found them very dull. I thought that it was easier and quicker to pick up knowledge from books.'

'But the books bored you too, since you didn't stay long enough to take a degree?'

'I thought perhaps I ought to learn languages.'

'But you could have done that in the vacations, and at Oxford too?'

'I suppose so.'

Floored.

The Chairman said: 'Sir John?' Sir John, very handsome and dignified, said:

'Now. I shall ask you an important question. You have spent some considerable time in Palestine. What do you think of the Balfour Declaration?'

All right. To hell with them.

'I think,' I said, 'that it's the most degrading document ever signed. England has sold itself to the Jews, and Palestine belongs to the Arabs. And that is what everyone in the Army thinks.'

The Chairman said: 'Thank you, Mr Fielden.'

I staggered out, down the long red carpet.

It was no particular surprise to receive, a week later, a polite letter to say that the Foreign Office would not be requiring my services. Adrian Baillie, however, had been given one of the eight vacant posts. I was angry. My work had been utterly wasted. The passing of the Foreign Office examination did not, so far as I could see, help me to any other work. I went to see Vansittart. He said yes, he thought perhaps I had been shabbily treated: he would see what he could do. A few days later I got a letter to say that the Foreign Office would be glad to take me as Honorary Attaché at Washington or Budapest. Vansittart added a note saying that, if I were patient, I should get into the service later. The prospect did not please me – I was not rich enough to be an Honorary Attaché – but it was Hobson's choice. Then as now, I had no desire to go to America, but Budapest seemed fairly promising. I went to see Sir Thomas Hohler, our Minister there, and at that time on leave in London. He was affable, and appeared delighted to have me. He told me to buy a fur coat. At lunch at my club, skimming the papers, I saw an advertisement for an examination for the League of Nations Secretariat. I had only vague notions about the League, and none about the Secretariat. However, I went round and put down my name. The examination took place almost immediately. Compared with that of the Foreign Office, it was simple. For the simple and yet fundamental reason that I did not care and was not nervous, I made no mistakes and came out by a long way top of the list. A week later I received a telegram from Geneva, asking if I would go there at once at a salary of four pounds a day. I had no doubt that there had been a mistake in transmission and that four pounds a week had been intended – just about what I should have got in the Foreign Office. I was quite content with that. I wired that I was coming, said a polite goodbye to Sir Thomas Hohler (and the Foreign Office), and departed for Geneva. Arrived there, I found that I was actually to be paid four pounds a day. It seemed a staggering sum. And in those days it was. I had suddenly blossomed into affluence. A glance at a newspaper had altered my life.

Geneva seemed beautiful. I had not become allergic to that shattering destroyer of beauty, the picture postcard. Morning by morning, the blue lake and snowy mountains thrilled me. The spacious Palais des Nations was filled with enchanting people, and I was happy as a lark. The League was indeed staffed at that time – as pioneering organisations of that land always and melancholically are – with idealists who believed sincerely that wars could be stopped. The work – after a week of two of agony – was not difficult, though it was arduous enough. The League, having started from scratch, had to build up an enormous array of files very quickly. Treaties, reports, the agenda of conferences and the proceedings of parliaments, had to be translated not only with rapidity but with accuracy. For this it was necessary to dictate translations very quickly. I had never dictated before, and I did not find it easy. My secretary, Judy Jackson, a darling person who later became secretary to Mrs Stanley Baldwin, tapped her shoe against the table-leg when I paused. I was infuriated, and drove my mind faster and faster. Thanks to Judy, I soon became expert at the job. Today I am horrified to think how that expertise has vanished.

My situation was now perfect. Sir Eric Drummond, the Secretary-General of the League, and his charming family, were very kind to me, and I spent many happy hours at their house. I was devoted to 'Tiger' Howard, that strange and unusual woman who was the *Eminence Grise* – or perhaps *Rose* – of the League. At week-ends we made up parties and went to Chambéry or Aix or Gstaad. There seemed to be no reason why I should not stay in the League Secretariat for ever, earning a larger and larger salary, and falling back in old age on a comfortable pension.

There was a reason, however, and it lay in my own character. I soon found Geneva not only boring but asphyxiating. The mountains stepped closer: the lake was shrouded in mist. I was fortunate in meeting the many celebrities who came to Geneva, and for Fridtjof Nansen I developed a hero-worship: but it was not enough. Geneva-for-life, however well-paid, was not my aim. The Genoa Conference of 1922 was just rising on the horizon, and I made it my business to go around saying that I was the only person in the League Secretariat who spoke fluent Italian. Nothing succeeds better than blowing your own trumpet, and I was successful. Six of us were sent to Genoa to help the Italian authorities. We were a harmonious and happy sextet. My salary was raised to five pounds a day.

At Genoa we discovered that the Italian authorities, though willing to spend any amount of money, had no idea about conferences. They had provided the sumptuous Royal Palace, with its private railway station below, and a blotting-pad and silver paper knife for every delegate: and that was all. We were by that time used to the procedure and requirements of conferences, and we went to work on roneos, typewriters, paper, clips, telephones, notice-boards, interpreters, and even hotel accommodation. For a week we worked extremely hard: we hardly slept: and I remember that the palms of our hands were bruised black and blue by roneo machines and rubber stamps. Then we relaxed: and for six weeks did almost nothing at all. Occasionally we were called in to translate or interpret, but on the whole we were magnificently lazy. And five pounds a day was a fortune in Genoa.

The Genoa Conference is long forgotten: but at that time it was a glittering excitement – the equivalent, and perhaps more, of a Summit Conference now. Thirty-four Prime Ministers attended it, an event which had never happened before: and Lloyd George (though a younger generation may not believe it) was then a more dazzling figure than Churchill ever became. On the top of all that, the Bolshevist leaders were to attend. Genoa seemed the hub of the world. If you could wear in your buttonhole the Conference insignia, you were *persona grata* everywhere. Trains from the royal station ran every hour to east and west of the Riviera: they were composed of Pullman carriages with deep armchairs: there was no payment: one could go (and we went) to San Remo or Rapallo for dinner or for the night. Splendid meaningless speeches were made by day: I can still see Lloyd George, swinging his pince-nez on a black ribbon, saying 'The thrill of peace has run through the veins of Europe!' And there was an unforgettable moment when, in absolute silence, the Russian delegates, headed by Tchicherin and Krassin, who had been brought down to the conference hall in a specially guarded train, walked to their seats. Everyone expected a bomb. (The bomb, however, took a different form in the Rapallo treaty.)

To my immense astonishment, the Italian Government now asked me if I would care to go to Rome to supervise the records of the conference. They would pay me five pounds a day, and it would last, they thought, about a year. It was a splendid invitation. I wrote to Sir Eric Drummond, asking if I could accept it. He replied that I could not. 'You are,' he added, 'constantly running away: you must learn discipline.' A fig for discipline, I thought: and I replied that I was going to Rome and the League could do without me. I burned my boats. The Italian Government said that they would not need me for a month, so I joined Sandro at Capri. There I swam and paddled canoes: and was spellbound by the red cliffs and the blue water. One day I received a letter from the Dutch Government, saying that they would pay me seven pounds a day if I would take a staff of translators and interpreters to the forthcoming economic conference at the Hague. I was now drunk with the possibilities of international conferences (and indeed they are still moneymakers today, if you are on the bandwagon). I threw over the Italian Government, and travelled from Capri to the Hague – a quite long train journey then. The Hague was enchanting, and the Dutch gave us a splendid time: I travelled over Holland and loved its fleecy clouds and flat views: but the conference was a flop. Litvinov and the other Russian delegates simply did not turn up at committee meetings: they went and learned to bicycle on the sands of Scheveningen. Soon it was over. I had bankrupted myself. I was unemployed.

The landscape, so far, has had few figures. That was inevitable. For six years I had not, with the brief exception of Oxford, ever spent three months in the same place or with the same people. Life had flittered past me like a row of lights seen from a train. And my compartment had been empty. In Geneva for the first time I had a small flat of my own, and took my place in what appeared to be a permanent social group. Apart from Sir Eric and Lady Drummond, their daughter Margaret, and Tiger Howard, there were R. H. Wilenski and his wife, for whom I soon felt a warm friendship: and they, though it did not seem so at the time, pushed me towards a greater knowledge of the arts, and the development of what talent I possessed as a painter. There was Hilary St George Saunders, who with the studious John Palmer wrote detective stories, and later made a name for himself by writing *The Battle of Britain,* and other such accounts, for the Government. There was Helen Foley the poet, whom Hilary later married. Geoffrey Dennis, then struggling with his first book, *Mary Lee,* was the intelligent head of our department, and working with him was the lively red-head Sheila Hall, whom he was to marry. There was Dame Rachel Crowdy, beloved by all, Chester Purves, a gentle creature whose heart was much in the League, and William Moloney, a genial madman whose heart was everywhere. There was the tall, handsome, commanding woman known as Dr Dixon, who, until you knew her, seemed like an incarnation of Hedda Gabler: and her friend Marjory Locket, with the kindest and warmest heart in the world, whose friendship was to go with me through life. Best of all my friends perhaps was Mrs Lilian Adam, a gifted member of the Baring family, who came out to work with us in spells, and was the life and soul of every party. There were, too, the visiting firemen, chief among them perhaps Philip Noel-Baker, whom I came to know well. Philip at that time walked in a cloud of glory, both as a very distinguished athlete and also as an architect of the League. He was to influence my future considerably. Just about this time I also came to know Gerald Heard and Christopher Wood. Christopher – not the painter – was a temperamental young man of great wealth, and a concert pianist. Gerald was a phenomenon. He had a brain like an encyclopaedia, a rapid wit, and an entirely original view of life. For some fifteen years he and Christopher became a part of my life. When, in 1937, they decided, with Auden, Isherwood and Aldous Huxley to decamp to America, I mourned their loss, and thought, as I still think, that their decision was fatally wrong.

I proceeded now, as young men should, to fall in love. Or didn't I? I thought that Ann was very beautiful, I loved being in her company, and was convinced that to pass my life with her would be heaven. But I did not alas, wish to kiss her, fondle her, or go to bed with her. I was not at the time quite aware of these ambivalent sentiments, because I was astonishingly ignorant. I had an idea that there was some deep division between sacred and profane love: as indeed there may be. At first it seemed to me that I could marry Ann, even if lust did not enter into the bargain: then I began to have doubts. Suddenly and for the first time this 'love' made me aware that, although I enjoyed the company of women and wished to be married, my physical desires flowed towards my own sex, and refused to flow towards the opposite one. And let me add here that, if such was my natural bent, born with me and inescapable, I myself certainly did not bend it or like it that way: it was a crippling deformity. Up to that time, I had never had a love affair with one of my own sex, and the idea of such a thing violently repelled, while also violently attracting, me. I suddenly saw that if Ann agreed to marry me, as I was fairly sure she would, I might do her a great harm. I resolved that this problem must be fought out: so I went to Zurich to see Jung, and his assistant, Oscar Pfister. I told them my tale, and they were charming and sympathetic. I said that I wished to get married, and to change the course of my physical desires. After several visits and a good deal of correspondence, they told me that they feared they could do nothing for me, unless I cared to be a guinea-pig for a delicate surgical operation (I think it had to do with glands and hormones), which might or might not be successful. This I funked. Soon afterwards I went with a party, which included Ann, for a ten day holiday in Venice. I had never seen Venice before, and it is a romantic place. My love flowered. The others left us much alone, and we drifted here and there in gondolas. I could not bring myself to a decision. Would Ann, once married to me, suffer from my sexual indifference? Should I, married to Ann, be miraculously cured of my homosexuality? I did not know. On the last afternoon of her visit – I had planned to stay for a few days longer – we sat on the wall of the Arsenal Gardens, looking over the lagoons. I decided that I would risk all, and ask the overwhelming question. At that moment Ann, who had stretched herself out in the sun on the wall, said: 'You know, what I most want is to have a dozen children.' Suddenly I saw it all: not only my own impotence, but a string of nappies across the years. The words which had risen to my lips remained unspoken.

The next morning I ran beside her departing train, and my heart shouted that I could not lose her. But I did. I shall never be sure whether that decision was right or wrong. I believe that it was right. Those whom Nature has condemned to be homosexual should not drag members of the opposite sex into their lives. At the time, I was plunged in grief. Venice became a melancholy place.

From the Hague, in a panic, I wrote to Sir Eric Drummond, asking if I could return to the League. He replied gaily that I could not do so in a permanent capacity: I was much too unreliable. But he added that he would be glad to have me on a temporary basis for the Assembly, which was due to begin in a month's time. When I arrived in Geneva, I found that Sir Eric had been indulging in a mild leg-pull at my expense. I could, if I wished, again become a permanent member of the Secretariat. But my wish was very feeble. Certainly the League offered security, travel, fairly easy work, pleasant surroundings, charming people – what more could one ask? I did ask more. What, I did not know: but not Geneva for life. That Assembly of 1922 was an awkward meeting: futile in the same way that, in a later era, meetings at Lake Success were futile under Russian vetoes. The Greeks, backed by Lloyd George, had embarked on a war which – so the English hoped – would take them to Constantinople and blot out the new nuisance, Mustapha Kemal. The French, on the contrary, thought that Kemal was the cat's whiskers. It was the old familiar story: two great powers at loggerheads, and all the rest trying to climb on one bandwagon or the other. The Greek armies were falling back in disorder, and a disaster was imminent. At public sessions the growing rout in Anatolia was avoided with the beautiful delicacy which does not recognize sodomy or masturbation. It was an altogether disgusting performance by thirty-six nations. Eloquent speeches were made about fishing rights, opium, river pollution, plumbing in Africa, the diseases of parrots, and other items of international significance. Never a word about Anatolia. Dear me no. Veils of hypocrisy and self-interest were daily drawn over the shocking picture.

The only delegate to grasp these veils and rend them at least temporarily was Nansen. Towards the end of the session he strode on to the dais, in spite of many efforts to restrain him, and delivered one of the most fiery and heart-warming speeches I have ever listened to. He trounced the assembled delegates for their cowardice and callousness. He pointed out, in his oddly attractive Norwegian English, that the object of the League was to avoid war, and that for a whole session a brutal war flaming on the threshold of Europe had been ignored. He said that he could only offer to go himself and instantly to the Near East, and do what might be possible for the million-and-a-half refugees who were being driven from the burning city of Smyrna. He hoped that in this work of mercy the League would support him. With a poor grace, and the staggeringly small sum of £32,000 from the assembled nations of the world, it did.

I was fired by Nansen's speech. Here at last, it seemed, was a thing to do and a man to follow. When I was given the opportunity to go with him, I leapt at it. Said Philip Baker, who was also going: 'We can't pay anything but expenses, you know: well, you can see that we can't.' I did see, and it did not seem to matter: I had, in spite of myself, saved some money from my salary, and it seemed enough. I did not quite tumble to the fact that other people would necessarily be paid, and that the unpaid worker is always suspect to the paid one. I was in a state of exaltation – a crusader who did not realize how futile crusades usually are. But Nansen had cast his spell over me, and it was a very potent spell.

During my life I have been privileged, as a flunkey, to meet a very large number of the celebrities of the world. No man or woman has ever given me quite the sense of human nobility and dignity which Nansen in his every action conveyed. And, mind you, Nansen had his faults and plenty of them. I was not hero-worshipping. Sometimes, in the days that followed, I could be hurt by what seemed his failures. Sometimes he appeared to make no sense at all. Quite often he acted rashly. It did not matter. Always one had the impression of a steadfast soul, incapable of a mean or trivial thought, incapable of selfishness or self-interest, incapable of the smallest cruelty, of a flicker of dishonesty, of discouragement, pessimism, harsh judgement or, and above all, arrogance. Such qualities may not add up to success, but they are a bright flame in the world of men. It seems to me sad that Nansen is now fading into the mists of history, and that no book so far written about him conveys the greatness of the man. There is now only one man alive, Philip Noel-Baker, who is in a position to write the epic which Nansen deserves.

Nansen was born in Norway in 1861. His boyhood was spent on a farm. The long hard winters accustomed him to snow and ice, skis and skates, and also, perhaps, to solitude. His interest fastened on physics, mathematics, geology, zoology, astronomy, and – an obvious product – philosophy. When he was twenty-one he, as he afterwards said, 'burned his boats' and sailed in the *Viking* to the Arctic. By 1882 he was Keeper of Zoology at Bergen, and in the following year he was studying the colouring of nerve-threads under Golgi in Padua. In 1888 he sailed in the *Jason* to Greenland and crossed it. At twenty-eight he was already famous. He became Professor in the University of Christiania, and went to lecture in England. In 1893 he took the famous *Fram* to the North Pole. From then on he was engaged in Polar exploration, but in 1905 the dissolution of Norway's union with Sweden drove him into politics, and he became the first Norwegian Ambassador in London. But his scientific interests did not slacken, and in 1911 he was studying a new trade route to northern Siberia, and went to Russia, where he was received with great enthusiasm. 1917 saw him in Washington, pleading for wheat for Norway: it was a natural step to the beginning of his great work of relief, starting with his work in Russia in 1921, and ending only with his death. The Nansen passport for refugees – the result of his personal intervention with each Government to get a number accepted – gave not only a place in the world, but new hope in life, to lost thousands.

The most striking facet of his personality was, to me, stillness. It was not an unfriendly or repellent stillness: it was the stillness of a deep pool. The pool could be ruffled by a summer breeze or agitated by a winter gale: Nansen's laughter was frequent and infectious, and his rages titanic; but his soul remained calm. He never put on airs: he was his natural self with anyone and everyone: he loved dancing and food and the ladies: and he loathed all cities. He was, perhaps, a mass of contradictions, and often a source of irritation to men who considered themselves practical.

Yet with him one felt curiously safe, as if caught up in a warm ascending air of kindness, toleration, and understanding. Moreover one was spurred to effort, because one could not disappoint him. His was a personality before which the human spirit might well do homage. Certainly I had never met his like before, and never shall do so again. He became, most uncomfortably, the yardstick of my judgement of all those who are set in authority.

Nansen now instructed me to take the Simplon Orient Express from Lausanne on the following day, and to wait for him in Belgrade, where we would arrive twenty-four hours later. Judy Jackson, who was to go as Secretary, would accompany me. We were told what to do in Belgrade to prepare for Nansen's visit there. It must here be explained that Nansen, though he had now become Commissioner for Refugees in the Levant, was still in the full flood of his negotiations concerning Russian refugees, and his arrival in any capital city was a signal for thousands of them to rush to him, demanding employment or housing or passports or food. It was also a signal for the Government authorities to prepare themselves for the demands Nansen would make, and to be ready with all sorts of complaints about the behaviour of the refugees, and the inability of the country in question to receive any more. These matters quickly added up to a formidable total of work. Judy and I were to prepare the necessary appointments for the twenty-four hours Nansen would spend in Belgrade.

We drove along the lakeside in the early morning, arrived at Lausanne, and found that the Simplon Orient Express had left an hour before. It was October, and we had failed to note an hour's alteration in the timetable. The station authorities assured us that there was no other train for Belgrade until the next morning. We were desperate. Judy was as zealous about the job as I was, and it seemed unthinkable that thus, at the very first stage, we should let Nansen down by sheer carelessness. It was also unthinkable to return to Geneva, and unthinkable to wait like two fools for the train which would bring Nansen. We decided that the only thing was to go towards Belgrade as best we could. We took a train to Milan, changed there, changed at Venice, changed at Trieste, and at Zagreb had so long to wait that we went for a walk. Zagreb in those days seldom saw a foreigner, and we were followed by a policeman and presently arrested as suspicious characters (spies, I suppose) and led to a police station. There we complacently exhibited our diplomatic passports, and were bowed out with apologies. Altogether it proved an amusing journey, and we arrived only two hours after the Simplon Orient Express in Belgrade. De luxe trains are not necessarily very fast ones.

In Belgrade it was raining heavily, and that city was then a fairly squalid and shabby place, remarkable only for acres of cobbles and particularly sticky mud. I did not care for it at all, and was bewildered by the Russian refugee chores. A little gilt fell off my crusader's gingerbread that day: but Nansen's arrival restored it. Constantinople, which I had missed once, glittered again on the horizon. But as soon as we were on the train, Nansen called me into his carriage, and said that he wished me to leave the train at Nish the next morning, and go down, alone, to Greece. He would, he said, write me a letter saying that I was his representative in Greece and the Levant, and asking all authorities to help me. I was flabbergasted. I could not imagine what I could possibly do in Greece, I did not want to be separated from Nansen, and I very much wanted to go to Constantinople. I stammered, 'But I have no experience of refugee work, and I don't speak Greek or Turkish. What d'you expect me to do?'

Nansen laughed loudly.

'I don't expect anyone to do anything, except what's under his nose. I didn't know Russian, or what to do, when I went to Russia, and I don't speak Greek or Turkish any more than you do. Every man of good will can accomplish something. You will be my eyes and ears in Greece. Act as you think fit. I have every confidence in you.'

There was no quarrelling with this, and in the early hours of the morning, feeling very cold and forlorn, I got down at Nish. It really is not a very pleasant place, and I waited for some hours with sinking spirits. It may seem strange that, since we were concerned with the influx of a million and a half refugees into Greece, Nansen was going to Constantinople. He did so because he thought, probably quite rightly, that his first step should be to meet Kemal, and persuade him to desist from the wholesale butchery of the Greek Army. 'If,' said Nansen, 'we are to have a million and a half women and children, without men, on our hands, the situation may be a little difficult.' In the event, that was what we had: but he could not have known that he would fail with Kemal, and Nansen had always an unconquerable faith that heart-to-heart talks would settle everything.

At this point it may be asked why I was not pleased to be going to Greece: and the answer is that I do not know. For some obscure reason, Greece is a country which I have never liked, either in thought or in experience. Many English people adore it and have adored it. Its dramatic ruins are impressive, its history seems a clarion-call to humanity, its treeless hills and mountains have a certain grandeur. But for me it was and is a forbidding country. As far as it is possible to dislike a whole people (which of course is not possible) I dislike all Greeks. In 1922, at the age of twenty-six, I did not rationalize my feelings in this way. I only felt oddly allergic to Greece. That did not mean that I was allergic to the job. Political thought was far from me: I wished to serve Nansen and to mitigate the sufferings of refugees, to whatever nation they might belong. Crusaders don't love natives.

When the train for Athens drew into Nish, I was quite unprepared for my reception. I had not grasped the fact that Nansen was news wherever he went. No doubt someone at Nish had registered the notion that I was of his company, and passed it on. I had no sooner got on to the train than I was surrounded by a mass of chattering, gesticulating Greeks. They informed me that conditions in Salonika were worse than anything I could possibly imagine: that thousands of destitute refugees were pouring in every day: that housing and food were non-existent: that plague was spreading: and what was Dr Nansen – who had all the money in the world – going to do about it? As I had not the foggiest idea what Dr Nansen was going to do about it, the questions were embarrassing. I could only say, endeavouring to put on an owlish face, that I was not at liberty to disclose Dr Nansen's plans. At the frontier I was received like royalty: there wasn't actually a band to play 'See, the conquering hero comes!' but it felt like that. My spirit retreated like a snail into its shell. I longed to be anywhere else. At Salonika I was met by a limousine with a military escort before and behind. I felt a bloody fool. I was whisked to the Governor's palace, and pushed through a mass of humanity to his room. He seized my hand and wrung it, then drew me to a large window, and, pointing dramatically, said: 'Look!' I looked: and saw a vast courtyard with high walls, and beyond some iron gates a black yelling crowd of struggling humanity. The Governor said: 'They are starving, and we have no food in the town. What is Dr Nansen going to do?'

The situation, had it not been tragic, would have been idiotic. Here was I, a silly young man with no experience and no instructions, being asked to perform a sort of miracle of loaves and fishes. The trouble was that Nansen's reputation as a miracle-worker was great. It could not, I felt, be smirched. But what was I to do? I could only say that my instructions were to collect the facts for Dr Nansen, who would doubtless act upon them. 'Facts!' said the Governor derisively. 'There are the facts in front of you!' I said that I hoped he would enable me to see the refugee centres for myself and decide what was necessary. Morosely he agreed.

There followed ten days of growing uneasiness for me. In a car provided by the Governor I visited the squalid makeshift camps which had been hurriedly erected for the refugees. The winter cold was beginning, and it was obvious that the lack of clothing, warmth, food, and medicines would soon present a formidable problem. The tents were inadequate and the refugees were mostly dressed in the thinnest rags. They crowded round me, asking when aid would come. I told my interpreter to say 'Slowly, slowly it will come,' and a woman replied 'Slowly, slowly we die.' After two days I sent a long telegram to Nansen. Rereading it now, it seems to me an adequate summary of the amounts and kinds of food, blankets, clothes, medicines and tents which would soon be a matter of urgency. My telegram was not acknowledged: Nansen was pursuing Kemal and had no time for me. But the Greek press had plenty. My every movement was reported, and the comments gradually passed from hope and welcome to irritation and anger. What was Mr Fielden *doing*? Mr Fielden, unfortunately, did not know.

I could not stand it, and decided to leave for Athens, where at least there was a British Embassy. Conditions at that time were so chaotic that trains could not be boarded in stations: if they came in to a platform, they were instantly overwhelmed by refugees. It was necessary to walk some way down the line in darkness, and climb on to the train in a siding. There was an uncomfortable sensation that the train might be mobbed. In Athens things seemed even worse than in Salonika, and Lindley, the British Minister, was not sparing in his criticisms of Nansen and, naturally, of me. The British residents had formed a committee to deal with refugees, and had started a large camp. Nansen had done nothing; and obviously I was a silly amateur. I sent another long telegram: there was no reply. Frustrated and ashamed, I went to work in the British camp, where our main business was to delouse the refugees, to dig latrines, and to persuade these

Anatolian peasants, with a whip, to use them. It was not romantic. But I was just saved from despair by the members of the
Greco-Bulgarian Commission, which had been set up under Colonel Corfe to supervise the exchange of populations consequent
on frontier alterations. Corfe and his deputy, Lindsay, were
towers of strength and humour. They laughed at my anxieties,
plied me with cocktails, took me to bathe at Piraeus, and made
me visit the Acropolis and Sounium.

After some ten days of this, I received a telegram. As I opened
it, I thought, with a sigh of relief, 'At last!' The telegram said:
'Kindly arrange for Greek Government to pay their contribution
immediately to my account Ottoman Bank. Nansen.' This was a
bit steep. The Greeks had, with other nations, contributed to
Nansen's fund, but it hardly seemed the moment to ask them to
pay. However, the drachma was falling rapidly, and it was clear
that the contribution would not be worth much if it were not
paid quickly. I had a somewhat unpleasant interview with
Doxiades, the Minister of Health: and the sum was paid. No
sooner was that accomplished than I received another telegram,
which read: 'Have thirty thousand blankets at three shillings
each: kindly induce Greek Government to buy.' I trundled back
to Doxiades, who told me: 'It's very kind of Dr Nansen, but an
Italian firm has already offered us unlimited blankets at two
shillings.' I don't blush easily, but I must have blushed scarlet on
that occasion. Presently a third telegram arrived. It said: 'Proceed immediately overland Adrianople and there take over grain
supplies as per instructions awaiting you.' This was too much.
I did not see myself taking a mad train journey through Mace-
donia, and finding myself again isolated. I had had enough of
Nansen's silence. I took ship and sailed for Constantinople.

Nansen, in the meanwhile, evaded by Kemal, had taken a
Greek destroyer and sailed, in a very rough sea, for the coast of
Asia. From the coast he intended to walk to Ankara and find
Kemal. The High Commissioners in Constantinople, who were
then the rulers of that almost beleaguered city, had other ideas.
To them Nansen was a nuisansce. A British destroyer was sent
down to intercept his Greek one, and he was picked off and
brought back to Constantinople. He arrived there, in a towering
rage, soon after I did. It was raining in torrents, and I see him
now, dripping and furious, his blue eyes sparkling with anger,
the water flowing off his oilskins and dripping on the floor. But
Nansen never blamed anyone: the fact that I had flouted his in-

structions did not matter. (I was by now in a sort of dotty haze: Constantinople seemed to be the most exciting city in the world.) Nansen explained that, under the Treaty of Mudania, the Greeks must now evacuate Eastern Thrace: but that an agreement (of which he gave me a copy) had been made with the Allied Commissioners to provide for the retention and removal of grain by the Greeks. It was a peculiar document (I still have it) which stated that 'civilians might take away all grain', and that 'military take all grain except what has been requisitioned from the Turkish inhabitants': and concluded with some menacing phrases, such as 'the protection and assistance afforded by the Allies would naturally cease the moment the Allied troops were withdrawn' and that 'Dr Nansen would have to make his own arrangements to protect such grain as might be left after their departure'. This really boiled down to the fact that Hilary St George Saunders had been (he had returned to Geneva) and I now was, Dr Nansen's 'own arrangements'. I departed for Eastern Thrace.

The train rumbled through the night. On either horizon villages, set on fire by the departing Greeks, were burning merrily. I had an almost undecipherable list of places where grain was stored, and of its Greek owners. Early in the morning, half-way to Adrianople, I got out of the train at a small stop whose name was on my list. I was marooned there for some hours. Then a car arrived with a peppery French colonel, who was in charge of one of the Allied Mixed Commissions. At this point of Thrace they had a French majority. He gloomily took me to their headquarters. The French officers there were cynical about England and the League, and pulled my leg unmercifully. In the middle of the night, trying to sleep on a hard floor, I overheard a wild quarrel between the colonel and the one British representative on the Commission. The Englishman was accusing the French of murdering Greeks right and left. I got up and put my head in: the colonel yelled at me to be gone. It was nightmarish.

But on the next morning the colonel, for some reason, relented. He gave me a car and a sheaf of papers from Greek farmers who had left their grain. I went circling around Eastern Thrace. It quickly became obvious that the whole business was absurd. The villages were in the hands of the Turks, and they were murderously determined to keep any grain that there was. It was in fact a rather frightening trip. I felt, and not without reason, that I might easily disappear. Eventually, I jumped on a train for Adrianople. There I went to the French Army Headquarters, for it seemed obvious that, if the Greek grain was to be saved, soldiers would be needed. The French general received me on the barrack square, and said that there was nothing doing: the Greeks could starve for all he cared. Tired and angry, I flared out that he would have to answer to the League for his callousness. He replied dryly that if I said another word he would clap me in jail. I returned to Constantinople.

Nansen as usual neither condemned nor was discouraged by failures. He nodded his leonine head gravely over my detailed report, said that clearly there was nothing more to be done in that direction. He suggested that I should go with Major X to the Sea of Marmora where, with shipping facilities, some grain might be rescued. It was now becoming urgent to obtain supplies of grain – for three reasons. Famine conditions were likely in Greece: the Treaty of Mudania had given only a fortnight's breathing space before Thrace became Turkish: and Nansen had been tricked into buying a large quantity of grain from Rumania, which had turned out to be unfit for human consumption, and had been sunk in, I think, Chios harbour. All in all, Nansen and Philip Baker had so far made a mess of things: the pursuit of Kemal had failed, nothing had been done for Greece, and a large part of our slender funds had been lost. Oddly enough it did not occur to me then or later to criticize Nansen for his rather scatty proceedings, any more than it occurred to me, years later, to criticize Gandhi in his silliest moments. Such men have a radiance which has nothing to do with practical results. I daresay that Mr Selfridge would have made a much better job of Greek refugees than Nansen ever did: but then, the Selfridges of the world don't do such things, and Nansen did.

I was not very pleased by Nansen's suggestion. Major X was a peppery little man who claimed to have been an officer in the Guards, though (and I cannot say why) I doubted this claim. He was all clipped grey mustache and glittering spectacles and fury, and I could not like him. Moreover the suggestion implied (and quite justifiably) that I hadn't done very well on my own. However, Nansen's word was law, and I embarked on a tug with Major X and sailed off down the Sea of Marmora. We had with us an interpreter, Marcou, and the Greek skipper of the tug, a shiftless dirty creature. The tug was tiny, uncomfortable, and filthy. The sea was extremely rough. We had, God knows why, no food or cigarettes. We were thrown about the tiny cabin, and at one time, when the skipper complained that he did not know where he was because he could not see the Eregli light, we seemed in danger of foundering. Stumbling about, I put my hand through one of the small cabin skylights and cut an artery in my wrist, losing a good deal of blood before I got a tourniquet round it. It was altogether a rather vivid voyage.

Major X talked in a boastful manner which increased my distrust of him. Yelling above the wind and waves, he assured me that we must 'stamp on the bloody Turks' and 'get the grain by force'. Yelling back at him, I attempted to convey a notion that representatives of the League couldn't have much truck with stamping and force. He roared back that I had made a fool of myself in Eastern Thrace, and I hated him the more. Presently we arrived at Sar Köÿ, near the entrance of the Dardanelles. It was a small village, but had been used in the past for grain shipments. There was a reasonable jetty, and several large warehouses full of grain, which was not, however, sacked. How, without sacks, could it be moved? 'You'll see,' said Major X, grimly. What I saw was that here also, as in Eastern Thrace, the Greek owners had fled and the Turks were likely to resist any transport of grain. And in fact Major X could do nothing: he said, grinding his false teeth, that we must return to Tekirdag to get assistance. I did not care for the sound of this.

At Tekirdag Major X went ashore, pointedly implying that I should not go with him, and climbed the hill to visit the Mixed Commission, which here was mainly British. While he was away I walked up and down the jetty with Marcou, who suddenly poured out his heart – or his lies – to me. He told me that Major X had been down here earlier, and had induced the Greek owners of grain to sign over their rights to him personally. He now held these papers, and, far from wishing to get the grain for Nansen, had made an agreement to sell it privately to a Greek firm, and thus make a huge profit. I should see, he told me, that a private ship would come to Sar Köÿ to take it. It might have been true: it might have been a tissue of lies: I could not tell. Major X returned with a platoon of soldiers, driving some ragged men before them. 'It's all right,' he said. 'I've got the caiques.' Sure enough a dozen caiques put out behind us. When we reached Sar Köÿ again, there was indeed a largish ship, flying (of all things) the Russian flag, standing out of the port. I said to Major X: 'But you aren't going to put the grain on *that* ship?' 'Mind your own business!' he returned. I said, 'Yes, I will: I'm going back to Constantinople.' He laughed and said: 'How?' How indeed. He

went ashore and left me. It was now raining in torrents and I
have seldom felt so deserted. And then, quite suddenly, there
occurred a miracle. A British destroyer swept up to the jetty. I
was asked what on earth I was doing there. I explained as best
I could. There were hoots of laughter: suddenly sanity returned.
'Could you take me to Constantinople?' Yes, they could and
would: a bit of gunnery practice first, which might amuse me.
I went aboard, and for the first, and I regret to say the last, time
in my life, discovered the magic of the Navy. After the muddle
and discouragement of the past months, I found myself miraculously in a world of smooth efficiency, sparkling cleanliness,
comfort, good humour and gaiety. I knew just enough about
gunnery to be able to appreciate what went on. I wondered (I
think) why I wasn't in the Navy and what on earth I was doing
fiddling around with refugees. It was as though I had suddenly
been caught up into another world. Then they dropped me in
Constantinople, and my problems returned. I learnt that Major
X was back there, and imagined that he had probably complained to Nansen about me. I went to the Tokatlian Hotel and
there wrote out a report for Nansen. When I had finished it, I
crossed the hall to get an envelope from the porter's desk.
I returned to my table to find that my manuscript had vanished.
I could not be bothered to write it again. I felt deflated: Nansen
could think what he liked.

Nothing was, in fact, said: a curtain dropped over the episode:
but no grain ever came from the Sea of Marmora. I remained for
some weeks in Constantinople, working in the Nansen office.
My experience had made me somewhat uneasy about what was
being done: and, as an unpaid worker, I myself was an object of
suspicion. But such embarrassments were offset by the glamour of
Constantinople at that time. It was not only a beautiful and
exciting city: it was also a dangerous and beleaguered one.
Kemal's forces were around the town: the bridges were mined:
rumour was constantly busy with a possible attack and massacre.
I had some friends in the Irish Guards, who were stationed there,
and Alexander, who was commanding them, insisted that I move
to their quarters out of the Tokatlian Hotel, which he said was
dangerous. Nevertheless we dined there every evening with Nansen, who would fascinate us with his stories of Polar voyages,
and his theories on ocean currents: and would then ask the
orchestra to play Grieg, and get up and dance to those melodies.
In the afternoons I would sometimes walk with Nansen (and a

walk with him was a considerable exercise) round the walls: sometimes he would talk vividly: sometimes he would be glum and silent and depressed. On one occasion I said, looking down at the Golden Horn: 'How beautiful it is!' and Nansen, with a sort of anger in his blue eye, replied: 'Do you think so? All cities are hideous to me: they bring out the worst in men.'

The Greek tragedy of 1922 has been so much obscured by later greater slaughters that it has dwindled to a pinpoint in history now. The tiny part which I played is now a commonplace experience of thousands of 'relief' workers all over the world, and merits no detailed description here. I returned to Athens to form, at Nansen's request, a Committee which might co-ordinate the rather untidy work of the various relief organisations which were now appearing – the Quakers, the Near East Relief, the Save the Children Fund, the British Red Cross, and, last and richest, with a million dollars to spend, the American Red Cross under Ross Hill. You might have expected such organisations to show altruism and team-spirit: not at all. They might have been a collection of prima donnas. Not one of them would disclose its plans or activities or funds to another; and they kept up, except for the Quakers, a quite disreputable struggle to requisition the best houses and the best cars. The results were that nobody quite knew how many refugees there were, or where they were, or what was wanted: and there was no long-term plan. Nansen was perfectly right in wishing to consolidate these activities: but, although I got great help from Bentinck of the British Embassy and Colonel Corfe and others, it was a task which defeated me. I travelled round Greece and the Aegean Islands (with a never-to-be-forgotten four-hour stop at Delos, the most magical place I ever saw) and collected a formidable array of figures, showing the numbers, sex, age, and (what was more important) occupation of the refugees. At that moment Greece had a great opportunity. There were, among the refugees, thousands of skilled carpet-weavers, farmers, wine-growers, masons, fishermen, and, oddly enough, jewellers. They could have been absorbed into the Greek economy. But it was not done. I pleaded with Ross Hill for a realistic view which would deny all aid to the refugees unless they worked for it: without that, they would simply sit on their bottoms and be fed, and at the end of the million dollars, nothing would have been accomplished. Ross Hill argued, with that maddening blind American grandiosity which has since so wrecked the world, that he 'could not enter into politics, and was only there to feed the refugees'. My hopes grew daily more threadbare: my enthusiasm waned. I sent (as I see from the papers I still have) angry telegrams to Philip Baker, saying that I was going to England and America to explain the position, and raise funds: and he replied gently, asking me to desist. I was also at loggerheads with the League, who wrote me that 'I appeared to be concentrating on *Russian* refugees'. I had indeed had to take these over in Nansen's name, and, since the wretched Cossacks in Greece (waiting for a problematical attack on Soviet Russia by Wrangel) had suffered more acutely than anyone, I arranged to send them back to Novorossiysk, thereby earning the enmity of Prince and Princess Demidoff, the Czarist representatives in Greece. You can see, I hope, that my position was complicated.

What with waning enthusiasm and growing exasperation, I found myself falling heavily in lust – it could hardly be dignified by the word love – with a blond young American who had come to work for the American Red Cross. He had large blue eyes and pink cheeks and was full of lofty thoughts and ideals. He was, I imagine, as much attracted to me as I to him, but homosexuality was for him a word never to be uttered. He assured me earnestly that we must go into partnership and remain together for life. That was not my idea. But the physical pull was so strong that when Hugh decided to leave Greece for America via Italy, I made up my mind to go too: and wrote to Nansen saying (as was true enough) that I did not think I could do any further useful work in Athens. The reactions to my decision were surprisingly strong. Nansen, though he never interfered in personal choices, deplored it: Adosides, the very charming Greek deputy who had been assigned to refugee questions, begged me with tears in his eyes to stay: Colonel Corfe said abruptly that I was behaving like a fool, that I now knew more about the problem than anyone, and that, if I had patience, I should be at the head of it all. My ears were deaf to all such advice, though I was slightly peeved when I overheard Adosides say, in Greek, 'It's the American who's pulling him.'

I found myself in a Florentine hotel with Hugh, and Sandro at once came round to see me. Having been introduced to Hugh, he exploded with mirth and his laughter echoed round my room. He asked me if I knew what a great fool I looked, gawping at this doll of an American: could I really be so silly as to suppose that this pink baby was worth a moment's thought? I looked at

Hugh through Sandro's mocking eyes, and the spell was broken. My lust disappeared like a flash of lightning. I said a brief good-bye to Hugh, whose blue eyes held astonished pain, and went south with Sandro. Lust, I suddenly felt, was no substitute for gay untrammelled friendship.

There now ensued six months which were perhaps the happiest, certainly the most carefree, of my life. Both Sandro and I were almost without money, but it did not matter: at that time it was possible to live quite adequately in Italy for three or four shillings a day, and Sandro was beginning to sell pictures here and there. By the cheapest methods of transit, and often on our feet, we wandered over Italy, Sicily, Sardinia and Corsica. Sandro painted for eight or nine hours every day, and I, sitting behind him, copied him as best I could, and learnt the technique of painting in a haphazard but delightful way. Laughter was with us, and we were always in the midst of silly adventures. Apart from finding myself swallowed up in Italian life, warm and gay and irresponsible, my eye was alerted to notice the beauty of people and places, skies and water, trees and grasses ruffled by the breeze, details of architecture and of painting. Every human being, no matter how small the talent, should make the effort to put down what is seen: a new clarity of vision is obtained, which adds for ever afterwards a new dimension to life. Finding this grow in me, I was entranced, and felt sure that I must become a painter and nothing else. Away with all ideas of relief, reform, organisation and the rest! The only life worth living was the life of the individual, roaming where he would, with no bosses and no routine! These brave ideas were a little deflated when Sandro's mother became suddenly and dangerously ill, and he was summoned home. Life without him was much less amusing. I decided that I must go and work at the Slade School. This was a foolish and conventional decision: I had an idea that it would give me a sort of respectable degree in art, and thus mitigate the disapproval of my relations and friends.

But to be poor in Italy was one thing, and to be poor in London was quite another. This particular facet of experience taught me how futile and mistaken are socialist doctrines which aim at equal standards of life for all. The pinch of poverty or the enjoyment of riches depends on many undefinable and shifting factors: climate, convention, character, snobism, age, upbringing, *et al*. In Italy it did not matter how I dressed or ate or lived: in London, because I knew people, it did. I was trying to act two irreconcilable roles: the son of a MFH at one moment, a shabby student in Gower Street at another. And the Slade was hardly helpful in reconciling me to this ambivalent life. Professor Tonks had 'passed' my paintings, and even muttered that they showed some promise: but in class, as was his way, he would ask me in a loud voice why I had ever thought of painting, and whether I shouldn't be better advised to take up knitting at once. I could have stood these pleasantries better if I had not had, on either side of me, Oliver Messel and Rex Whistler, who, blithely ignoring both Tonks and the model, drew with a facility which I knew, with desperate melancholy, was altogether beyond me. With each conscientious sketch, I saw my talent more clearly for the poor little thing it was.

Destiny chose this moment to move Philip Noel-Baker to ring me up, and to say that Lord Parmoor, who had become Lord President of the Council in the new (and first) Labour Government, needed a secretary for League of Nations affairs, and I was the very person. I was depressed, and the prospect of being secretary to a Cabinet Minister was glamorous. I knew that everyone, from my father onwards, would applaud. I wrote to Tonks telling him of the offer, and saying that, since he had so much discouraged me, perhaps I should take it? I hoped by this letter to sting him into some expression of faith in me as a painter. As I might have known, nothing of the sort occurred. Tonks replied briefly that if I had not the perseverance necessary to an artist, I had best give it up immediately. I thought at the time he was right, but I have since realised that he was entirely wrong. Perseverance does not make artists. Only talent does that. Talent may bring perseverance in its train, but the artist is born, not made. Tonks's letter, in any case, put paid to my career at the Slade.

I went to interview Lord Parmoor, and, in response to his questions, told him a great many fat lies. Among other things he asked me if I wrote shorthand, and I said that I did. This claim was expiated later in tears and sweat, when I had to take down not only letters dictated by him but also minutes of committees. I used to scribble what I could in longhand and make up the rest from memory. Parmoor and other celebrities used to mutter 'I don't think I said *that*,' and I would reply quickly, riffling through my notebook, 'But I have it down here.' I am amazed to think that I got away with it, but I did.

So there I was. A new life began. Pin-stripe trousers, black

coat, bowler hat, arrival at the Treasury at nine a.m. every morning. I was absolutely the world's worst secretary. I forgot
everything and muddled what I did not forget. Fortunately I was
young and my mind was quick, so that I could often recover
myself. I did not at all like Parmoor, who seemed to me a rather
unpleasant and silly old man. But at first I was a good deal
impressed by the job. Paley, the tremendously dignified porter
of the Treasury, treated me with great deference, and I had not
had any deference for a long while. I had access to the Cabinet
room, which then seemed very thrilling. I sat in the secretaries'
box in the House of Lords, and ran down to correct, in Hansard,
the many mistakes which Parmoor always made. Dignitaries of
all sorts, from the Archbishop of Canterbury onwards, sat in my
room waiting to see Parmoor. We even had visits from Queen
Mary. My room looked out on the Horse Guards Parade, and it
was all very grand. Best of all perhaps were the red boxes containing despatches from Ambassadors. I had a key for these, and
it so happened that they travelled, by routine, from Buckingham
Palace to my office, so that I was the first to see anything that
the King had written. On one occasion, when Alexander of
Yugoslavia had done something dictatorial, the King had taken
a new sheet of paper and written on it, in blue pencil, 'Dear!
Dear! Whatever are we coming to?' I thought this direction of
foreign policy so delicious that I was temped to extract the sheet
and frame it – for who, except the King, could ever know, and
what could he say? I desisted because I thought it would not be
believed.

Society now drew me into its orbit. Because I was young and
a bachelor and (I suppose I must add) an Etonian, as well as
being in a position which people might regard as promising a
political career, invitations poured in and all doors were opened
to me. A week-end at Arundel, the Duchess of Devonshire's Ball,
the reception at Londonderry House, and so on. The road of
success was opening before me. But I felt myself a tramp on that
road. I wanted to hide in the ditch. I tried hard to be at ease but
never succeeded. Between these glamorous people and myself
some chasm yawned. I was hopeless at all parlour tricks: poor in
small-talk, stupid at bridge, a bad dancer, a rabbit at tennis and
uninterested by racing. I came to know the faces photographed
in *The Tatler,* but I was never quite of their company. I could
just get by, and that was all. Gradually everything went sour on
me. I began to loathe Westminster and the long dreary debates I

had to attend. I was cured for ever of any desire to become a politician: it seemed to me, as it still seems, the most boring life imaginable. When the Labour Government fell, I was delighted to be free. I thought gaily that I would return to Italy and join Sandro again in the best sort of life I had ever known. And at that moment, like the sudden toll of a bell, came a letter from his uncle, saying that Sandro had died in Tunis. It enclosed a pencilled scrawl, written during his last illness, asking me to 'come out soon'.

This was a deadly blow. Italy had, I suppose, if only half-consciously, remained at the back of my mind as a refuge, a delight always to be rediscovered. Now it vanished. Without the gay company of Sandro it was unimaginable: and indeed for many years I did not return to it. What was I to do? Despondently I looked at myself. I was twenty-eight, and when you are twenty-eight (with the dreadful thirty looming on the horizon), you may begin to feel that you are a failure. I had run around a good deal, but had nothing to show for it. I was no good at anything. I did not even know what I wanted to do – except to run away, somehow, from all organised life. It did not then occur to me that a varied experience of life may be valuable. I saw only (as others may see) a long sad succession of scatterbrained globe-trottings. So, when Oliver Baldwin suggested that I go and live with him on a poultry-farm in Oxfordshire, I thought, madly, that this was perhaps my destiny and my proper place.

Oliver was a remarkable person, and I was much under his influence at that time. I had known him slightly at Eton, where his very individual behaviour had amused me. I had also come to know his family. I had been at Aix-les-Bains with Stanley and Lucy Baldwin when Oliver returned from his six prisons and two revolutions in Turkey and Armenia. He was then in a rather daft, but splendidly daft, state of mind, with a sizzling white-hot anger against the world in general and his father in particular, in spite of the fact that Stanley Baldwin had rescued him, by an exchange of prisoners, from a condemned cell. He paced up and down the room at Aix, unfolding to my admiring ear his plans for a better world, and I was spellbound. Possibly the fact that his father was Chancellor of the Exchequer increased the spell, though I don't think so. I was at a stage of life when all rebellion seems glamorous. And Oliver, besides having a good mind, was a witty and engaging companion. I was convinced that he was marked out for a great career, and even now I am puzzled that he failed to scale the political heights. In 1924 I was quite ready to become his disciple on a poultry-farm. I was in a strange mood of self-abasement, and felt that the further I could get from the madding crowd the better. Thus I fell into a kind of slavery, which astonishes me when I look back upon it. In the evenings I was Oliver's attentive audience, listening with respect to his speeches, writings, and plans. In the day I did all the chores, pumping up the bathwater (a quite heavy task), and cleaning out the houses of the hens and geese. Oh, the damned geese! I had done some dirty jobs in Greece but nothing compared (as anyone who knows it must agree) with the filth of geese. I grew to hate them so much that I could not even eat them. When they hissed at me, I would have liked to cut off their silly heads. But I was not in the least unhappy. The country routine suited my state of mind: Oliver entertained me: and at week-ends there was always a sprinkling of intelligent and amusing guests. I was quite content to remain a sort of background for Oliver, and might have so continued had I not, after some seven or eight months, fallen desperately in love for the first time in my life. The object of my affections (so reason told me) was unlikely, improbable, and unsuitable. It did not matter: I was caught like a rabbit in the glare of physical attraction, and blinded to all else. I could think of nothing (except when I was in a turmoil of jealousy) save one person and one act. I became, naturally, an unmitigated bore. Oliver, finding the attention of his disciple apt to wander, grew impatient with me. I saw that my days at Watlington were numbered, but I did not care. My love burnt itself merrily out, and exploded with the usual agony. I descended into a suicidal melancholy. Nothing mattered any more. Escape offered itself suddenly in an unexpected letter from William J. Locke, the novelist, who wrote asking me to go and stay with him at Cannes. I had met him and his adopted daughter Sheila by some chance, and had liked them very much: I had not met Mrs Locke. It seemed quite a good idea to go to the Riviera, which I had never seen, under such auspices. (I think that I had some vague idea that I might blow out my brains in the Casino, after losing my all.) I travelled to Marseilles with Oliver, who was going to visit his uncle in Algiers, and proceeded to Cannes.

I sat on a sunlit terrace while Sheila dispensed cocktails. Presently Mrs Locke appeared. Seeing me, she stopped dead in her tracks, and exclaimed: 'My God! It isn't possible!' Introductions were made, and no more was said: I wondered if she was not right in the head. A few days later, she asked me whether I would care to go over to Monte Carlo with her. I said that I should be delighted to see Monte. When we arrived, she directed the chauffeur to the Royalty Bar, and as soon as we were seated there, called a waiter and told him to go across to the Park Palace – a nest of luxury flats just opposite – and ask Madame d'Alvarez to come down. After a time an elegant figure emerged from the Park Palace. Faultlessly dressed in the manner of eighteen, Diana d'Alvarez might have been anything between forty and sixty. She was certainly good-looking in a ravaged way. When she saw me, she paled in a manner which I have read about in fiction but never seen before or since. The rouge on her cheeks stood out like two setting suns. Staggering to a chair, she murmured: 'Brandy!' The brandy was brought at the double. I thought, all these people are utterly mad.

We had lunch with Madame d'Alvarez, and when we left she pressed my hand and said: 'Come and see me when next you are in Monte.' I assented vaguely: I did not expect to see her or Monte again. But shortly before the end of my visit, Mrs Locke told me that she was sending the car to Monte Carlo, and perhaps I would care to go. I said that certainly it would be fun to try my luck at the tables. But after an hour of the Sporting Club, I wearied of that form of pleasure. I had very little money to lose and I lost it quickly. When I emerged into the sunshine, I wondered what to do while waiting for the car. It struck me that I might get a cup of tea off Madame d'Alvarez, and I made my way to the Park Palace. Arrived there, I saw through the double doors that a bridge party was in progress, and tried to make my escape. But Madame d'Alvarez came rushing out, propelled me into a small boudoir, and hissed: 'Wait here, I'll send them all away.' I stammered, 'But I shouldn't dream ...' But she was gone. There were voices and then silence. Madame d'Alvarez returned, and settled herself on a sofa. Tea was brought in. 'They've all gone,' she said. 'Now we can talk.' What on earth was this, I asked myself? Curiouser and curiouser. Was the woman mad? She asked what my plans were, and when I said that I was returning to England in three days time, exclaimed: 'Oh, but *why?* Look, I've got a party for Maurice Maeterlinck's birthday the day after tomorrow, and I'm having the whole restaurant decorated with blue birds: there'll be the King and Queen of Montenegro and the Grand Duke Andrew and the Phillips Oppenheims and Lily Langtry and Mary Garden and others: now why don't you come over and be my special guest?' In the light of today, such a party may sound a ludicrous bore: I suppose I must have thought it very exciting: I fell for it. I moved over to a small and cheap hotel in Monte. When the party was over, Diana d'Alvarez said: 'Now the Oppenheims have invited us to lunch at Sospel tomorrow, and the Grand Duke wants us for dinner at the Negresco – you can't refuse *that*, it's a Royal Command!' And, hey presto, I had become a Riviera gigolo. It did not, of course, strike me like that, because I kept to my hotel, and went out only to the large parties which she or others gave every day: I was fascinated by the raffish Riviera life, and the streams of money thrown away: and every day I decided to return to England tomorrow. And every day postponed it. I was dazzled by the pageant of wealth and also exhausted by it. Parties went on into the small hours every night, and at eight in the morning the indefatigable Diana would be ringing me up to announce another and another. It took me about three months to realize that, in Riviera eyes, I had become the *cher ami*, the lapdog, and the property of Madame d'Alvarez. When this eventually dawned on me, I made haste to depart. Diana d'Alvarez was aghast. 'But,' she cried 'why, why, why?' I tried to explain that I couldn't spend my life on the Riviera, and must find a *job*. It did not, in that environment, sound at all convincing. 'A *job*?' exclaimed Diana, staring at me. 'Well, if you must have a *job*, I hold about half the shares in Dry Monopole, and I suppose you could go into the Paris office, couldn't you?' I thanked her very much, and said that I did not think I should be any good at selling champagne. Madame d'Alvarez paled behind her rouge. 'I must talk to you seriously,' she said. 'I'll tell you what, we'll go over to tea at the Negresco.' On the way along the Corniche road, she developed a new and staggering plan. 'I see,' she said, 'that you're bored with this Riviera life: well, perhaps it *is* boring. I'll tell you what. I sell pills all over the world. You see, I got very fat at one time, and had to go away and starve myself – lie under sandbags and all that. It was very successful and I came back quite slender again. People wanted to know how I did it. So I invented some pills – nothing in them, of course, but they've had a great success everywhere – oh yes, America, South America, all over the place. Now I'd rather like to go and see if I'm getting the profits or being cheated. What say we take the Rolls and the Peugeot and go all around the world? How would you like that?' Well, I thought, it's quite an offer. To go round the world in comfort and *gratis* wouldn't happen to me again. There was a moment of dreadful temptation. Then I saw myself trailing in Diana's wake. No.

That evening, when I saw her out of the car at the Park Palace, and accompanied her into the hall, she fainted, or pretended to faint – I shall never know. She fell in a heap at my feet. I picked her up and carried her to the flat, and laid her on a sofa. The next day I left for England. I never saw her again. It isn't a moral tale.

I arrived in England. My father, stepmother and sister were just about to leave, with a girl called Myrtle Kellett, on a Mediterranean cruise. My father, as I have indicated, hated 'abroad', and I don't think he ever intended to go. At the last moment he fell diplomatically ill with influenza. Everything had been booked and couldn't be cancelled. I don't think it's much of an exaggeration to say that, like the *Snark*, they had forty-two cases all carefully packed with their names clearly painted on each – to say nothing of my stepmother's lady's-maid, already on board. My stepmother said that I must take the girls. I protested that I did not want to go on any cruise: I had to stay in England now and find a *job*. She pooh-poohed that, said I had been wasting my time anyway, and another six weeks would not matter. I found myself on board the *Otranto,* with two seventeen-year-old girls in tow. It was my first, and undoubtedly my last, experience of a cruise. I would prefer Hell. There was a Master of Ceremonies, and a grisly never-ceasing attempt to make everyone 'matey' – and nearly all the horrid people on board wanted to be just that. We were expected to join merrily in deck games, lotteries, whist-drives, and dances. Every other night there was what was called a 'running' dinner, which meant that everybody was forbidden to keep to his own table but must join another and be matey. At Tangier we poured off the ship in waves of crowded boats, and, once on shore, found ourselves with the darling passengers wherever we went. It was the same in the Balearic Islands, the same in Barcelona. Then, to my horror, I found that we were steaming up to Monte Carlo. God in Heaven, I said to myself, I am now going to be mixed up between Diana and these two girls. I think I must have been sweating with apprehension by the time we arrived in front of the Casino. Fortunately for me, Marguerite van Buren, an American lovely with whom I had made friends, was circling the Place in her car. 'What on earth are *you* doing here?' she cried. I hissed at her: '*Is Diana here?*' 'No, gone to Paris'. I breathed again. Marguerite whisked us up to her flat. From that moment everything became brilliant: we were offered lunches, cars, boats, anything we fancied. People came rushing in to see me. I drew Marguerite into a corner and said: 'But what is all this *about?* People here were never so nice to me before.' She opened wide blue eyes and replied: 'But don't you *know?*' I said I didn't know what she was talking about. 'But nobody would ever dare to invite you – you were Diana's beau!' 'I wasn't anything of the kind!' 'Of course you were – but didn't Mrs Locke *tell* you?' 'Mrs Locke told me nothing.' 'But, don't you see, Diana had a beau called Captain Chesney, Mary Garden's half-brother, and he died in Deauville just before you arrived – and *you were the exact image of him!*' She added: 'Wait a moment,' opened a drawer and showed me a photograph: it was indeed very like me. 'You see?' I did see, at last. 'We are all fond of Diana and she was desperate: Mrs Locke thought you were a gift from Heaven: so did Diana.'

We were magnificently entertained to lunch and dinner, sent to drive along the Corniche, taken to the Sporting Club. Myrtle and my sister, who had been getting more and more bored by the *Otranto,* thought this fine. In the evening a gale blew up, and we were accosted by a dim little man off the ship who warned us: 'Better get back, last launch leaving!' Our hosts laughed and said that they would send us in their private launch. So we set off at one a.m. in a rough sea and scrambled dramatically aboard. All this made the girls feel that Monte was tremendous and they pleaded with me that we should leave the *Otranto* at Toulon and return there. It was a mad idea but I agreed. Thompson the lady's maid was packed off in angry tears to London, and we sent a wild telegram to the family: 'Feel *Otranto* definitely unsafe: going Monte Carlo.' The odd thing about that was that the next night the *Otranto* ran into Cape Matapan and buckled her bows, and the passengers were sent home. The family were of course scandalised by our action, and angry wires arrived. However, we had about a hundred pounds between us and decided to spend it. How to do so was obvious. Myrtle and my sister had already worked out, alas, a 'system'. We spent a week at the tables, and had just enough, at the end, to get us back to London.

Thus with a whimper and no bang I came to the end of ten years wandering. I was now not only without a job, I was also without the smallest idea of what job I wanted or how to get one at all. I pulled what strings I could without avail, and then, descending lower, began to read and reply to advertisements. Round and round I went, to publishers, to business firms, to oil companies, to advertising agencies, waiting in queues and sometimes being interviewed. The nadir came when I applied as a commercial traveller for Kelly's Directories – and was turned down. I daresay I was not very prepossessing and my record was not good: but there was one definite blot against me everywhere – that I had been connected with the Labour Government. In those days that was still a crime. Depressed and anxious, I became ill. I had for a long time been dogged by a recurrence of Gallipoli dysentery, and I was now advised to see Aldo Castellani, the specialist in tropical diseases. He put me into his clinic in Putney and there for three weeks I lived on three glasses of milk a day and had emetine injections. I emerged as light as a feather, and at this moment Philip Baker flew into my life again. He wrote saying that Hilda Matheson, the Talks Director of the BBC, was looking for an assistant, and perhaps I would like to go to lunch in Eaton Place and meet her.

I had never listened to a radio, and had only a very vague idea of what the BBC was or did. However – any port in a storm, and I gratefully accepted the invitation. On the morning of it I was seized with a paralysing dysenteric tummy cramp. Furiously I rang up Castellani, and told him he hadn't cured me. He said, 'Come round here.' I went to Harley Street where, as was usual in Castellani's practice, patients were waiting all over the house and even sitting on the stairs. Presently he came, jabbed a needle into me, and said, 'Now you'll be all right.' Miraculously I quickly was, and took a taxi to Philip's house. In the taxi I began to feel that my feet were turning into huge balls of cotton wool, and the driver's head got further and further away. In Eaton Place I just managed to get out, rang the bell with an arm which seemed to be a mile long, and fell down the steps in a dead faint. And so I first met Hilda Matheson, and, after Irene Baker had treated me with strong coffee (and I had cursed Castellani and all his works), talked to her. My fifteen years in radio began. But only after difficulties which will be related later.

I had left the bypaths for a main road, and exchanged variation for a career. Was it a good thing? No: it wasn't. The world, of course, does not approve of people who run from one thing to another, and does not crown them with success. The brief span of human life allows time for only two kinds of success: brilliance or application – the genius or the plodder. I was neither brilliant nor a plodder. I was that uneasy misfit, the artist without talents. Such an individual is happy only when he is not tied by routine, by bosses, by regulations, by ordered hours of work, by organisation and organisations – in short by all our civilized slavery. But he has no wings to lift him above this man-made swamp of – to him – despair. He can choose only between the frustration of the clerk and the failure of the artist. In 1927 I was enchanted to be 'safe' at last – to have a settled place and a salary, to be part of a rapidly-developing institution, and to be offered what seemed to be (and indeed to a large extent was) congenial work. Looking back, I now think that my first great mistake in life was my letter to Tonks: my second was lunch in Eaton Place. Not that I am ungrateful to Philip Noel-Baker, who certainly did his best to turn me into a useful member of society. But that was not my role. I should have been a mediocre painter but a competent one. Perhaps I should have drifted into making lampshades or designing dust-covers or ladies' hats: and maybe I should have had my private and individual moments of anger and frustration: but never, I think, the great black asphyxiating anger and frustration with which bureaucracy, for the next twenty years, enveloped me.

Chapter Three

*I conceive some scattered notions about a superior power
to be of singular use for the common people, as furnishing
excellent materials to keep children quiet when they grow
peevish, and providing topics of amusement in a tedious
winter-night.*   JONATHAN SWIFT

IN THAT YEAR, 1927, when my faltering footsteps first crossed the
anything-but-august threshold of Savoy Hill, the British Broadcasting Corporation was born, and Mr J. C. W. Reith became its
first Director General. (The company had, of course, existed
since 1922). 1927 also saw – or heard – the first two racing
'commentaries' (the Grand National and the Derby), the first
'commentary' on a football match, and the first broadcast of a
symphony concert from the Queen's Hall – this last an innovation
greatly resented by listeners. Another year was to pass before the
first broadcats of a BBC Dance Orchestra (under Jack Payne),
and yet another three before Adrian Boult conducted a BBC
Symphony Orchestra. In 1927 the BBC was poised for its flight
into the ether, and it was precisely this flutter of untried wings
which was, at least for me, its chief and great attraction. Almost
nothing was known about the transmission of sound through the
microphone, and the shape of things to come was still fluid. Mistakes were constantly made, and every day was an experiment.
The future was still uncertain, and money was in short supply –
one guinea for a quarter-of-an-hour talk; programmes were
scrambled together from day to day, and, when they failed or
ran short (for we had hardly begun to learn the possibility of
exact timing) there were no easy gramophone records, or even
Bow Bells, to fill the gap. The gaps were filled in those days by
the charming Cecil Dixon, who tinkled Chopin on the piano, and
announced each number in a shy little voice. She should have a
place in any BBC history. Fleet Street, so much more ancient and
pontifical, looked upon this new toy with an amused and indulgent eye, though there were some, like Lord Riddell, whose
eye held a faint alarm. In the formative years before 1932, the
BBC was a new and exciting dish, sizzling over the fire, with

Reith as *chef de cuisine*, and perhaps too many cooks spoiling the broth: by 1932 it was the heavy though doubtless healthy pudding which it remains – rather soggy now to my taste. When I listen today to the same old variety shows, the same old feature programmes, the same old commentaries, all so smooth and efficient now, and the plummy announcers' voices with their bedside manner of conveying expurgated news, I sigh for the muddles and mistakes of the past. We may have been silly, but we were never complacent. And, God save us, we really believed that broadcasting could revolutionize human opinion.

When Hilda Matheson had seen and approved me, despite the effects of my polyglandular injection, she told me that she herself could not appoint me. For that I should have first to be 'interviewed' by Reith and Admiral Carpendale, the Deputy Director General. Remembering Burlington House, I quailed a little at this. I also remembered the series of unsuccessful commercial interviews. I was not much good at it (perhaps, I thought, I have halitosis or BO). And my record would not appeal to any pundit. Why did you give up painting? Why have you been so long unemployed? Why did you not take a degree? Questions without answers. I approached Savoy Hill and Mr Reith in no easy frame of mind. And Mr Reith made it no easier. Since I am two inches over six feet myself, I am apt to get an inferiority complex, or an attack of bad temper (much the same thing) when anyone towers over me. And Mr Reith not only towered, but intended to tower. Instantly I had the impression – quite a mistaken one – of an insufferable tyrant. Reith in fact had and has one of the largest inferiority complexes ever known to man and, as is the way of such things, it makes him arrogant. I was intimidated, as who would not have been, by this giant with piercing eyes under shaggy eyebrows, and the scarred cheek which somehow suggested ruthlessness. He snapped at me immediately: 'Why d'you want to come into broadcasting?'

I had no answer to that one. Or rather, the correct answer wouldn't do. 'Because I've been turned down even as a commercial traveller for Kellys Directories, and I'd take any damned job that offered.' I murmured some bromide about a new development which had immense possibilities. 'Getting in on the bandwagon, eh?' I reflected that perhaps there was something in that. Since I was extremely vague about what I should have to do in the BBC, I could not say that I should be good at it. 'I suppose,' pursued Mr Reith, with a cutting edge to his voice, 'you know that you won't make any *money* here? This is a dedicated service: we don't want people who are after money.' (I wondered what his salary was). He added abruptly: '£400 a year – that's about all you're likely to get.' Since I was earning nothing, and did not seem likely to, this remark did not bother me: what I wanted at that moment was not money but security. I had, however, an uncomfortable feeling that, once again, I had made a bad impression. Reith, after giving me a long stare which seemed to expose my mildewed soul, said: 'You'd better go up and see Admiral Carpendale.'

Carpendale, a handsome blue-eyed man with a barking manner, said, 'Miss Matheson recommends you, but I don't know why. What can you *do?*' These questions were frightful. *Do?* Well, Admiral Carpendale, I can paint in water-colours rather badly, I can speak French and Italian and a little German, and I'm rather good at digging latrines. I stammered that I had a fairly good knowledge of literature and poetry. 'Literature and poetry?' barked Carpendale. 'My dear chap, this is *broadcasting!*' He considered me for a while, and then said: 'Better try you out as an announcer.' He rang a bell, and said to a secretary: 'Take this man to Number 5 and give him a news bulletin to read: put it on a closed circuit.' This was my first sight of a microphone or, come to that, a studio. I stumbled through the news bulletin. 'Well,' said Carpendale, with a sort of snarling satisfaction, when I returned to his office, 'no good as an announcer, that's a sure thing.' I left Savoy Hill with my tail between my legs.

I was not, therefore, surprised when Hilda Matheson told me that Reith and Carpendale had not approved of me, and did not wish me to be appointed. 'But never mind,' she added, 'I'll get over that: you'll see.' And so she did. In due course I became a member of the Talks Department at £400 a year. I felt that I was there on trial and on sufferance, and I sensed a strange hostility towards me among the BBC staff. I therefore strained every nerve to carry out the tasks assigned to me with scrupulous care, and to exercise what charm I could. I had a positive terror that at any moment I should be sacked. And that is, now, a strange thing to look back upon. I was completely wrong, and I did not realize my error until thirty years later. In 1957 Gerald Cock, who had settled in San Francisco and was making a tour of Europe, came to stay with me in Italy. Gerald had been a highly successful administrator of the BBC. He was, among other things, the first Director of television, and the first representative of the BBC in America. I had not known him well, and had sometimes thought his fizzing energy a little exaggerated: so that I was surprised when he invited himself to stay. Gossiping about the past, he said: 'Ah! how well I remember the time when you came to the BBC. You were the 'wonder boy' who had been everywhere and done everything. We were all terrified of you.' I was staggered by this. I replied that I didn't believe it: it was I who had been terrified. 'Oh no,' he said, 'we thought you would be Director General.'

Two years later, I had a visit from Florence Milnes, that charming intelligent woman who battled (and it was a battle) for thirty-three years to build up the BBC Library, and was thereby – and will be – of matchless assistance to countless programme builders. When we were in doubt about any personality, any date, any event, any reference, a trip to Miss Milnes in the library would settle the matter without fuss and without apparent effort. She too should have a place in any history of the BBC. When she came to see me in Italy, she had already retired, and I had not seen her for many years. I happened to express my surprise at Gerald Cock's remark, and she said at once: 'I can tell you exactly what people thought when you came to Savoy Hill. You were the man of courage and money who *would stand up to Reith*. People were frightened of you, because they thought that you might make them lose their jobs.'

I imagine that these two quite disinterested opinions must be somewhere near the truth. At the time I was a million miles from imagining anything of the kind. I thought that I was badly equipped for the job, that I might easily get the sack, and that the whole staff, with the exception of Hilda Matheson, despised me. I had, as I now see, an opportunity which I failed to seize. Equally, I am inclined to think that the BBC might have made more use of my services than it did. My experience, disorderly and aimless as it might have seemed, fitted the BBC, as it then was, perfectly. I had travelled more than most young men of my age, I had made the acquaintance of a great many distinguished people in various walks of life, I was by that time well read and had a wide knowledge of English poetry, I spoke four languages, knew something about art and politics, and was musically fairly well educated. This dilettantism was exactly suited to the needs of the BBC. I was of course a flunkey: all broadcasting officials are flunkeys, bowing the arts in and out of the studio: but a BBC flunkey could have considerable effect on programmes. And a

BBC flunkey, to be effective, had to be a queer kind of mongrel: in racing parlance you might call him Entertainment by Impresario out of Scholarship. As in all mass entertainment, there was always the danger that, in the words of Burke, 'learning will be cast into the mire and trodden down under the heels of a swinish multitude'. Such a danger is illustrated today by programmes such as Mrs Dale's Diary and by the BBC Variety programmes – the most vulgar broadcasting in the whole civilized and uncivilized world. There is also the danger of preaching to a minority of the converted by becoming too highbrow, as the Third Programme now does. The broadcasting flunkey has to steer a course between vulgarity and obscurantism, pulling the one up and the other down, until a lucid and agreeable programme is obtained. It is not so easy as it sounds.

The phenomenal rise of broadcasting has never yet found its troubadour and probably never will. Yet it could be a great song. From the whiskered crystal set of 1920 ('I can actually hear a *voice!!*') to the mammoth of Portland Place in 1932 was a giant stride. Reith, with his volumes of beautifully written and detailed diaries, should have been the man to sing that song: but his voice failed him. (And there were reasons for that.) Many others have attempted it, but none, I think, with success. I have no desire to compete. I was, as I have said and shall say again, no more than a flunkey of the microphone.

The tenemental building in Savoy Hill, with its creaking lift and narrow stone staircase, where the solemn Mr Chilman (still, I believe, with the BBC), presided over a tiny reception desk, was the reverse of glamorous. The 'studios' were mostly small rooms with distressing echoes, and by no means soundproof. The atmosphere was one-third boarding school, one-third Chelsea party, one-third crusade. Or possibly the crusade bulked a little larger. There was the same feeling of dedication and hope which had characterised the League of Nations in its earliest days. All causes seem good when they are new and untried: and all, in the end, except individual creation, are spoiled by human mediocrity. Hitler was perfectly right when, in *Mein Kampf*, he wrote that no organisation should ever be run by more than a dozen people at most: proliferate your staff, and you're done for. At Savoy Hill, luckily for us, we were short of staff and money, and there was violent and healthy competition between the various 'departments'. 'Talks' thought that 'Variety' was vulgar: 'Variety' thought that 'Talks' should not exist: 'Talks' and 'Variety' thought that 'Music' over the microphone was hopeless: 'Sport' seemed an odious frivolity: as for 'Drama' – well, I ask you, plays which you couldn't *see!* At about this time Aldous Huxley wrote me a letter which I still possess about 'broadcast' programmes – 'plays I cannot take: these disembodied voices make me physically sick.' In fact we had no more idea than the makers of silent films of the shape which broadcasting would eventually take: in the meantime, every day was a challenge.

I was often asked, in the years that followed, 'but what do you *do?*' Well, what does a broadcasting official *do?* The answer is that he can, if he so desires, mould public opinion exactly as he wishes. Or perhaps not exactly, but very nearly. I don't believe that there was any time in my years at the BBC, when, had I been fanatically convinced by Communist or Labour or Tory doctrine, I could not have puffed it enormously. (Luckily for me, I never was convinced by any doctrine.) Authority can never control broadcast programmes: in the last resort, it is the producer who controls them, and, if he is ingenious, he can 'put over' any point of view. The music 'director' who likes Scarlatti or Bach or Mozart or Bartok will – even unconsciously – slant programmes in their direction, and listeners will become familiar with them: the play producer who likes Shakespeare or Ibsen or Pirandello or Noel Coward will do likewise: and so on. Greater dangers await the producer of the 'spoken word'. Try as he may to be 'impartial' – that fearful symmetry which is never possible – he will, through his own taste, slant programmes towards what he likes. The elemental fact about broadcasting is its tremendous output. You may have all the authorities and restrictions and committees and regulations: but they are all defeated by the rapidity of successive programmes. Once, with Peter Fleming, I did a summary of the year's news (on New Year's Eve, of course), and I think that almost every phrase in that broadcast was controversial and dangerous. But we used four experienced broadcasters, speaking very rapidly, and although many listeners were outraged, none could remember exactly what had been said. That is an illustration of the fact that broadcasting gallops so fast across the hours that its impact is not consciously felt until it is too late to protest. Mr A or Mr B, the broadcasting official, may be and indeed is a cypher, but his tastes will gradually sway millions. They will not of course do so in one broadcast programme or even a dozen, but if (and this is difficult) the thousand odd programmes produced by a man or woman over, say, two years, could be examined, the drift of that producer's tastes and belief and influence would become evident. This, though obvious, is an important point, because all the careful regulations and safeguards are defeated by it. Whatever rules you may make, in the last resort public opinion will be formed by the men who actually produce programmes. The men who sit at the top, the ageing generals, the chairmen of gas boards, the ineffective professors, the uninspired journalists (Heavens! what strange people have been put in charge of the BBC!) know almost nothing about what is going on under their noses: they cannot – for who on earth can follow the details of sixty or seventy daily hours of programmes? And here I speak from personal experience, because when later I had my own broadcasting organisation in India, I madly tried to follow all programmes, only to find that it was quite impossible. The men who make the programmes (generally underpaid) sway the crowd: the administrators and authorities (usually overpaid) do not.

In the early days at Savoy Hill, we had one aim and one aim only – to find Voices to fill the Hours. If they were distinguished Voices, saying what we thought should be said, so much the better: but if not, programmes had to be invented to support poor voices. The first objective was to avoid silence. And this was not, at first, as easy as it sounds. We had no financial carrots to dangle, and many distinguished people fought shy of risking their reputation on the unfamiliar microphone. Fortunately there were some who did not. I remember best the trinity of E. M. Forster, Desmond MacCarthy and H. G. Wells, who all gave us freely of their time and wise counsels, and would sit round our gas fires at Savoy Hill, talking of the problems and possibilities of broadcasting. Desmond was, of course, a superb broadcaster: the only difficulty with him was to keep him to his script, for he would easily wander, in the Irish way, into a flood of reminiscence. E. M. Forster did not, as a speaker, quite reach the standard of his beautiful prose, but he was a wise and sympathetic counsellor. H.G. was a hopeless speaker with his squeaky voice (we built a special non-echo studio for him, but to no avail) but he was wise, even if, while always preening himself with women, he tended to be offensively rude to men and especially young men. At a slightly further remove, and in very different ways, were Arnold Bennett, Walter Elliott, and Hugh Walpole. A.B. could not broadcast on account of his stammer, but had a childish enthusiasm for all things new, and helped us enormously in discovering talent. Walter Elliott, then tipped as a certainty as future Prime Minister, was a tower of strength in things political. And Hugh was a Niagara of verbosity and as harmless as water. Whenever a speaker failed, it was ten to one that a telephone call would produce Hugh, ready to speak without a manuscript, and to say nothing controversial, for exactly a quarter of an hour or twenty minutes or whatever time was needed. These six were great props. And then, of course, there were the 'established' popular broadcasters whose number steadily grew. It would be invidious, as they say, to list too many names here: it seems to me that Vernon Bartlett on international affairs and Ernest Newman on music criticism, were the first two, closely followed by Walford Davies, who was the best broadcaster I ever knew. He was that partly because he was by nature a stunningly gifted teacher and exponent, and partly because – a very rare gift – he was entirely unaffected by the microphone and the whole para- phernalia of broadcasting. Anyone who watched his antics in a studio - dropping music on the floor, blowing his nose, rubbing his spectacles, or throwing an odd remark to someone in the room – might have thought he was putting on an act: in fact he was simply his natural self, and a very engaging self it was. Nobody in all BBC history has succeeded in transmitting as he did a love of and enthusiasm for music. Ernest Newman was a law unto himself, refusing always to submit any manuscript or even to have one, but invariably producing beautiful talks.

I shared an office with Lance Sieveking. Lance lived some- where among the rolling clouds of his vivid and sometimes er- ratic imagination, and occasionally from these clouds there fell a shower of brilliant ideas. His impact on broadcasting, though it cannot be measured by any statistical standards, was consider- able. He was in the forefront of all experiments and afraid of nothing. He was a stimulant. It is always dangerous to say that any one person is or was responsible for an innovation, but it seems to me that it was Lance who fathered the first experiment in Baird's television – right back in 1930 at Savoy Hill – which took the form of a play, *The Man with a Flower in his Mouth*. It was jagged and hazy, but it gave us, even then, an idea of what television was bound to be. And with his play *Kaleidoscope* – at about the same time – he started the use of multiple studios with a 'panel' to control and 'mix' them. As a stable companion he was unpredictable and sometimes irritating. He would arrive (late) in the morning, and bending over his table towards me, would say something like this: 'Have you *ever*, my dear Lionel, have you *ever* walked down a long *long* passage, with a mirror, a *huge great* mirror, at the end of it, and walked slowly slowly *slowly* until you got up to that *huge great* mirror, and looked into it, and seen . . .' and here his voice rose to a shout, 'NOTH-ING!!!!' And I would say, 'Oh really, Lance at this time of the morning, do for God's sake shut up!' And Sheila Wynn-Williams, our admirable and charming secretary, would giggle in the background. It was Lance who invented and had printed and framed a notice which stood beside the microphone: 'If you *sneeze* or *rustle papers*, you will DEAFEN THOUSANDS!!!!' With some difficulty I got these notices removed, as they caused great alarm and despondency among talkers. All the same, they remain an indication of the kind of fright which the microphone produced at that time – and not without reason: on one occasion a policeman who was broadcasting for me about his duties, and whom I had carefully rehearsed, had a last minute idea (which he did not communicate to me) that it would be fun to blow his whistle: he did so, and the whole BBC went off the air for several hours.

Every day and in every way, the organisation of broadcasting went ahead, and nobody could quite keep track of it. At first Hilda Matheson was the undisputed arbiter of the spoken word, and we were her disciples: but gradually other arbiters began to emerge – Derek MacCulloch, with his immensely successful Children's Hour, Mary Somerville with her programmes for Schools, Stobart with a very thin end of the wedge known as 'Adult Education', Henty with News, and, last but not at all least, the growing number of talks and commentaries on Sport – all these threatened the powers of a single 'Talks Director'. Very gradually, though it took a long time to come to a head, a squabble developed among these interests. But for most of the time at Savoy Hill no squabbles arose: there was too much to do. It was, for instance, difficult at first to decide how *long* any 'talk' should be: nowadays the fifteen minute period has been accepted as basic, but at that time we had little idea whether listeners would accept five or fifteen or thirty or sixty minutes. Eric Maschwitz, a man of sparkling ideas, threw quite a spanner into our works by inventing the highly popular 'In Town Tonight', in which talks were cut to a drastic two minutes each: and it did seem that perhaps that was enough for most speakers. On the other hand, the 'National Lecture' (what a name!) was invented for very distinguished people and lasted an hour: occasionally, as in the case of Dr Glover with his 'Challenge of the Greek' it could be arresting: but usually it was a highbrow flop. Or, at least, so it seemed to us.

In this backward glance it is worth considering for a moment our own ideas about the future. Although broadcasting was empiric and faltering, we had some fairly clear notions about its ultimate development. Television, we knew, was bound to come: we also thought (and it is still a thought, because the requisite cheap sets cannot yet be manufactured) that microwaves were likely to give us thirty or forty separate programmes, and we had definite plans for (a) a continual news programme always on the air, always available, always being added to by the latest events; (b) a programme of light music and waltzes, without the intervention of any announcer (a great number of people wanted this 'background noise'); (c) a programme of continuous readings from the classics, always demanded by hospital patients; and so on and so forth. We also of course thought in terms of a 'Third' programme, essentially highbrow. Reith however was very much against any such specialization, and I think now that he was right. He invented what was known as the 'Phi' system: roughly speaking, this meant that certain programmes of value – a concert by Toscanini, a talk by Einstein, a starred production of Shakespeare – were made obligatory for the whole BBC network: other programmes of less importance but still of some moment could be queried by regional stations, which would have to suggest an alternative, and that alternative might or might not be accepted by London: a third category of programmes could be accepted or rejected by stations as they wished. Reith's argument (I trust that I have understood it) was that by this system listeners would automatically hear the best things and grow to like them: if you had a special programme for every taste you would merely be preaching to the converted, and get no further. That is a point of view which may be debated: I am inclined to think that the Third Programme, as it is today, is something which belongs to the private gramophone and the university lecture room, and not to broadcasting. Broadcasting should continually enlarge the listener's horizon, and if it does not do so it falls into a rut of routine: but it must never jump too far. I am aware, of course, that such arguments will be out-dated by commercial television and sound: sound and vision, spurred by advertisers, will, like the newspapers, follow popular taste: but do not ask me to believe that that is the best solution. The real degradation of the

BBC started with the invention of the hellish department which is called 'Listener Research'. That Abominable Statistic is supposed to show 'what listeners *like*' – and, of course, what they like is the red-nosed comedian and the Wurlitzer Organ. But anyone who has studied the letters received by the BBC knows that (a) only Abominable people ever write to it, and (b) hardly a single letter is a valid criticism. Hilda Matheson and I always wanted (and I am sorry that we never had the courage to do it) to put a speaker on the air saying tomato-tomato-tomato for a quarter of an hour: we were convinced that we should get letters of praise. (And my later experience at the Ministry of Food showed just how daft English letter-writers can be.) For the broadcasting official there can be one rule only – to do what he believes to be good and to spare no trouble in the doing of it. Once he begins to follow what is supposed to be popular taste, he is on the road to stagnation.

It is time that I mentioned two other people who, in their different ways, contributed a great deal to broadcasting in those early days. One was Stephen King-Hall: an example of a man who made himself into a broadcaster. I 'discovered' him because Oliver Baldwin took me to see him, saying that it was a shame that anyone so talented should be unemployed and nearly starving. I thought he had a lively mind, and invited him to try his voice at Savoy Hill. He asked me what he should talk about. I said that it didn't matter: anything that interested him. He decided to talk about the Mediterranean. He produced a quite good talk, which I did not think would set the Thames on fire. But, when he had finished and walked rather disconsolately away – that happened to many speakers, who felt that the lack of applause at the end of a talk was somehow discouraging – he got on to a bus in the Strand. Behind him were two men, and one said to the other, 'D'you know, I just heard a fellow on the wireless talking about the Mediterranean. It got me. Damned good he was. I shall go there for my next holiday.' This conversation produced in Steve (so he has told me since) a sort of conversion of St Paul: he suddenly saw the possibilities of broadcasting, and set himself to work at it. And he worked with concentration and care. He learnt just what to do with his voice, and he kept a card index of every fan letter, and sent everyone a card at Christmas. Thus he built up an enormous popularity which probably counted for much when, later, he published his books and his News Letter and stood for Parliament. The other – a very different character – was a Civil Servant called Lambert, who told stories under the pseudonym of A. J. Alan. His was a natural gift, and I have never known anyone quite like him. His stories began nowhere and ended nowhere, but he had an authentic Sheherezade gift, and could hold you enthralled. He was a pernickety broadcaster, never appearing more than four times a year, refusing all interviews and photographs and publicity, not submitting any manuscript beforehand, and vetoing all printed or written copies of his tales. Recently a member of the Third Programme told me that she had heard 'recordings of A. J. Alan' and thought them 'poor'. I was surprised, because I find it difficult to believe that he ever permitted a recording: it may be so. At any rate, he was in a class by himself.

We worked very hard. By this I mean (as far as I am able to mean anything) that at the end of three years I had a nervous breakdown of shattering magnitude through overstrain: a breakdown which left me with persistent insomnia for the rest of my life. 'Work' is one of the most unsatisfactory words in the English language. Like 'love' it covers too many different things. There is manual labour, digging, heaving, lifting: there is rushing-about labour, errand-boys, commercial travellers, pilots, engine drivers: there is standing labour, shop assistants, waiters, bus conductors: there is skilled labour, surgeons, doctors, scientists: there is brain labour, accountants, civil servants, writers: there is the undoubted labour of a socially climbing hostess, or, come to that, of a prostitute: and so many more. What on earth is 'work'? All that you can say is that it is activity. Certainly we were active. To gather enough people – always new and more people – for the microphone meant a constant alertness: the reading (or at least skimming) of every new book, the seeing of every new play and film, the attendance at every party to which one was asked, the journeys around England, to points where one thing or another created interest – slums, unemployment, pageants, new factories, a murder trial, a scandal, anything and everything: but above all an ear constantly cocked, at parties, in buses or tubes, at exhibitions, in shops, in the street and on the farm, for the Promising Voice. Never were there enough (and never are there now) Promising Voices. Many people would think that our 'work' was not work at all, but a constant round of pleasure. But we could never forget it: every moment of experience could be grist to the microphone. And then, when a voice or a personality was 'captured', there was the business of audition (no, I am so sorry, your voice doesn't *go* on the microphone), and rehearsal (please do it just once more), and support for the actual broadcast (don't worry, just talk naturally ... thank you so much, it was SPLEN-DID. Let me get you a taxi). And demand grew with the growth of broadcasting: special programmes of every kind for Tom, Dick and Harry, not only throughout the day but throughout the night too. There seemed no end to it.

From a snob point of view, we were enviable. At first I approached celebrities with caution, usually through some mutual friend: but as broadcasting developed it became possible, and even a part of 'work', to write to every celebrity who lived in or visited England, suggesting a broadcast: and the offer was rarely refused. Thus we were – if only as flunkeys – in a position to meet anyone and everyone. It seemed, at first, intensely exciting to do this. It was only after experience that one learned, with grey and grisly disillusionment, that the Great Ones of the World were indistinguishable from ordinary people, and indeed were very often more captious and touchy than the average man. Naturally there were glowing exceptions, but on the whole one became aware that the chief advantage of meeting 'distinguished people' was to fill (if one so desired) a book of autographs. I was seldom able to make friends of the Great. Probably I was too unimportant and boring for them: possibly I did not often want to. In the process of meeting half-a-dozen celebrities every day, one became conscious of the classes into which they fell. Men and women. Women were (and are) almost never good broadcasters. I don't know why this should be, but it is a fact. You can reel off lists of men who have been, or are, stars of the microphone: but you will have a job to find any women who equal them (I refer here only to Talks). And that, certainly, was never our fault. I am sure that no famous woman was ever neglected by us. Lady Rhondda, that champion of feminism, once wrote of me in *Time and Tide* (after a luncheon tussle with her and H. G. Wells at the Ivy) that I was a 'highly-cultured hop-pole' – a description which has always delighted me. But the Lady Rhonddas of this world can say what they like – no woman yet has ever been a real star of radio. It is a strange fact. Then there were the different worlds of literature, science, music, travel, the theatre, the films, industry, politics, law, medicine, engineering, painting (never a subject for sound radio), gardening, architecture, archaeology, and so on and so forth *ad infinitum*. Gradually, as these various worlds moved through the studios, one came to recognize the broad characteristics of each. Actors and journalists were the two groups with which it was easiest to deal, because both actors and journalists realized as a matter of course that they were giving a performance and earning a fee, and both were ready to co-operate in doing the job well. Writers were more tricky: unpunctual, arrogant, and easily offended, they resented all criticism, and endeavoured to create an impression that they were doing us honour by deigning to come to the microphone at all. Scientists, engineers, mathematicians and all technicians, including civil servants were, though polite and conscientious, nearly always dull when it came to the spoken word, and the business of trying to persuade them to use simple English was long and tiresome. Of all groups, politicians were by far the worst; not only were they convinced that they knew about public speaking much better than we did, but they also translated our efforts as attacks on their party politics, and we were always set down as Reds or Reactionaries. I remember that I used to funk the rehearsal of every political talk, and wish the speakers at the bottom of the deep blue sea. I can only recollect one exception to this rule, and that was Megan Lloyd George, who was not only a naturally good broadcaster, but also a person of great charm and gaiety, with whom it was always delightful to work. Dazzling exceptions cropped up, of course, in every group: men like Bernard Shaw and Sir James Jeans (to take two examples at random) took to the microphone as ducks to water, and their visits were holidays for us.

It may be asked how far a producer can assist a speaker to be successful at the microphone, and this is a debatable point which deserves a careful reply. We know from the theatre that good producers are scarce, and that the gift of persuading a performer to modify voice and movement is rare. We also know that you cannot make a good speaker out of a bad one, and that the microphone has an odd way of flattering some personalities and extinguishing others. (Lloyd George, for example, in spite of all our efforts, was never able to broadcast successfully: deprived of a live audience, he went flat.) Therefore there are two imponderables: the natural gifts of a speaker, and the natural gifts of a producer. The broadcasting official who listens to voices every day and almost all day must, if he is not a complete fool at the game, gain a sort of sixth sense about voices which are (a) naturally suited to the microphone (b) capable of improvement, and (c) hopeless; (a) will look after itself and (c) must be tactfully thrown out. But (b) is his problem. He can suggest, sometimes with great effect, the raising or lowering of the voice register: he can make changes in pace and pauses and emphasis: and in the last resort (though I was and remain violently opposed to this) he can 're-write' the talk in simpler or more conversational language. Whatever he does (and here we are far from theatrical practice) he must be extremely careful not to destroy the essential personality of the speaker. Ten rehearsals *may* produce only a mediocre talk: but sometimes they may work miracles. You never can tell. Moreover, you may find, to your astonishment, that a voice which sounded splendid on a dais or in a room develops on the microphone some strange and hideous accent or intonation. It boils down to this – that the gifted, sympathetic and imaginative producer *can* very often help the nervous or inexperienced speaker *if the speaker is willing:* and this is a necessary part of all broadcasting because there are never enough gifted speakers to fill the programmes. Apart from this, the broadcasting official can make things easier for speakers and writers by inventing frameworks. In the early days of broadcasting, we found it extremely difficult to obtain 'spontaneous' debates (now made much simpler by the then impossible process of recording), and, to meet this difficulty, we invented a series called 'Conversations in the Train'. It was a simple sort of idea – train noises under a discussion of live issues. Writers and speakers were tickled by it and debates became better: moreover I was able to do without censorship because, with gramophone records of train noises running throughout the discussions, I could always drown a risky sentence under a whistle or the roar of a tunnel. In such ways – and there are always hundreds of them – speakers and writers may be helped by an imaginative staff.

Looking back, it all seems faintly ridiculous. Perhaps in retrospect all bureaucratic effort seems that. There is no sense of achievement. You cannot say, I painted that picture, I wrote that symphony, I designed that house. If you are honest with yourself, it is obvious that the wheels went grinding on and would have done so, as well or better, without you. Why did we cudgel our brains in all our waking hours for new ideas, why did we rush like panting terriers after new voices, new writers, new methods of presentation, why did we spend long hours of overtime in the studios, trying out new permutations and combinations of sound? What did it all amount to? Today, as sound broadcasting sinks into its grave with the silent films and the blunderbuss, what is the result of all our efforts? Mrs Dale's Diary and the red-nosed comedian at one end, the gabble of an Isaiah Berlin and the scrapings of a Stravinsky at the other. The splendid conquest of the ether has turned into a dull drug, a lullaby for foggy minds. What did we hope for? I think we hoped for a clear voice which would cut through hypocrisy and half-truth. Not any longer the quiet voiced elders, bequeathing merely a receipt for deceit. Something more decisive: a Voice of God, perhaps. One shouldn't complain, I daresay: after all, Christianity is in much the same boat, and that had Jesus Christ to inspire it. We made the mistake of thinking of radio as a new religion, when it was merely a new channel for the same water. And maybe the use of the plural pronoun is wrong: most people in the BBC were probably content to earn their salaries and produce popular entertainment. I hoped, in a rather vague way, for something better: and so did Hilda Matheson.

Hilda drew my admiration, respect, and affection almost instantly. I had at first thought that it would be strange, perhaps impossible, to work under a woman, but that feeling soon faded. Hilda was never preoccupied by power, never lectured, never laid down the law: she ran her department on a loose rein, encouraging, helping, sympathising, and yet keeping herself firmly in the saddle. She was in the saddle because she was usually right. She was not supremely intelligent or supremely beautiful or supremely chic or supremely anything: she was just one of those people who are made of pure gold all the way through. You could not imagine Hilda panicking about anything, or failing to meet any situation with composure and charm. She had the rare gift of making all life seem an adventure, and she was always the best of good company, with a blessed sense of the ridiculous. I grew devoted to her, and my years at Savoy Hill were perhaps glamourized by this devotion. What happened later was all the more appalling to me.

Placed as I was, with the arc-lamps surrounding celebrities throwing a reflected light on me, I stumbled to new social heights of snobbery and fatuity. My stepmother, seeing that I was established in London, and fairly respectable for a change, conceived the idea that it would be a good plan for us to share a house, to which she could from time to time escape from my father. It was, as we might both have known, a quite horrible idea. Her friends were drawn from the huntin' shootin' and bridge-playin' set, and bored the pants off me. She thought that my theatrical and literary lions were beyond the pale. However, since I, with my total £700 a year, wasn't rich enough to entertain as I wanted to do, and she, with a great deal of money, wanted someone to run a house in London for her, it seemed a good notion at first. A long low house in Wilton Street, admirably suited to party-giving, was bought and furnished: in its panelled hall I gathered all the famous people I could lay my hands on, and they came because broadcasting was beginning to look like a paying proposition. The doings at Wilton Street were duly reported and photographed by *The Tatler*, and I was 'in the swim'. My stepmother had a knack of arriving in the middle of a raffish assembly, and I erupted with theatrical whirlwinds into her most pompous bridge-parties. But it did not much matter: I was too busy for niceties of class. I was pleased with my job, with London, and with, above all, myself.

Slowly this picture began to change. As with all such changes, it is difficult to put a finger on the exact causes. The BBC was growing rapidly, and, as in all cases of growth, became less flexible in the process. The first major change was the introduction of 'administrative officers' to control our budgets. In the early days we – that is to say, the programme producers – could allot fees as we thought fit: now we began to have worthy people of a civil service type who decided whether Priestley or Edgar Wallace or T. S. Eliot was worth two guineas or ten. Or indeed whether we could afford them at all. This was an almighty mistake: domination by the mediocre had begun. Worse than that, squabbles began: the chasm yawned ever wider between bold experiment and cautious compromise. Also the BBC, with its growing influence, was coming under fire from all sides for suspected favouritism of one kind or another: too Tory, too Labour, too Red, too Reactionary, too many symphony concerts or too few, too many talks or not enough, nepotism on the staff, bad coverage: any old stick would do to beat this huge Aunt Sally. At the same time, since the BBC was now obviously a bandwagon, there were plenty of people trying to climb on to it or up it. Rifts developed and grew among the staff: pioneering days were over.

In the course of collecting voices, I had, inevitably, approached many people who in those days were labelled 'progressive'. (I need hardly add that now, thirty years later, they are all staunch old diehards, which is the natural fate of progressives.) As a result of this, Hilda and I attended a good many parties, in

London and in country houses, where intellectuals – to use that pompous word – were gathered together. Gentlemen in the Athenaeum Club were soon whispering to Reith that he was being 'run by a Gang of Reds'. Reith began to turn an enquiring eye upon the Talks department, and sent sharp little notes to Hilda suggesting that so-and-so held eccentric or subversive or atheistic or anarchistic views and was not a suitable person for the microphone. Hilda, jealous of her friends, retorted no less sharply, and the battle was on. Reith soon reached a point of saying that so-and-so *was not* to broadcast: Hilda implied that he didn't have enough culture to know what he was talking about. I became a highly uncomfortable buffer state, trying at one moment to persuade Reith that Hilda was valuable to the BBC, and at another trying to stop Hilda from writing offensive memoranda. It was all to no purpose: Hilda was forced into resignation, and left the BBC for ever.

At this point I must try to keep Reith in sharp focus. He became and has remained one of my most valued friends, and my admiration and affection for him are immense. His saga as first head of the BBC must be one of the strangest tricks that Destiny ever played on a man. From the not very important managing director of a wireless company he rose in a few short years to be a kind of Arbiter of Religion, Morals and Taste. It would have been a severe trial for the most brilliant saint or seer. Reith rose magnificently to his opportunities, and if it can be said that any one man 'created' the BBC, he was certainly that man. His stamp still remains on it, and nobody since has greatly altered it. Undoubtedly he gave it dignity, integrity and respect. But no man can be expert in everything, and no man is entirely without prejudices. Reith had his limitations. His presbyterian cast of mind is not wholly at ease in the artistic world. One of his favourite remarks was that 'broadcasting should be in the van, but only just in the van'. This meant roughly, to use a painting simile, that you might dare to go from the National Gallery to the Tate, but not so far as the London Group. I don't know that he was wrong: listeners were easily huffed by anything too startling. But his influence did tend to hold the BBC back from all things provocative, or even bold. Moreover – and this was perhaps his worst fault – like most men in power, he did not take kindly to criticism, and was apt to surround himself with yes-men. Many years later, when I raised this point with him, he said quite frankly, 'Yes, if you have a man like me and get rid of him,

there is a case for getting rid of all his staff at the same time.'
Certainly I felt, when after his departure I returned temporarily
to the BBC in 1940, that a vivifying influence had been lost, and
that, behind the Director-General's door there was no longer any
personality at all. He was perfectly within his rights in ousting
Hilda Matheson in 1929, but in my view (which, as you will
shortly see, was a partial one) he made a mistake which has since
affected the whole development of the spoken word on the
microphone.

Hilda's downfall caused a whole lot of new forces to come into
play. Chief among the leading personalities were Mary Somerville, the Director of Schools Programmes, and Charles Siepmann, who was butting his way upwards from Adult Education.
All this took me somewhat unawares: I could not really believe
that Hilda would go, and it did not then occur to me that I
might succeed her. I don't think that I even wanted it. But between not wanting it and having Charles jumped up over my
head, there was a vast difference. And indeed this was the first
formidable row in the BBC. A stink of intrigue went up, and
people felt uncomfortable about their own jobs. Nine of us, in
the Talks Department, decided that we would resign in a body.
Hilda, however, deplored any such action on our part, and took
us to Walter Elliott's house, where he harangued us, and pointed
out that we should be forgotten in a week and would succeed
only in harming the BBC. So our gesture was dropped. But my
instinct shouted very loud and clear, it came and shouted in my
ear, that my days in broadcasting were done, and that I should
cut adrift without more ado. And this instinct was neither (as I
now see) wrong, nor was it entirely or even preponderantly a
matter of selfishness or sour grapes. There were at least five valid
reasons for me to leave the BBC. One was that I believed and
still believe that a mass form of entertainment such as the BBC
should never be served by a permanent and pensionable staff. If
you want variety – and you do – you must vary your staff. The
most brilliantly original thinker will not stand up to a daily
bleeding of his originality: he must become stale. Another very
valid reason was that my loyalty to broadcasting, and my pleasure in it, were conditioned by my admiration for Hilda, and had
nothing whatever to do with the kind of cautious civil service
which the BBC was becoming. A third was that promotion in the
BBC led to desk work, and desk work was exactly what I did not
want: I wanted to live in the studios and produce programmes.

But the higher you and your salary rose in the BBC – and this, this damnable fact, is true today – the less you had to do with studios or programmes. (I wish that the BBC charter made it compulsory for all BBC 'directors', from the Director-General down, to produce at least one programme a month under their own name; we should soon see how much these highly-paid gentlemen know about broadcasting.) A fourth and very valid reason was that, however much I hated the idea of becoming a desk-bound Director, I hated even more the pressure that would turn me into a Director-frustrated impresario. And, say what you like, that problem is always with us: put the administrator above the creator, and you make a hell. And a fifth reason was that I was temperamentally unsuited to be an ageing, routine-bound member of a huge timid Corporation. But, alack and alas, I had tasted the fleshpots and was ready to sell my soul.

Charles Siepmann quickly made it clear that he was prepared to pay for my soul. He took me to dine at the Athenaeum – naturally he belonged to that club – and assumed his saintly air. He spread the butter of flattery thick, told me what a fine fellow I was, and how great was my contribution to broadcasting, waved his hands in a gesture of hopelessness, and swore that if I put my intention of resignation into effect, the standard of pro-grammes would fall, and his own reputation would suffer. There was a germ of truth in this. Fortuitously I was the one person in the Talks Department at that moment who on the one hand had a quirk of imagination and on the other a vast knowledge of the voices and pens necessary for programmes. That does not mean that I was in any way exceptional: hundreds of people like me could have been found: it just happened that the BBC had not found them just then. Had I resigned, the programmes would certainly have suffered for six months or so, because the machine-ry would have been temporarily lost. And Charles was aware that if they suffered at the beginning of his reign, his reputation would be harmed. So he produced (just like any international gathering) a Treaty of Compromise. He would divide the Depart-ment into three – News, Adult Education, and General Talks, and over the last I should have full authority. I did not like it, but I liked even less a return to the days of my unemployment, and I doubted if I was fit for any other job. I said weakly that I would try it for a year: and I should have been astonished had I known that the trial would last for five. Now, as I look back, I know that I made a terrible mistake.

The additional work and anxieties caused by the gradual dis-
integration of Hilda, and the storms which followed, now sent
me into a nervous breakdown of madhouse proportions: and this
was followed by shingles of the fifth nerve, which, as anyone
who has had it knows, is a trying disease. When I emerged, somewhat shaken, Anthony Asquith invited me to ask the BBC for a
month's leave, and to go with him to Malta for the filming of the
Gallipoli sequences of E. T. Raymond's *Tell England*. The Company wanted my advice on the choice and arrangement of the
'Gallipoli' beaches, and would be glad to pay my expenses,
though, since I was a member of the BBC, I could not technically
be 'employed'. I was devoted to Puffin Asquith, who is one of
the most charming people on earth, and I jumped at the offer.
So I travelled down through Italy and Sicily, and spent one of
the most diverting months of my life in Malta. The film was
financially underwritten by an industrialist called (I think)
Little, whose son had been killed in Gallipoli: and was looked
upon with favour by Authority, which meant that we had at our
disposal the British Mediterranean Fleet and some 5,000 soldiers.
The Company, which was headed by the endearing Bruce Woolf,
treated me with great kindness. The whole month was punctuated
by One Ridiculous Incident After Another: ORIAA. Puffin and
I started with the whale of a gaffe, going to make a formal call
on the Admiral in the flagship, and omitting to realize that it
was the King's birthday. We arrived on the stroke of noon, when
the ship was dressed overall (if that is the right term) and the
guns were about to be fired. Our Laurel and Hardy appearance
at the gangway created consternation, and we were hurried below. The Brock's bombs which we carried everywhere, to simu-
late the explosions of shells, proved a great deal more deadly
than anyone had supposed, and were always exploding in the
wrong places. On one occasion someone dropped a cigarette-butt
into a case of twenty, and I, who was down on the beach, saw
Puffin vanish in an atomic cloud of black smoke. Puff, though
an admirable director, had an Oxford voice which tickled the
licentious soldiery: when he said, through the megaphone, 'Would
you *mind* moving a *little* further to the right?' (they were wading
in the shallows, rehearsing 'the attack') the words were taken up
along the shore 'Would you *maind*, mai deah fellah, would yer
maind?' But the soldiery objected very violently to the idea that
they should drown in the shallows among the barbed wire, taking
synthetic blood into their mouths and letting it out into the

water: that was too near the knuckle. Surprisingly, the film gradually built itself up in a vivid way. There came a stupendous moment when Puffin and I, in a little boat in the middle of Ghain Tafeia Bay, were able, by wireless, to direct the British Fleet. '*Revenge,* a mile nearer, if you please: *Barham,* a mile back.' Then came the scenes of the landing, with the boats from the ships dividing on either side of our tug, and rowing away towards the land, where the Brock's bombs were already bursting with great effect. Oddly enough, it was very moving: I could have cried. However bad or good the film eventually was, that reproduction of the Gallipoli landings had great validity. I had bought myself a full-size Bell & Howell cine camera, and with this I clicked away merrily until I had exhausted ten reels. When we left Malta, the Company's film was sent (by some arrangement with the Customs) by sea, but I fastened my ten reels about my body with tapes and said nothing to anyone. There was a horrid moment when the Customs man at Dover recognized Puffin, and, after asking him how the filming had gone, handed us a list of forbidden goods: and Puff passed it to me, saying, 'Have we got any of these, Lionel?' I put on my best poker face, and clanked away towards the gates. Roddy, the camera man, who was in front of me, was stopped and prodded by the man on duty, and I broke into a cold sweat. But I was untouched: and when the train drew out of Dover, I proudly exhibited my reels. Everybody was furious: it was pointed out that I could have wrecked the film. I took my film to Grierson, a good friend of mine and then looked on as a great expert, and asked him to 'cut' it, which he did so badly that I had another copy made and cut it myself. It came out as a beautiful and amusing 'trailer'. The staff at Welwyn were greatly impressed, and Bruce Woolf remarked, 'If it all comes out like this, we've got a winner!' Later, the whole film was run through in the presence of Mr Little, and I thought it first-rate. Mr Little did not, and in an hour made alterations which wrecked it. I protested to Puff against this vandalism, but Puff, polite as ever, shook his head and said that without Mr Little it would never have been made. So it was a flop.

Returned to London, I found that my stepmother, tired of the Wilton Street experiment, had let the house without informing me. That did not matter, because I was sick of London life and parties. I decided that I would take a cottage in the country, and see how commuting suited me. I was lucky in finding instantly not only a dream cottage at Merstham, but also a dream housekeeper in Rose Edgington. This darling woman cooked for me superlatively, kept my house spotless, and looked after me and my guests like a mother, for five years. The mad nonsense started by socialists, their dear delusion about the degradation of domestic drudgery, is a fake and a sham. Rose was happy with me, and I was happy with Rose. Why in God's name should you admit that one man is a mechanic, or a politician, or a painter, or a musician, or an accountant, and in the same breath say that no one is a cook or a housemaid or a butler?

Delighted by Merstham and Rose, I now bought a tumbledown old house at Windlesham. It had been inhabited by an eccentric old bachelor who had let it go to rack and ruin. It had five acres of land, mostly bog into which you sank ankle-deep, through which ran a purling stream. The house was two old cottages knocked into one, with one primitive bathroom, two sitting-rooms, and five bedrooms. Great elms grew alongside it and made it dark and damp. But it had promise and I bought it for £800. At this point my father played a trick on me. Or did he? To this day I don't know whether it was a trick, or whether he was mean, or whether he thought he would give me a salutary lesson in economics. Since I had no capital, and wasn't likely to have it, I asked him (after taking some time to screw my courage to the sticking-point) whether he would give me an advance for the house, which I would repay. He replied that if I wanted capital, he would do a business deal with me. He would commute my allowance of £300 per annum, and give me £6,000 in lieu of it. I was delighted: £6,000 seemed to me a fortune. I thanked him effusively. He then wrote to his solicitors and instructed them to hand over to me six thousand pounds of deferred railway shares. When I asked the solicitors for the £800 to pay for the house, they looked down their noses and said that I had better arrange for a mortgage. I asked why, if I had six thousand pounds. With immense difficulty it was explained to my addled brain – which had never dealt with shares – that deferred railways were standing at about forty, and that this meant that they were worth not six thousand but two thousand five hundred. Since they 'might' recover, it was inadvisable to sell. I hadn't a clue about this. I rang up everyone I knew in the City. Some said, 'Hang on to them': others said, 'Get rid of them'. I vacillated: and every day they went down. When they reached two thousand pounds I sold them. And I was right because they never recovered. My father got out of it nicely: I lost £300 a year, and gained two thousand. This experience cured me for ever of any desire to experiment with stocks and shares. I paid for the house, and had just enough money over to buy a modest amount of furniture, to paint the rooms myself, and to spend some money on draining the bog. Luckily for me, the summers of the early thirties were magnificent, and my work paid off. The bog became an enchanting garden, and the house, when a few trees had been felled and some coats of whitewash applied, a gay little abode. Five years later, when I went to India, I sold it for five thousand guineas, and thus I very nearly (though not quite) got back on Father.

By the time that I returned to the BBC, I had begun to take a different view of my job, though I don't suppose that at that moment I was conscious of any great change. But in fact I was no longer a dedicated man with a crusade. For various reasons the gilt on the BBC gingerbread had worn a bit thin. I realized that we were going to get more and more cautious, and that things were going to be run not by inspired decisions but by slow committees. I also realized that although I could continue indefinitely as a programme man, I was unlikely to get promotion into the ranks of 'administrators'. Apart from that, I now had a house and a garden which focussed a lot of my interest, and I was no longer inclined to work overtime or worry myself unduly if programmes were bad. I knew that I knew enough to get away with my job as well as anyone else, and that seemed to suffice. In brief, I had taken that fatal step which most men take when they marry, and when a job, while essential, is only a way of paying for a home life. Mind you, I don't think that the BBC suffered from any inefficiency or laziness on my part: they got what they paid for, and probably what they wanted – a man who did his stuff reasonably well and was afraid of the sack. Isn't that what all employers want? But strictly speaking, I ought to have been sacked. I had grown a deadly hatred of the ingrowing BBC respectability and longed to upset it. I was an employee with a chip on my shoulder.

On two points only I was able to preserve a crusading spirit, and a feeling of magic. These were historic events, and poetry. I thought, and I still think, that sound radio was and is a fascinating medium for both, and that neither had or has been exploited as well as it might be. My excursion into history came about by chance. On the occasion of the marriage of the Duke of

Kent to Princess Marina, the BBC issued one of their especially stupid 'orders' – to the effect that no programme outside the actual broadcast of the ceremony was to deal with the marriage. Such orders always spurred me to disobedience. I put in two programmes, one called 'Epithalamion', and the other 'The Arrival'. I was fairly sure (and I was right) that nobody in the higher echelons of the BBC would know that 'Epithalamion' had anything to do with marriage, and I planned a super-reading of Spenser's poem with a backing of Elizabethan music. 'The Arrival' was to cover the wedding of Princess Alexandra of Denmark to the then Prince of Wales, which had some things in common with the Kent wedding. This programme exceeded all my expectations, and was perhaps the most successful programme I ever did for the BBC. I was helped in it by Kenneth Adam, who waded through a large part of the immense amount of contemporary papers which, to my surprise, were available. The result was that we could follow every detail, from the first visit of Queen Victoria to Denmark, and her remarks about Alexandra, on through the absurdly insincere speeches in Parliament, and so to the arrival of the yacht at Tilbury, and the journey to London by the new railroad, which went 'at the astonishing speed of eight miles an hour'. Then came the drive through London, enlivened by the collapse of most of the stands, built by dishonest contractors, and a perfect riot of drunkenness. And then came the arrival at Windsor, with Queen Victoria 'waiting with all my daughters in the long drawing-room till we heard the carriages approaching', and then the whole lovely service, with the original music and the comments of contemporary diary-writers, and so to the moment when the Queen walked away by herself to Frogmore. The programme was helped by a brilliant cast, and Kate Cutler as Victoria gave a great performance. But that was not the whole story. It just happened to be one of those rare programmes which, as soon as the handles of the panel controlling the studios began to turn, leapt to life. One saw the whole scene, and one was suddenly conscious of the immense possibilities of sound radio. Television would not have done it: it was a matter for the ear and the imagination.

Its success was undoubted. We had shoals of letters, and Reith called me down to his room and told me that he thought it one of the most spectacular programmes ever produced. If I could do that, he said, why did I not give up the idea of India (which had just then swum into my ken) and devote myself exclusively to programmes of past events? I was a little shaken by this, and sketched out some ideas for other similar programmes on the South Sea Bubble, the fall of Charing Cross Station, the opening of the Crystal Palace, Disraeli's purchase of the Suez Canal shares, the death of the Prince Consort, and other such byways of history. But I was bitten with the Indian idea (as I shall later make clear), and nothing came of them.

My other crusade was less popular and more arduous. From the early days at Savoy Hill, we had been intrigued but defeated by the possibilities of verse-reading on the microphone. It seemed that not only the medium but also the listeners were ideally suited to it. No country in the world has equalled England in poetry, and although Englishmen may often laugh it off, there is a deep poetical strain in the English character. Here you had a medium which did away with the often embarrassing *presence* of the reader, and could perhaps reach back to epic days. We tried one thing and another: poets reading their own verse, groups of poems under a single theme or idea, anthologies (we actually published a book), competitions, and so on. Nothing quite came off. People, so far as we could make out, switched off as soon as a poetry programme was *announced*. I began to try a different method: no announcement at all, but a gentle introduction of good music, leading into a poem. Gradually I began to think that perhaps there could be a connection between a piece of music and a poem and a voice, just as there is a scientific connection (because they are all vibrations) between light, heat and sound. I embarked on a series under the generic title of Mosaic. In these programmes I endeavoured to take an idea – self-sacrifice, the country or the town, war, peace, travel, Christmas, government, what-have-you – and push poetry and music into that idea. I pushed ruthlessly, cutting poems and music as I fancied. Often I failed miserably: sometimes, for an ecstatic moment, the programme rushed to life. I was not popular and the programmes were not well received: but poets from W. B. Yeats to Robert Nichols were interested, and came to argue with me. I had not and have not the faintest doubt that I trembled on the edge of a discovery which could (and still can) make radio programmes of poetry thrilling: but I never quite captured the exact recipe. Each quarter-of-an-hour programme that I did cost me three months of evenings devoted to repetitions of music and poems: whatever people may have said against them (and they said a lot) they were the product of much work and thought. And I have the impertinence to think today that, though they were far from perfect, the BBC has never since done anything that remotely approaches them.

By 1934 I was an old hand at the BBC in so far as there could be any 'old' hands in that new pursuit. I churned out programmes, interviewed speakers, made appointments, ran a subsection, entertained crowds of folk at Windlesham, dug my garden, and got into a thorough muddle with myself. I was sick of the whole business. What did I want? I did not know: but not this everlasting repetition of the same old chores. During my eight years of my first steady job, I had made – as was inevitable in that position – a great host of more or less distinguished acquaintances, and a few friends. It was a little sad, from a snobbish point of view, that distinction and friendship did not seem to go together. I should have liked to be an intimate of the Great, but I wasn't. I did however make three women friends who each had her own distinction - Margot Oxford, Sybil Colefax, and Marie Tempest. These three charmers, all so different, added so much affection, so much cosiness, so much confidence to my life that I miss them at every hour, even today. Different as they were, they had one thing in common: if you were once their friend, their loyalty was unshakeable and they never let you go. Margot had a devastating candour which earned her many enemies: once you got past it, and realized that it was no more than a childlike innocence which concealed no malice, she was the best and liveliest of friends. When I had my appendix out, she came to see me every day, bringing great tomes of her scrap-books (and they were quite something) to amuse me, and sparing no pains to raise my spirits. And, after all, I was small beer for her. Sybil Colefax was a not particularly intelligent lion-hunter, and made no bones about her social climbing. But, whether you were important or not, she never let you go once she had made you her friend. I spent many happy hours in the lovely Argyll House, as I also did in Bedford Square. Both these women were great hostesses, and the great hostess, who has a perfect intuition about mixing and dominating her parties, is not to be despised. Good conversation and good food in a happy atmosphere are not so easy to come by. Marie Tempest was, of course, in a different world. She was not only a great artist of the theatre, she was a great artist of life. I don't think that anyone I ever met justifies that description better. Her conversation, her movements, her clothes, her hair, her houses, her gardens, her food, her cars, the whole smooth arrangement of her life, were managed with a quite extraordinary precision and intelligence. She was the most fastidious person I ever knew, and I think the most attractive. I ran to her with all my troubles, and never came away without a saner view. It was a pleasure to look at her, a pleasure to listen to her, a pleasure to be with her. I don't know where she sprang from, from the gutter perhaps, but she was the greatest lady I ever knew. I don't think I have ever missed – and continued to miss – any human being as much as I miss her. She decorated life.

Like any other young man in a large city, I fell in and out of love. The English language, normally so rich, is quaintly poor about this monosyllable. Mother-love, love of mother, asexual love of friends, love of a dog or a horse or a house, physical love lasting a week or several years, love of power, of humanity, of the arts, of God – all these infinite variations and many more go under one name. I don't believe that (in the Paolo and Francesca sense) I was ever truly in love: I was quite often in lust. I preferred my own sex to the opposite one: whether that was ineradicably born in me, whether it was the result of war, or whether (as sometimes happens) it arose from a fear of emotional entanglement, I don't know. I have a theory (which nobody is going to squash) that when a boy is surrounded in youth by older women whom he reveres, the idea of going to bed with a woman appears to him an act of sacrilege. However that may be, I found my experience of sex so painful and daunting that, in my early thirties, I decided that I must cut it resolutely out of my life. Plenty of people do that, and it isn't fearfully difficult. The only trouble is that absence of sex creates a vacuum which needs to be filled by some over-riding interest: and that I never quite found. Thus, I suspect, I assumed a mask of frigidity and indifference which made many people find me disconcerting and unsympathetic. In retrospect *(si vieillesse pouvait)* I am inclined to think that, when, at the gates of heaven, I show up my nice paper of a Chaste Life, St Peter, far from awarding me full marks, will give me a zero and send me downstairs to get a bit more experience. Sex is a business into which, whatever silly laws are made, one should adventure boldly. I merely ran away.

When, in 1927, I had managed to squeeze myself past the shaggy eyebrows of Mr Reith, and become a member of the BBC, Eric Dunstan, the 'golden-voiced announcer' of his day, was just leaving England to take charge of Indian broadcasting. I envied him in spite of the low value which we attached to broadcasting in those days. I envied him India; I envied him what I conceived to be the business of transmitting barbaric music on jewelled instruments to a population of Indian princes in the intervals of holding profound converse with sages of charm and infinite wisdom. In 1930 he was back, mortified, humiliated and enraged; and Indian broadcasting had gone bankrupt. This was a puzzle to me; and although I forgot about India in the breathless task of feeding the ever-hungrier microphone of Britain, it remained, in the back of my mind, a puzzle which I intended to solve. And if one's intentions are even moderately firm and consistent, they are often realized. Early in 1935 I heard, by chance, that junior members of the BBC were being asked if they would care to go to India. No such invitation had come to me, so I took myself downstairs to Mr Administrator Nicholls, whose signature appeared on those issued. Nicholls, looking startled by my irruption, said: 'You seem to be a ram caught in the thicket.'

'I haven't the remotest idea what you are talking about.'

'I mean,' he said, bald head flushing, 'well – you have a claim.'

'Claim?' I said indignantly. 'And why not? You are asked to send someone to organise broadcasting for a whole sub-continent, and you issue the invitation only to juniors.'

'Yes – I don't know why it didn't go to you.'

'I suppose most people here are too comfortable to think of going to India.'

'The pay and prospects aren't very attractive.'

'But the job might be?'

Nicolls shook his head. 'Well, I was born there. I wouldn't go. Funny country. Government of India's the most bureaucratic in the world. You mightn't like that.'

'Do you think,' I asked, 'someone else would do it better?'

'Well,' he said, 'there's Beadle.'

The first Great Man said: 'Your record's not very good, y'know, for this kind of job.'

I asked: 'Why not?'

'H'm – all over the place – sticking to nothing long –'

'But surely taking an interest in a good many things, perhaps even learning something about them – isn't that what you want for broadcasting?'

'Unstable –'

'After all, I've been here eight years.'

'Nobody's going to deny that you've inspired programmes. But organisation's another thing.'

I get mad when anyone says anything of this kind.

'Organisation,' I said, 'is nothing but an invention of mediocre people to prove that they can do something.'

'Quite. You always overstate a case. This job isn't going to be programme-building; it's going to be hard, systematic desk-work. See my desk? Is yours as tidy?'

'I don't have three secretaries. And how many worth-while people in the world's history had "tidy desks"?'

'You must remember that I'm assuming a responsibility in recommending you.'

'Certainly. Then send Beadle.'

'I wanted to talk about that.'

The Great Man got up. He was very tall: his chair was very high; the visitors' chairs were an abasement. There was almost no possible visitor above whom he couldn't tower. Nevertheless, the towering business, if somewhat babyish, was also in an odd way endearing. I always had an insane desire, during these interviews, to clamber on to my chair before speaking.

'Yerrs,' he said, adopting a well-known and caricatured attitude, and staring out of the window. 'Beadle, ye see, has a wife and family. The salary of two thousand pounds which they are offering won't be enough for him, although, mark you, it might be for you.'

'I'd go for two hundred.'

The Great Man turned his eyes away from the window, and fixed them upon me.

'Now doesn't it strike you that that's not playing the game – taking an unfair advantage, in fact? You say you'd go for two hundred simply because you have private means, whereas Beadle –'

'It's you who are unfair. Just because I always have, always do, and always shall, spend every penny I earn, all you people jump to the conclusion that I'm rolling in private means. You can look at my bankbook; you'll find zero or something damned near, and no securities.'

'Well, I confess you surprise me. If what you say is true, it surely doesn't argue well for your foresight and prudence. After all –'

'I ought to save money? I have never been able to see why. I like so many things so much better than bank balances or stocks. I think they *are* better.'

'You are suggesting that it's a good thing, an admirable thing, to be a spendthrift?'

'Not at all. I happen to like my house and garden, and I like spending money on both to the utmost limit of what I earn.'

'And what's going to happen to all that if you go to India?'

'I haven't faced up to that yet. Anyway, it's not decided; and you don't seem very keen on the idea.'

'I never said that. It's my business to weigh things up.'

There was a pause, I found myself looking, as I always did in this room, at a large gilt-mounted globe which indicated not only twenty-four hour time but also the BBC's failure to impose it on the mildly-amused but unconvinced British populace. 'This is London calling. The time is now fourteen minutes past fourteen . . .' The corner of my eye took in the Great Man's boots on the hearthrug, and I knew that he was irritated. As always, I felt like a small boy in the headmaster's room, and this inferiority complex made me wish to say something exceptionally rude. I must pull myself together, I thought; after all, I want this job.

'What were you going to suggest about Beadle?'

'Yerrs. What do you yourself think of him?'

'Beadle? I scarcely know him. I believe he's thought to be a good administrator.'

'And isn't that what's wanted?'

We're off again, I thought.

'No. What's wanted is smashing drive, and a whip-up of enthusiasm in a country which has scarcely heard of broadcasting.'

'That's part of the job, I grant you. But isn't it just as important to build a good steady foundation?' The Great Man stared out of the window again. 'I often think you want two people for this job. T'chk! The Government of India should have been more generous — much more generous. Yerss. About Beadle. I was thinking that perhaps you would stand out for the salary that he requires.'

'How much does he require?'

'Well, we thought about three thousand. After all, he would be giving up very good prospects here —'

'And I shouldn't?'

'You gave me to understand that you didn't approve of sticking to anything for long.'

'Perhaps there's something in that. So I am to refuse anything less than three thousand?'

'We thought you might be willing to compete with Beadle on equal terms.'

'So I most certainly am,' I said, nettled. 'But I also happen to know that other outside candidates, including Eric Dunstan, have applied for this job. Is the BBC going to guarantee that they compete on equal terms?'

'And how did Dunstan know anything about it?'

'I told him.'

'Why in the world did you do a thing like that?'

'But I'm not afraid of competition! As a matter of fact, I wanted to find out something about the back history of broadcasting in India.'

The Great Man stalked to his chair, put on a pair of horn-rimmed glasses, and made a note with a gold pencil on a perfectly new block.

'Yerss. I see that this somewhat alters the situation. Very well. I shall write to the High Commissioner and ask him not to discuss salaries at all. Will you agree to that?'

'Certainly. What do I do if he does?'

'I presume that if I ask him not to, he will not. Eh? Anyway, I shall wait until I hear from him.'

Fifteen minutes past sixteen on the globe. I went out.

'We are summoned to the High Commissioner at 12.30,' said Beadle.

I found this irritating for several reasons. First, it was Beadle who had been informed, and then informed me; I felt that he had somehow got a start. Second, I did not know Beadle at all well – later I came to respect and like him immensely – and some mischievous person had told me that he thought it beneath his dignity even to compete with me; and this was quite a probable theory, because the contempt felt for 'programme people' by 'administrators', and vice versa, was immeasurable. Third, the idea of going together appalled me; I had visions of sitting on a bench with Beadle before the High Commissioner, who would see which of us was the better at answering general questions.

Uneasily, therefore, I accompanied Beadle into the very small waiting room at India House. Beadle was silent. I continued to think that he thought me an impertinent interloper, and remained silent also. There were some terrible trade journals on the table, and no view from the window. We were thus constrained to rub our chins and gaze vacantly at the framed photographs which hung on the walls - pictures of a type with which I was soon to become too dreadfully familiar. 'State Dinner given at Gurkbetta by H.H. the Maharajah of Gurkbetta in honour of the visit of Their Excellencies', 'H.E. the Viceroy with the Nawab of Phootal after a day's shoot at Phootal', 'Lady Piles opens the new Beedabhoy Feedabhoy Hospital in Poona'. In Beadle's prolonged absence these pictures began to get on my mind. Beadle had been called first to the presence. It was a relief to know that we were not to be interviewed together, but why Beadle first? A, B, C, D, E, F - was it alphabetical or an insult? Why was he so long? Probably it had all been decided long ago between the BBC and the High Commissioner. The whole thing was a farce. Phootal. Anyway, I said to myself, I don't want to go to India; what on earth induced me to embark on this crazy idea. A State Dinner, a day's shooting. No. In any case, I should be a hideous failure; they are quite right. I think I'll just go, I said to myself; I can't stand the idea of this interview. Sir Bhupendranath Mitra. Sir Bhupendranath Mitra. It's a name I can never pronounce, never. Beadle will wear stiff collars to office, play tennis, shoot on appointed days, attend State Dinners. Perfect. Beedabhoy Feedabhoy. Sir Bhupendranath is now saying 'I congratulate you, Mr Beadle.'

Beadle returned. Very deliberately he put on his coat and hat, took up his umbrella, gave me a nod, went. Without a word. Well, I said to myself, what do I make of that. You'd have thought, wouldn't you, that he'd say 'Nice old boy,' or 'Terrible,' or 'Good luck,' or *something*? Not a bit of it. Mum's the word. Lady Piles opens the hospital. Will you come this way, sir?

Sir Bhupendranath Mitra sat in a room shaped like an L. The long arm of this L was empty, and gave the impression, when one entered it, of being just an empty room by itself. After an echoing exploration of the polished floor, one came quite suddenly upon Sir Bhupendranath in the short arm, as one might come upon an elephant in the jungle. And indeed there was something of the elephant about him. He was large and spreading, with small eyes and a tough black skin. Quite obviously he had the charm of an elephant too. He raised his massive bulk, shook hands silently, and we both sat down. I felt much better. Sir Bhupendranath, I said under my breath, with something approaching assurance.

Clearing his throat, Sir Bhupendranath said: 'How much do you want?'

This, of course, was the very last question I had expected. Various insane replies flashed through my mind. Nothing. Six-pence. Half-a-millon. What had Beadle said? Must I say three thousand? Play the game, old boy. I'm damned if I do. A day's shooting with Lady Piles. I said: 'I was told quite definitely that you had agreed not to aiscuss salaries.'

'But, my dear chap,' expostulated Sir Bhupendranath, blowing a spray of saliva over his blotting pad, 'that's rubbish. I want to write to India by the airmail tomorrow, and we've got to go through to brass tacks – cash, I mean.'

Now what do I say? 'I'm not interested in cash.' No, that'll sound as if I would go cheap. 'Three thousand.' No, I won't; it's far too much for India; it will prejudice the whole thing.

'I'm afraid, Sir Bhupendranath,' – got it – 'I can't discuss that at all without referring to the BBC.'

'Very well, very well,' said Sir Bhupendranath testily. 'Then there's nothing further we can discuss here.'

We shook hands solemnly. Was there a twinkle in his eye? Perhaps he was laughing at me. Feeling as flat as a pancake, I retired down the long arm of the L. So that's that. Of course he knew at first sight that I was useless. Not even the decency to ask me a few questions. Beadle and Lady Piles after a day's shooting at Phootal. Of course; I should have known it. Ring, ring, ring, isn't the lift working? The whole place is half-asleep. Damnably, I have been damnably treated. Good morning.

The second Great Man, who had been a Viceroy, said: 'Well now, what can I do to help you?'

He's immensely tall, I thought and looks extraordinarily young, but why wear a grey frock coat? I really haven't the foggiest idea why I came to see him.

'Well, sir, you have such a vast experience of India. I thought perhaps –'

'I'm afraid I really know very little. The longer one stays there, the less one knows. And besides, one so soon gets out of touch.'

'Perhaps you could tell me something of the people I ought to see or consult?'

'I doubt if it would be quite proper for me to do that. I expect the Government of India will do all that is necessary.'

I am muffing this interview. There must be something to be got out of him; he is a Great Man.

'It's rather difficult,' I said, 'to know what line to take. I mean, broadcasting is or should be, shouldn't it, a tolerant kind of business – I mean,' I said, getting more and mare confused, 'that it's influence should perhaps be used –'

'I'll tell you what,' he said. 'Always remember the difference between influence and power, and remember that the first is the greatest.'

And with that I had to be content.

The third Great Man, who was Very Great Indeed, sitting in a very historic room and smoking.a pipe, said: 'So you're going to one of the most important jobs in the Empire.'

'Do you really think that?'

'Of course I do. Broadcasting for four hundred million people. Why, your influence might come to be greater than that of the Viceroy himself.'

'Can I dare to ask whom you are sending as Viceroy?'

'A good man. An excellent man, I promise you.' He waved his pipe in a gesture of enthusiasm. 'No, I can't tell you his name at the moment. But I promise you shall see him before you go. Of course you must. And he'll want to see you. It's a most important job.'

'Your Secretary of State doesn't share your opinion.'

'What makes you think that?'

'I asked him for an interview, and his secretary wrote saying that he was too busy to see me before I left.'

'But that's nonsense. I'll see that he sees you. Here, I'll do it now.' He picked up a telephone. 'What about going to the India Office straightaway now? Could you manage that?'

'Of course.'

He spoke into the telephone.

I should not, I felt, be popular at the India Office.

There was a tremendous to-do about seeing the fourth Great Man. This puzzled me, for I had known him fairly well, and thought him intelligent, good-natured and unpretentious. Eventually I found myself being received with more pomp than is usual even in Mayfair, and ushered by several butlers (I thought) into a long, heavily overfurnished room in which I waited for some time. The Great Man at length arrived in what seemed to me a processional aura. I stood up, very nearly saluted. Felt that I heard the National Anthem somewhere. I was offered a cigarette from a goldmounted box; the Great Man took one. He towered. I thought, I am obsessed by towerers. He sat down. I sat down. His expression was sombre; his face longer and paler than I had remembered it; his chin immense. Looking down it – a veritable Russian steppe, it must have been, seen from that angle – he said: 'I think perhaps a Commission.'

'To do what?' I asked, appalled.

'To tour India and report upon the possibilities of broadcasting.'

God forbid, I thought.

'Yes,' I said.

At this moment I developed acute appendicitis. Clearly the effect of too much towering on my internal organs.

Over lunch, convalescent, I said to Sir Bhupendranath: 'But what really made you choose me?'

'Perhaps I had a crunch.'

'Hunch.'

'Hunch, yes.'

'I don't believe it. Why, you only saw me for two minutes.'

'Quite enough.'

'No,' I said, 'I'm bothered. I feel I've somehow got in under false pretences. Beadle's so obviously the man for the Indian Civil Service; he'll be sociable, play games, shoot, and be generally popular.'

'Quite true.' Sir Bhupendranath twinkled.

'I shan't do any of those things. And I'm an untidy sort of person.'

Sir Bhupendranath twinkled even more.

'India's rather an untidy place.'

'But do you really think I can do the job?'

'I haven't any doubt about that.'

But I had. Anticipation and struggle were better, I found – as most of us do – than realization. While Great Men faintly disapproved, and Beadle was in the way, it was easy to be determined to grasp the prize; but the prize in my hand felt extremely heavy. I was committed to what might prove a foolish venture, and my own undoing. I was almost certainly ill-equipped for it; I did not know India, or any Indian language; my knowledge of broadcasting was lop-sided and did not include engineering, the elements of which I should have to learn; I had burnt my boats and sacrificed a pension, since the BBC would give no undertaking to take me back, and I had not pressed for it; I should have to give up my house, servants and dogs, for all of which I had a considerable affection; I was thirty-nine and therefore perhaps too old a dog to learn new tricks. Indian broadcasting, or what remained of it, was in a mess; the people out there were, I had reason to believe, extremely unenthusiastic about my appointment; I might be, probably was, the wrong kind of person and, apart from India hating me, I might hate India.

These reflections were a good deal magnified by appendicitis and my friends. I felt queasy; and my friends seemed to divide themselves into three classes of Job's comforters. One, which included Aldous Huxley and Gerald Heard, put down my action to a sadly mistaken spirit of bravado and ambition. Gerald made play with the CIE, generalised on the efforts of a lust for power, and missed no opportunity of saying that 'Lionel was going to devote himself to making little Indians radio-minded'. Put that way, it didn't sound so good to me. Another, more frivolous, asked with lifted eyebrows why I was exiling myself; India, he said, was a one-horse place anyway; I should hate it; I was making a great mistake. And a third, including my family, sighed and thought it a pity – though the kind of thing I would insist on doing – that I should fly off the handle when I had settled down so nicely and successfully with the BBC.

So I decided to take a trip to Russia, Germany and Italy: and see if thereby I could make myself less ignorant.

Berlin, Moscow, Rome. Snow, twisted coloured domes, the Unter den Linden, jewels in the Kremlin, the clinic for Reformed Prostitutes, Lord Perth entertaining Roman society. In Berlin a good time was had by all. The staff of the Rundfunk were quick, charming, kind; the efficiency of German broadcasting enthralled and appalled me. The never-stopping lifts were symptomatic; just as you never waited for a lift, so you never chatted in a corridor. The precision of the whole machine was an impact, an assault. I liked it; human beings seemed more lively there than in the BBC. Compared with the Rundfunk, the BBC was dawdling, with a lost motive of action. This whizz of purpose gave me an inferiority complex: I told myself for comfort that this kind of sophisticated, expensive broadcasting wouldn't do for India; Russia would provide a much closer parallel.

Staggering under an immense fur coat which I had hired from a theatrical costumiers, I approached the Russian Reith.

'How do you vet talks?' (Languages and distances of India).

'We don't.' Kergentsev smiled benignantly.

'You're not asking me to believe that in Soviet Russia –'

'Perhaps you'd like to come to one of our meetings.'

Why don't I know Russian? Of course everyone will say that I have been fooled. Can they really have a staff of listeners to cover every programme? It seems like that: vetting after, instead of before, the event. Perhaps it's a better way of doing things; too much 'vetting' spoils all programmes. I get the idea, and it's decidedly a natty one. Leave the transmitters on after the programme is finished, and then: 'Kharkov!'

'Sir!'

'Your talk at 8.30 was inconsistent with Soviet ideology. Report to Moscow.'

Something like that. And the public listen. Do they listen? Broadcasting here is the direct opposite of Berlin; shabby studios, out-of-date equipment, bad timing, pauses. I try to look at it from the listeners' end. The clinic for reformed prostitutes; the hospitals; the factories, the hostels. (Four people in this room? Yes, why not, ask them anything you like – aren't you a bit crowded? – ah! you don't realize what our conditions were before the revolution!) Everywhere the cone-shaped loud-speaker, twittering, twittering. Nobody listening.

'What are you doing here?'

'Oh, we're building a studio for the factory.'

'But why?'

'We have our own orchestra.'

'And what's this?'

'Oh it's a public address system for the clinic.'

'But why?'

'The Central Programmes are a bit dull.'

Decentralization. Is that something to be aimed at? I go to the villages. Heavens! What roads! But it's like a fairy-tale – these gaily painted houses in the snow! Here's the cone-shaped loud-speaker again, twittering. Nobody listening. It strikes me that the USSR has overdone broadcasting. Too much propaganda. It has become a mere background noise.

All the same, Moscow is entrancing. I am so fantastically entranced that I feel like throwing India to the winds and staying here for ever. Unstable, as Reith said. Why on earth do I like it? There is something exhilarating in the air: perhaps it was always like that. The ballet, the theatre, the glittering golden domes and dull red walls of the Kremlin across the river, the incomparable St Basil's Cathedral, straight out of a fairy-tale: these are Old Russia, of course: but somehow I had never expected to find them so glowing. Kiroff has just been murdered in the Kremlin, and hundreds of people, so we're told, are being shot every day. Can't help it: it adds to the glamour. I suppose it must be frightful to be Russian: but the young Communists are invariably charming with their brilliant childish candour and endless talk. They have something we've lost – faith – maybe in a bad cause – which gives a sparkle to life.

I said, looking through palisades at an expanse of mud: 'The Palace of the Soviets doesn't seem to have got very far?'

'Oh, not yet. We've only had twenty years. And you've seen the architects drawings, haven't you?'

'Lots, and grand. But never anything finished.'

'They will be.'

'Now this is a photograph of the Peckham Health Centre.'

'No, no. That must be somewhere in the USSR.'

'But I assure you that it's in London.'

'Nothing like that in London. We know. The capitalist system –'

They *knew*. They knew because in all their twenty years they had been taught to 'know' that Russia is the finest country in the world: just as we have been conditioned to 'know' that Bolshevism is a plague. Human beings, all plodding stupidly towards the impossible moment when every Tom, Dick and Harry is healthy, wealthy and wise, separated by propaganda into warring nations. Why do I have anything to do with broadcasting?

'It's a wonderful station. All that marble! And what beautiful lighting! But why don't the trains run?'

'They will. Moscow will have the finest tube-service in the world.'

'London has quite a big one, you know.'

'No, no. Very old-fashioned, if it has one.'

Talk and more talk. In an interval during the ballet, we stand and watch the couples parading in the foyer, two by two, in dreadful orderliness. G, who is never ill, says: 'I want some air.'

The Bolshoi theatre is a labyrinth. I say: 'Dashed if I know where it is.'

Moving along the red-carpeted corridors, G says: 'Sorry, very sorry. I'm going to faint on you.'

She does. I stagger to a settee with the body. Cholera? Typhus? I can't speak a word of Russian; and nobody takes the slightest notice of us. I rush along the corridor, find a commissionaire dozing, seize him, drag him. (Shall I be shot for this?) He evinces no surprise: takes G's head, motions me to take feet: we proceed. No one even faintly interested. We arrive at dressing-station in the theatre – would you believe it? Doctor and nurse in white coats: bottles: Red Army man, apparently dead, on stretcher. Doctor applies valerian under G's nose. Her eyes flicker: I know that she sees Red Army man. 'Damn it all,' she says in a small voice, 'I only want a loo.' Yes: and how am I to make the doctor understand that? He applies valerian again: G waves it away petulantly.

'Write it down, you fool!'

I write w.c. on a scrap of paper, show it to the doctor, who ignores it and applies valerian again. I am too panic-stricken to remember that oo is the official sign in these parts (why don't we internationalize these things: surely they're just as important as the Post Office?). I shake the doctor: it's a heroic gesture because I feel sure that I shall be shot for it. No good. Valerian again.

G says in a weak voice: 'Give me the damned paper. After all, I'm an artist.'

She draws vividly. The doctor's beard wags in delight. They disappear together. Presently G comes down the grand staircase, laughing.

'Funniest thing that's happened to me for years.'

'M'm.' I say. 'Funnier still if you had cholera.'

I was frightened. Why? Because one senses something callous and unsympathetic? In a crisis, human life and feelings don't count as they do with us. Yet the doctor and the dressing-station were efficient. But not, somehow, comforting.

It's a puzzle. Never in my life have I felt so unselfconscious. If ever one breathed a free air, it is here. Because I'm English? I don't know. I have the impression, and God knows that it isn't based on any communist propaganda, that these people, in spite of bad living conditions, in spite of poverty, in spite of the OGPU, have somehow grasped the secret of living *together*.

There is an absence – perhaps in Russia there always was – of envy, greed, malice, and (above all) convention. I am not in the least surprised or offended when Soviet youngsters drift into the American Ambassador's box in the intervals of the opera. They crowd me out of it, lean over the balcony: if an Englishman came out of the gallery and did it, I'd hit him. And I'd hate him, because he'd do it out of spite. These people do it because it's perfectly natural that anybody should go anywhere. Impossible to explain this. It's ten thousand miles from the sneers of a *Daily Worker* or the complacency of a *Times*. Everybody taking everybody on trust in a vague, incurious, delightful way. Perhaps incurious is really the keyword. When I look out of my window in the morning I have the feeling that if I cross the Red Square in my pyjamas and sit in meditation in the snow on the top of Lenin's tomb, no one will take the slightest notice. That kind of attitude frightened me, of course, when G fainted: yet, if it's a general attitude, doesn't it free one from a million restraints? Is it perhaps the elementary step to freedom to let one's neighbour do as he likes without peering and goggling, without saying – or even thinking – 'What's that fellow up to? What *right* has he ... What a funny-looking man ... What peculiar clothes ... What a nasty, lovely, strange, odd, bad, good, face ... 'Live and let live' – we English pride ourselves on that: yet, Cheka or no Cheka, I never began to understand what that really might mean until I went to Russia. And in spite of bugs and what not, I said good-bye to Moscow with regret.

Snow and more snow and the frontier station again. I smuggle a bottle of vodka through, for no other reason than to see if it can be done. It can be done. At the centre table, young officials read all my books with apparent attention, and at great length. We wait, but it doesn't matter; nothing in Russia seems to matter quite so much as elsewhere. We drink vodka and avoid looking at the excellent maps and graphs which cover every wall; we have seen too many graphs; Russians are graph-mad.

We rumble on over snow-covered plains. Poland. On and on and on. Monotonous dazzle. Why do men fight continually for this frightful bit of country? Warsaw. The snow disappearing. Forests. I ought to have flown this journey. Yet it's amazing how swiftly one achieves it. Innsbruck and snow again. Gay parties of skiers. Through the tunnels. Sunshine, and the soft Italian language. The dome of St Peter's across the Campagna and a sense of homecoming. What country in the world can compare with Italy?

Lord Perth is entertaining. Ribbons, sashes, diamonds. Glitter of sleek heads and silks. 'Like to see the Big Boy?' 'The Big Boy?' 'Yes, I'll take you to the parade tomorrow.' Yes, I'd like to see the Big Boy. Here I am on the dais. I feel embarrassed and self-conscious. Do I look all right? My clothes. *Eccellenza*. Alfonso next to me – they think here that he has the evil eye. Orderly crowds. Speckless cavalry. Smart is the adjective for everything and everybody here. And now there's a distant sound of cheering – but no, it isn't cheering, it's just two staccato syllables. '*Du – ce! Du – ce!*' Even cheering has gone smart; I must say they do it well, and it's exciting in a mobbish way. The Big Boy is here; I can touch him; goodness, I could even kill him. Perhaps I ought to. The crowd's enthusiasm is immense. It's exactly like Mac-Leish's *Fall of the City*. 'The armour is empty; there's nothing inside it.' All the same, I am rather carried away myself; as a dramatic spectacle, it's superb. And, after all, why not *panem et circenses*?

The cavalry goes through its paces. That famous slither down the steep bank. But after it, a new venture on this occasion, come whippet tanks, forty of them, coming at forty miles an hour. 'We can do it as well.' Over the steep bank they go. Some of them fly off the edge and fall the thirty feet, plump, bury their noses in the ground. How do the men inside stand it? Off they go again, over the horizon; we all move too, and find ourselves looking down into a wide valley, at the bottom of which the tanks are re-forming. Then up they come, straight at us, in close formation, a mass of rushing steel. Everyone makes an involuntary movement to step back; the Big Boy is amused; the line of tanks stops dead just in front of us. We are invited to examine them. Well. Very interesting. No, thank you, though; I don't come to Italy for this kind of thing.

All the same, Rome is improved, I thought, on my way to the EIAR. This smartness and gaiety have their effect; no feeling of depression here. The old trams gone; no vehicle allowed to sound horn or siren. That's as it should be; why don't we all do it? Once so noisy, Rome has regained peace; what's more, everybody drives better. The enchanting Lisa Sergio receives me at EIAR.

'How many languages now, Signorina, nine or ten?'

'You always flatter. But I'd like you to hear our new American announcer.'

'Signorina Sergio, no doubt.'

'Listen and tell me if it is.'

Italian radio listeners, compared with the millions of Germany, England or Russia, are scanty – a mere fifty thousand. Why? Well, says Lisa, the Italians are a peaceful people, not very interested in international squabbles; and then, they mostly make their own music, and prefer it to tinned stuff; and, above all, spend most of their time out of doors. I wonder if that applies to India, too. Italian radio, though comparatively poor in funds, is spruce and inventive. A system of simultaneous broadcasting by short-wave relays is a useful tip for India. Multiple studios and panels, those sacraments of the BBC, are derided; everything and anything can be done from one studio. Yes, I think it can. I watch through a glass window a whole symphony in full blast, and not a sound reaches me; uncanny sensation, I feel that I have suddenly gone deaf. But such sound-proofing is miraculous. 'Every village must have the radio,' says the Duce. So a village set has been evolved by competition among the manufacturers. The result is much better than the German state-made 'people's set', though a bit more expensive. I am beginning to have radio indigestion. Good-bye, Lisa; may you never do propaganda against us! Good-bye, Rome; may you never be a forbidden city.

Visit a perfectly kept garden, and you may feel some dissatisfaction, though not necessarily envy, when you return to your own. The ground-elder is getting the better of you; the lawn is a disgrace; the hedges need clipping; the whole lay-out is, after all, rather inept. Any non-pachydermatous traveller visiting totalitarian or communist states in the thirties must have felt some pang of uneasiness on his return to England. Something was amiss, but what? The aspirations and actions of Germany, Russia, Italy, might be misguided, as one was led to believe, but had England any source at all of aspiration or action? In Rome, Berlin, Moscow, eyes might flash with sinister intent, still, they flashed attractively; perhaps the walk was Gestapo-pricked, still, it was supple and alert; but what about Bond Street and Hammersmith Broadway, and the Old Kent Road? If, as our propaganda had it, the apparent vigour of three European nations was prompted only by revolvers, were the fishy eyes and listless faces of England so much more to be commended? And if unemployment had been abolished by ruthless methods, was there nothing ruthless about Jarrow and the Rhondda Valley?

141

Perhaps we know the answer now: perhaps we don't. My reactions in 1935 did not amount to much more than a feeling of impatience, a sense of disappointment in the England to which I returned; London seemed suddenly more dingy, faces in the Tube more pasty, shop-windows less bright. But in my own field, that of broadcasting, I felt indignant. Though many of us had for some time been conscious that the flame lighted with enthusiasm at Savoy Hill was burning low, it was the contrast with other broadcasting organisations which, for me at least, threw the elephantine bureaucracy of Portland Place into startling relief. How had we come to this? At Savoy Hill we had regarded broadcasting as a crusade; at first, perhaps, as only a small one, for I don't think many recognized its full potentialities, whatever may be said now; but later as something to which we should and must devote our whole time and energy. We had become broadcasting bores; we could not go to parties without looking for possible performers, discussing possible ideas; we could not read books or hear music without applying the author or the composition to the microphone; all our waking hours were given, and given with immense pleasure, to the methods of making the microphone serve humanity. We believed, we really did believe, strange as it may seem, that 'Nation should speak peace unto Nation'; and, short of staff, blundering through technical ignorance, searching, inventing, failing, rehearsing, we felt pride and happiness in the job and never doubted that:

> ... *music's prison'd rapture and the drown'd voice of truth*
> *mantled in light's velocity, over land and sea,*
> *are omnipresent, speaking aloud to every ear,*
> *into every heart and home their unhinder'd message*
> *the body and soul of Universal Brotherhood*

But now?

Now, in the first place, the programme was no longer the thing. It was wiser, in the BBC of 1935, to be a 'good administrator' than to have any original ideas; better to spend your time cutting down artists' fees than rehearsing the artist; more paying to use a blue pencil than your mind. The Controllers appointed by Reith were men who had never distinguished themselves in the programme field; their ignorance was an accepted joke. Fast and furiously they were crowding the swollen staff with men of their own type, just as Waterfield and Macadam were to crowd the Ministry of Information four years later; and where one lively person had sufficed to run many programmes every week with vigour, there were now six tired young men, each complaining that to 'look after' one talk a day was too much. Perhaps it was, considering the amount of time which had now to be wasted in arguing about fees with 'Executive' or 'Administration', in 'covering copyright', in holding 'conferences', in 'setting down your reasons on paper', and generally in doing anything except applying oneself to the real business of thinking out programmes and producing them effectively. *That* was at a discount.

Perhaps all organisations, as they grow, must become bureaucratic, for the very simple reason that a very small proportion of the human race possesses inventive ability and resource, and some place and purpose has to be found for the great majority, the mediocre. Certain it was that pomposity and bureaucracy, conspicuous by their absence at Savoy Hill, established themselves firmly at Portland Place. And for my part I vowed that, wherever I reigned in broadcasting, 'administration' should never get the upper hand. Thus I put myself against the majority, and the course of my rake's progress might, I am sure, have been predicted by any nicely-established civil servant. I wasn't, myself, altogether unaware that my success would almost certainly also involve my failure.

Journeying, convalescing, and meditating upon larger aspects of broadcasting than had hitherto come my way, I also kept three permanent nightmares in the background of my life. One was a Hindustani grammar; a second was the Government of India Act, 1935; a third was broadcasting engineering. In hospital I had waded laboriously through two volumes of grammar, and spattered much paper with my gawky Urdu script; that engaging old bluffer, Sir Denison Ross, had provided me with a teacher (English) who omitted to tell me that his accent was deplorable, and that to learn the printed script was a waste of time. Nor did I realize the immense gulf between European and Oriental languages. I put my slow progress down to advancing age, and despaired.

I also despaired quite a lot over the Government of India Act. Central, Provincial, reserved subjects; communal electorates, creeds, castes; Princes, Hindus, Muslims, Sikhs, Indian Christians, Buddhists and Backward Tribes; district commissioners, police superintendents, legislatures, *tahsildars;* the Government of India comprises the Governor General in Council, the Finance Member, the Law Member, the Member for Industries and Labour, the

Commander-in-Chief, and Uncle Tom Cobley and all. A meritorious document, balanced, precise, just, readable (just); it lamentably failed to engage my attention. It was too like the BBC, faces in the Tube, pinstripe trousers; not a flicker of humanity marred its august pages. Painstakingly I searched for a reference to broadcasting; for surely, I thought, as problem after problem was unfolded, examined, and placed on its appropriate shelf, surely, in this immense, sprawling, illiterate country, broadcasting could educate, unify, and direct as no other medium could. The spoken word could run like fire once again through India. But the grey volumes said no, we don't deal in fire, and we don't like new things; our findings are based on a careful study of the status quo and how it can be maintained without upsetting Imperial traditions in these upsetting days when natives have the face to object to being called natives, and we actually have to change the name of Imperial Delhi, which we built with twenty million pounds of good Indian money, and call it New Delhi. So don't, said the grey volumes, talk about broadcasting and unity, because unity, except as a pious aspiration, is a dangerous thing; and that's just why the benevolent British Raj finds all these problems so terribly difficult to solve, and writes about them at such length. But you will, added the grey volumes, find that we haven't forgotten about broadcasting in Section 129. And I read:

(1) The Federal Government *shall not unreasonably refuse* to entrust to the Government of any Province or the Ruler of any Federated State such functions with respect to broadcasting as may be necessary to enable that Government or Ruler

    (a) to construct and use transmitters in the Province or State

    (b) to regulate, and impose fees in respect of, the construction and use of transmitters and the use of receiving apparatus in the Province or State:

Provided that nothing in this subsection shall be construed as requiring the Federal Government to entrust to any such Government or Ruler any control over the use of transmitters constructed or maintained by the Federal Government or by persons authorised by the Federal Government, or over the use of receiving apparatus by persons so authorised.

(2) Any functions so entrusted to a Government or Ruler shall

be exercised subject to such conditions as may be imposed by the Federal Government, including notwithstanding anything in this Act, any conditions with respect to finance, but *it shall not be lawful* for the Federal Government so *to impose any conditions regulating the matter broadcast* by, or by authority of, the Government or Ruler.

But, of course, there was the usual catch at the end.

(5) Nothing in this section shall be construed as restricting the powers conferred on the Governor-General by this Act for the prevention of any grave menace to the peace or tranquillity of India, or as prohibiting the imposition on Governments or Rulers of such conditions regulating matter broadcast as appear to be necessary to enable the Governor-General to discharge his functions in so far as he is by or under this Act required in the exercise thereof to act in his discretion or to exercise his individual judgement.

The last three lines, from 'to enable', are recommended by me for insomnia. Did the Romans, or anyone else, ever make quite such fantastic legislation?

But what did it all mean? It meant, no doubt, like most of the Sections, that somebody was trying to 'check' something: but what it seemed to me, more threateningly, to imply, was that the Reforms would pave the way, not to a unified system of broadcasting but to its opposite. Every Government and every Prince could cash in on the new medium. And how! Every State would have its Luxembourg, its jazz or Indian equivalent, its advertisement racket, its playing-down-to-the-lowest-common-factor-of-taste. Unless Indian broadcasting could, within the next year or two, acquire, so to speak, an All India Personality, which would hold it together, something of that kind was bound to happen. Or so I thought. Perhaps I was wrong, perhaps right,* but after reading that section, I felt an urgent sense of time's winged chariot which guided a good many of my subsequent actions.

And then there was the accursed machine itself. My stupidity as well as my ignorance baulked me here. I listened to the crystal-clear discourses of Sir Noel Ashbridge, took radio sets to pieces and put them together again under the charming eye of Mr Pulling, visited transmitters, wandered about the Control

---

* The Federal Government never, of course, actually came into being.

Room endeavouring to cope with the ribald comments of Mr Bottle, and evermore came out by that same door as in I went; or so it seemed. In fact, I learned something; as much, perhaps, as any Director of Broadcasting should ever know. The captain of a ship should not fiddle too much with the engines. But subsequent experience convinced me that the BBC system of separating engineers from programme staff, and letting neither know what the other was doing, was and is a bad one. Programme people should know enough to have a healthy respect for the difficulties of engineers; and engineers should be encouraged to take an interest in programmes, and to help programme directors actively in the placing of artists, the use of the right type of microphone and studio, and so on. Failing some effort to bring this about, you get, in almost any broadcasting organisation, a state of idiotic jealousies arising between the two sides; the engineers talk contemptuously of the programmes as 'stuff', and find programme directors supercilious and irritating; programme directors write off the engineers as nit-wits because they themselves understand nothing of engineering difficulties. The BBC remedied this to some extent by the establishment of their 'school' in 1936; but it was a rather feeble remedy for a chosen few.

I, certainly, had very little wisdom. I was fatally undecided as to whether Broadcasting in India was Fun or a Mission. I could debunk myself up to a certain point but no further. Reason informed me that the appointment of a lightweight like myself was, as far as Government Departments, Dignity, Decorations and Decorum went, absurd: and that my wisest course was to extract every possible ounce of amusement from an adventure which would end in an explosion. Emotion and vanity told me that I was a Saviour, speeding to the rescue of poor black people, to whom I should be most frightfully nice (so long, said Reason, as they are most frightfully subservient to you). Ambition told me (and still does) that I was capable of creating a much better service than the BBC. I was in a constant state of falling between all these stools. And so, I fancy, whether they knew it or not, were most people who went to India. The immensities and potentialities of India were exciting: the temptation to exchange argumentative Britons for admiring submissive Indians was great: and the ease (if they weren't sufficiently admiring and submissive) of sliding into files, golf, a good salary and a perfect climate, had practically killed all English decency and initiative in the Indian Civil Service. India was a Paradise for those who were willing to sell the pass in the sense of supporting, over innumerable whiskies-and-sodas, an imperialist oligarchy which was as dead as the dodo, and failing to realize that the real Britain might be a close friend of the real India. But I can't claim that I was any better. I fought madly, and perhaps quite stupidly, in what Mr Gandhi told me was 'a No-man's-land in which everyone will throw stones at you'. In other words, I hated Indian inefficiency, Indian inferiority complex, Indian noise, and Indian dirt, just as much as I hated British cruelty, British patronage, British complacency, and British bad taste. And so, loving nobody, I found myself, so to speak, in the middle of an Asiatic Rugby scrum in which I kicked everybody and everybody kicked me. But that, of course, is not the whole story. Kicks or no kicks, India took your heart: she would not let you ever again see complete righteousness in the dark cities and stuffy enclosures of the West.

> *Broadcasting House, London, W1*
> *August 13, 1935*

My dear Fielden,

I felt particularly inadequate this afternoon to cope with the momentous issues of your departure but, as I said, you can imagine lots that I didn't say; and probably at one time or another I have said them – in part anyhow.

You certainly realized the supreme responsibility which is committed to you, and what you have it in your power to do. I don't know that anyone – not excluding the Viceroy – can do for India what you can.

Don't mind my urging you again to tread like Agag – very delicately – and to be very wary. Perhaps the less you say the better for many months to come. I know what it will be – the suffering of fools, to say the least; but one gets that in every walk of life and it is always hard for men, like you, of quick intelligence and eager disposition. Impatience and such qualities are gifts of the gods and they're also instruments of the devil.

It is your kind of temperament which is required and essential for this work. It is your temperament which will in due course, make a triumphant success. But do remember that it's also – quite as much – that very same temperament which, in a minute or a week, can produce disaster. It's therefore not just temperament but your temperament conditioned and controlled that is wanted. And I believe you will need to do a powerful lot of conditioning and controlling of it – and so many won't do that. They think it's an insult to their intelligence or capacity. It isn't. The strongest man is the one who, with mighty abilities over others, submits, is patient and never loses hope.

One other word which even to write is a great embarrassment to me: I believe profoundly that if you ask the Almighty to run this business and take you through all the troubles and perplexities and irritations, and believe as you ask, then you'll have something impossible, quite likely, otherwise.

All good go with you,
Yours very sincerely,
SD. J. REITH

Chapter Four

> One man in every five is an Indian. The other four are,
> let's say, an American, a European, a Negro, and a Chinese.
> Doesn't that make you feel very important? It is rather a
> staggering thought, isn't it, that we Indians are not much
> less than a fifth of the human race and that, next to China,
> our country has the biggest population in the world? And
> doesn't it make us feel keen to take our proper share in the
> ordering and settling of the world's affairs?
>
> MINOO MASANI - OUR INDIA

Saturday August 17th. On board *SS Poona.* Called by revolting
Goanese steward – where *is* Goa, anyway? – at 7.30, which I consider an insult on board ship. Ships give me claustrophobia; why
didn't I go by air? Told that breakfast is at 8.30 – monstrous!
Fan in cabin below making noise like aeroplane; can't sleep, so
get up. Seldom seen a filthier cabin; one bathroom apparently to
sixty cabins. Peerless day; sea like blue silk and not a cloud; a
light breeze gently fanning. Endeavour to skulk to unassuming
table in diningroom unobserved; no good; marshalled to Captain's table and placed firmly between Colonel Grating (agent
for Standoni's wireless transmitters in India) and Mrs Grating
(agent for Colonel Grating). Almost positive that Gratings have
specially arranged to sail on my ship; shall have a complex about
Standoni's. Mrs G very refayned, with black frizzy hair, eyes
intended to be starry, and absolutely blinding row of false teeth
which she clearly considers indistinguishable from real. Colonel
G whitehaired and monocled, with desperate battered remains
of good looks: persuasive cringing manner and mean face. Skipper, obviously intentionally, looking exactly like George V:
opposite him Major General Somebody, head like a red-hot egg
and extraordinary manner of repeating everything, e.g.

Mrs Grating: 'Ai always say, General, that kippers are the
very *best* things for breakfast!'

General: (very slowly) 'Kippers are the best things for breakfast.' (Pause) 'Yes, by jove, kippers are the best things for breakfast, eh!'

There's a fat white woman whom nobody, surely, can ever
have loved – though East of Suez you never know – going to
Cairo; she's jolly, I fear.

'Lovely day! Bright and early! These trips are *such fun!* And
the Captain's such a *dear!* So many times I've sailed on the dear
old *Poona!*'

Yes, yes, yes, Mrs Watson: you wait, I'll murder you presently.
I bet you play deck quoits and have a fancy dress.

Colonel Jolly. Indian Medical Service. Belies his name. Dour,
dried-up, silent. I rather like him.

'Not been East Before? You wait for the Red Sea. Innoculat-
ed?'

Don't know that I do like him. Cornelia Sorabji: I've met her
before; Parsee lawyeress, wedded to Imperialism. Thought Par-
sees were Hindus, what an error! Said I believed in the trans-
migration of souls.

'I don't want to be a fly, if that's what you mean,' said Cornelia.

No, no. Do I want to be a fly? Cornelia is exactly my idea of
a witch. I don't like witches, however clever.

Fourteen days at this table will drive me demented.

Stealthily I go on deck; ambushed; forced into deck chair by
combined and skilful Grating manoeuvre. Do I know about the
Peshawar experiment? Yes, I do. Yes, I know that Standoni's
have lent a transmitter and village sets. The whole thing in a
nutshell? Well (looking as wise as I can) I don't know. Dammit,
I *don't* know. Engineers? Oh, certainly. Where from? Well –

'Ai don't want to talk business!' says Mrs Grating, archly. 'This
is the taime to enjoy ourselves!'

Well, I must go and write letters. Yes, really. You see the BBC
gave me a present: lots of names inscribed in a book; I have to
write to them all before Port Said. Yes, really! What was the
present – why, a gold cigarette-case, what else. Yes, this one.

'Oh, ai do think you're a lucky, lucky man!'

It's impossible to sit down in my cabin, one must lie or stand,
so I pace it, thinking, am I a lucky, lucky man? Adopt the Coué
principle: 'I am, I am, a lucky man.' Assuredly yes. Who would
not envy me, spreadeagling the globe to set up a new service in a
huge country? Why the devil, I ask myself, don't I get more kick
out of it? A jeering imp sits in my soul, and will not be dislodged.
'After all, what do you *know* about India?' 'Nothing, but –'
'Very little about broadcasting if you come to think of it?'

'Dammit, eight years –' 'Oh, but not in engineering or publications or the legal side or administration.' 'Damn administration!' 'They'll expect it – they won't like your type.' 'They? Who's they?' 'Well, you've never been a popular person, anyway.' 'No, I know, but –' 'Ah, India will be just the same – and then you don't even know the language properly, fancy that!' Shut up, imp, shut up: I must do my Hindustani grammar, and go through the 1935 Act again. This cabin is dreary beyond belief. 'Yes, read your silly books: they won't get you anywhere because you're much too old, old, *old!!!*' Dear imp, please imp, leave me alone: the die is cast: I must have confidence. Could I fly from Cairo, I wonder? Because this ship really is hell to me. A funny thing that, when you think about it: what's heaven to some is hell to others: a satisfactory after-life is unimaginable and so is Marxism. A ship is hell to me because I hate being inactively shut up: but then, why should an aeroplane be better? Because it goes faster. Sheer escapism, perhaps: I can't face the imp. If I arrive in Delhi by air ten days earlier than the scheduled Bombay by boat, what happens? It might be spectacular, but the Government of India, I suspect, won't care one bit for spectacular subordinates. Do I care whether they care or not? A moot point: they pay me, after all: but then the money is Indian money, and loyalty, said Liddell Hart once, may mean only a conspiracy of mutual inefficiency. I think I might fly.

Wednesday August 21st. The evening star glitters in an orange sky as we slide into the Canal. Young man on the bridge tells me that he is going from Sandhurst to join the Ethiopian Air Force: General Red Hot Egg (who turns out to be enchanting, and clearly uses the repetition formula as camouflage) points out the mast specially created to tether R.101. To *Thee*, I think, be ascribed all might, majesty, dominion, and power – that's what they all say every Sunday. And I'm going to India: yes, and on this confounded boat. Would the shipping line cash my cheque? 'No, sir, we never do it.' 'But, dammit, you've got all my luggage, plus a car, on board: you can risk it.' 'No, it's against regulations.' 'But Imperial Airways have offered me a seat from Palestine onwards.' 'Sorry, sir, you might try in Port Said or Cairo.' 'But how long is the *Poona* stopping?' 'Can't say: depends on the shipping in the Canal.' I haver angrily: rush ashore at Port Said: no cashing of cheques there: shall I take the train to Cairo? No: daren't: might get stuck. And then what? Oh, for God's sake, I tell myself crossly, do have some courage and decision. And return feebly to the *Poona*. Now our searchlight throws its long beam down the straight black glimmer of the Canal, and silence seems to be closing drowsily behind us as the quiet ship glides on: once again, gratefully, I hear that Eastern silence, broken only by the far, hysteric yap of a pi-dog among the sand-dunes. Bombs on Ethiopian villages, a mast for R.101: the night broods over man's follies.

Friday August 23rd. The Red Sea in August has the attributes of a mild nightmare. The temperature mounts, 84, 87, 89, 95 – not so very high, but humidity mounts too, and a white mist descends, enveloping the ship so closely that even the sea disappears, and dim sweating shapes falter across decks suspended on warm cotton-wool. The heat does not thaw the ice of small-talk: a stoker, the Captain tells me, has just run up the funnel and gone overboard; 124°, he adds, down there. 'They often do it.' Can I go down? Well, no. The Captain changing the conversation, adds that I may be interested in the old wireless apparatus, which has only a two hundred miles range. Of course, the *Poona* is to be broken up in the Far East at the end of this voyage: this progression through cotton-wool is the last of her many voyages down the Red Sea. A ghostly ship about to become a ghost: what happens, I wonder, to things like baths and settees and panelling and port-holes when ships are broken up?

Monday August 26th. Aden behind us, we pitch gently through the Arabian Sea. The Captain (who evidently enjoys giving passengers a good dose of alarm and despondency) announces with a chuckle that a ship ahead reports 'heavy swell', while the *Kaiser-i-Hind*, which left Bombay on Saturday and will pass us tomorrow, caps that with 'strong wind and high seas'.

Tuesday August 27th. Cornelia Sorabji examines me in Urdu, which (if I knew it) is rather like a Greek examining an American in French. I now know the life-history of the Gratings. General Red Hot Egg achieves eighty circuits of the heaving deck, sweat pouring in his wake. Queasy, I follow his example: exercise restores me. I begin quite suddenly to think the whole business is great fun, and I have just as much capacity as the next man to undertake it. A change of heart? Mrs Grating tells me a funny story about the Englishman who said to the Indian 'Are you a good sailor?' and got the indignant reply 'No, sir, I am a first-class passenger.' I laugh at this, and check myself: good heavens, am I laughing at Mrs Grating's jokes? Obviously my standards have fallen.

Thursday August 29th. How much more, I ask the Captain, while I nervously clutch the bridge, *can* she roll – without going over, I mean? He says, glancing indifferently down the decks. 'Oh, about ten degrees.' I go below, and wedging myself into a settee, try to collect my thoughts. I must write down something about Indian broadcasting. Can't think of anything to write. Take a pad and write 'Indian Broadcasting' and draw a line underneath that. That seems to be all. After a time I write 'The first principle of any broadcasting organisation . . .' At this point Colonel Grating staggers towards me with a whisky-and-soda, and, laying a hand on my knee, says in a voice of deep significance, 'Well, my boy – well my boy, this time tomorrow . . . you will be a member of the Government of India.' And I very nearly heard him say, under his breath, 'Incredible!'

ONE OF THE SIX THOUSAND LETTERS WHICH AWAITED ME

14th September, '35

My Lord,

My Lord, it is on the 2nd of this month that I had sent one envelope to you, my Lord, as a stranger requesting therein to forward and recommend my application to Mr E. J. Belton. My Lord, in writing to you I had had an infusing idea that I was writing to God and that God being kind to helpless creatures is sure to help and hence taking you, my Lord, as God to me I had every hope that you would help me.

My Lord: the Govt of India Gazette shows that you have taken over charge from Mr Belton and now therefore I have a greater hope of achieving the post of the Programme Assistant. When everything is in your hand and when writing to you I have an idea that I am writing to God direct in heaven who is a helper of the helpless, a recommendation to those who are devoid of recommendations as in these days, success follows those who have sources and recommendations but I being lacking in these aspects beg to approach you, My Lord, whom I have taken as a God to me, to favour me. The applications were to reach up to n th of this month and today it is 14th *but no mandate I have entertained from you, My Lord.*

If I could not get success through you, my Lord, my God, I would think myself to be the most unfortunate as unfortunate according to my views are those who do not get success when they leave to the mercy of God and as I have entirely taken you as God and have left myself entirely on your mercy I am either to get success or term myself as 'most unfortunate and devoid of God's help'.

My Lord: think of my sentiments to you and to my Mother Mrs Fielden she is a Goddess to me and I expect every favour from my Mother.

My Lord, my God: grant me an interview before you select others for these posts.

My Lord, my God, accept my homage to you and to my dear Mother, Mrs Fielden.

Awaiting a reply from you,

Yours obediently,

SHIRA SHANKAR

With infernal cheek and of my own free will, I went to India to place myself at the head of a cultural organisation in a country whose history I scarcely knew, not one of whose two hundred languages I had mastered, whose customs I had not bothered to study, whose dress I should not copy, whose art was a closed book to me, whose literature was a dim translated shadow: and I thought, God bless me, that it was very good of me to go at all. Of course that's putting the case rather violently: still, there's an element in British make-up which does make us think *au fond*, however much we hide it, that we confer a distinct favour on all foreigners by deigning to visit them: and it's quite enough to earn the very cordial dislike of other races. India, in my experience, ranked snubbing as a greater sin than Imperialism, and put good manners and intelligence on a higher plane than nationalism or the colour of a skin. And that's what the British, not excluding myself, failed to grasp. I, with a touch of exhibitionism, might sit upon the floor or talk to prostitutes or stay at Wardha with Mr Gandhi: but in my heart of hearts I am sure I felt a bit superior to it all: and nobody recognizes that hidden feeling quicker than an Indian. In other words, both reactionaries and extremists were essentially right about India: it is the cursed

154

moderates who were wrong, always. Rule India with a rod of iron and a tremendous swagger and India liked it: love India genuinely and humbly and India loved you: but put on pinstripe trousers and write judicially and impartially on files and India knifed you – rightly. Or pretend, like me, to be awfully nice and broad-minded, and India made you know in the end, with some discomfort, that you were sitting on a lonely fence.

If the future is a mirror towards which the past marches to meet itself, any such looking-glass held up to me as I rolled towards Bombay on the *Poona* might well have induced me to purchase a return ticket at once. In it I could have seen, it is true, the Success of my Mission in terms of fourteen glittering transmitters and a staff to do them service in a most efficient way: but I should have been appalled to see also the End of My Fun, in the shape of personal loves and hatreds, rages and frustrations, and an eventful bankruptcy of faith: worse still perhaps, the dreadful use of the instrument which I had created, the harnessing of broadcasting to the obscene chariot of war. I think, I hope, I should have turned back then, in 1935.

But mirrors to the future aren't yet in general use, and my arrival at Bombay was simply dull. I think I must have expected glamour: I'm sure I didn't expect smelly darkness, drenching rain, and a temperature which forced the sweat to soak one's clothing before the rain could. I leant over a wet rail and looked down on desolate glistening quays, spattered with swaddled sleeping coolies: and felt vaguely that, as Controller of Broadcasting to the Government of India, I ought to do something. And although it was four in the morning, the absence of Somebody Important to greet me ruffled my temper: it was inefficiency or an insult. If the Indian officialdom (or even Indian curiosity) wasn't asleep, it should surely meet all boats on the chance of interesting passengers: not least, I felt, the first Controller of Broadcasting. But nothing stirred, and hot heavy silence brooded over the port. I returned, perforce, to my cabin, and awaited the day.

It brought *The Times of India*, very dark and incoherent, knocking at the door. What were my plans for Indian broadcasting? What was the state of British Broadcasting? 'None and lousy; and I'm not giving an interview,' I said. I was angry, because I wished to walk delicately with the Indian press. Reith had warned me of the pitfalls – rather overwarned me perhaps: visions of Reith and Riddell manoeuvring for a place in the public sun. However, I had tried to be good by sending to the Government of India the text of what I proposed to say to the press on my arrival, asking them to modify or alter it as they thought fit. And now here I was, without an answer. Beans I could spill in plenty, but should I? I could have said a mouthful about the purposes of broadcasting as I conceived them: but the conceptions of Delhi and Simla would be, I feared, very different from mine. How often, afterwards, did I wish that I had then spilt every possible and impossible bean, rammed the press of India full of the wildest ideas before anyone could stop me. But no: caution and Reithism prevailed, and I awaited Mr Gog, the Bombay engineer, who probably had my orders in his lazy pocket. I hereby caution all who find themselves in similar positions to spill the beans and damn the consequences.

The colourlessness of my cabin and the apparent colourlessness of Bombay – for even at night there is colour or not colour about a place – gave me to brood on vocations generally. I had been born a painter, and a painter I remained and should remain, whether fulfilled or unfulfilled no matter. It may seem a matter irrelevant to India and broadcasting, but I must go on about it, because missed or mistaken vocations seem, increasingly, a characteristic of our 'civilization': most men can do one or two things with spirit, skill, and pleasure: but the educational formulas and conventions of a mechanical age tend more and more to iron out the individual, to erase rather than encourage his particular bent. In the year of grace 1943, when we were plunging everybody into factories and expecting them all, irrespective of their characters, to go to it, we were still unable to realize that people who like machines will work them well, and people who prefer puddings or pictures won't. Anyhow, in that year of grace 1935, I was really an unhappy painter, born by some error to a wealthy Master of Foxhounds, and gently propelled by him into decorous pursuits such as the Army and the Foreign Office, until I had finally come uneasily to rest in the mezzo-artistic but still respectable sphere of broadcasting. Of course, I was good at my job, because even the semi-artist is much more clever than the bureaucrat: but I was shinning up the wrong tree all the same. Like so many people who can't find a nice quiet creative outlet, I had a craze for crusades: being unable to improve canvas with paint, I set out to improve humanity: a grave error. It took India to teach me that Browning couldn't have been righter about the awkwardness of playing with souls.

I didn't attempt to play with the soul of my second visitor. He was an emissary from that fuzzy, self-made saint, C. F. Andrews, an emissary, so to speak, from the stricken people of India. I ought to have warmed to him. But somehow I just didn't; I couldn't keep my attention on him. Again and again, in the five years that followed, he would appear in various places throughout the length and breadth of India and in a soft voice remind me that he had been the first to welcome me: as frequently I failed absolutely to remember his name and face. I am certain that he was an estimable character with a heart of gold: but he had no colour: he was colourless: and never have I been able to pierce a dull exterior to discover a heart of gold. I need people to be colourful saints or scamps: and now you may begin to see the kind of trouble which was brewing for me in the attempt to create a whole broadcasting organisation from scratch. But now the unnamed – whose name even now escapes me – pointed over the rail and said: 'Here comes Mr Gog.'

I looked down and saw a fat body and part of a dark fleshy face under a vast solar topee ambling foreshortened towards the gangway. Even before Mr Gog, speculator in radio's problematical future, gained the deck and flashed at me his oily ceremonial smile, I knew that he and I were destined to quarrel.

Now, now, says reason, for this is a reasonable age, how in the world could you know any such thing? You cannot, says reason, judge a man by his looks or his walk or his solar topee. I must reply that I certainly can. Whatever else I have been doubtful about in this mortal life – and God knows it gets more puzzling every day – I have never had any doubt at all about what I look for in human beings. The trouble is that God has arranged my grey matter to demand a combination of qualities – bad or good makes no matter – which seem distressingly rare. And my eight years of broadcasting in London, that daily meeting with, and testing of, the supposedly 'great', had narrowed, rather than amplified, my quite blatant summings-up of men and women. Cocksure, if you like, I was, on this point at least: but cocksure only because I had at one time or another interviewed almost every distinguished man and woman in the great world of London, and watched them giving, over the microphone, their mostly dusty answers to the world. One after another, I had been thrilled to meet them, and my thrill at meeting new human beings remains: but I had watched so many of the great developed, so to speak, in these broadcasts, from the negative to the positive, that I had acquired a fairly reliable judgement of the value of the film. And I knew, pretty well, how the film ought to look.

I hope, of course, that I wanted more than that. I did, I think – however much I debunked myself – see a Mission in Indian broadcasting. I believed, without analysing the belief too closely, that the spoken word, rightly handled, could perform miracles for a vast and illiterate country. Once get the ear of those masses, and pour into that ear the wisdom of its own great men – and what huge balance of sanity could not be thrown into the uneasy tilting scales of the world? In some such vaguery my thoughts ran. But to get the ear – that was the first, the crucial, point. Without that, all else failed. Therefore, of man's two great qualities, those of intellectual vision and emotional drive – and there are no others worth mentioning – I wanted, first, the latter. If I could find both in one man – the rarest thing in the world – so much the better: if not, I could for the time being – so I insanely and mistakenly thought – myself supply sufficient of the former. But, however blind I may have been to my own shortcomings, I had no doubts about my ability to recognize either quality or both, or the lack of them, within three seconds of meeting any man. And Mr Gog quite definitely had neither.

I wasn't, therefore, altogether at ease as I sat and drank coffee on the balcony of the Taj Mahal Hotel with Mr Gog and his brother, Magog. I felt positive that I wasn't behaving as a Director-General ought to behave. It was extremely hot: I wanted eggs and bacon, but dared not demand them, in case their consumption conflicted with some Indian usage. The Gogs, while gently probing me with obvious disfavour, left me the conversational ball: and I found it dangerous to roll. As a Director-General, I had to be omniscient: and as I knew very little about broadcasting, and just nothing about India, I felt not without reason that every phrase might betray me. In any case I knew, and I knew that they knew, that I was at war with the Gogs. Gog the elder had been selected, as I was later to learn from a Government file, because 'he has a large private income and seems just the man'. Magog was a shock to me: he had been selected only two days before my arrival by Belton, who was doing – in his own despite – a sort of John the Baptist for me. Gog was to go to the new Station at Delhi: Magog was to take his place in Bombay. All this without reference to me: I boiled inwardly, and looked with rage upon the magnificent panorama of the bay.

Gog and Magog, I reflected, provided at least two reasons for the strange fact that Indian broadcasting, with a potential hundred million listeners, had in fact about fifteen thousand. A group of Indian business men, fired by the financial success of European broadcasting, had floated a company in 1927 and, with a too-meagre capital, built two weak little stations at Calcutta and Bombay. In the following three years they had gathered some seven thousand listeners and lost a great deal of money. They decided to go into liquidation. The Government of India, which then and later – with considerable wisdom – thought broadcasting a curse, was thereupon bullied by the vested interests of radio dealers to buy up the transmitters. Having done so, it proceeded, quite naturally, to economise: file-writers in Delhi could hardly be expected to sanction public expenditure on music, drama, and similar irrelevancies: it seemed obvious that all such frivolous waste should be avoided. The programmes accordingly deteriorated even from their former low standard: and Indian broadcasting would have spiralled down to complete eclipse had not the BBC, at the critical moment, started an Empire programme on the short wave. Europeans in India rushed to buy sets: and since the Government had, by way of strangling broadcasting altogether, put an import duty of fifty per cent on sets, even the eight thousand extra sets purchased brought quite a deal of money under the broadcasting head. The dealers cried that broadcasting's profits must be used for broadcasting: the Government replied with the offer of a new station at Delhi and a man – me – from the BBC. But, however much English residents of India listened to the BBC – and to the radio dealers it did not matter, then, who listened to what as long as sets were sold – Indian broadcasting remained what it had always been: and Gog and Magog were characteristic of it.

How characteristic I learned when we visited 'the Station'. This was housed on the top floor of a dingy building, the rest of which was given to offshoots of Post Office administration. A dilapidated lift wheezed and creaked us to the fifth floor, the ragged liftman unconscious of my eminence: arrived, and ready to assume Director-General-like dignities and condescensions, I was confronted with an empty, and exceedingly dirty and untidy room, some fifteen by twenty feet, cluttered with a medley of paper-strewn tables and bounded by a partition of wood and glass. Percolating through this, I was in Gog's office, and out of it opened the eight by ten sanctum of the 'Directors of European and Indian programmes'. Beyond this was 'the Studio', a dark room hung with dirty cotton curtains of a peculiarly atrocious magenta, and furnished with a large grubby divan in pink and gold, a battered piano, and a harmonium. The atmosphere was that of a bankrupt brothel, and the noise of the street, no small assault on the ear-drums, rang and reverberated through it. In one corner a stuffy alcove housed an out-of-date gramophone turntable. My soul freezing within me may have caused a slight rise in my eyebrows, for Gog remarked carefully, and unnecessarily, that the staff were not yet here, but that they 'would arrive somewhere about ten'. He then put on a large pair of hornrimmed spectacles, seated his burly form at his desk, and proceeded to sort out letters. Magog, who in great contrast to his brother was a slim and epicene young man of a Bloomsbury type, meanwhile asked me if I would care to listen to some gramophone records: he had, he said, the largest collection - of course European - in Bombay. I said curtly no: but felt that Gog and Magog had undoubtedly won the first round.

I never could 'assert myself', and I didn't now. What I should have done I don't know: perhaps never gone to the studios until all the staff were assembled: perhaps pushed Gog out of his chair: perhaps - yes, alas, it was an infallible rule of India - shouted at him. I did nothing except take the chair opposite him, the chair, quite clearly, of a subordinate, and accept the letters which he handed to me. Among these was one from the Honourable Mr Mitchell, acting Minister of Industries and Labour in the absence of Sir Frank Noyce, which told me (a) that it 'would be wiser to say nothing to the press at this juncture' and (b) that 'he had thought it better to defer my visit to their Excellencies' and that I should, 'when I came to Simla, first stay with us.' This was infuriating: to have my careful press statement thus abruptly dismissed was bad enough: but to upset the invitation from the Willingdons, which I had moved heaven and earth to obtain, was a disaster. I had known vaguely that Indian broadcasting was disreputable and down-at-heel: and I had divined, not quite incorrectly, that the immediate homing of its new Controller to the Viceroy's House would raise its prestige: now, when the need had been reinforced by experience, I was defeated. The Military Secretary to the Viceroy, clearly unaware of Mr Mitchell's design, had also written to say that Their Excellencies would expect me on the following Monday: should I ignore Mitchell and wire acceptance? Was it worth enraging the Department? Looking back, I think it probably was: I was destined to enrage them anyway: but, whether owing to the Gog and Magog, the studio, or the lack of a substantial breakfast I hadn't the courage.

And now the staff began to trickle in. First came Blenkinsop, the 'Director of European programmes'. As the Bombay station broadcast for some five hours a day, about an hour of which was devoted to 'European' programmes consisting mainly of gramophone records, his job was not arduous. Blenkinsop was pale and shrinking and slovenly, as well he might be on the beggarly wages he received: his hands were wet and shook like those of an old man. He was, I suppose, about thirty years old; he shocked me, because he was the first down-at-heel white man I saw in the East. Trembling, he poured out a tale of woe, to which I felt that the Gog and Magog, on the other side of the partition, were listening attentively. The burden of the story was that he, Blenkinsop, should be appointed Station Director; he had worked for ten hours a day for eight years, Magog knew nothing, and so on. Blenkinsop, given opportunities, was perhaps no fool: but fresh as I was from the BBC and infuriated by the look of the studios, I could only shrink from his plaints, and wonder what his 25,000 hours of work had been devoted to. Blenkinsop suffered by meeting me when I knew nothing of Indian conditions, and was moreover irritated by Gog and Magog: I wrote him off.

Next came Chakravarty, the 'Director of Indian programmes'. The trouble about Chakravarty, as far as I was concerned, was that his English was so thick and strange as to be almost unintelligible: and even had I been able to converse fluently in Hindustani it would have availed me nothing since he came from Gujerat. Chakravarty, even through the barrier of language, could be recognized as a trier: one of Nature's slaves, slow, willing, fated to be bullied. He had soft brown eyes in a round scared face: he conveyed to me, as best he could, the idea that although Gog and Magog were great people he, Chakravarty, would possibly make the best Station Director. From this awkward subject I endeavoured to wean his attention to programmes: so far as I could gather, they consisted of an unvarying rota of three or four singers and a couple of instrumentalists. Each artist performed for two, and even three, hours at a stretch, and had apparently done so for years. Chakravarty's mind obviously did not run to any interruption of the hallowed routine.

I passed out into the main office, and six weedy clerks rose wearily to their feet. Should I make a speech? Talk about the greatness of broadcasting? The nobility of their calling? How Gog and Magog would laugh behind their partition, if I did. I shook hands with Mr Gomez, the accountant, a dry little man with waxed mustaches and shifty eyes. I looked at his books, which were unintelligible to me. I knew that I ought to make some brillant criticism or suggestion, and could think of nothing to say. The atmosphere round me was one that I had never encountered – the atmosphere of slavery. These people were interested neither in me nor in broadcasting: they wanted only to be left alone, to earn what they could, to do as little as possible for it. Mr Gomez, however, made it relatively plain, over a discussion of figures, that the proper person for the appointment of Station Director was an accountant. I retreated to Gog's office, and said I was ready to drive to the transmitter.

So far, so bad, I thought to myself in the car. I can make no impression on these people, and I dislike them all. Gog, with his fat face and body, his sly smile, his obvious grossness and utter ignorance, is no man for me or for broadcasting; yet here he is, a fixed constellation in my sky: what do I do with him? Magog, with his music and his effeminacy, is perhaps one better for broadcasting, but he will never keep order and nobody will respect him. Blenkinsop I don't trust: Chakravarty is incapable of original thought: the rest are not even capable typists. Where do I begin? How can broadcasting ever come to life under·such people? As we flashed through the tree-shadowed avenues towards Worli, Gog and Magog pointed out this and that – the house of a millionaire, the Willingdon Club, the Race Course. India? Yes, I supposed, Europeanized India, of which Gog and Magog were evidently a part. But they could tell me little about the serried rows of tenements huddled under the smoke-stacks of Worli. Was that India? Yes, the India of the underpaid cotton operatives, poor relations of their contemporaries in Rochdale and Todmorden. And at the transmitter were two of their kindred: mechanics earning £2 a month. I was now an employer of sweated labour, no less. The transmitter was a replica of the old, out-of-date design of 2LO: that it still functioned seemed a miracle. Pannikar, the Station Engineer, handed me a petition: it said – and I knew without reading it that it said – that he, Pannikar, was the proper person to appoint as Station Director.

We drove on now towards Thana, some twenty-five miles outside the city, where Belton had proposed that a new transmitter should be erected. For me who knew nothing about transmitters, this was one more awkward problem, to which I could apply only common sense and cryptic utterances: I was vaguely against the whole idea, partly because I knew little about Belton, whose vague associations with India's dying broadcasting seemed half-hearted, and partly because such a project would involve large expenditure, and finance was going to be one of my most ticklish problems. Nor did there seem to be any great urgency about building powerful transmitters until programme and studio management had been drastically reorganised. The old trans-mitter was certainly out-of-date, but it did function: it was sub-ject to interference, but twenty-five miles of cable might well prove a source of trouble as well as expense. As we drove along, therefore, I made up my mind that the Thana project should be delayed, and got a certain kick from having, if only in my own mind, decided something. The drive was enchanting enough: the warm golden air caressed us as we swept past glinting water-logged paddy-fields and village bazaars bright with colour, where sacred bulls with necklaces of turquoise blue wandered at will; and the whole landscape was aflame with the startling blossom of the gold-mohur, trees as high as elms flaunting a profusion of gold and crimson orchidaceous blooms.

Gradually the villages became more deeply embedded in the countryside; mud walls tanned by the sun to beige, shadowed by rustling palms, with rutted winding lanes which I longed to explore. Village women moved with superb elegance through the sunlight, the bright brass pots poised on their heads, gold and purple petticoats swinging with their stride. Beggars with long beards and emaciated legs, who might be sages for all I knew, sat about, and the lovely white oxen, with their melting eyes, pulled carts upon which gleaming black bodies, crowned with crimson turbans, slept or meditated in a golden trance.

'With these damned carts you can't get along at all,' grumbled Gog. Maybe. Did I want to get along? In this sleek car with Gog and Magog I was a million miles from India, just as I was a million miles from it in my capacity as a government-wallah. I wanted to get out and lose myself. But of course, I didn't. We very seldom have the courage to do what we want.

Soon we came among thicker trees and scrub, and the car bumped and panted over rough tracks, branches sweeping the roof with contempt and dislike. The jungle, I thought: lions, tigers, leopards, snakes – no, after all, not so near Bombay, Actually in five years of India I never saw a lion, tiger, leopard or snake; and only twice an elephant. But at this moment I was romantically inclined, and when we finally lurched to rest in a hot green shade, I could think of nothing but the beauty of the trees.

'The proposed site of the transmitter,' said Gog, consulting a large map, on to which his forehead dripped beads of perspiration, 'starts from that big tree over there, you see the red –'

'Isn't that hibiscus?' I asked.

'Hi *what*?' said Gog, put out by this.

'No, nothing,' I replied quickly. 'You were saying that the site started from that tree –'

'And goes on up the slope to that sort of yellow bush – what?'

'Nothing. Go on.'

'And then down past that dead tree with the creeper and round that bit of open space –'

'I'll just get out and go over it. Give me the map.'

I took the map and charged into the jungle. If I follow the most prickly places, I thought, I will get away from Gog and Magog. But they are watching me: what ought I to do? Nobody at the BBC ever prepared me for this. If only I had some sort of *instrument:* something which buzzed or clicked. The hibiscus is a dream, and that jacaranda – I must look intently at the ground, as if I knew something about it - then scan the whole area, so . . . Yes, and I must take some time about it. Or not? I should rather like to sit down on this piece of lush grass, but I can't think that an engineer would do that. If I have a garden, I shall plant a lot of jacaranda . . . but then, the whole thing is hopeless, I ought never to have come at all. Fool that I am, and damn Gog and Magog . . .

I returned, looking as thunderous as I could, and said: 'I don't think it'll do at all.'

'You wish to return to Bombay?'

'Yes.' (What on earth did he expect me to say?)

Almost immediately we lost our way. With interest and some surprise I noted – for I was new to the linguistic gaps of India – that Gog and Magog had considerable difficulties in understanding, and making themselves clear to, the locals. This was not encouraging to me. The language of those parts was presumably I thought, Gujerati: I didn't understand a syllable. In England I had plodded through a whole Hindustani grammar, and knew by heart every exercise in it: how much is it, I should like a bath now, bring me some tea, how is your grandfather? More, indeed much more, I had learned to read and write the printed Urdu script. But here in the Bombay area all this meant nothing at all. And even Gog and Magog, it seemed to me, were pretty well floored. This tower of Babel was not a promising place for radio.

We arrived back, eventually, at the echoing magnificence of the Taj Mahal Hotel. I said that I would send a telegram to Belton, and go to Delhi that night. Gog and Magog were horrified by this: they wished to give a party for me, champagne and an excellent dinner, they said, in the freezingly air-conditioned ballroom of the Taj. I thanked them, and supposed in a guilty way that I ought possibly to meet some more people: but the day had frightened me, and I was impatient to get on to Delhi and see what Fate had in store for me there. In any case, I felt that, in the moist heat, my dignity, intellect and wisdom as Controller of Broadcasting to the Government of India were ebbing through my pores. I was in no mood to face a dinner-party.

So I climbed on to that train which, proceeding quietly over some 2,000 miles, was known as the Frontier Mail. I had as yet no bearer – that personal servant who is indispensable in India – because I was suspicious, not quite incorrectly, of a bearer recommended by Gog and Magog: I thought he might spy upon me. This was only a vague kind of thought, a dim intuition: but had I known how much truth there was in it, I might have felt even more nervous than I did. As it was, I realized, on this first acquaintance with Indian trains, that a bearer was desirable. I was, so it turned out (and that almost never happened to me again) the only European traveller on the train. I had a roomy compartment, with two berths covered, like a Victorian horse-hair sofa, with particularly slippery upholstery, and a shower-bath leading off it. It seemed luxurious. Gog and Magog would not allow me to unroll my own valise, although I said that I was capable of doing so: they had brought along another young member of the staff, who did it for me. And after doing it he handed me, surreptitiously, an envelope.

The train pulled out. I waved to Gog and Magog and opened the envelope. It contained, and I knew that it contained, a plea that he, Hussain Ali, was the only person really suited to be Station Director of Bombay.

Some people used to enjoy railway journeys in India. In fact, to judge from the rarity with which the poor little air lines were used whilst I was there, the majority did. I didn't: though on this first occasion I expected nothing less. Crossing Romantic India, I said to myself: the wide lonely spaces: the Indian night. I peered out of the window into the Indian night: hot, stuffy, black. Not even a star. I stretched myself on the horsehair and slept. I awoke chewing dust, with the sun burning a hole in my head. Drawing the blind, I considered dust. I had never seen real dust before. It was not only in my mouth, it was in my hair and my ears and my nose, it was on the pillow and under the sheets, it lay like snow on the floor, it covered my hairbrushes and my towels and my sponge and my books and my clothes: it seemed to increase and multiply with every moment. Hastily I put myself under the shower and gratefully remained there for a few crystallizing minutes: then shook my bed and belongings, only to find that I had accumulated a positive icing of dust on my wet skin. I returned to the shower again. With a repeat of the process I became comparatively dust-free and looked out of the window. Crossing Romantic India. Never had I beheld an uglier landscape: flat, tired, naked earth stretching to flat horizon under a grey and heavy-clouded sky. The jungle? A Rajput castle? A tiger? Some ruins? Blue mountains? A little deer, perhaps – oh God, give me a little deer at least! No, no, said God, Hampstead Heath, but flat.

It went on like that.

We arrived at Delhi in the evening, and it was dark. I realized for the first time – and I never quite got used to it – that in India the sun sets punctually at six-thirty, more or less, all the year round: there are no long evenings and no short ones, a monotonous state of affairs. So Delhi drifted by me for the first time only in rain-mirrored winking lights, the empty spaces of the Ceremonial Station, and finally the sudden bustle and clamour of the terminus. I stood in the doorway and a voice under a topee said:

'Fielden?'

'Yes?'

'Belton.'

I got down. We shook hands. He said nothing more. A coolie was removing my baggage. The station was full of noise, tremendous noise, and bustling human figures in all manner of dress and undress, and behind it all was the swish of heavy rain which gleamed in the arc lights and spouted from the carriage roofs.

'That's all your luggage?' shouted Belton.

'Think so,' I yelled.

'Come on, then.'

I thought, really, I doubt if this is the way a Controller of Broadcasting should be received, however I must be patient. (Conditioned and controlled.) I followed. We clambered into an antique, weather-screened Ford. My luggage, in which I had lost all interest, seemed to have disappeared. We drove off through sheets of rain, which banged and rattled on the canvas screens. Puddles in red earth spouted up in the headlights. The engine wheezed and spluttered.

'Blast!' said Belton, above the noise, as the car skidded. And then, suddenly, he shouted in my ear – 'I suppose you *know* that you've come to the most God-awful country in the world?'

'It certainly seems wet now,' I bellowed, 'but why God-awful?'

'Because,' bawled Belton, 'you can't get a thing . . .' the rattling of the side-curtains carried his voice away, and it came to me only in gusts . . . 'think you're coming to put everything . . . not a thing, I tell you . . . blue-eyed boy at first . . . frustration, madness . . . not a thing *done*.' He seemed to relapse into silence, though I fancied that he was still muttering. The car drew up on some wet gravel: the shape of white modern buildings was dimly discernible.

'*Boooy!*' yelled Belton through the dripping darkness. White blowzy figures scuttered softly. Belton got down, slamming the door, and I followed him, squelching, round the edge of a dim building and then through gauze doors into a large, empty, absolutely featureless room, in which, round the single bulb that glared from the ceiling, a strange cloud of insects danced.

'Do for you, I suppose?' said Belton, and I caught the implication that I supposed myself too high and mighty for such a room, which, of course, was true.

'Excellent,' I murmured, thinking how much I hated camp beds. 'Where am I?'

'Oh,' said Belton. 'This is the club. Sorry, thought you'd know. Nobody much in Delhi this time of year. Find yourself a house, no doubt, though they're damned difficult to get, I may tell you. Anyhow you're due to go up to Simla tomorrow night to stay with the Mitchells. I shall take you, of course.'

Everything, I thought in a mad rage, is being arranged for me.

167

Regardless of any wishes I might have. Why the devil am I so weak in accepting it all?

'You'll be able,' pursued Belton, throwing a brief Hindustani execration at the 'boy' (aged about sixty) who was unfolding my camp bed, 'to see the studios tomorrow. I've taken a house. Hope it'll do. Couldn't delay longer.'

Anger bubbled up in me. The damned interference of the man! The studios for the new Delhi station were *my* affair, and I had my own ideas about them. And now a house had been taken . . .

'I'll get rid of it if it's unsuitable,' I replied in a flat voice.

'Probably won't find another if you do,' retorted Belton. 'You don't know Delhi. Which of these bearers do you want? They've both got good references.'

Two aged figures swathed in white bowed and tottered before me. With clasped hands and eyes lifted to the rainy skies above the roof, each assured me that I was, most inexplicably, his father and mother, and that to me his life's devotion was assured. Both were hateful. Had I not pictured to myself something so vastly different? Slim, intelligent youths, with the eyes of gazelles, worshipping me with silent, but so effective, service? What had I to do with these old monsters? But I was too tired to argue. I said 'That one'll do.'

'His name,' said Belton, 'is Khuda Baksh. You'd better look at his papers.'

'I absolutely can't,' I replied, 'look at any papers.'

And Khuda Baksh, whom I never ceased to dislike, started, there and then, to remain with me for five long years. So much for will-power and decision.

I found myself, next morning (after Khuda Baksh had, to my unspeakable horror, made the most violent but unavailing attempts to bath, dry and dress me) at a breakfast table with six lightly-clad sweating gentlemen, each reading with deadly concentration a newspaper, periodical or magazine. The atmosphere was one of excruciating surliness. I felt a spasm of laughter welling up inside me, though I wondered too, whether Delhi hot weather would reduce me to the same condition. I need not have wondered. It did.

Mr Belton then drove me to the transmitter. The sky was blue, though heavy clouds rolled on the horizon: damp tremendous heat enveloped us. As from a Turkish bath, I stared in growing wonder at New Delhi, that thirty-million-pound monument to British grandeur which looks like the immaculate conception of

a frozen suburb. Whitely down the straight, straight roads gleamed the bungalows of A, B or C variety according to your station
and salary: whitely gleamed the fence-posts of the circle from
which five white straight roads led each to another circle from
which five white straight roads . . .

'I can't imagine how you find your way *at all*,' I said to Belton.

'This is Princes Place, and there are the Secretariats,' replied
Belton. 'You'll soon get used to it.'

Exactly, I thought, what Russia would like to be. Whitely
gleamed the statues of past Viceroys, meditative white heads
rising from white robes. Whitely gleamed the meretricious domes
of the Secretariats: and away away, characterless, featureless, almost limitless it seemed, flowed the Kings Way, ending only in a
distant stumpy elephant which was the Arch of Victory. Whitely
gleamed the great pillared roundabout, so like a gasometer (and
always thus known) which was the Assembly House.

But then, through a long white vista, abruptly came something
of a very different age and order – the three great pearly bubbles
of the domes of the Great Mosque, a sight to uplift the heart.

> *These are thy wonders, Lord of Power,*
> *Killing and quickening, bringing down to hell*
> *And up to heaven in an hour:*
> *Making a chiming of a passing bell.*
> > *We said amiss*
> > *This or that is:*
> *Thy word is all, if we could spell . . .*

Am I, I asked myself, spelling badly, as we bumped and banged along the now mercifully curving and not-so-good road between the fairy-like ethereal grace of the Jama Masjid and the
beautifully severe lines of the Old Fort, poised above the hazy
reaches of the Jumna? These at least are products of human
hearts and hopes; not of A, B, or C engineers: and for the India
which could build them I felt, for the first time, an entirely
natural friendliness and admiration.

We jolted through the gates of Old Delhi, along the wide untidy streets where, in the dust strips before the houses, all manner
of delightful untidy conversation pieces, cooking, squabbling and
games were going forward, through the cantonment, where wed-
dingcake architecture and greater decorum prevailed, and so

along flat empty roads to the transmitter. This, I was glad to observe, was in a frightful mess. I had no desire to be forced into a sudden opening of a brand-new station with staff not as yet recruited. I listened without any regret to the sad stories of the Marconi engineer – red tape with the Public Works Department, impossible to complete the approach (which was a mass of rocks and rubbish), gear unprotected from the rain, the Posts and Telegraphs Department unaccountably slow ... Belton interrupted, talked technically: the Marconi engineer shouted, I looked blank. I was calculating that I should have at least six weeks to recruit and train a staff, fit up studios. But six weeks only!

Bumping back to the studio, Belton informed me that he had already advertised for staff ('couldn't delay longer') for the new station. My hackles rose through my aertex shirt. How many, I enquired.

'Oh, well,' said Belton airily, 'I decided that three would do for the station and three for the transmitter. Like Calcutta and Bombay, you know.'

'And at what pay?' I queried, trying to sound as though I really believed that three people could run a daily broadcast programme *in toto*.

'Oh, usual rates, you know,' replied Belton. 'Let's see, the Programme Director would get two hundred rupees - that's £14 a month – and the assistants sixty – that's about £5 – a month. Quite good pay for Indians.'

'But not, surely, for brains or originality?' I suggested.

'Well, of course, you can try to get them put up. You'll see, you won't. Government of India scales. Anyway, they're quite attractive enough. I've got six thousand applications already.'

'*Six thousand?*' I gasped. I felt like rolling over into the back seat and yowling like a scalded cat. '*Six thousand?*'

'Yes – I'm going to hand them over to you,' said Belton. A flicker of a grey eye through spectacles came round at me: he had scored. 'You'll have to go through them, I suppose.'

'But,' I ventured, cowed, 'don't I have a clerical staff *at all*?'

'Oh, yes. There's Rashid Ali and a few clerks at Headquarters, wherever you *do* make your Headquarters. They're at Simla now. But you couldn't trust *them* with applications.'

'Why not?' I asked.

'Oh, my dear fellow, a Muslim would choose nothing but Muslims, a Hindu Hindus, and so on. You have to keep an eye on communal representation. Have to explain that to you. Besides, they'd choose their own brothers and sons and nephews – God knows where you'd be. Anyhow, here's the studio.'

I perceived, in a daze, that we had arrived at the portal of a undersized and peculiarly hideous wedding-cake. It was a bunga-low wedding-cake, but that did not prevent it from having thrown out stalagmite-crowned turrets with gothic windows of coloured glass, and a crenellated portico of plaster. A derelict garden – in India correctly called 'a compound' – lay gasping around it. I followed Belton through a high small hall, which smelt like a tenement, into a central room – the largest, obviously of the bungalow: indeed you might say the whole bungalow reft of its turretries.

'Used to belong to the Maharajah of Bumph,' said Belton, complacently surveying the impossible room. 'Rather a lot of bathrooms, I'm afraid: otherwise not bad. Not bad at all.'

I sat down in the middle of the floor and contemplated the solar-plexus of my beautiful new broadcasting organisation. It was about thirty feet long, at least thirty feet high (with a pain-ful addition of coloured clerestory windows) and about twelve foot broad. It echoed like a tomb. No orchestra could fit into it, no singer could sing in it, no talker talk: it was inconceivable that it could be applied to broadcasting. I thought of England, Home, Beauty, and the BBC. Belton said:

'Here is Boshi, the Station Engineer.'

A plump figure with a brown, flat, penny-like face, came waddling up to me and bowed profoundly. He was wearing khaki shirt and shorts, and between them an enormously wide white leather belt to which multitudinous medallions and hiero-glyphs were attached. Bowing over me, he purred: 'It iss my prout honour to welcome to the studios our incomparable leader.'

I wondered if I had heard that correctly. But the purr con-tinued: 'We haff been as a sheep without a rudder. You, sirr, haff come as a saviour to uss.'

Belton had wandered out into the garden. I said, feebly: 'Well . . . do you suppose we *can* broadcast from this studio?'

'Sirr? Undoubtedly we shall broadcast gr-r-reat things from this studio. We need perhaps some curr-r-rtains, yess? . . . But we haff other studios . . .'

Deferentially – what a perfect butler! – he led me into bath-room after bathroom, octagonal, hexagonal, turretted, blue-win-dowed. Not bathrooms in the Ritz sense, no: rooms, merely, where a bath might be put upon a cement floor, to be filled from a tap and emptied into a hole. Bathrooms in which the human voice echoed and re-echoed. Something, I decided, must be done to Belton about this: a plot began to spin in my mind. Also getting the measure of Mr Boshi, I said: 'I see that you are very experienced in broadcasting.'

The penny expanded into smiles.

'Sir-r-r, with the sole exception of Mister Istapleton, I am the oldest member of the Indian S-S-State Broadcasting Service.'

'And undoubtedly,' I said, casting discretion to the winds, 'you will do it great honour.'

The penny became serious.

'Sir-r-r, I have a s-s-small communication to make to your Honour.'

From below the belt he produced a letter addressed to me. Too well did I know what that letter contained. I shook him warmly and wetly by the hand and hurried into the garden.

'Well!' I exclaimed, smiling like a Cheshire cat, 'that's all splendid! I'm most grateful! And now, can't I make some amends for all your trouble by giving you some lunch?'

The face of Belton went through a series of phases. It fell, looked doubtful, sneered, rose, and finally beamed.

'Glad you're pleased. Yes, it *is* about tiffin-time. Where would you like to go?'

'You're the expert. Where can we eat and drink most effectively?'

On the way, I spoke of alcohol with appreciation and respect, and discovered in Belton a taste for white wine. Over lunch therefore I plied him with the best that the hotel could produce, carefully filling his glass while he looked elsewhere, so that the desired explosion came as I anticipated. Looking darkly across the dessert, Belton shot suddenly at me: 'D'you know *why* you've been invited to Vishregal Lodge? Because you've been to *Eton,* tash why, thash *all —*'

'Not at all,' I retorted. 'It's because I intrigued to get there.'

But that wouldn't do. Belton was off and wasn't going to listen to me.

'*You* know *noshing* about broadcasting! Anyone can shee *that!* And let me tell you, you're not *wanted* in India, not *wanted!* I *know.* Do *you* know,' he hissed across the table, 'do *you* know that the Govment of India *wrote* to Shectary of Shtate shaying *reconshidered* decishion, didn't *want* you. Shectary of Shtate shaid contract shigned, noshing to do ... Yesh, and you wont lasht a year, not a *year* ...'

His voice went on. It was funny, comic, horrible, revolting. It was probably true. Belton had maybe wanted the job, probably deserved it: between me and the Government of India I knew there could be only rage. I looked out at the swimming-pool and the trees, felt unutterably sad, ordered oceans of black coffee.

Belton, getting into his car, said: 'Afraid I've talked awfully stupidly. I always,' he added grinding the gears, 'say damn silly things. Sorry.'

He was disarming, and after all, I thought, likeable. But looking out on British India, I did not feel excessively exultant.

The train, bumping through the night across dusty plains, deposited you at Ambala at four in the morning. You could then whisk out of your carriage and catch – with a minimum of time to spare – the first Diesel rail-car which took you to Simla by hairpin bends over boiling precipices on a line which seemed too narrow for a nursery train. Or again you could sleep a little more in the heat and clangour of Ambala station and catch the second rail-car. Or again you might sleep still more and take a taxi, though that, on the curling roads, made some people sick. I should have preferred the first or third course: Belton firmly imposed the second. This, he said, before disappearing into the station lavatory, was due to the fact that (a) his bowels must work regularly and couldn't be hurried and (b) the taxis charged too much. My own bowels, I knew, had no intention whatsoever of working in such circumstances, and as I was being paid £2,000 a year, a perfectly dizzy income for me, I didn't care a damn about expense.

However, the second rail-car it was: and we curled and curved over dizzy and dizzier ravines, through hosts of chattering grey monkeys – but not a flower to be seen – until the mountains stretched endlessly below us, contour after contour, identical, lifeless, barren, ugly – reminding me a little, though less colourfully, of the illimitable ranges which spread below Madrid.

Belton, now solicitous, warned me: 'You must be careful. Very careful. 8,000 feet plays the devil with the heart. Don't walk too fast. You'll probably faint.'

He went on with this until I felt myself distinctly growing paler, and heard the wheels repeating 'Probably faint, probably faint, probably – probably faint ...' And so, when I beheld a hill in front of me after descending at Simla station (the rickshaws with their human ponies I could not face) I walked with such idiotic slowness that I must have appeared to be ninety. '*Am* I fainting?' I asked myself. 'How do I feel?' After a bit myself said, 'Personally, I feel bully: what's wrong?' So I walked a little faster. Admittedly the way was steep, and admittedly I (resentfully) puffed and blew. But faint, no. I rather wished that I *could* faint. Simla frightened me.

After the station hill came a long straight road, the backbone of Simla, and the backbone, for that matter, of the hill upon which it was perched. It was an awkward backbone, like that of a goat, shelving away quickly, and allowing only a precarious straggle of houses along its brim. One of these was the Hotel Cecil, centre (though I didn't yet know it) of the political or amorous intrigue of which the Government of India was chiefly composed. Past this rackety building, which looked as though it might slide at any moment into the abyss (but in which, by diabolical ingenuity, the builder had contrived to make a lounge without any view whatsoever) slid rickshaws innumerable, pulled by panting natives dressed in the liveries of a vulgar Venice. In the rickshaws (which, when I came to look at them, were simply bath-chairs uptilted) reclined elderly gentlemen with massive paunches, cigars, and white topees, assiduously reading documents or nodding with distant dignity to a passing acquaintance. The rickshaw-wallahs, except for their sweating brown faces and tired, flat, brown feet were costumed in blue and scarlet, green and purple, violet and gold, and exceedingly bad taste. I smelt not quite Huntingshire and not quite Suburbia, but an uneasy mixture of both. Snobbery rampant, taste couchant, in a field azure, crossed with Decorations.

Up, up, up we went through the trees, the mountains dropping to our ascent, until puffing and perspiring we reached our goal - Inverarm. Inverarm, a black-and-white monstrosity in the Tudor style, with a red corrugated-iron roof. Here lived the Mitchells: here would live the Noyces, the Stewarts, the Clows, my successive presiding genii: here I was destined to have endless quarrels, embitterments, disillusions, and boredom in excelsis.

But the Mitchells, on this one occasion when I visited them, were charming. They, about to retire, had no stake in my future and thus no anxieties about my character. With them, after a pleasant lustreless evening I arranged to go to Viceregal Lodge next day. I wanted, badly, to get there. I was terrified of going there, because mutual friends had told me that Lady Willingdon was a Dragon, who would impose the sternest of conventions on her guests, and that life at Viceregal Lodge was a continual slavery. But, if I couldn't get the ear of the Viceroy, I was done for. I felt sure that, under a benignant Viceregal eye, Indian broadcasting could begin to flourish: without it, never.

So, feeling absurd as well as nervous, I was pulled in the Mitchell rickshaw under the Viceregal Gate House, where the Indian guard (magnificent, it must be said) came with a great clank of arms to the salute of my nervous person. Up the drive we went, I anxiously consulting my watch, through hordes of grey monkeys which hardly bothered to move to make way for us. And then I was getting down, flustered (my tie? this suit? my hair?) at the portico of a Very Large Wimbledon Villa, and being taken by an ADC (witheringly polite) across a galleried hall, and into a loggia where a party sat.

And instantly it was quite all right. I made my little bows without difficulty. The Vicereine made none of the anticipated comments on my appearance. Instead, I felt perfectly at home. I knew in a flash that the Willingdons were charming and I couldn't fail to get on with them. I knew that she was dominating, a human dynamo if ever there was one, but I also knew that she could be knocked off her perch very easily by words. I knew that Lord Willingdon was genial, kind and sympathetic: there, I thought – and thought rightly – I shall have a friend. I was enormously elated.

We all strolled out into the garden in the sunset. It was one of the perfect Simla evenings which are rare. Behind us, towering into the deep blue sky, the snows of the Himalayas brooded: in front, the immense dropping contours of the hills, purple and violet and blue, disclosed the distant plain and a curving gleam of the river. Stars began to glitter. Lady Willingdon said: 'Come, come! Lost in dreams? But you've got a lot to do! Can't afford to dream here, y'know! Now I'll show you the rose garden while there's still some light!'

She took me firmly by the arm.

But I was glimpsing the long silly road of the future: the miles of paper that I should cover with hopeless arguments: the endless recruitment of unsatisfactory personnel: the quarrels and frustrations, the growing languor and indifference: the hatred of Indian and Englishman alike: Mr Gandhi saying ' . . . if you choose to keep your job by virtue of the guns behind you': the slow building of stations and the ignorant fight with language and music and habit: and at last the dim departure, no trumpets sounding, into the muggy clouds of war . . .

But the rosegarden was beautiful.

English literature and English anecdote have been considerably weighted, in the last century and a half, by Indiana. I do not propose to add very much to that burden. No Poonah stories, I hope, will be retold here. None of us, however, can entirely escape the mould of our times. Whether we are sociological or political or scientific or artistic or agricultural, we have to take up the pattern of human life, of progress or regress, discovery and research, at the point where it exists on the loom when we sit down to it. We can alter the pattern only slowly: the carpet goes on growing, much the same, even through revolutions. We cannot change what is already done. When I (or anyone at that time) went to India, I could not make a mental exclusion of events and trends. And because I was new to, and ignorant of, India, such trends and events probably made more impact on me than they could to those who had spent long years either in India itself, or in the services in England which controlled it. I did not think of India as a permanent vassal of the British Raj, and I thought the British Raj rather Kiplingesquely ridiculous: on the other hand, I did not think of India as independent, and I supposed the British Raj to be in some ways grand and glorious. I had a muddled but somewhat glamorous picture. The foregoing pages will have shown, I trust, that my expectations in this respect were not entirely fulfilled.

Among events and trends, the first was the menace of war. Nobody could doubt, in 1935, that the pathway to war was open. Therefore the planning of a radio network for India had, willy-nilly, a strategic note. It was for this reason (to take one example) that I decided to link stations – I had learnt this from Italy – not by telephone cables, as in Britain, but by a system of relay transmitters and receiving stations, which could operate and modify a series of wave lengths, free from any sabotage.

Second came the change of influence in India – a change to which the Indian Civil Service chose to remain blind, but which was apparent to any newcomer. The quality of the British was deteriorating: the quality of Indians was improving. It could not be otherwise. The Indian Civil Service had once been a coveted career; younger sons of the nobility had gone into it, and, even if they had behaved atrociously, been drunk, had their Indian mistresses, embezzled funds, and died young, they had seemed, to the Indian minds of the time, glamorous, damnable, and lively. In their place, by 1935, we had the younger sons of Clapham and Surbiton, plus their suburban wives. And at the same time Indians, educated now in the universities of England, America, Germany and Japan, no longer regarded the English as supermen, even in a damnable sense. They thought them merely ignorant. Moreover, India was now wide open to new currents of thought flowing from Russia and Germany. These were the trends which threw the shadow of extinction over the British Raj. I have often been accused, in later years, of 'siding' with Indians, or 'being disloyal' to the British Raj. Neither was true. I came as a new boy to India, and the situation was clear. We had to do better, or get out.

And there was a third trend. The British, always paying lip-service to self-government (though seldom at the right time or with the right proposals) had invented the 1935 Act, which gave some measure of autonomy, but too little and too late. Compromise, as usual, muddled the picture. The Indian Civil Service, shadowed for the first time by the threat of unemployment, became more rigid and more obstinate: Indian nationalists, seeing the glimmer of independence, grew intransigent and wild. In the middle sat the Indian collaborationists or quislings (I don't think the name is unjust) who hoped that temporary subservience might earn them, in the end, high tyranny. The political weather in India, however you might look at it, was not promising.

That was the Indian end. The English end was – at least for me – even less attractive. England in the thirties had seemed to be stepping downhill, with a decline of enterprise and inspiration, and a growing class hatred. Mr Baldwin was whimpering of safety first, and Britain seemed to like that whimper. As a contrast the totalitarian countries, however thin and ugly their façade, gave an impression of liveliness and decision. People may deny, nowadays, that they felt like that, but it was a common feeling nonetheless. I myself had a special anger against the BBC pudding and its ways: this had grown out of personal experience in cases too numerous to be mentioned here. But I will mention two. In the early thirties the BBC, like any other group or organisation, had been preoccupied by unemployment. The BBC staff had been, I think, exceptionally generous with their money and time, and had run an unemployment centre at Gateshead.

Much effort had gone into programmes that might help. I devised a series which could, I believe, have much reduced the growing discontent. Many people were interested, including Edward, Prince of Wales – always quick in human sympathy. But the Labour Party stamped on it: and I had the clear impression, not only that the BBC would never fight in a good cause, but that Labour wanted and prayed for a split in English opinion, as they do today. That indeed may be good party politics: I began from that time, and have continued, to believe that party politics are due for the scrap heap.

My second quarrel, which left a permanent scar on my mind, was and must remain concealed in the virtue – or vice – of our social attitude and laws of libel. I can say only that it dealt with the effect of advertising upon truth. Few people, even today, realize to what monstrous lengths our huge advertisement concerns can go in their struggle against truth. 'Publish that article, and we stop your revenue!' Newspapers, after all, in the majority of cases, could not exist without their advertising revenue. And advertisement is nearly always exaggerated, false, and misleading. We all really *know* this: does anyone seriously believe that those yellow old tusks will become white as driven snow by the application of Hoodlum's Toothpaste, or that that muddy old skin will become roses and jasmine after a dose of Laxative B.?

I had imagined that the BBC, which did not depend on advertisement, would be immune to these influences. I was wrong. The revenue from advertisement in BBC publications was so colossal that it could not, or would not, be ignored. And it did, on occasion, seriously impinge on programmes. That is to say, we were prevented (and it is still the case) from attacking or even criticizing a product which experts had condemned. This so enraged me, and made me rage, that High Authority eventually sent me a memorandum pointing out that, if I wished advertisers to cancel their contracts, my Talks budget would be severely curtailed. I replied that I would rather have no talks at all. Exaggeration was perhaps my middle name: but I still rage against advertising: and wonder why it is allowed, tax-free, to stain men's minds, and the countryside, with its vulgar lies. The BBC could have blown the advertisement racket wide open, and it didn't. If it had, there might be no commercial television today. I am bound to admit that the BBC, if pusillanimous when it came to a fight, was and is a thousand times better then the commercial horrors people gape at now. Dear Sidney Bernstein,

I like him immensely, he is a first rate showman and does a fine job: but no, no, a thousand times NO: to dazzle people with unnecessary luxuries in the name of art or entertainment is harmful In those days, of course, we were far from commercial radio: all the same, I was not inclined to model my Indian puzzle on the lines of the BBC.

The five years which I spent in India were, undoubtedly, the loneliest years of my life. The ache of loneliness was with me al·ways. On the one hand there was the conglomeration of English officials and their wives – the most ignorant, insensitive, arrogant, and stupid conglomoration that the world has ever produced. During my first winter in Delhi, I went out to dinner with them almost every night. It was a terrible experience. Not only were their houses and furniture identical – they were built and supplied to the same pattern – but also the food, the guests, and the conversation were identical. There were always twelve people, and usually the same twelve. The dinner was always thin soup, wet fish, tasteless beef, and caramel custard. Since you were forced by etiquette to sit in an order determined by your salary, you sat almost always next to the same people. And, of course, you wore full evening dress. Very soon, I wanted to scream. The extraordinary thing was that any human being could stand it. Not a book was read, or owned, in those trim, respectable bungalows: not a play had been seen: not a note of music was known: never was there even an echo of real laughter. In the similar roads with similar lamp-posts and similar gates, it was as though one was shut up with a crowd of actors in an out-dated pageant, a dusty fusty representation of Versailles, with occasional struts before a distant sullen audience, inattentive and unknown. It was a sad spectacle of third-rate tyranny.

If this was (as it struck me) the English side, the Indian one, from which one might have expected more help and gaiety, was even more inscrutable and opaque. Indians saw in me (especially when I went out to dinner so much) just another stiff-necked British official. Why should an Englishman (and why indeed, I echoed) run their broadcasting? My efforts to be courteous were regarded as cunning: my attempts to speak Urdu and eat Indian food were a sly form of hypocrisy. The CID sent me a packet of intercepted letters from Indians, in which it appeared that (a) I knew nothing of broadcasting and had never had anything to do with it, (b) that I was a close relative of Mr Baldwin, and that was how I had got the job, and (c) that the BBC had sent me to

179

India because medium-wave transmitters were now out-of-date, and they hoped that I could sell off their old ones to the Indians. I was incensed by the idea of intercepted letters, and returned them to the CID, saying that they should cease sending them to me: but the poison did its work. I felt that I was up against a stone wall of misunderstanding, on which I might knock my head in vain.

These were the broad lines of discouragement. Of course there were exceptions, and very happy ones. Chancellor of the Exchequer (in Indian parlance Finance Member) was P. J. Grigg: and with him and his wife Gertrude I found an instant bond of sympathy, and a warm friendship which has never, and will never, grow dim. P.J. has one of the most piercingly brilliant brains that Nature ever made: he is unafraid, angry, violent, and devastatingly honest: and, in spite of all that, a man of modesty and humility, capable of great compassion. Gertrude, in her different way, is no less of an individual. These two might have been sent to me by God: I think I should have run away from India without them. That did not mean that we did not quarrel like three cats: they thought that India needed a rod of iron, and I didn't. But we recognized each other's point of view and respected it. At moments suicidal, I could run to the Griggs and be assured, not of agreement, but of warm and happy argument with underlying sympathy. Of all the English houses in Delhi or Simla or Madras or Calcutta or Bombay, the Griggs' was the only one in which I could feel unbuttoned and at home.

There were also the Willingdons. If I say that Willingdon was a good and perceptive Viceroy, Linlithgow the worst disaster that ever struck India and Micky Brabourne (removed by untimely death) the most promising Viceroy of his times, I am merely stating a view which resulted from my personal contact with all three. They were good or bad, that is to say, as far as I and broadcasting were concerned. Of other matters I have scant knowledge. Willingdon was a man who combined great natural dignity with an easy manner and a sense of fun. I can't imagine anyone – not even nationalist Indians – disliking him personally. He was keen on the possibilities of broadcasting and approved my plans for it. I had an entrée to the Viceroy's house at any hour. If (as frequently happened) I asked him to help me about something, he would tell me of the difficulties in detail, and then go about the business with infinite tact. When he failed (as he quite often did, for red tape was sometimes too much even for

Viceroys) he would put his head in his hands and say, 'My dear boy, I'm afraid I have let you down: we must try again.' Lady Willingdon liked me for different reasons: she liked anything new, and anybody who made the fur fly. In these two I had a cosy last resort, which was an immense help in my first six months, which were also their last in India. The Government of India soon got wise to this private line – so to speak – between me and the Willingdons, and when Linlithgow arrived, he was requested never to see me unless a Minister was present: a piece of advice which he decided, not I suppose unnaturally, to accept. Lord Brabourne, on the contrary, who was Governor of Bombay and then of Bengal, and the obvious selection for the next Viceroy, was completely sold on the idea, and my ideas, of a great extension of broadcasting, and through some uncomfortable years I visualized an end to all my troubles when he came to Delhi. But he died in Calcutta. Had he not done so, I believe that the history of Anglo-Indian relations would have been a very different, and much happier one, and I doubt whether Pakistan would ever, with its attendant massacres, have been created. It was a death which altered an Empire.

There were exceptions, too, on the Indian side. Dr Ansari, the forerunner of Mr Jinnah, was a man of exceptional charm, wisdom, tolerance and goodwill. Like Willingdon, he was born to be loved. He gave me a warm welcome, and I found in his house a fount of instruction about Indian ways and thoughts. Unluckily for me, he died suddenly about two months after I arrived in India. But fortunately, I gravitated from his house to that of his lieutenant, Asaf Ali. Asaf Ali, a Muslim of course, had married (a rare occurrence in India) a Hindu, Aruna, who (as I write) is Mayor of Delhi. These two showed me great kindness, and although I thought Asaf Ali rather a weak man, and Aruna far too extremist and fanatical, I spent many very happy evenings with them. They also introduced me to Sarojini Naidu, who became, for a time, a fast friend. Sarojini was the poetess of India, and no mean one. She was fat and ungainly, and looked like a benignant frog. That did not matter at all. Her enormous warm sympathy and her unquenchable sense of fun flowed over you like a warm bath. She was the best woman speaker – with the possible exception of Annie Besant – that I have ever heard. Perhaps for best I should substitute the most magnetic: it was quite difficult to remember, in both cases, exactly what had been said, but while they were speaking, they held you entranced. Evenings at the Asaf Ali's were different from those with English officials. The food was attractive and surprising (with a good deal of laughter at my reactions to it), the conversation was uninhibited and gay, and after dinner one sat on the roof and watched the pigeons. This Indian game is great fun. You send up your flock of pigeons into the evening sky, and the game is to see how many of other people's pigeons they can lure back with them, or, of course, how many you lose. The pigeons wheeling against the calm sky make an entrancing pattern, and the excitement, when your eyes are quick, is as good as that of a racecourse, and much more subtle. I enjoyed those evenings.

Also, there was Gandhi, and there were my Station Directors. But those came later.

The winter in Delhi, as anyone who has experienced a Delhi winter knows, was a miracle of perfect weather. June days, September evenings, and all the flowers on earth.

My first job was to scrutinise the 6,000 applications for jobs. This was one of the most baffling tasks I have ever attempted. For they were all the same. The Government of India had laid down a sort of formula for applications – or perhaps one should say, implied it. Each letter started with the words 'I am a young man of active habits'. It went on to say that the young man had been to such-and-such a university, and had emerged with a degree, or (ancient but true joke) as a 'failed BA'. It then stated that the young man's father 'had fought for the British Raj in 1914' and that his grandfather 'had fought for the British in the Mutiny'. And he was, yours obediently. Poor youth of India! I was saddened by these letters. What could I do, when broadcasting was in question? I could only strive to pick out a phrase or a signature which had some individuality. In this way I chose some 300 applications – all, and more than all that one could interview for twelve jobs – and put them aside. Then I had to recheck them, in order to be sure that they contained the requisite communal proportions of Hindus, Muslims, and Anglo-Indians. Had I not done this, I should have instantly been accused of favouritism, and questions would have been asked in the Assembly. These things being accomplished, I had to convene a Selection Board: no one official in India could make appointments: they had to be made by a Committee, and to that Committee were attached the same rules – communal percentage of Hindus, Muslims, and Anglo-Indians, plus a Member of the Assembly.

Daft, do you say? It was daft all right. I approached the Government of India for advice about the Selection Board. They looked down their noses and said that they could not advise me: it was entirely a matter for the Head of the Department. I said that I knew no one in India. They said that that could not be helped. After a time, partly with the help of the Asaf Alis and Mrs Naidu, partly with the assistance of letters from England from E. M. Forster and others, I got a Board together. It included A. S. Bokhari, a Professor at Lahore University, who was destined to play a considerable part in my Indian scene.

One day I went to a party at the Willingdon's attended by Emerson, the Governor of the Punjab, and his ADC, Walter Skrine. Talking to Skrine, I voiced my bewilderment over the applications, and my fears that to train a broadcasting staff would be a long and difficult task in a country where the theatre hardly existed, and few books were read. He told me that he knew an Indian who was employed in the Army Headquarters at Simla as an examiner in languages: a very intelligent fellow, he said, who had produced plays and even written them, as well as a good deal of verse, with great success. 'I should think,' he added, 'that he would be exactly your man.' I took the name and said I would send him an invitation to attend the Selection Board. The name was Zulfaqar Bokhari. The first name stuck in my mind because it was unusual: but I did not connect him with Professor Bokhari of Lahore, since I was in a fair muddle about Indian names, and trying to get myself to slip round such tongue-twisters as Vijiaravagacharya, Rajagopalachari, and Ramaswami Iyer. Zulfaqar wrote to acknowledge my card, but said that he was well-suited to Army Headquarters and had no interest in broadcasting. I was slightly ruffled by this, and wrote him a letter telling him that he was an ass if he did not at least try, since broadcasting was bound to lead to positions and salaries of distinction. This brought him down to see me. I was staying at the Hotel Cecil in Delhi, and when he arrived was typing (it was ferociously hot) dressed in a bathing slip and nothing else. He recoiled on seeing me. I thought that perhaps he was embarrassed, so I told him to go away, and to come back later and have lunch with me. In later years he told me that it was not only the first time he had ever seen an Englishman in, so to speak, undress uniform, but it was also (and he had been for ten years in Army Headquarters) the first time that an Englishman had asked him to a meal. Over lunch I teased him a bit, and came to the conclusion that he was very much what was wanted: I persuaded him to put down his name for the Selection Board. When he arrived at the office, Gog, who was presiding over the arrangements there, rang me up and said that Bokhari was entirely unsuitable for broadcasting, and would create havoc. I said that havoc was what I most desired. Thus Zulfaqar started his long career. And some havoc there was. Later he became Director General of Radio Pakistan.

I now began to 'tour'. This 'touring' was a comic business. The Head of a Department in the Government of India was not permitted to go off on his own: every detail of the tour, including train departures and arrivals and all engagements, had to be stencilled and circulated to all departments well before he left. This did not add much gaiety to travel, and had the unfortunate effect (unfortunate to me, anyway) of encouraging raids by newspaper correspondents at hotels and stations. It was perhaps necessary, since much touring was necessary in a country as large as Europe, that the Government of India should know where its officials were. I had written to Reith (who then and thereafter gave me every assistance in his power, and constantly cheered me with wise letters) asking for the loan of an engineer, since I did not feel competent to make a five-year transmitter plan for India. He sent me Kirke, the Head of the BBC Research Department. Kirke was a great charmer, as well as a highly efficient technician. With him I escaped, when I could, from Delhi, and began to know the extraordinary variety of the Indian continent. Slowly a 'coverage' plan began to emerge.

The Selection Board now met, and interviewed the 300 candidates. The standard was depressingly low. (That, of course, stemmed from Lord Macaulay, who decided that young Indians should be trained as clerks, and nothing else.) Zulfaqar made an immediate impression. When his turn came, Professor Bokhari whispered to me 'This is my brother: had I better go out?' I said he had. The Selection Board gave Zulfaqar first place, and he became, to Gog's rage, the first Director of the Delhi station. I asked one of the candidates: 'Do you know what is meant by the reproduction of programmes?' He replied: 'I think, sair, the Indian masses are too weak to indulge in much reproduction.' I wondered what I was going to do with these people.

It was now high time to train the staff for the Delhi station, and to arrange the programmes for it. It was the first high-powered station in India, and much might depend on its success.

184

Army Headquarters refused to let Zulfaqar go, and were furious with me for taking him. I had a battle royal before I got him. When he arrived, I thought that I had made a frightful error. He was used to army ways, and I found him one morning drilling the whole staff on the verandah, and teaching them to form fours. Gently I tried to explain that that was not exactly what I required. He said, 'But these people must be disciplined.' However, he was quick to adapt himself, and threw himself into the work with enormous zeal. Without him I don't think that the Delhi station would have started at all: the hurdles were unexpected and tremendous.

None of the staff, of course, had ever seen a microphone before, and they found great difficulty in using it, or in believing that it was of any use. Since Indians in general (and who shall say that they are wrong?) do not find that Time and the Hour run through the smoothest day, the punctuality of programmes left much to be desired. Noise and chatter in the studios seemed incurable. In spite of all that I could do, acoustics were appalling. But the worst hurdle was the performers. Music and mummers were matters held in low repute, rather as Quakers might have regarded them a century before. When I got to India they were almost entirely (the ballet was an exception) in the hands of prostitutes and pimps. No man or woman of the upper or middle classes of India would stoop to the practice of music or acting. This posed a serious problem. There was I, supposed to produce an entertainment service for India, and there were my most likely clients, holding up their hands in horror at the very idea. Moreover, the notion – rapidly spread and embroidered – that I was going to pay colossal sums to all performers, naturally made matters much worse. I was encouraging prostitution, that was what it came to: and it followed, of course, that the favours of all prostitutes were mine at will. It was Zulfaqar who, with great tact and ability, induced a campaign to show that 'prostitutes' was a misleading word. And this was true. It was an Indian custom (and a very wise one) to send young men of seventeen or eighteen to learn about manners, art, and love from women who might be called courtesans. Many of these women had exceptional dignity, intelligence, and grace: they were in fact among the most intellectual Indians of their time. By applying very strict rules in the studios, sacking any performer who behaved badly, and picking only the best singers and instrumentalists, we gradually surmounted the initial fury. But it remained a problem. I was bombarded with letters from 'respectable' people, saying that their daughters could 'sing a little': you may imagine what their singing was like. Apart from that, most of my artists ate opium, and refused to come to rehearsal in their 'opium-time'.

I must make a slight digression about this. The Western world thinks that opium is a terrible thing, and God knows how many committees and conferences have been held to abolish it. But India gave me a very different impression. The smoking of opium, and the taking of an opium pill, are two vastly different things. Opium smoking, which I tried to see what results it had, is completely horrible: it can induce a certain euphoria, but its effect on health is disastrous: that I know from personal experience. But the opium-pill is quite another thing. It is, like garlic, a disinfectant: it is the quickest and surest remedy for stomach troubles. I do not believe that is has any deleterious effect. I had among my artists an old man of seventy – and I think he is still alive – who was known as the best *sarenghi* player of India. The *sarenghi* is a kind of violin, but very much more complicated. It needs great agility of fingering. This old man was without doubt a beautiful executant, and he told me that he had taken an opium pill every morning from the age of seven and had never been ill. I was impressed by his story (and the similar stories of other artists) and convened a meeting of Indian doctors, to get a ruling from them. They were outspoken on three points (a) that opium pills did no harm, and probably protected against disease (b) that the West had not begun to understand the healing qualities of opium, and (c) that cancer could be arrested, or at least kept at bay, for thirty years or so by the use of opium pills. I had not, of course, the means or time or knowledge to make any scientific check: but I did find myself eventually in the odd position of obtaining and distributing opium as the Head of a Government Department. Later, when I had an especially painful operation in London, and the English doctors refused me drugs, I wondered whether Indian opinion might not be right.

I now began to skirmish with Authority. The studio premises were appalling, the rates of pay were enough to degrade any organisation, and the whole business of building up a broadcasting network was generally regarded as wasteful and unnecessary. I had to fight for every penny. One announcer per station was thought quite enough. In Government budgets I was 'credited' with the very small amount flowing from license fees (not only were there few listeners, but most of those did not pay), but not with the much more considerable sums arising from the 50 per cent duty on each imported set – and no sets were manufactured in India. Thus, at the time of every budget, I was a target for questions such as: 'Why are Indian finances burdened with this losing concern?' If the Minister replied that the Government thought that India should have a broadcasting service, the supplementary question came pat: 'Why isn't it run by an Indian?'

My progress was largely controlled by the Cabinet Minister (or Member of the Viceroy's Council) who was answerable for broadcasting in the Assembly. I had three of these in succession, and I should not have chosen them myself. The first, Sir Frank Noyce, was a harmless man who had risen from the ranks, made a successful career in India over forty years, and was about to retire. What he most wanted was to have no Bothers. I was a Bother. He did not care – why should he? – if Indian broadcasting succeeded or failed: it was a new gadget, and as such rather suspect. My careful and sometimes angry arguments were shot at his immense paunch and glittering pince-nez, and bounced back. I might as well have talked to a feather-bed. The second, Sir Thomas Stewart, stymied me whenever he could. On one occasion, when I was pressing some matter which he opposed, and which I thought of critical importance, he said blandly: 'My dear Fielden, you waste words. You do not seem to realize that I can do, and I shall do, exactly as I choose.' I was so angry that I still see him saying it, with a photo of the Parthenon behind his head. 'A damned little twopenny dictator,' I thought. However, his brother, Sir Findlater Stewart, was Permanent Under-Secretary at the India Office. I could often have murdered Stewart, but somehow I could never quite dislike him. He had charm. But the third, Sir Andrew Clow, was far and away the worst of the three as far as I was concerned. He was a pious Presbyterian, and he suspected that broadcasting was wicked, and that I was its Mephistopheles. He would summon me to Simla at a week-end, and there, in the antimacassarial glories of Inverarm would play hymn tunes by the hour on an upright piano, and very badly. He loved anything which reflected badly on me, and would carefully read every translation of gossip-columns in the many little scandal sheets of India, and then confront me with them with a long face. Once when I was accused of homosexuality, his pious sermon so annoyed me that I said, 'And if it were true, Sir Andrew, what business is it of yours, if I do my job properly?'

I thought he would explode. It was the kind of remark which annihilated him. He thought it incomprehensible and Samsonic. He liked to live in blinkers. One day he said to me 'Last Sunday I listened, reverently, to a Divine Service on the BBC. And at the end they said *that it had been recorded!!!* Now is not that a blasphemous scandal?' He caused me much trouble, did Sir Andrew, and I never got on with him at all. These three gentlemen were, I suppose, fitted for the posts which they occupied, but nobody on earth could say that they were good for Indian broadcasting.

I worked extremely hard, and I don't think anyone could have spent more time on the job than I did. Whether I spent intelligence is another question. Arnold Bennett once said that nobody ever died of overwork: they died only from disorganised work. A short while ago I came across, in an old book, a detailed table of my engagements. My office hours were from 7 till 1, and from 5 to 7 – this was an arrangement prompted by Indian heat. In the intervals I went to the Station to examine programmes and supervise rehearsals: I slogged through lessons in Urdu: I attended to Indian visitors, mostly white-bearded, who would usually come at 6 a.m. or at 4 p.m., and I tried to think out future plans for stations, staff, programmes, and salaries. I got malaria, as everyone in India did. Malaria in India is rather like the common cold in England, except that it is less annoying, but runs a higher temperature. If your temperature was less than 102°, you went to work as usual, and did not feel anything much except a headache. But when I got malignant tertian, it was a different matter. I was very much surprised when I put a thermometer in my mouth and saw it register 105.5°. I was surprised because I did not feel particularly ill, although I was shaking like a pneumatic drill. I don't know quite what malaria does to one's body (and I doubt if anyone else does) but it seems to me that, when you once have it, you have it for keeps. When I left India in 1940, I did a long cure of quinine, and it appeared that I was cured. But when I went back to India in 1950, I had not been a week in Karachi (and it was winter, when malaria scarcely appears at all) before I went down with a ferocious attack of it. I conclude that it is a permanent guest. In any case, whether through malaria or overwork, I developed – though, I did not then know it – tuberculosis. And no doubt that affected my temper.

When I had been in India for about six months, two curious (and subdued) events occurred. The first was that the Prime

Minister, Mr Baldwin, wrote me a letter which was opened by the CID. The letter was marked 'Prime Minister', and was both written and addressed in his own hand. In it he agreed with some of my conclusions, and said that the Viceroy (oh Heavens!) would be directed to give me better assistance. I had known for some time that many of my letters were opened, because one of my clerks had been in the CID office and knew all the tricks. And they were surprising. I learnt – fairly easily – how you can break and replace any seal with a thin hot knife: and I learnt also, which surprised me more, how a letter can, with a special pin, be rolled up and drawn out of the bottom corner of an envelope, and then replaced. Nobody looks at the bottom corner of an envelope. I learnt many other such tricks. I knew when letters were opened. I was infuriated by the case of Mr Baldwin's letter. Not only would it infallibly stop Baldwin from writing to me again: it would also earn me more hatred from the Viceroy and the Ministers. I took a hundred opened envelopes and went with them to Sir John X, Head of the CID. I asked him why he opened my letters. He laughed. 'You neurotic people,' he said, 'get such queer ideas. We don't open your letters: you imagine it.' I threw my bunch on to the table, and exclaimed: 'Let me tell you how these letters were opened.' He made a face and said: 'Well, well, that's just bad luck: a certain number of letters are opened as a routine: yours have just happened to be unlucky.' I said: 'Sir John, what have you got against me? Do you think I am working for Gandhi?' He shook his head. 'No, no.' 'Do you think I am a Communist?' 'Oh dear no.' 'Then,' I asked, 'what have you got against me? You have stolen my keys and searched my house, among other things. May I not ask you why?' He replied: 'You are talking a lot of nonsense: but if you want it straight from the shoulder, India is no place for Left Intellectuals.' Two years later I went to his funeral, and felt no grief.

The other event was curiouser - straight out of *Alice in Wonderland*. To make it clear, I must explain (bear with me) some details of the Government of India as I knew it. India, as I have said, is a sub-continent into which you could put the whole of Europe. The Pathan and the Bengali are as different, and as remote, from the Madrasi as the Swedes or Finns from the Spaniards. This conglomeration of races was ruled by some 1,500 English Civil Servants and a small army of about 60,000 men. The whole budget (because the country was so poor) amounted to about one-twelfth of an English one. Therefore the problems of

India were largely insoluble. You might have excellent men, but distance, disparity of views and customs, and shortage of money could confound the best policies. And Indians did not like us. These facts tended to a sort of hopelessness, a feeling that so much and no more could be done, but that Authority must be preserved at all costs. And from this it followed naturally that the Government must live apart, in a sort of Holy Heaven of its own, like the Gods in Tennyson's Lotus Eaters. This grew into a passion for secrecy. The Viceroy and his Council, and their staff, became Untouchables. The files in which the Viceroy and his Ministers wrote were never allowed to percolate down to the Departments, which had other staffs and other files. But the people who allowed this to happen were such nitwits that they failed to realize that the Cabinet Staff of Indians would inevitably contain some rebels, as well as a great many clerks who were related to clerks in the Departmental staffs. Thus the 'Very Secret' notes of the Viceroy quickly reached the Departments. A kind of absurd spy system was set up. But there was more to it than this. Faced by the enormous difficulties of their tasks, the officials of the Government of India had begun – as bureaucratic officials often do – to resent any suggestion of haste. They had to have time to pass the baby around, and sometimes to let it quietly die. As in India small notice was taken of any criticism of the eternally-fixed Government, this attitude was free to develop: and it developed into an astounding inertia. Gradually it became *praiseworthy* for an official to have as many files (pending) as possible in his office. It was almost a point of honour. To my astonishment I saw many high officials surrounded by piles of files which covered the entire floor space of their office. Some were six months old. And so far had this process gone that the Government of India had actually issued a general order which prohibited any Head of Department from reminding the Government about a pending file until six weeks after it had been sent in. Now it happened that broadcasting was not amenable to this process. I could not defer for six weeks or longer a decision to replace an announcer who was ill, or to decide whether some ceremony should be broadcast or not, or to send an order for valves to Marconi's. I therefore went in person to badger officials, and they did not like it. I don't suppose that I was either tactful or polite. At the same time I was growing tired of English parties, I refused to join the European club, I made a number of

Indian friends, I would not have a Government-allotted house, and I went quite often to see Gandhi.

These things and others made me extremely unpopular with the Government. They began to think (and who knows if they were right?) that under my guidance broadcasting might develop not only into a great nuisance, but also into a great danger. I might act rashly – which was not done in India. But they were in a pickle about getting rid of me. They could not say that I did not work: they had no actual crimes to put against me, and in any case they had 'chosen' me and signed my contract. So somebody suggested that a Commission should be set up to declare that I was of unsound mind. This news was conveyed to me by my own staff, who advised me to be careful. I laughed at them: I did not believe a word of it. So they brought me the Council files: and there, incontrovertibly, it was. It had been turned down as impracticable, but the suggestion had been made. I was dumbfounded. For a while I asked myself whether perhaps I *was* of unsound mind. My anger against the Government of India increased.

So far, I have painted this picture of India, in 1936, in sombre colours. But nobody, as far as I know, has ever set down these rather trivial facts: and any historian worth his salt must take them into consideration when he considers the downfall of the British Raj. And downfall it was: don't let anyone make the mistake of thinking that Attlee or Mountbatten or England made a great and noble gesture of renunciation. We got out of India because we ruled it so ineffectively that we were forced out – and also, of course, because we had neither the troops nor the money, after the 1939 war, to hold it by force. No credit is due to England for the events of 1946 and 1947. It was not, as Lawrence had hoped, a noble gesture: it was a feeble one.

But few lives are altogether sombre, and mine in India certainly wasn't. To travel round India as I did, with a purpose and a welcome everywhere, was an adventure and a delight. From dusty Sind to the rugged North West Frontier: from the dramatic snows of Darjeeling to rainy Chittagong, up the wide sluggish river to Dacca, and to the sprawling human ant-heap of Calcutta, where in the palatial English swimming-pools five hundred fat naked Englishmen were sedulously dried by black slaves. And so to the temple of Puri and through the jungles of the Central Provinces and down to Madras, a city which seems to turn away disdainfully from the great rollers which break along its humid

shores. And Mysore so different, with its Sussex-like downs: and
the dreamy lagoons of Travancore. At Hyderabad I had an unforgettable dinner with the Prime Minister, the wise and gentle
Akhbar Hydari, sitting alone with him in an immense garden,
with thirty-four huge fountains playing for our benefit. He sent
me in luxury to see the cave paintings of Ajanta, which no one
who sees them will forget. And so to other palaces such as those
of Baroda, Jaipur, and enchanting Udaipur: and to others still,
where Maharajahs were crazy enough to reassure me about my
own sanity. It was a splendid experience: and I gradually came
to learn something about Indian life and customs, and of the
very varied races which inhabited the sub-continent. I grew perplexed about the application of broadcasting to this Tower of
Babel, but also grew to love the sprawling muddle of India
better. Established Western habits began to seem less valid. Were
not Indians perhaps right when they said that you should wash
always under running water, and that to sit and soak in a dirty
bath was disgusting? Was there something to be said for their
horror of used cutlery, when you saw Indian fingers manipulat-
ing food with such delicate dexterity, and such careful washing
before and after it? Was not there something charming in the
attitude that silence is never embarrassing, and 'small talk' foolish? And surely the *dhoti* (when you saw it at its best, as in
Bihar) is a mode of dress far more becoming, simple, inexpensive,
and clean than the extraordinary Western array, where a man
needs at least ten different garments before he is clothed, and
usually keeps most of them far from clean? Not that I could
exactly see English squires hunting and shooting in a *dhoti:* still,
I pondered over these and many other such matters, and wondered whether the BBC conception of broadcasting might not be
entirely wrong for India.

By the time that I had spent eighteen months in India, things
were beginning to move fairly favourably. New stations were
coming along, the nucleus of an excellent staff had been assembled and trained (partly with the help of the BBC school),
programmes were improving, and the general attitude to broadcasting had become much more respectful. Even Mr Rajagopalachari, the Prime Minister of Madras, who had argued with me
furiously against any broadcasting in India (and, in my opinion,
he was and he is the wisest man in India) had come round to it.
I had managed to change the name of the organisation, and this
trivial event pleased me. I had never liked the title ISBS (Indian

State Broadcasting Service) which to me seemed not only unwieldy but also tainted with officialdom. After a good deal of cogitation – which may seem ridiculous now, but these apparently simple and obvious things do not always appear easily – I had concluded that All India Radio would give me not only protection from the clauses which I most feared in the 1935 Act, but would also have the suitable initials AIR. I worked out a monogram which placed these letters over the map of India, and it is now about the only thing which remains of me in India. But, when I mooted this point, I found that there was immense opposition in the Secretariat to any such change. They wanted ISBS and they thought it fine. I realized that I must employ a little unnatural tact. I cornered Lord Linlithgow after a Viceregal banquet, and said plaintively that I was in a great difficulty and needed his advice. (He usually responded well to such an opening). I said I was sure that he agreed with me that ISBS was a clumsy title. After a slight pause, he nodded his long head wisely. Yes, it was rather a mouthful. I said that perhaps it was a pity to use the word broadcasting at all, since all Indians had to say 'brodcasting' – *broad* was for them an unpronounceable word. But I could *not*, I said, think of another title: could he help me? 'Indian State,' I said, was a term which, as he well knew, hardly fitted into the 1935 Act. It should be something general. He rose beautifully to the bait. 'All India?' I expressed my astonishment and admiration. The very thing. But surely not 'broadcasting'? After some thought he suggested, 'radio?' Splendid, I said – and what beautiful initials! The Viceroy concluded that he had invented it, and there was no more trouble. His pet name must be adopted. Thus All India Radio was born.

By 1937 I had become – as Indian officials were apt to do – an intolerant little dictator. Although I got some doubtless salutary checks from above, I was a king of my growing dunghill. I took greater pleasure in flattery and less in contradiction. Doubtless the appointments which I made (or persuaded a Selection Board to make) suffered accordingly. I began to like yes-men. All India Radio was not exactly robust, but it was a growing and healthy child. I had a nucleus of Station Directors who knew their jobs admirably. There were one or two flies in my ointment. Before Kirke had returned to England, he had interviewed all applicants for the post of Chief Engineer, and had concluded that none of them could quite stand up to the business of creating a whole new network. (Or perhaps, to put it in another way, Indian engineers in highly-paid commercial jobs were not attracted by the salary I could offer.) I was very much against the appointment of an Englishman, and invitations were issued to Indians in England. But they came to nothing. Eventually it was agreed between the various interested parties that an Engineer should be sent out from the BBC. This was Cecil Goyder. Goyder was a conscientious, hardworking, proficient man who did a great job for India, and it was largely owing to him that All India Radio, in its early days, had few technical failures. Goyder fitted beautifully into Anglo-Indian society, but he did not fit me. From the moment I saw him descend from the aeroplane, wearing a high stiff collar and an outsize topee, I knew that my relations with him could never be cordial. I don't think that we ever quarrelled; on the other hand, I doubt if I ever held any conversation with him which was not official. He did not like me and my ways, and I could not warm to him. This was a pity, though only a small one: it widened the gap which always exists between engineers and executives, whether on a ship or in a factory, and thus tended to feuds within the AIR. Still, one can't have everything, and Goyder was a first-class technician. The other flies were a bit more serious. Impressed by Zulfaqar Bokhari, I had jumped to the conclusion that his brother, the Professor, would be no less valuable. When it became obvious that a Deputy-Director was necessary (particularly when I was away on tour) I asked for the Professor. Zulfaqar warned me, with perfect good sense, that I was making a great mistake: his brother, he said, was a scholar who would hate the rough-and-tumble of broadcasting, and I should run into great trouble by employing two brothers. But I had become dictatorial and I would not listen.

When Ahmed Shah Bokhari arrived, he had made up his mind about me, not quite correctly. He thought that I was a rather silly Englishman, and that he would succeed me, and he was correct on both points: he also thought that I should become a figurehead which he would control, and in this he was wrong. He started out by coming every evening to my house, and reading aloud to me from the English poets. Since I had selected and listened to the best English voices for eight years, the fearful Indian pronunciation and intonation affected me like a piano out-of-tune. To escape, I ran away to the Station and talked over, or listened to, programmes. There Ahmed Shah would pursue me, and, coming into office or studio, would say to his brother 'Get out!', and would then sit in the chair opposite me and put his feet on the table. Since I had chosen him and he was my Deputy, I could not object. But a cold war developed, and I was no match for this Krushchev. He was one of the wittiest men I have ever known, a brilliant conversationalist with a wide culture. Gradually I became aware not only that he was damning me with faint praise to all my Indian friends ('Poor Fielden, he means well, but of course he knows so little about India, and he thinks you're a damned fool') but also that he was carrying tales about me to the Government of India ('Fielden has just been to see Gandhi: Fielden has had a secret meeting with Nehru: Fielden loathes the Viceroy'). When I taxed him with these things, his tears would drip on to my blotting-pad, and for a while they convinced me: but soon there was incontrovertible evidence of his attitude. And there arose a Whispering Scandal, which I don't doubt originated from him. It was said that the AIR should be rechristened the BBC – the Bokhari Brothers Corporation. This, though only a whisper, was damaging: it seemed best to send Zulfaqar to the new Station at Bombay, where he was successful and, as far as I know, happy: but I never got as good a Station Director for Delhi, and my interest in the programmes there waned, which was doubtless what Ahmed Shah desired. I am far from attributing any blame to A. S. Bokhari: he was a brilliant man who did what to him seemed right. I was up against (as in the BBC) a man whose thoughts ran naturally to the power of broadcasting, rather than to the quality of its programmes. Such men probably hold all the best cards.

The Indian Congress leaders have so far had no place in this narrative, and it is time that they did. Some three months after my arrival in India, Gandhi had come to Delhi and established himself, as was his wont, in a camp outside the city. I asked the Home Minister if I might go to see him. The Home Minister said no. I asked why. The Home Minister said that I was 'too close to the Government'. I said that I did not see how I could run broadcasting if I did not know the point of view of Indian Nationalists. He was obdurate. I went to see Mr Gandhi next day. (At that time, I should have been quite glad if the Government had sacked me.) Mrs Naidu met me at the entrance to the camp, and said, laughing: 'So you've dared to come to see our Micky Mouse!' But, Gandhi, standing in the verandah of his hut, only smiled and scribbled a note which was handed down to me. It said: 'My dear Child, This is my Silence Day: so you can talk, but I can't.' I could only say: 'No, no, Mr Gandhi, that won't do: I shall come back tomorrow.' So I came back tomorrow. It was evening, and he was lying on the floor of his hut, with a hurricane lamp beside him. I put the case for Indian broadcasting as best I could. He kicked his legs in the air, throwing wild shadows over the gleaming rush matting, and said: 'I see what you are – a milk-and-water Liberal. You have no place in India. This is an armed camp. Be on one side or the other.' I said that I could no more be on one side than a telephone could be on one side: I was only a transmitter. He replied, 'Don't blame *me* then, if both sides throw stones at you.' In spite of such exchanges I soon had a great affection for Gandhi: and I think that I can say without immodesty that he liked me. When, later, I pressed him to broadcast, he said: 'My dear Fielden, you know and I know that if I do so I shall increase the number of your listeners by four or five millions overnight: if I knew that you were going to stay in India, I might do it: if you don't, I shall merely increase the strength of my enemies.' There was no denying this. Gandhi was, I think, a much lesser man than India has chosen to imagine him: he was, aesthetically, blind and deaf: he had not the smallest understanding or knowledge of music, painting, sculpture, architecture, or even Nature: and his literary knowledge was absurdly limited. His favourite author was Thoreau, and one can well understand why. Such a man could not really see all sides of life clearly. On the other hand he had an endearing Puckish humour, an enormous love and compassion for the human race, and a very shrewd brain. He had a remarkable intuition about people, and pierced through all hypocrisy to the heart. It was always fun to be with him. Legend credits him with a skeletal body and an ascetic life: in fact, he was quite plump, and his huts and food, though simple, were as attractive as any average man could wish: I, a sybarite by nature, could have been quite happy with them. I was immensely impressed by his theory of passive resistance, which has been much misunderstood: in the light of later events I saw clearly how true it was that, given no collaborators and an absolute refusal to help an enemy, the enemy could in the long run be defeated without weapons. Once, when I was arguing with him about this, he said: 'My dear boy, I don't cheat myself with any belief that India would be with me: perhaps only a thousandth part would be with me; perhaps my gospel will not be understood for a thousand generations, perhaps never: but that does not alter the fact that it is right.'

Jawaharlal Nehru was a very different character: a man of

great culture and violent temperament, he had, and has, his feet in both Indian and European tradition. He is a man of immense and compelling charm who can quite often act like a spoiled baby. On one occasion he rang me up at ten o'clock at night from Gandhi's camp, and said: 'Look, there's no food here; could you give some to Nan (his sister) and me, if we came over?' This was so astonishing and unusual that I was almost struck dumb. I stammered that all the servants had gone to bed (in India they live outside the house), but that I could scramble some eggs. 'Fine,' said J.N. 'But no politics, mind.' They came over and we spent a delightful evening, during which Nehru remarked that my drawing-room was 'stately, but hardly cosy' – a remark which I threw back at him when I visited him in 1950 in the luxurious palace of the Commander-in-Chief. It wasn't possible not to like such a man, or indeed his very charming sister, Mrs Pandit. When, in 1936, I was struggling with misery and frustration, I wrote to both Gandhi and Nehru, asking why they would not lift a hand to help me. Both replied in personally-written letters, and here they are:

Segaon, Wardha

Dear Fielden,

I value the confidence you have given me. My sympathies are with you in your troubles. But you have to take them philosophically, if you must stick to your post: even though it be for the good of the country. Any attack on your personal character is a vile thing. But any society has its share of blackmailers. These you should laugh at. Then there are the critics. You may not expect informed criticism. Very few write for the public good: most write for money. Then there is the third class who don't come to you as you would have them to do. They don't in spite of themselves. Those who know you would like to avail themselves of the facilities you may give them but they know that the harm done by such co-operation will be greater than the good intended. Take Raj Kumari herself. Even she can go only a certain distance and no further. You must not grieve over this but take it as inevitable in the circumstances surrounding us.

Yours sincerely,
M. K. GANDHI

My dear Fielden,

Your letter reached me and it made painful reading. I am afraid you are a misfit in that job or in India: but then all of us are. What is one to do about it? You blame others (including innocent me!) but does not the fault lie really in the environment, in circumstances which are bigger than individuals, in the unhealthy relation between India and England, in the topsy-turvy world itself? Broadcasting is a great thing, I believe in it. But it is after all a part of a much larger whole, and if the body is sick how can you treat a finger or a limb?

I cannot write to you all I want to. I am writing this note in haste. I am off on one of my interminable tours and for seven weeks I shall have no rest. But even if I had more time I doubt if a letter would convey to you all I feel. I wish you could come here and spend a few days with us. Both my sister and I would be happy to have you and perhaps you might feel better and calmer for a change.

I have had to put up with a great deal which might have embittered me and filled me with hate and yet I have survived. I feel pretty lonely often enough but not bitter against anybody. Why should you succumb to this bitterness and hate? I suppose Delhi, Imperial Delhi, is partly responsible for it. It is not easy to remain sane there and even I cannot stand it for long.

India is a very friendly place. It has so many hateful aspects but so many more lovable ones. You must get behind the mask and get in tune with it. Unhappily you have started at the wrong place, with the wrong people. Not your fault of course.

I wish I could help you. Perhaps I can in some odd ways. Write to me sometimes about books and pictures and anything else that you like. Your letters will be welcome. In spite of politics, I have not lost my humanity.

Yours,

JAWAHARLAL NEHRU

In July 1937, when I was due for a two-yearly six weeks leave in England, I went to say goodbye to the Griggs, whom I should not see in India again, since their time there was finished. I said to Lady Grigg: 'I hope that my aeroplane crashes: I have done all I can, and I see no future for me.' She said, naturally: 'What utter nonsense you talk!' But it was not quite nonsense. I had come to a dead end, though my words may have been prompted partly by a tired body. I was not in the habit of weighing myself, and I did not know, or even suppose, that my weight had declined from ten stone to eight. As I am six foot two, this was a bad business. But I was far too busy to realize that I was ill. I was even too busy (and here I am afraid that Arnold Bennett's dictum about disorganisation applies) to make proper arrangements for my journey from Delhi to the airport of Jodhpur. As a result, I found myself in a small train crossing the Great Indian Desert in the height of summer, and without either airconditioning or the block of ice which I had failed to order or, come to that, a topee. I am sure that eggs would have fried in three seconds on the roof of that carriage, and I fried inside it. I arrived at Jodhpur in a state of near-collapse. As it happened, two cousins of mine, Derek and Peggy Walker, were travelling by the same flight. Peggy told me later that they were so appalled at the sight of me that they actually made arrangements as to what they would do if I died on the journey. Peggy was to continue to London, while Derek supervised the funeral arrangements. Indeed when we came down for the night at Baghdad, I thought that my number was up. I lay on my bed and sweated, and felt that I was falling through endless blackness into everlasting night. At Croydon my friends were even more appalled than the Walkers had been. My eyes had sunk into my head, and my cheek-bones stood out white. My doctor, Isaac Jones, most endearing of men, who always on principle denied the existence of any disease, said heartily that I was a bit run down, and should drink four quarts (or something like it) of milk every day. I did this, and soon recovered. My TB went unrecognized. I had a whale of a time in London. I had spent very little money in India and my bank balance was higher than I had ever known it. I took a luxurious flat, entertained largely, and bought a Jaguar car. I also wrote two turnover articles for *The Times* on Indian broadcasting: and Philip Graves (I think) followed them with a leader. I put a strong case against the meanness and inertia of the Government of India. The articles caused a fluttering of many dovecotes, and the Government of India were silly enough to issue a formal communiqué, stating that 'they were not in agreement with the views of the writer'. They must have been fairly certain that the writer was myself, but *The Times* was silent as the grave about that, and Robin Barrington-Ward never gave me away. The *démenti* merely had the effect of focussing attention on the articles, and popularising them in India. Was I wrong to write them? Well, that is a debatable point. How far should the 'loyalty' of a civil servant extend?

I now felt very unwilling to return to India. Indeed the thought of it gave me a sinking sensation. This was a temporary aberration, and did not mean that I disliked India *per se*. It was a compound, I imagine, of ill-health, a distaste for further inevitable quarrels with Bokhari senior and the Government of India, an unenticing contrast between dreary Delhi and my gay London holiday, and, most of all, of a feeling that I had played my part, and it was over. I had given a rude shove and kick to All India Radio, which was maybe in the right direction, and maybe in the wrong one. But I was not temperamentally fitted for the steady push which was now required. I understood for the first time why Reith had got bored with the BBC. Pioneering is always fun, and seems worth while: organisations once formed are inevitably dreary, and the motive of action is lost. I endeavoured to put a buffer between my holiday and my return by arranging a motoring trip through Germany with my friends Patrick Baggallay and Harry Dakeyne. And it was a charming trip. Strangely enough, Germany in 1937 seemed to us extremely pleasant. After the war, a great deal was said to the effect that the people of Germany ought to have known what was going on and stopped it. All I can say is that we, as tourists, found only what seemed a very friendly, prosperous, and happy country. There was no sign of fear or cruelty. When I waved good-bye to my friends at the Munich airport, my heart was sinking: by the time I reached Athens, and nodded to Indian officials in the dreary dining-room of the Grande Bretagne, it was in the sole of my shoes. In melancholy mood, I drove myself from Jodhpur to Delhi, breaking down and getting stuck at Alwar *en route*, but avoiding a repetition of the horrible train.

I shall not linger over my two subsequent years in India: and you may be glad of that. I have painted the picture as I saw it and it did not greatly alter. All India Radio grew, and grew inevitably out of my control. I felt as if I were being slowly hoisted into a curtained howdah on the back of a swelling elephant. Pioneering days were over. I had done my utmost, with careful rules of promotion, to avoid the rise of clerks who knew nothing about programmes, and to keep rewards and prizes for those who possessed originality and vigour, however intractable their personalities might be. But I could not stop the growth of red tape or the accumulation of a deadly routine. Gradually I myself was swamped by problems such as the development of foreign broadcasts, the imminence of war and the attendant preparations, the maddening contracts with gramophone companies, the mass of Parliamentary questions, the welfare, housing, and pay of an increasing staff, the international quarrels about wave-lengths, the printing and circulation of radio publications, the tenders for new stations, the purchase of land for studios and transmitters, the question of acoustics, and the relations of All India Radio with Provincial Governments. These and many more such kept me chained to my desk. Earlier I had known every member of my staff, and his or her family history: now I hardly saw them after a brief encounter at a Selection Board, and even Selection Boards had to be held in my absence at outlying stations. I was being, so to speak, squeezed upwards and outwards, and I did not like it. More and more I tended towards isolation: and Advani, now Station Director at Delhi, dubbed me – not without justice – 'The Prisoner'.

Occasionally I played some little games with the Government. Sir Thomas Stewart, who had now become Governor of Bihar, rashly promised his Prime Minister that 'he would make Fielden give them a radio station'. The Government of India requested me to go to Patna and discuss it. I replied that such a journey would be useless: Patna did not, and could not, rate as a necessary centre under our five-year plan. The Government nevertheless replied that I must go to Patna 'if only to explain the Governor's promise'. I said that I would do no such thing. The Government then sent me a 'secret' letter (two envelopes and two seals, and common property of all the clerks) saying that I was 'ordered' to go to Patna. I went to bed, and said I had malaria. My clerks brought me the Council files, which said: 'The Controller of Broadcasting is being obstinately disobedient.' Another secret letter arrived, stating that I should proceed to Patna as soon as my health permitted. I proceeded. It was a twenty-four hour journey. At Patna I was met by the Prime Minister, his Cabinet, and a lot of his friends. We adjourned to his house for a merry dinner. I was asked to make a speech. I stated the facts, i.e, that Patna would be 'covered' by the new Calcutta station, that I had no money for another, and that I would gladly build one if the Prime Minister would give me the cash. My train left at midnight and I repeated the twenty-four-hour journey. Next morning the Indian papers were full of my speech – with an acid comment from the Patna Government that the Governor had promised something he could not fulfil. The Government of India sent me a secret and angry letter saying that I was forbidden to 'give any more interviews to journalists'. I replied that I hadn't done so in the Patna case, since I had not opened my mouth except in the Prime Minister's house: but that I was delighted to be freed from journalistic interviews and would in future tell all journalists that the Government did not allow me to speak to them. A furious secret letter came back saying that I was 'deliberately misinterpreting' what had been said, and that I was of course free to give interviews, but that *'I must not speak on matters of policy'*. To that I replied rudely that whatever I said must inevitably be a matter of policy. A week later I went down to Madras. The Editor of the *Madras Mail,* an amusing fellow (and English), wanted to know what I was going to do in South India. I said smugly that the Government of India did not permit me to speak on matters of policy. Next day this was all over India. The Government sent me a Letter of Censure. A Letter of Censure was, for the Civil Service, a dreaded instrument: it blocked all promotion and titles. Since I wasn't interested in titles or promotion, I sent back the rudest letter I could write, saying that I should be delighted to have ten thousand letters of censure, and they would not alter my point of view about the Government's stupidity.

A more comic incident occurred when one of my Station Directors decided to have a series of talks on the butterflies of India. It happened that an English civil servant, then retired, had made himself an expert on these, and my Station Director, quite rightly, wrote to him in England asking if he would record a talk. This old gentleman – and it was typical of the ICS – was infuriated by the letter, and sent it to the India Office in London, asking how on earth it came about that *an Indian* was allowed to write to him directly, instead of the British Head of the Department. The India Office took the matter most seriously, and it was passed from office to office in that building, with queries and counter-queries as to what Indian broadcasting was, and who I was, and where the butterflies came in. When it reached the Government of India, it was already a formidable file: and, of course, the series of talks had long finished. The Government of India added to it at great length ('*Is* a Station Director of AIR entitled to write to anyone in England? Your comments, please.'). When, eventually, it reached me, I wrote on it: 'The only answer to all this nonsense is the plural of two globular objects.' And I made assurance doubly sure by getting hold of the Viceregal file, and writing the same remark on it. My clerks, of course, never knew what it meant. The Government of India (in a secret letter) said that I was to remove it from the files. I said that I would resign sooner. Nothing more was heard. I hope that it still exists.

I had, when I arrived, decided that I would not, like other Heads of Departments, spend the months of April-October in Simla. It was of course a fairly natural thing to do: most departments could be 'run' from Simla, and their staffs thus escaped summer on the plains. But it was clearly impractical for broadcasting, and especially for broadcasting in its initial stages. I had to be on the spot: indeed I had quite often to take the place of the announcer. I was told that I should be ill if I stayed in the plains in summer: and I was agreeably surprised to find, in 1936, that this was quite untrue. When the thermometer rose to 122° in the shade, I found it an amusing new experience, and managed to get through my work quite well. But as one summer succeeded another, I got on much worse. I don't know if this is a general rule, and whether (as I have been told) the blood gets thinned and one is less able to stand the heat. Or maybe my general health deteriorated. In any case, by the summer of 1939 I was finding Delhi almost impossible to take. The day did not matter so much: it was the night, when the temperature remained above 100°, which was ruinous. It was not possible to sleep in or on a bed: one had to stretch oneself on the ground on a bit of rush matting. The blazing gold and scarlet of the gold mohur trees (whose orchidaceous flowers, when you pick them, stink like rotten meat), and the repeated piercing cry of the brain-fever bird, became symbols of nightmare. In June 1939 ill-health began to interfere with my work, and the Indian doctors thought that I should have an abdominal operation. I therefore asked the Government for medical leave, which was granted. I felt too queasy (which now seems absurd) to face the air journey, and decided to go by sea. I had a faint feeling that war would be declared before I could return, but I did not think very clearly about anything. In any case all the arrangements had been made for that eventuality. And I had no doubt that All India Radio could get along very well without me: I was not indispensable. In short, as Samuel Butler remarked, just as confidence breeds power, so the want of it breeds impotence. In India I had lost confidence not only in England and the West, but also, and seriously, in myself. Four years of hard labour had produced fourteen transmitters and a competent staff – and in four years the four hundred million people of India had bought exactly eighty five thousand wireless sets. It was enough to make a cat laugh. It was the biggest flop of all time.

Chapter Five

WAKING IN A cloud of chloroform in St Thomas's Hospital, I found by my bedside a long official envelope, and in it a marathon of a letter. It was addressed from 6 Burlington Gardens and dated 1st August 1939: signed A. P. Waterfield. Accustomed by this time to official letters, I looked at the end first. It ran as follows:

'*Accordingly, we decided to ask the Government of India if they would lend you to us, if you were willing to come, for this purpose and under these conditions, for a few weeks beginning on September 1st, which we chose since some of us hope to be away on holiday during a part of August.*'

Fateful days for holidays.

'*The telegram containing this message went off on 16th June, and the Government of India have replied that they have no objection, if you are willing, but that in fact you left India on the same day on medical leave and may require an operation which would incapacitate you for three weeks. I suggest therefore that, if the suggestion appeals to you, and your health permits, you should, when you get this letter, get into touch with Sir Campbell Stuart and Ivison Macadam, both of whom I believe you know. I should hope that, after you have had a talk with them, you will be able to judge whether you would like to help us in this way and under these conditions, for a few weeks, preferably from September 1st onwards, if your health then permits: and I shall be glad if you will let me know your decision as soon as possible, so that I may let the Government of India know, through the India Office.*'

Evidently the letter offered some excuse for me to remain for a time in England, and, at this moment of crisis, the thought was welcome. But what precisely was I expected to do? I turned back to the earlier part of the letter.

'*In the light of these facts, we reached two conclusions. First, that we should in all probability need to employ a man with broadcasting experience in the Ministry, but until we had made further progress with our planning it would be difficult to say exactly what qualifications we should need to look for in the holder of this appointment. And secondly, that the best plan would be to invite someone with such experience to come and help us for a short time on our planning work, without either side being committed to offer or accept a whole-time appointment in the Ministry in the Event of War.*'

August 1939. In the Event of War. Under these conditions. Further progress with our planning. No commitments. Exactly what qualifications? A short time. Difficult to say exactly. My thoughts went back to Italy, Germany, Russia. Would they be writing such letters? But I was still in a haze: a chloroform haze, perhaps. I turned back to the letter again.

'*On the one hand, we shall have close and constant contact with the* BBC, *who will remain constitutionally independent, but will naturally act under Government instructions . . .*'

H'm.

'*. . . so far as may be necessary, in matters that concern the national interest and the conduct of the war . . .*'

No doubt about war, then? I could not believe it.

'*. . . our position in relation to them will more or less resemble that of the Foreign Office and Colonial Office today. That is, we shall be concerned with the general principles of publicity in war-time . . .*'

Principles?

'*. . . including the supply of news and publicity material and the censorship: they will be concerned with the problem of how best to convey such material to the listener by means of broadcasting technique, in which we should not seek to interfere.*'

But I should. My experience was not with supply, but with the presentation of supply. The letter did not enthuse me. On the other hand, I knew that Waterfield was an amiable and conscientious man: under this official verbiage might lurk an opportunity worth pursuing. Not that I was consciously pursuing anything very much: like many others, I was trapped by the thunderous future.

Scent proved very poor in my hunt for Campbell Stuart and

Ivison Macadam. Covert after covert was drawn in vain. Either they were away, or unavailable, or engaged in some hush-hush conference. Finally cornered, they gave me a cool, not to say frigid, reception. Vague hints of their own burdens and anxieties were conveyed to me: but they were not disposed to speak of Waterfield or of me. What was I to Waterfield, or Waterfield to them? I never did discover. I could only pursue Waterfield.

Waterfield was not elusive, but he was surrounded by a dense crowd of aspirants to posts in the Ministry of Information. Last of the queue, I staggered into his office at seven o'clock one evening. I found an exhausted and harassed man: and no wonder. He was Britain's answer to Goebbels, and without plans. I could only feel sorry that I had burdened him with yet another useless interview.

Courteous though weary, he shook me warmly by the hand, and said: 'Ah, you are a man of ideas, and we need them badly.' I asked: 'But *what* ideas?' 'Anything, my dear fellow, anything.' Suddenly I realized that he was repeating a formula: and that he had not the slightest notion who I was. 'Ideas about India?' I queried. 'Certainly about India, if you like.' Suddenly he dived across the room and opened a cupboard, from which a mass of files fell to the floor. 'I think we have something about India here.' 'Shall I write down some ideas about publicity in India, press, radio, cinema, and so on?' I asked. 'Yes, do be a good chap and do that.' I left hurriedly, feeling that he was overdue for a drink and dinner. I was overdue for them myself.

I was told next day that seventy-one Directors of the Ministry of Information had been appointed. (I believe it was really only half a dozen, but anything seemed possible at the time). Among them was Harry Hodson, who became Director of Empire Publicity, or some such title. I wrote, as best I could, my ideas about publicity in India. I doubt if anyone ever read it. I took it to Harry in Belgrave Square, and there discovered quite a large nest of Indian civil servants and businessmen, also writing memoranda. Sour grapes, I don't deny, were not far from me. Hodson, it was clear, did not relish my presence, but he handed me a letter from Waterfield, who, he said, would like to see me at once.

In a taxi I read Waterfield's note. It was courteous, even affable. No doubt, it said, I must be worried about my position, and whether I should return to India or not. He and Lord Perth, it said, 'were trying to fit me in'. Would I come across and see him? I thought to myself, as we passed the Ritz, do I want to be fitted in? Perhaps I have no alternative, said Piccadilly Circus. The Indian business is over: you have fought too much with the Government of India, and in wartime it will be worse. But, said Shaftesbury Avenue, it will be worse here too: there is sunshine and space in India: here there are only seventy-two directors. Give it all up and buy a nice farm, said Bedford Square. But the towering grey Senate House frowned down at me, and said that I had no money, and money is power, and power was what I liked. All these people scuttling about the polished floors were in the race for money and power, and why should I be left out? My little taste of power had corrupted me.

Waterfield, who now appeared calmer, informed me that Sir Findlater Stewart had been appointed Director General of the Ministry. That, as far as I was concerned, was a stunner. Sir Findlater was a typical civil servant – he was Permanent Secretary at the India Office – and wouldn't care for my type at all. Moreover, I had been at loggerheads with his brother, Sir Thomas, in India. Fate had dealt me a poor hand. Apart from that, I thought (and still think) that the appointment was a queer one. For propaganda you needed a Beaverbrook, a Reith, a Priestley, a Coward – surely not a civil servant. But these thoughts were swept away by Waterfield's next announcement.

He said that they had been considering me for the post of Chief of Broadcasting in the Ministry, but had come to the conclusion that the post must be filled by someone who knew nothing about broadcasting. 'We don't want friction, you see.' I must confess that I had hoped that some such task might fall to me: opportunity fell with a dull thud into the past. Waterfield said that they had appointed Sir Kenneth Lee, the Chairman of Tootal Broadhurst. Later I saw Sir Kenneth, a charming man, and found that he ably fulfilled Waterfield's ideas about broadcasting. He asked me rather tepidly whether I would stay and help him.

It was time, I concluded, to book my passage to India. There at least I could work out the last seven months of my contract, and I should not be idle.

But, before leaving, I started a grand quarrel with the BBC and the India Office. I was convinced that the Germans would start a short-wave service to India, and that, since my own medium-wave transmitters could not compete with it, a similar service must be started by the BBC. This was a complicated engineering matter, which arose chiefly from the fact that, in the absence of any manufacture of cheap medium-wave sets in India, all sets were geared to short as well as medium wave. Short waves jump considerable distances, and are best received from far away. It was obvious that a German service which made fun of the British Raj, would be an instant success. But neither the BBC nor the India Office would have anything to do with it. I persuaded Waldorf Astor to ask a question in the House of Lords. That put everyone into a tizzy. I was summoned to the India Office, and stated my views to an assembly of old gentlemen who had never listened to any radio. They said, with some spleen, that they would cable to the Government of India. I retorted that the Government of India was illiterate about broadcasting: and in due course that Government sent a cable to say that Fielden was, as usual, being an alarmist. The only thing that I could do was to ask Hilda Matheson, who had started an organisation for the recording of English life and English aims, to take a few Indians on her staff. Hilda, as always, did not fail me.

I flew back to India in a mood of dejection and discouragement. It was a strange flight, with windows talc-frosted (in case we were spies, I suppose), and a descent on, of all places, the Sea of Galilee. I did not wonder what Jesus would have thought about his Christian followers: even after 1940 years, his teachings were clear enough.

Chapter Six

The Congress has further laid down that the issue of war and peace for India must be decided by the Indian people, and no outside authority can impose this decision upon them, nor can the Indian people permit their resources to be exploited for Imperialist ends.

STATEMENT BY THE CONGRESS WORKING COMMITTEE 1939

To ESCAPE FROM winter, wartime, austerity and muddle in England to the remote and sunlit places of India was one thing: to discover the political effects of war in India was quite another. The Government of India was entirely chairborne: and, as we all know, nobody is so bellicose as the gentleman behind the comfortable and distant desk. And when civil servants are presented with coloured labels printed with the words 'Very Secret' or 'Most Secret' or 'Top Secret' or even just 'Secret', you may be sure that such labels will be multiplied as recklessly as chips in a game of poker. Very soon it became, more or less, necessary to convene a Committee to decide whether the Viceroy's visit to Baroda for a tiger-hunt should be treated as 'Most Secret' or 'Top Secret'. Since it was obvious, my dear chap, that the Enemy (pretty well engaged in Poland just then) should *never* knew how many valves All India Radio held in reserve, or how many staff it employed, all telegrams – whether to say that the Station Director was down with malaria, or a new microphone was required – had to be in cypher. The cypher was complicated enough (at least I thought so) to test any Senior Wrangler: once a month a Top Secret Messenger arrived to present me with a *Top* Secret Envelope (with five seals, all doubtless opened by the clerks *en route*) which gave me the new *Word* of the month, and by that word alone the cypher could be decyphered. A. S. Bokhari and I alone could know it. The result was that Ahmed Shah and I spent many hilarious (and sometimes angry) nights endeavouring to pluck some meaning from groups of figures which probably meant 'Roof of studio three in need of repair: please sanction expenditure of Rs. 400' but, since the Station Director, poor devil, often got a letter wrong, might come out as 'Goon ka foodle brhaa to seen' or something of the sort: and thus, after

· a few hours of hopeless work, we should be obliged to send another (of course encyphered) telegram back, saying 'Don't understand: please repeat' – and I don't doubt that we also got this wrong sometimes. Work was a good deal multiplied. Among other things a meeting was convened at which I was solemnly asked whether I could 'guarantee that none of my artists would send, in songs, plays, or talks, Messages to the Enemy'. I could only reply that I had upwards of 3,000 regularly employed artists on my lists, and that I could not guarantee one of them. Fortunately for me, the Army was present at this meeting, and the Army was entirely reasonable, and even very much on my side. Had it not been so, broadcasting in India might have been shut down for the duration of the war: that had been contemplated. And there was, no doubt, a logical argument for that from a British strategic point of view: if we were to hold India by force for the duration of the war, there could be no sort of certainty (as in a homogeneous country like England) that radio would not be used for seditious ends. And this thought made it necessary to have soldiers to 'guard' the transmitters and studios, and, naturally, to institute 'passes' which everybody forgot or lost, and which in any case were seldom understood by the 'guards' and could very easily be forged. But these and other wartime measures were as nothing compared to the political upheaval.

On the 15th of September 1939, the Indian Congress Working Committee issued a statement which – at any rate to me – seemed reasonable, eloquent, and moving. The gist of it was that if England, as it was said, had embarked on a war 'for freedom', the freedom of India was part of it. I doubt if anyone, reading that statement today, could find anything amiss with it. The Viceroy's reply was long delayed, and, when it eventually materialised, was so vague as to be almost incomprehensible. These two statements threw me into a crusading mania which excluded almost everything else from my mind. I was convinced (as indeed I am still convinced today) that we could have come to terms with Indian nationalism with the happiest results. Our case for refusing independence to India rested on four main points. First, the hoary old argument that India was 'not yet fit for self-government'. Second, that we could, much more easily than under an independent Indian government, attract Indian soldiers by high rates of pay. Third, that an independent Indian government might easily decide to 'go over' to the Enemy. And fourth, Mr Jinnah.

All these arguments were shaky, even if a logical case might be made out for any of them. The first argument was sheer nonsense. India had had four years of the 1935 Act, and the Provincial Governments had functioned very well. There was a large nucleus of trained Indians in the ics. And only a fool could say that the Viceroy and his Council were more intelligent or capable than the very distinguished men of the Indian Congress. The second argument was more telling. Since the British Raj had left the 700,000 villages of India in a state of misery and near-starvation, it was obvious enough that regular pay and good conditions would attract a large percentage of India's millions, and that they would no more care what they were fighting for than a mason would care what kind of architecture his daily stint of bricks was making. (And indeed, the Indian forces fought with extreme gallantry during the war, and never, as far as I could make out when I talked to them, had the remotest idea what they were fighting for.) A good case could be made out for the third argument, but it was based on a misconception of the Indian point of view. India was not friendly to Britain, while Britain held her in subjection: it did not follow that India welcomed subjection by other countries. Gandhi, of course, might well have wished to turn India into a larger Switzerland, and to welcome all nations as guests but none as rulers: at the same time, he, like other Congress leaders, was powerfully affected by English language and English habits, and was not in the least deluded about German or Japanese aims. Nor were any of the others. It is worth remembering that Nehru was the one and only statesman who, passing through Rome, deliberately rejected an invitation from Mussolini. So far as I know, there was not a Congress leader who would have 'gone over to the enemy', with the sole exception of Subash Chandra Bose, who came to an unhappy end in Japan. The fourth and last argument was the worst of all. Jinnah had presented the British Government with the perfect instrument of Divide and Rule. Once a Congress leader, he had quarrelled with the Congress and made himself a Saviour of Muslims against Hindus. India could not have independence, according to Jinnah, until the races were divided. This suited the British Raj perfectly. I knew Jinnah well, and the remarks made by Mr Attlee, in a television interview in 1958 (which caused such indignation in Pakistan) seem to me perfectly just. He was an agreeable, well-dressed, shrewd and capable small-town lawyer, and he was very little more. Circumstances presented him with a unique opportunity to climb the ladder of fame on the rungs of a religion to which he was completely indifferent: and he climbed. I did not dislike Jinnah: on the contrary, I found him delightful. But to erect a great mausoleum to him, to which thousands ascend on bended knees, calling him a Saint, is about as ludicrous as to do the same for, say, Sir Roger Casement – who, probably, was as good and sincere a man in his way. Jinnah, through egoism and self-importance, did great harm. And the British Raj did no less. The massacres of 1947 were prepared in 1939.

I was in an awkward position. Whatever my political beliefs were, I could not use All India Radio to further them. That would have been treason (whatever treason may mean). I don't think it even occurred to me to do so. It would hardly have been practicable: it would certainly have been dishonest. At the same time I felt that it was urgently necessary that some sort of bridge of understanding should be made between the British Government and Indian nationalists. And there were some weak signs that this was not impossible. Sir Andrew Clow asked me (and this was revolutionary) whether I could 'bring Nehru to see him'. I arranged this, and, as far as I can remember, Edward Thompson drove us to have tea in the Clow house. That tea was a terrible business. Lady Clow made bright conversation about the weather, and Nehru sat looking incredibly gloomy, and wearing, I can't help thinking purposely, just about the most threadbare old *ajkhan* I have ever seen. It was obvious that a cat and dog would have got on better than Clow and Nehru. And yet, today, I am as sure as I was then that if England had risen nobly to her opportunity, not only should we have had a far more powerful (and less troublesome) war ally in India, but also a much greater friend in later times. At the time of which I am writing, Sir Stafford Cripps came out to India, and appeared to feel exactly as I did. But, of course, he was then in the Opposition. When, in 1942, he came out again as a Member of the Government, he *said* the same things, but either failed or was not permitted to act upon them. In a broadcast from New Delhi on March 30th 1942, Sir Stafford said, among other things: 'it is for the Indian people, *and not for any outside authority,* to discuss and decide their future constitution. We shall *look on with deep interest* and hope that your wisdom will guide you truly in this great adventure.' But in fact, since the British Government never believed that 'their wisdom' would guide them truly, unless they decided to remain a subservient colony, these words meant nothing: perhaps Cripps thought that they did. In any case the opportunity was missed, and India had to go the way of massacre and partition. And so, between 1939 and 1943, I became obsessed by the idea of immediate Indian independence, and this greatly affected and confused my thoughts and actions – confused, because, as was natural, I was no less obsessed by the necessity that England should win the war. It seemed to me that there was little to choose between, say, Hitler in Sudetenland and England in India. I wished that we could be wiser.

Suddenly, as I had – not with great intelligence – prophesied, Germany started up a powerful programme in Indian languages. The Germans had a beautiful and easy target. They could make common cause with the Nationalists, laugh at the 'freedom' which we failed to give, caricature the Viceroy and Government, make fun of the topheavy bureaucracy, and point to all the muddles of Mr Chamberlain. The effect in India was instantaneous and smashing. Indians quite naturally found German rudeness (and, I must say, German music) much more entertaining than what All India Radio could provide. The Viceroy and his Council were alarmed, and the first thing that they did was to cable London to the effect that Sir Zafrullah Khan, who was there, should make an immediate answer on the BBC. That was the measure of their ignorance of radio. Obviously Zafrullah, witty man though he was, couldn't replace, or even answer, a daily programme. So eventually – and perhaps it was my one triumph in India – a cable went forth from Delhi, drafted by Maxwell, the Home Secretary, which contained the extraordinary words; 'Fielden was right, and we were wrong,' and asked for an immediate regular Indian service from the BBC. There followed an acrimonious correspondence, because the BBC was not prepared to abandon its position. But it had to yield. It then became a question of how an Indian section should be constituted. I had by then got one or two trained Indians with Hilda Matheson, so a nucleus was there. But who was to command it? The BBC sent to the Viceroy a list composed entirely of retired Indian Governors, hardly any one of whom had ever listened to a radio. Even the Viceroy was appalled. He asked me whether I would go. That was a 64,000 dollar question. I knew that I should not be welcomed: I had, so to speak, started all the trouble. But what could I do? I said that, if he thought fit, I would go to organise it, but that I thought it should be controlled by an Indian. A long cable was sent by the Government of India to the BBC, to the effect that the Government of India considered that I was the one suitable Englishman: as indeed I was. The BBC refused flatly. This, after what I had done – however little – for broadcasting both in England and in India, came as a shock to me. I had not realized that I was so hated. The Viceroy sent for me again, and said that, 'as the BBC seemed so keen on titles', we might perhaps find somebody titled in India who would work with me. I agreed, though with a sinking heart. Sir Malcolm Darling was summoned to Delhi. Sir Malcolm was (and is) a man of great charm, intelligence, and kindness: unfortunately – though I did not realize it at the time, – he has a strong jingoistic streak which at times makes him subscribe to the policy of 'my country right or wrong'. He had had a splendid career in India, and had written two remarkable books about it: nobody could say that he did not know India, and nobody could say that he didn't love it. But at the bottom of his heart he believed (so it seems to me, and he has since been to stay with me in Italy) that India should be governed by the British: and this was a fatal gap between us. In our conversations with the Viceroy, I did not tumble to this: I thought Sir Malcolm enchanting, and on his side he assured me that he would leave programmes to me. And so, not without great reluctance on the part of the BBC, it was agreed that the section should be run with Sir Malcolm as Head, and with me as Editor. I was, of course, a colossal fool to agree. But I was bemused, as I have said, by the idea of Indian independence, and I thought that I might serve it in this way. Quite apart from that, I saw no future for myself in the fights which would undoubtedly occur in India. Reasons are seldom clear-cut: I daresay I had many selfish interests. In any case, this put *finis* to my Indian days.

I left India late in April 1940. The signs were threatening enough. Our KLM air-liner could go no further than Naples: and Italy was on the brink of war. I had tried, so far as I was able, to keep my departure from India secret: once divulged, it would inevitably involve me in parties, presentations, and emotional occasions, sincere or insincere, which I wished to avoid. Nevertheless, the Station Directors of AIR clubbed together to present me with an imaginative and touching gift: and at Lahore Rashid Ahmed and Din Tyabji (now a seasoned Ambassador of India) gave me the most beautiful party I have ever attended in the Shalimar Gardens, with millions of tapers twinkling along the still lakes. I travelled to Karachi alone. No trumpets sounded for me there, nor, as you can guess, on the other side.

Chapter Seven

Poor fellow! He has done his best, but what does a fish's best come to when the fish is out of water?

SAMUEL BUTLER - THE WAY OF ALL FLESH

It seems to me ... that the character of war has changed in our time ... We have made it not merely a means to something, but once we are in it an end in itself — a religion and a god, in whose service anything is proper except to lose it: a very jealous god to whom we are prepared to sacrifice everything, even the very principles for which we are fighting ... So at the end we are a little disillusioned to find ourselves suddenly without any god at all, only a dead war.

HOWARD CLEWES — AN EPITAPH FOR LOVE

LONDON IN 1940. The black-out. Is it really necessary to stumble around like this, and hide behind black curtains? How much, really, is the value of supposed safety against the depreciation of psychological depression? Daylight raids don't seem frightening. Is it supposed that, even in a lighted city, aeroplanes at 20,000 feet can hit Downing Street or Buckingham Palace? And what matter if they did? Wasn't there some sort of argument in favour of lighting your cities gaily, and dowsing your factories? And then, evacuees all over the countryside, making hell of it and ruining it: and getting sick of it. Food gradually getting worse: inevitable that, in an island with too many people and too few ships: but still, not gay. Dunkirk and a sense of despair. Blood and tears and toil and sweat. Backs to the wall. Growing hypocrisy. The blitz. Squalor. Noisy sleepless nights. Churchill talking from Agincourt. Long dusty office days: evenings with the stirrup pump and the ambulance. Not really a way in which one would have chosen to spend a part of this brief journey from cradle to grave. And what was it all in aid of? Hitler and his gang were international highwaymen, no doubt: but you don't make the roads safer by tearing them all up, and killing most of the road-users. Hitler, it might be said – probably inaccurately – had killed a million Jews: however that might be, the situation isn't improved by killing ten million Gentiles. Wars are futile. Who can like a world ruled by fear and bad temper?

Nevertheless a lot of people did, and perhaps always will. The English, when roused, are a bellicose race. Many for whom peace was a dull and dreary routine, with few rewards, found a new glamour in life. Purpose, which had been vacillating in the twenties and thirties, found a new aim. Win the war: quite simple. Don't bother about anything else. Eric Maschwitz, over a cocktail at the Café Royal, said to grumbling me: 'But, Lionel, it's *wonderful* to live at such a time! The Great Blank Page of the Future! Think of it!' I thought of it, and was not comforted.

My assigment to the BBC, which lasted for just six months, was exactly what, had I not been such a dunce, I might have expected it to be. The authorities had not wanted me and did not like me. I could not admire 'Freddy' Ogilvie, the new Director-General. I had never been friendly with Sir Stephen Tallents, now Director of Overseas Programmes. However, these did not greatly matter: they were generally lost in Olympian clouds. What mattered more was that I felt like an unwelcome stranger in the BBC. The staff had increased and changed enormously since I had gone to India: once I had known nearly all of them: now I knew surprisingly few. I felt rather as if I had been transferred from the Travellers Club to the RAC. It wasn't exactly bad: but it was strange. And I, probably, was regarded as a former Director-General, who would put on airs: perhaps I did put on airs. (And who cared twopence about India, anyway?) As second-in-command of a tiny Indian section, I was a nobody: and it's quite difficult for any of us to come down to being a Nobody, if we have been a Somebody Somewhere. Maybe it is very good for us. After a good deal of unpleasant fighting, Zulfaqar and I managed to start a service to India just before the Hitler offensive of May 1940. We had made a careful study of the German broadcasts to India, and the means of offsetting them. Of course, when you are on the losing side, your propaganda is always lame, as became evident in the German broadcasts at the end of the war. The Indian staff in London, however, knew their India: and I still think that the service which we started then was on the right lines – which does not, of course, mean that it had anything to do with BBC dignity and restraint. It was rude and lively. But when

Sir Malcolm Darling, who had been dallying in India, reached England about ten days later, he made it clear that this would not do at all. And who shall blame him? Rightly or wrongly, he thought that English broadcasting should be courteous and non-committal: and he wished to stand well with Authority, as represented by Ogilvie, Tallents, and the India Office. I was the nigger in the woodpile. Even the Indian staff – aware that I was a much lesser person in England than in India, and rather enjoying the excitements of London – did not greatly care about the quality of our programmes. I became a useless fool, and in November 1940 I resigned. Mr Ogilvie – or was he Sir Frederick? – said: 'I am afraid I have no option but to accept your resignation.' That was that. Philip Jordan, a friendly soul, wrote a searing article in the *News Chronicle*, saying that I was right and Ogilvie wrong: Harold Nicolson said that I was 'much too passionate'; and so I passed into oblivion.

One small incident, which probably affected my future, occurred in these months. A certain Major Harrison had been imported into the BBC as 'War Office Adviser' – or something of the sort. I was infuriated by the very idea of War Office Advisers. I was rude to Cecil Harrison on every possible occasion. The ruder I was, the more he liked me. I cannot imagine how he tolerated me at all. Perhaps I amused him: certainly the feeblest joke might have seemed funny in Pompous Portland Place. People are fond of saying that the BBC did a magnificent job in the war: but, with the exception of Tommy Handley and the Brains Trust, there were few outstanding programmes. The Indian service, on which I had pinned so many hopes, degenerated into a bad Hindustani translation of English news bulletins (incomprehensible to most Indians) with nice dashes of English music-hall. Am I biased? I am.

On the day after I departed, unwept and unhonoured, from the BBC, I joined the Ministry of Food, towards which Howard Marshall had been insistently beckoning me for some time. I had a crazy idea that, as a not very convinced belligerent, I might do better at alleviating hardship than in creating it. It proved to be an uninspiring affair. Lord Woolton was pleasant and at times charming: at the time of my arrival he was considerably frightened by Churchill, who used to send him the usual 'half-sheets of notepaper' saying that 'the British working man must have his steak', while at the same time allowing Beaverbrook to seize all the available storage space in the country for aeroplane odds and ends, thus keeping about fifty food ships waiting in the Bristol Channel. Woolton must have had a difficult time. But he was never criticized. In his memoirs he says that this was due to the fact that he had lunch at the Ritz with Lord Kemsley. I very much doubt it. As far as I know (which of course may not be very far) it was due to the fact that the Ministry of Food paid the press some £10,000 a week for food advertisements, and no paper would risk this lovely advertising revenue by criticism. When, later, I wrote a 'profile' of Woolton for the *Observer*, I mentioned this fact, but he would not let me print it. Quite right: in his place I should have done the same. In the Ministry of Food I gathered, among other things, an odd assortment of people, including Lilian Braithwaite, Jeanne de Casalis and Evelyn Laye, who cheerfully got up at 2 a.m. to travel uncomfortably to hideous places and proclaim with hideous untruth that a carrot a day made you see perfectly in pitch-black darkness, or that a Woolton Pie was the ultimate triumph of a cordon-bleu chef. I also had the good fortune to meet Lettice Cooper, the novelist, who had the unenviable task of answering the multitude of letters which poured in to Lord Woolton. ('Lord Woolton is greatly concerned about the state of your canary, and recommends . . .') She was about the only person in the whole great building who had and kept an excellent sense of humour, and she more or less saved my life and reason, and turned into a lifelong friend. I scarcely know how she saved her own reason at times: among her letters I remember one which included a long and scholarly argument for throwing into the sea the bodies of people killed in the blitz, thus fattening the fish and improving Britain's food supplies. I drew in the charming Margery Locket and Pamela Frankau to work with her and it was quite a gay party. But it seemed a more and more futile one to me, and after six months, I had enough bad temper, and a small excuse, to get myself out. The excuse was provided by Robin Whitworth, a charming and intelligent person whom the BBC had thrown out for being a Conscientious Objector, and who applied to me for a job. I thought that the Ministry of Food was the very place for Conscientious Objectors, but Lord Woolton did not. So I swept out in a fury. On the next day I joined the Ministry of Aircraft Production, where my friend Stephen King-Hall had been roped in to do a report on what I can only call the Mental State of Workers in Factories, with recommendations as to An Increase of Productivity. (I seem to have heard these words quite often.) He wanted me to do some running around which he had not time to do himself. But I cannot now go on with ministries, which are fearful things at the best of times: and I shall pay a visit to my aunts. My aunts are really much better fun than any ministry.

At this time, 1940, I had three Fielden aunts living. They were Una, who was eighty-five, Sarah (whom you have met before) who was seventy-eight, and Beatrice who was a mere seventy-five. They all had that peculiar toughness which seems to be characteristic of mid-Victorian England. Was it upbringing, good constitution, absence of worry, or what? Una was destined to live to a hundred, and both the others far into their nineties. They were neither very rich nor very poor: I imagine they each had about £1,200 a year. Sarah and Beatrice had been married: Una was a robust and unrepentant spinster. Una had an exquisite little house in Alexander Square: Beatrice had a flat in Albert Gate: Sarah lived at Eastbourne, where she worked madly on a beautiful garden (and could exhaust any guest) and did a lot of quiet good works. All three got direct hits from Hitler, and emerged scatheless and quite unshaken. When Aunt Una's house was reduced to rubble, and she had been extricated from the ruins, she merely said: 'My word, that was the hell of a bang!' Beatrice was considerably annoyed, and said that Hitler must be made to pay for her Egyptian collection. Neither of them could be induced to leave London. As for Sarah, she had returned from Sunday morning service and was reading in her drawing-room when the bomb fell on the house. Her cook and maid were taken to hospital, but, although the windows of the drawing-room and all the glass-fronted book-cases were blown out, Aunt Sally received not a scratch, and, politely declining the neighbours' offers of assistance and lunch, made herself cheese sandwiches in the shattered kitchen. When I saw her that evening in London, and asked her how on earth she had escaped, she said tranquilly 'My dear, I think it was the Service: we had a particularly nice Service this morning.' She moved without any fuss into a new house, concentrated with delight on a new garden, and was very pleased with the price she got for the ruins.

Una and Beatrice, homeless, presented me with a problem, and in my spare moments I ran around hunting for a flat for them. They had to live together: that was inescapable, though neither relished the idea. Flat-hunting was difficult, if only because one had to make as sure as possible that the premises were not going to be requisitioned by the armed forces or the civil service. Indeed, in spite of all my care, they were ousted in a month from a flat I had taken for them in Hyde Park Gate. Eventually I established them in an attic flat in Sloane Street, and in this they lived happily until they died in the fifties. I used to go to see them very constantly. I used to find the flat frightening. At the height of the blitz, bombs seemed to be rushing about all over the roof. Una would insist on playing backgammon, and, when I ducked under the table, would say 'Your move – what on earth are you looking for?' Beatrice would discuss Browning or Bergson, and lift surprised eyebrows if I jumped at a particularly loud bang. 'Aren't you feeling well, dear?' These old ladies were certainly a tonic.

Some ten years later, Beatrice, then eighty-five (Una being a gay ninety-five), wrote some memoirs of her life. I tried, but lamentably failed, to get them published: and I was sad about this, not only because it would have pleased her, but also because I thought them striking. My own writings may share the same fate, but if they do not, I think it is not out of place to include some of hers here. They are an authentic description of a life now almost forgotten.

'I was born in 1866 – a long, long time ago. In the years that have passed, I have lived through peace and great wars, and a bloodless revolution.

No wonder if we are all dazed and puzzled and have lost some of our balance in all these happenings. Let us hope that our suffering will eventually be for the good of mankind, though we may well regret the passing of so much that was good and noble in the past and the greater freedom we then possessed, which has perhaps gone for ever.

In the days of my youth we could travel all over the continent without passports or visas, and could take what money we needed for the journey without question, and though we had to pass through the Customs House on arrival, the examination was conducted with a friendly courtesy and apparently an inborn belief that most of us were honest folk.

We were, I think, more friendly with foreigners, in those days, than we are now, in spite of all the talking; we may have laughed at each other's manners and customs, but we believed in each other's sincerity where now we are full of doubt and suspicion. Should we believe then that in the New World people are less honest than they were? An unpleasant thought that points to the downfall of civilization rather than to its upraising, for honesty is the very life-blood of all friendship and understanding.

Rationing may be a necessity but under it the consumer has lost all his rights. Anything may be palmed off on him and he has no redress. The shops are not responsible for what they sell, and the Food Ministry is a bogy of indifference. A young butcher once offered me some bad looking beef, and when I remonstrated with him, he said "Take it or leave it."

"Then I will leave it," I replied. His surprise at my answer was ludicrous. He literally goggled with astonishment. He was of course young, and had not lived in the days when customers ha(still some rights and expected good service and civility.

Our happiness lies in our everyday freedom more than ou. politicians seem to realize. We should quote them the wise words of Chang in *Lost Horizon*.

"Ah, but you see we believe that to govern perfectly it is necessary to avoid governing too much."

These words should be printed in large type and hung up in the House of Commons for all the members to read and re-read.

My father was one of three brothers, rich cotton spinners living on the borders of Lancashire and Yorkshire. My grandfather was John Fielden, who carried the ten-hours bill through the House of Commons in the teeth of violent opposition. A man of great integrity and conviction and a sticker to the end. It was the first act of Parliament ever passed to help the workers. And let us remember that the ten-hours bill was only for the little children working in the mills and not for the men and women. A state of white slavery for children that it seems almost impossible to realize in these days.

I have in my possession the medal that was struck to commemorate the event; it is a small silver medal about the size of half-a-crown, with the head of Queen Victoria on one side and an engraving of a man and woman and two children in a room together on the other, representing a home perhaps.

There is an old family story that when the ten-hours bill was at last passed, my grandfather returned to Manchester, and rushing into the office where his brother, Joshua, sat at work, exclaimed: "I have finished it, Joshua, I have finished it!"

To which my great uncle Joshua, an astute and portly old gentleman, replied: "Finished it, John? Finished it? You mean you have only just begun it."

What my grandfather did in Parliament to further the cause, Richard Oastler did among the people, speaking and encouraging the workers to fight against the tyranny of their masters. He was called the Factory King for his labours and was adored by the workers. He must have been a very engaging and exceptional personality. When his wife died, a niece went to look after him until he died. As a dear little old lady she would sometimes come and stay with my mother, and as a child I used to enjoy some of the stories she told me of those exciting times. One story that remains fixed in my memory was of a great meeting Oastler organised at York where thousands of workers were to assemble on a certain day: some of them walking twenty and thirty miles to attend it, and how he promised them bread and beer on their arrival and how unfortunately their enemies, the mill owners, hearing of the meeting and the promise of food, bought up all the bread and beer in the town, so that when the weary marchers reached their meeting place, tired after their long march and many drenched to the skin, for it had been a stormy night, they were naturally furious to find the promised food not forthcoming. When Oastler arrived at the hotel he was told of what happened and advised by his helpers to keep away from the meeting, as in the present temper of the workers they feared he might by lynched. He refused to listen to such advice and went at once to the platform where he received a great ovation.

In the meantime he sent his helpers to the neighbouring towns and villages for the much needed bread and beer which eventually was found and distributed. At the end of the great meeting, Oastler, instead of riding home as he had intended, decided he would march at the head of the workers on their long tramp back. What as a child I used to listen for was the end of the story as told by his niece, who always finished the recital in the same words: "When we took off his socks we took off the soles of his feet too." A rather lurid description of bleeding and blistered feet which of course filled me with admiration for the hero.

I also have in my possession a letter from Richard Oastler written to my grandfather, John Fielden. It was written in December 1847, six months after the passing of the bill. It seems to have been written on account of a movement on the part of the mill-owners to try and repeal the ten-hours act. He writes: "And so, they are at work again! I gave them credit for more sense! Never mind, if we must have another try, I shall, if I meddle, be for *Eight* . . . Remember it is not I who have provoked the new strife, it is the mill-owners. If I do start I will hoist the banner of *eight Hours* and God will speed the right."

It was a great fight for a good cause and naturally I am proud to think that my grandfather, although a mill-owner like the rest, saw the evil of this child-slavery and determined to better it, if he could not abolish it. He installed the ten-hours day in his own mills long before it became law, determined to do what he thought was right if it was a monetary loss. Perhaps I should add as a moral to the story that John Fielden was a Unitarian – anathema to the Churches, yet it was he who did the work of mercy and not the other mill-owners who, no doubt, in those days attended Church regularly with their well-dressed families.

My ancestors were working men, spinning the cotton on hand-looms in their cottages like the rest of their neighbours. Evidently they were able and reliable spinners and honest hardworking men. When my greatgrandfather had finished a bale he strapped it on his back and walked twenty miles across the moors to the Manchester market. He was soon known there for his good spinning and honesty and the buyers would give him more for his bales than the other less competent spinners.

It was natural, perhaps, that the other spinners should suggest that he should sell all their bales of cotton for them. Whilst they would supply a trap to drive the bales to market, he was to sell them there. He tried to do so, but soon found himself in trouble as the spinning varied so much in quality and in the end he suggested to his fellow workers that they should all work together in a barn or room, so that he might see that the work was done properly, and help those who needed help in their work, so that they might do it more perfectly and more thoroughly, and thus took the first step towards the family cotton mills.

Honesty and commonsense seem to have been the great gifts of my ancestors. Gifts making for firm foundations on which to build. Commonsense not only teaches us how best to make use of the present, but seems to have a mysterious power to see into the future and its coming necessities.

To imagine we can build up a great new civilization on lying, stealing and murder, even if done for the State, as some would have us believe, is foolish thinking and as impossible of lasting success as trying to build on bog or sand. The end will be ruin however fair it looks to start with. Truth and wisdom are the only lasting foundations on which to build, nationally or individually, with any hope of success, and let us add the love of freedom to cement the whole together, and we shall all be able to rejoice at the result.'

The Fielden family, to judge from what history I have of them, must have been an obstinate and dogged lot. From about 1640 onward they were Quakers, and in 1683 Joshua Fielden of Inchfield, Rochdale, was fined for absence from church to the extent of fifteen shillings and fourpence: in the following year the church seized his bedding, worth five shillings: and in 1685 he was fined again and 'goods were taken, viz. a pewter and a Bible, worth seventeen shillings, to pay the fine.' They remained Quakers nevertheless. My aunts were clearly in the same tradition. They held strong beliefs: I was muddled.

So now, in 1941, I became a sort of Inspector of Factories, a situation which would have made my greatgrandfather howl in his grave, I should think. I knew absolutely nothing about factories. I travelled up and down the country and hated it, because train-services were bad, and factories almost always difficult to get at. It also seemed to me that Hitler decided to bomb whatever town I was in, and the Southampton blitz in particular reduced me to almost gibbering terror. The factories themselves seemed to me nightmarish: they were mostly lit by what was called 'daylight lighting' which made everybody look as if they had severe jaundice and a hangover. People were reduced to automata. I remember especially a woman whose job it was to examine the insides of gas shells. These were coated with a flesh-coloured preparation, and the coating had to be perfect. They were rolled down to her on an inclined plane, and she rapidly examined, and passed or rejected, them. I asked her to let me do it for a few minutes. Soon I staggered back, feeling that I was in a dream of whirling intestines. I asked her 'How long have you been doing this?' 'Two years.' 'You like it?' 'Suits me fine.' But others were not so well suited. After all the blah about our wonderful workers, it was odd to see that at 5.10 p.m. (hours of work being till 5.30) everyone was queueing up to go to the greyhound racing, or what have you. Overtime my foot. The British worker, as I saw him then, couldn't have cared less. It was also very noticeable that, on the whole, women did much better than men. They were much spryer, looked better, and seemed to do their jobs easily. The men looked haggard, and were sullen. I talked to many managers and shop stewards, and three points emerged clearly. First, a loss of pride in craftsmanship: repetitious jobs which he did not understand bored the worker. Second, much more interest in higher wages than in the war. Third, the ability of women to run a machine with half their mind, and think of a new hat, a dinner, and the children: and the anxiety of men to make machines do something different and more interesting. And of course there was a lot more too – transport, housing, canteens, temperatures, lectures, entertainments, and so on. An old story. A report was written. At that moment the Minister changed, and the report went straight into the waste-paper basket. Stephen left, and I remained suspended in a kind of vacuum. Sir Archibald Rowlands, the Permanent Secretary, to whom I took my troubles, said 'My dear Lionel, you have a nice office overlooking the Thames, and a nice salary, and nothing much to do. Why worry?' Archie was a dear fellow, but I couldn't sit and stare at the Thames. I got myself out, and swore that I would do no more bureaucratic work. But what was I to do? Nobody wanted me. And quite rightly. In this world of war I was useless.

India still sat in the forefront of my mind, and I somehow found myself a member of an 'Indian Freedom Campaign' under Fenner Brockway. Fenner is a dear soul, a champion of lost causes, well-meaning and (to me) very confused. I need hardly say (since it always happens to Fenner) that the Indian Freedom Campaign had no money at all, and even less organisation. Fenner's ideas about Equality reach a point which is hilariously funny and very tragic. When we decided (after a hideous struggle about finance) to employ a secretary, and various ladies were due to be interviewed, Fenner said to me 'I am so afraid that they will feel *embarrassed* if I sit behind a desk: so let us take our chairs into the middle of the room, and talk to them there.' The ladies were considerably startled, and not at all, as Fenner hoped, at ease. I was now sent to make speeches about Indian Freedom all over England: but for the most part in extraordinary (at least to me) places like Newark, Grantham, Stoke-on-Trent and Newcastle. I was falling rapidly in the social scale. Since we had no money, I had to travel cheap, and I was 'put up' in the various towns, not by the working class, which might have been amusing, but by rather dreary commercial travellers, who were indeed very kind to me, but with whom I could find no common ground. The nadir was reached in some frightful town (I cannot remember where) in which I talked in a Wesleyan chapel to an audience of thirteen: and, after expounding at great length and (as I thought) with unanswerable logic the case for Indian Freedom, I was faced by an old gentleman with no teeth who rose and demanded: 'You aint arsting us to believe that Indians can govern theirselves, ay you?' However, this idiotic stumping did teach me to 'think on my feet': and presently I was taken up by the Commonwealth Party under Sir Richard Acland, as their 'Eastern Expert'. The Commonwealth Party had some nice people in it, such as Vernon Bartlett and Tom Wintringham, and for a moment I believed that it might be our salvation. Under its auspices I spoke to a large meeting at the Central Hall, Westminster: which nearly frightened the pants off me. Soon, however, the party fell to pieces – perhaps Acland was not quite the ideal leader. But all this speaking resulted in an approach to me by Martin Secker, who suggested that I should write a book on India. I did not at all want to do so, because all writing is a tribulation to me: but I had got myself into a groove, and thought that I must not refuse. In a haze of gin I ground out a book which was called *Beggar My Neighbour*. I was an ignoramus about publication, and when Martin Secker asked me whether I would prefer a de luxe edition, which would take a year to print, or a cheap one which would take three months, I opted for the latter. I did not realize that at a time when 'austerity' made all books look cheap, a cheap edition would look terrible. Secker by that time did not like the book, and did not spend much money on advertising it. It was so badly printed that it was almost unreadable – at least, that is what many correspondents told me. Nevertheless, the reviews of it were – to me – startlingly long and startlingly good. There were some exceptions. Eric Blair, otherwise George Orwell, who had a particular dislike of me, wrote no less than 6,000 words about it in *Horizon*, tearing it to bits and calling his article 'Gandhi in Mayfair'. I thought that this was a bit too much, and asked the Editor, Cyril Conolly, whether I could write 6,000 words in reply. Cyril, a very fair man, agreed: and I did my best to stab Orwell in all his vulnerable points. He then asked Cyril for another 6,000 words to reply to me, but Cyril, quite rightly, had had enough. I made over the proceeds of the book, if any, to the Indian Freedom Campaign, and to this day I haven't the vaguest idea of the number of copies sold. It was banned by the Government of India, which I thought flattering: later it was reprinted in India by an American firm, but I never saw a copy of that edition.

These peculiar activities suddenly flowered in a surprising way. Waldorf Astor, the proprietor of *The Observer*, had a quarrel with J. L. Garvin on a Wednesday, and Garvin left. Lord Astor rang me up and asked me if I would write the main article in *The Observer* in his stead, beginning on the following Sunday. I must explain, however, that the invitation was not quite what it – at first – sounded. Obviously Lord Astor had to have somebody to write, and, equally obviously, he did not want to take any sudden and binding decision. I was a useful pawn which could be played without much risk: moreover, the Cripps Mission was about to leave for India, and my knowledge came in handy. Limits to my future were quickly set. It was made clear to me that, when the war was over, David Astor would naturally inherit the Editorial Chair: also that in the meantime there would be an acting Editor. This was at first Geoffrey Crowther of *The Economist*, secondly Wilson Harris of *The Spectator*, and thirdly the dramatic critic of *The Observer*, Ivor Brown, who eventually (and surely it was an even stranger appointment than mine) became Editor until David took over. In spite of all this careful hedging, the invitation came as an immense bolt from the blue. I was much more appalled than pleased. This now seems strange to me. I had written a good many articles for *The New Statesman* and other papers in BBC days: in India I had grown accustomed to making speeches and writing articles by the yard: in England I had spoken a good deal, and written a book. Writing for a Sunday newspaper should not have appalled me. I imagine that it was a fear of Garvin. I had known him, and read his articles, it seemed to me, from my childhood on: he appeared to me a great figure with an encyclopaedic mind. I did not see how I could possibly rival him. I foresaw him (and indeed everyone else) laughing at my absurdities.

Work on *The Observer* was quite different from anything that I had expected. I never saw the acting Editors. The staff was much smaller than I had thought possible, and it always seemed to me a miracle that the paper came out at all. As far as I was concerned, I had one assistant, who was Miss Barbara Ward. She has since attained fame, but if you think that she wrote my articles for me, you are mistaken. She seemed to me then a mousy little person, and if I asked her to get hold of a contributor or write a factual note, she obliged with great efficiency. And, to do her justice, she never attempted to interfere in the smallest degree with my ideas or articles, and was entirely charming to work with.

The week on *The Observer* followed a regular pattern. On Monday I lunched with Waldorf Astor at (God knows why, but he chose it) the Holborn Restaurant. In his courteous way – he was one of the gentlest and most endearing men I ever knew – he would say, always, very much the same thing. 'My dear Audax,' (that was the pen-name they had given me) 'you wrote beautifully yesterday. I especially liked etc, etc, etc . . . But don't you think you could outwrite Scrutator? I think you could. I should be so pleased if you would.' (Scrutator was the military expert of *The Sunday Times.*) In some distress – for I longed to please him – I would reply: 'But, Lord Astor, I know nothing, and care less, about military matters: and I think that *The Observer* would be so wise if it concentrated upon what is to happen *after* the war.' But I could not convince him. On Tuesday David would either see me or ring me up, and develop some rather Utopian attitude of his own: and from this it almost invariably followed that I was visited on Wednesday by some hush-hush individual (an escaped prisoner-of-war, a German refugee, an American observer) who confided to me various things which seemed to me to make nonsense. On Thursday I had to attend the solemn meeting of bigwigs who made up *The Observer's* Board of Governors, and each of them would have a different suggestion to make for the next number. On Friday, thoroughly baffled and confused, I wrote my article or articles: oddly enough, I found that the best place to do this was lying on the ground in St James's Park. I had the impression, rightly or wrongly, that with people moving round me, I had a sense of what England was thinking. On Saturday David arranged a dinner-party, perhaps with Mr Anthony Eden, to keep us all in the swim. And so, for a time, it went on.

I had one delightful compliment. Bernard Shaw, on a week-end visit to Cliveden, said to Lord Astor: 'I don't know who your Audax is, but he writes much better than Garvin ever did.' Lord Astor, disappointingly, did not divulge my identity: but I treasured the remark. Nevertheless I was bound to fail in the end. I was not the right person, and I had not the necessary staying-power. It came to pass that I wrote a spiteful article about a Churchillian visit to Moscow. I don't think it was stupid: but it was undoubtedly tactless. From that moment I was in retreat. Waldorf Astor was much too nice to sack me: but gradually I did less and less. I went out not with a bang or even a whimper, but in a sort of polite diminuendo. I remain grateful to *The Observer* for an interesting experience.

I was now (somewhere about the beginning of 1943) in a bad situation. I had, it seemed, tried almost everything and failed everywhere. I was forty-seven, unfit and almost penniless, and I took myself off to the family abode at Kineton. The house was half-converted to a hospital, and the family were living in a part of it which had been so badly divided as to be almost unmanageable. My sister, a grass widow while her husband was fighting, had abandoned her lovely house and come to live in a cottage on the estate. She very efficiently looked after such things as the chickens, goats, rabbits, and what garden remained. My father had developed cancer: but, since the doctors thought that an operation at his age would be too risky, was kept unaware of it. The only servants in the house were Clark the butler and Mrs Wellard the cook, a woman of great personality and dry humour, who cooked beautifully but was not going to stir out of her kitchen for anyone. From the room where we fed to the kitchen was fifty paces of dark stone corridors. Clark, though very willing, was usually in a haze of gin. Someone, therefore, had to lay tables, change plates, wheel trolleys along the corridors, and wash up. I was amazed to discover the etiquette which ruled – still ruled – behind the baize doors. Glass and silver had to be washed and stored in, and fetched from, the butlers pantry: Mrs Wellard would throw it out if it reached the kitchen. China went to the kitchen. The rule was immutable. My stepmother and I would take turns at washing-up. Our treasure and terror was the last, the very last, murderously thin port-wine glass used by my father. He simply did not like port out of any other glass. Stupid perhaps, but there it was. I rather share his feelings. Wine is better in a beautiful glass: tea is undrinkable in a thick mug. Anyway, with my stepmother and me, it became a case of 'It's your turn to wash it' – 'No, it's yours' – and when Clark, thoroughly ginned-up, finally broke it, we were, although sorry for my father, greatly relieved. On the whole it was, I suppose, the sort of crazy family life which was common in England at that time. With a dumb despair, I felt myself slithering into a dependent waster with a few domestic chores. There seemed to be no future at all for me.

In that, however, I was mistaken.

The brief War Office letter, enquiring whether I would be 'willing to accept a post as major in connection with the administration of occupied territory', did not even faintly thrill me. I did not altogether believe it; after my experience of the Government of India, two Ministries, the BBC and *The Observer*, and with my reputation as a seditious pacifist and author of an angry little book, it seemed plumb crazy that I should join the British Army in any capacity whatsoever. I wrote an affirmative reply and went to wheel in the trolley for lunch.

I had written an affirmative reply because I could think of no particular reason for writing a negative one: do what I would, I should inevitably be caught up before long again into some form of 'national activity': so why not this? 'Do you make your own life or do you allow circumstances to make it?' was a question found in a fortune-telling book in the spacious days of peace: I never found an answer to it. But perhaps the blessed word Italy did linger, a flickering flame of hope, in the recesses of my mind . . . the hillsides round San Gemignano, brave towers against the blue sky, the *contadino* down there through the grey haze of the olive-trees calling '*Vai!*' to the white oxen ploughing the slope . . .

Suddenly, a week or two later, I was facing a Colonel across an office table. He didn't look in the least like a Colonel to me; his whiskers and nose were long, his manner suave; he was not at all intimidating. Quizzing me in almost deferential fashion, he asked: 'Are you quite sure that you want to accept a post of – er – major – er – rather – a small post. I mean,' abruptly he exploded, 'people with your sort of record generally want a governorship at least!'

I was not, as I should have been, dumbfounded. I did not, as I should have done, pull myself together and say, with firm conviction, that although for the moment I could waive the right to governorship, my record deserved no less than the rank of a brigadier. That was what he undoubtedly expected me to do, and in the light that has now dawned upon me in regard to that particular period of history, I have little doubt that the requisite number of stars would have landed upon my most unmilitary shoulder. The authorities believed, quite inaccurately, that we were about to conquer and administer the whole of Italy: they had not got the men for the job: and the odd mess of my life, which included a fairly good knowledge of Italy and its language, as well as some years of Indian administration which, albeit ending in fury and disaster, had earned me the CIE as a consolation prize, made my value high. The Colonel gave me every opportunity: but I, who had risen in the last war to the dizzy rank of major, then considered elevated, replied as meekly as any sheep that I was content with what he offered. Opportunity thus fell with a thud into the irreclaimable past.

Did I then, said the Colonel, now pursuing his questions with, naturally, a greater degree of contempt, mind working with Americans? I said that I didn't, on principle, mind working with men of any nationality; whether I should quarrel with individuals was another matter. The Colonel seemed satisfied with this, and asked me if I could sail at a week's notice. It was on the tip of my tongue to say (for I had been considerably humbled by the years of brutalization) 'You're not really going to *take* me?' – instead, I said, in the noncommittal manner which all really good Englishmen use, that I could, but would prefer not to.

On the way home it began to dawn on me that this thing might perhaps actually be happening. A major in Amgot – incredible, absurd; my friends would explode with laughter. To be regimented again after the years of fighting against regimentation in any form, against obedience, against discipline, against loyalty even, all the vices which our civilization extols as virtues, was unendurable. To be part of a machine without a head, trampling over Italy – how could I contemplate so odious a burden? Yet how could I contemplate the alternative – the drifting state of frustrated fury in the desolate garden? I wondered, as the autumn landscape slipped past the train, whether, after all these years, I could still speak a word of Italian. Better have lessons, I thought idly. Better 'put my affairs in order' – sail at a week's notice. Better, perhaps, order a uniform. Two, three, how many uniforms? But I did not believe in the future and I did nothing at all; except, of course feed the hens and chickens and bring in the goats. The afternoon sun cast its long shadows over what had once been the terrace, the lawns, the herbaceous borders; a tangle of weeds and trampled hay.

On that Friday came a letter with URGENT marked at the top in a nasty shade of green. It said that I had been selected for appointment as so 11 CA Italy – whatever that might mean – that I should hold the post of acting Major, and that I should report immediately to the London District Assembly Centre, prepared to embark. A sinking sensation was evident in that part of me which had so decisively rejected war and everything concerned with war. Also in that part of me, forty-seven years old and mulish, which was diffident, lazy and sybaritic. Humanity everywhere was vile, and why should life be better at San Gemignano?

Two days sank quickly under the ripples of time, and I was walking, feeling rather sick, into the London District Assembly Centre, which was in fact none other than the overwrought and melancholy building known in less secretive times as the Great Central Hotel, Marylebone.

I had not at any time frequented this somewhat gloomy tavern, and since receiving my sailing orders had visited it only once, although officers and men under sentence of departure were supposed to answer a roll-call there twice a day. I had done no more than hurriedly draw the camp equipment available: a process which involved one in the peculiar orgy of trying to 'fit' appallingly ill-fitting shorts and bush shirts in a maze of staggering officers engaged in the same practice. I had seen the equipment marked, packed, and despatched together with the two suitcases allowed: and observed the instructions, scrawled on a blackboard in the dimly lit hall, to the effect that my 'draft' (known as RZOFK which seemed to belong more to an oculist than an assembly of men) would parade for departure at such and such a time this evening. The consequence of my inattention to roll-calls was that I alone, out of some seventy officers, was improperly dressed. And the impropriety was hideously evident, not to be disguised. I was wearing service dress and a British warm, all very nice and new and snug: the rest (according, as I later learned, to Army Council Instructions, all laid down, my dear fellow) were buried in battle-dress and sank beneath the weight of tin hats and veils and gascapes and haversacks and revolvers and convolutions of webbing holding up other impediments. The officers, as far as one could see anything of them beneath the bulgings of their armament, were not youthful: their movements were of a slow, creaking and clanking nature: the whole effect was, I thought, nightmarishly that of great slugs stirring below ironmongery. I was somewhat fretted by my impropriety but nevertheless glad of my saner clothes; and glad too, in an angry way, of a previous war's teaching that to ignore stupid orders is right and proper. The Army Council instruction which decreed that officers should take a long night journey in Great Britain dressed as inconveniently, though less attractively, than the White Knight, was just plain silly. The only possible justification for it would have been, and in point of fact probably

234

was, that men were going, as in the last war, straight into the firing line next day; whereas none of us could get to any possible firing line for weeks, unless it was submarine warfare, in which full equipment would have been a disadvantage.

There was no particular virtue (except to myself) in my want of ironmongery under the dim lights of the Central Hotel, but when I discovered the little round man – not without difficulty since he was almost extinguished by iron pans and webbing – who was our 'Colonel in charge', and displayed my condition, he uttered a fretful 'TUT-tut-tut' and told me that I should go straight to the station ('St Pancras, but don't *tell* anyone') to get my luggage out of the van and change into ironmongery on the platform. There were absolutely no lines in my hand to indicate that I should ever do such a thing, and I told him no. I said the War Office had rushed me away at a moment's notice, and that they could have me in a British warm or not at all. The Colonel emitted an indignant clank and said (very reasonably I thought) that even if I thought myself a Field Marshal I should have to do as I was told. I adjusted one of his helmets which had got entangled between a mosquito-net and a gascape, and told him no again. He did nothing more. I suppose he could have had me arrested. I should have been delighted. I saw with hideous clarity, now that it was too late, that I had been a double-dyed fool to get myself into khaki again.

Depressed, having answered to my number, I climbed into the large open lorry. We sat in rows facing each other, on long wooden seats. The faces under the tin hats seemed to me revolting, and revoltingly similar. But then I have never loved my fellow-men. I saw these faces staring at me down endless days, in sleep, at the trough, on the road, in the hut and the tent, the barrack and the billet, the trench and the brothel, the street and the latrine, close breathy smelly faces from which one could not escape: and there was infinite dreariness in me. In a stream of lorries we rumbled down the Euston Road. Extraordinary sensation! Twenty minutes earlier I was in my flat in Park Lane: ten minutes earlier I was in a taxi, still master of my fate. Now I was an unrecognizable brown ant in a swarm, an ant becoming dirtier, less recognizable, with every passing minute. The passers-by in the Euston Road gave us heedless stares, turning away to their shops and buses: for us the threads of fate were now drawn tight. No turning back for us on this journey to nowhere, this space of time which for its space and time, possibly for ever, would obscure us. It was possible, here and now, to hail a taxi and drive to Park Lane; and I could no longer do it.

Dark St Pancras absorbed our shambling figures, heavily clattering out of the end of each lorry: on a long platform we waited, cold and purposeless and silent. Diffident whispers ran among us, and now for the first time I heard the mutter of a 'dry ship'. The thought appalled me. I had visualized a perpetual stock of Dutch courage on any ship, and to shrink soberly from submarines seemed unthinkable. However, there was nothing to be done; it had not even occurred to me to bring a supply of alcohol.

A long unlighted train came sibilantly to rest beside us and we clambered in – a proceeding requiring acrobatics from all but me. Helmets and haversacks were hopelessly wedged in doorways, hooks and handles tore at webbing and capes. Inside the dark coaches there was just enough seating room – just. Racks and floors were quickly littered with coats and caps and rolled capes and tin hats with string shopping bags tied over them and revolvers and pouches and haversacks and the inevitable complicated webbing, a variation on red tape in khaki, encircling us all. Almost instantly, it seemed to me, some people began to snore – lucky folk so speedily oblivious to their surroundings. When the dim lights came on, they illumined a most convincing picture of grey-green battle disarray. It was 6.45 p.m. We were due, so it was understood, to arrive at our destination, wherever that might be, somewhere around nine o'clock next morning. Meanwhile we had each been provided with a packet containing a couple of gargantuan sandwiches of doubtful content, and a couple of buns guaranteed to wreck a denture.

Opposite me was a large lieutenant, still awake: my attempts at conversation fought a losing battle against his sleep. He was a policeman, but a City policeman: that distinction he was most careful to draw. He had been through the blitz and the city fire: I learned how this and that pal had been killed or rescued. Now he was going to do something of an Amgotically police nature, without, of course, knowing a word of French or Italian or German. He did not much care about going and did not know at all what his duties would be: but promotion, so he had been told, would be accelerated by his going, and so there he was. He had a family, he said, yawning. Boy of ten, girl of seven. Must provide. His head nodded. Seven-fifteen. How on earth, I asked myself, do people sleep so easily? I cannot sleep. Great people, it is said, always sleep easily: *ergo*, I cannot be great. The train bumbled on to nowhere. I ate my sandwiches and wished that I had been born in a different age.

Sometime after midnight the train stopped at a long empty platform. It was said to belong to Northampton or Nottingham – no matter, a canteen served us with tea at a penny a cup and I blessed it. I had to borrow a mug because, in spite of a quite serious attempt to think seriously about military necessities, I had brought neither mug nor water-bottle nor, of course, anything to drink. Mugs and cutlery and water-bottles ought to have been hanging round me, according to the Army Council instruction: and they weren't. That this was reprehensible I fully realized: I was a burden not only to myself but also to the officer who had to stand by while I took his mug away, thereby probably depriving him of a second cup: yet even if I have to take part in another war when I am eighty, which seems highly probable, I feel sure that, at critical moments, I shall be without a mug, a water-bottle, and a drink.

The train trundled on: it crawled: it stopped altogether for long silent periods. Between one and four o'clock we might have covered, by my reckoning, some twenty miles. Did all troop trains thus wander vaguely through the English night? A flick of envy I had for comfortable civilians, travelling by express. Dirt in my finger-nails: and should I be able to use my electric razor on board the ship? In the Army, in the Army, slowly said the wheels.

I dozed: and we were running across moors into the dawn. Factories scarred them: more and more, bigger and bigger factories: at length in the distance derricks and the gleam of water. With groans and yawns and creaks and clanking, impedimenta were rearranged. Presently we shambled out and stood in dejected, untidy groups on a small deserted platform. Everyone looked surprisingly ancient, and I reflected, with early-morning gloom, that I must not only look, but actually be, the same. There seemed to be no one to give us any orders: we waited. I moved around evasively, feeling my lack of ironmongery conspicuous, and seeking a face to talk to or receive talk from: but found none. After a time a round little man whom nobody, I think, had ever seen before and who carried no badge nor even armlet to identify him, demanded our identity cards: and to him humbly we offered them up, not without (except for me) a great disarrangement of impedimenta. He did not ask our names or check our faces (such as they were) against our photographs: he merely collected and removed, in an untidy bundle, the sole proofs of our identity. The train drew out, disclosing big dock sheds across the lines. Raggedly we trailed over.

Through high doors the grey sides of our ship stared at us: and we, shambling to a standstill, stared back. I disliked those grey sides immediately. Ships have a personality. The *Olympic*, my first ship, *en route* to Gallipoli in 1915, was a gallant handsome creature: she had majesty and force: you felt proud to be of her company. *Aquitania* by comparison, was a stout and fussy matron, common and rather unreliable: *Mauretania* a perfect bitch, though attractive in her way: *Normandie*, so much later, had undoubted charm as against overdressed *Queen Mary*. They were the great and glorious ones of my recollection. Among the less great were some charmers too – *Caledonia*, for instance, which took us away from the flaming beaches of Gallipoli to idle sunny Egypt, and *Kaiser-i-Hind*, sturdy but unattractive, which took me, and incidentally Colonel Lawrence, from Alexandria to Marseilles in the joyful October of 1918: and the graceful *Contes* of the Lloyd Triestino, running from Bombay to Venice, and arriving there always, or so it seemed, on the stroke of noon, when the pigeons flew up in their automatic cloud to the sound of the cannon: and last and worst of ships of my acquaintance, the gloomy grimy *Poona*, rolling me for the first time through the Indian Ocean. A hateful ship the *Poona:* and the grey sides of the ship I now stared at were definitely Poona. And on top of that, I thought, as we stumbled up the gangway, *dry*.

Squeezing in an impatient mass, though there was no hurry whatsoever, past the empty lift-cages up the uncarpeted stairs, we disposed ourselves and our impedimenta about the lounge. The lounge, as lounges go, went badly: its architecture was of the early Pullman period, decidedly the worse for wear; it had a high middle aisle surmounted by blackened glass and boxed by a derelict balcony stacked with rifles: and two low-ceilinged wings with windows permanently shuttered in deal. Faded cretonnes on battered sofas and bedraggled green curtains hanging sadly against the shutters bore witness to past glory. Having rushed up the stairs like sheep, in a hurry to get nowhere, or perhaps with an idea that first comers would get somewhere, we now sat staring, hoping very much with a hope that was destined to disappointment, for breakfast. A solitary nurse in the QAI uniform held her place on a sofa and enjoyed our sidelong glances: we, I daresay, felt that the ship was somehow safer, and certainly more gay, if women were aboard.

Presently an old gentleman – his age was later confidently asserted to be seventy-one – with the fiercest possible face set in a halo of red tabs and gold braid, and a rainbow of medals on his left breast, bustled up to a table and, after fumbling with a mass of papers, addressed us in a series of short barks.

'Gentleman – this a full ship – very full ship – not a berth empty – not a berth! Do our best for all – but full ship! Take it as you find it! Wartime emergency! Short shipping!'

We dumbly registered loyal assent and disgust.

'Get down to business at once – Cabin A – cabin with a private bathroom! Eight colonels, please, for Cabin A!'

After some hesitation and muttering, eight elderly gentlemen pushed their way through the jungle of webbing and received billeting slips at the table.

'Eight more colonels, now, for Cabin B – cabin B – cabin with private bathroom!'

Yes, there were eight more. A lot of colonels, I thought. A cackle of colonels. A concentration of colonels. A regular consti-pation or even a conflagration of colonels. Eight colonels to a bath, eight colonels to a bed. A chorus, a confluence, a catastrophe of colonels. Eight colonels to Cabin C. I cannot stand it.

'Eight more colonels for Cabin D . . .'

No, there was something amiss. Muttering and hesitation.

'Isn't there another colonel heah?'

Nothing in the webbing jungle stirred. Bad show, chaps, bad show.

'Very well then – I want one major to go with seven colo-nels . . .'

Somebody let out a smothered gust of laughter. I looked round and caught a twinkling eye in a large face which was attached to the most untidy imaginable body. Somebody laughed, who laughed? I was filled with delight. Somebody else had visualized a major perishing under the weight of colonels sevenfold. I wasn't alone on the ship. So I shifted around and spoke for the first time to Teddy Croft-Murray, the most intelligent and endearing char-acter who ever went to Italy under the banner of AMG. In a few moments I learned that he came – the Ancient Monument he called himself – from the British Museum and was destined to report damage to works of art in Sicily. God be praised, I said, for someone like this, and I forgot even to feel anxious when, with seven unknown majors, I was handed a slip with c37-c written on it.

Down we went to C deck. Rather uncomfortably low, I reflected, for torpedo attacks: on the other hand well-protected from rocket-bombs and such: one can't have everything. I don't know quite what I expected in the way of cabin accommodation, but I think the reality startled us all. Eight bunks, wooden-bottomed (except for one), built in two tiers of three and one of two, round a cabin which might just have contained two moderately comfortable peace-time berths. The bunks were built of rough deal, and upon them a single naked bulb in the centre of the ceiling shone dimly: the space of floor left vacant could not have measured more than five by three. In this little vault, we eight were to sleep and breathe and have our dressing and undressing, as well as our baggage. And I, for my sins, was destined for one of the bottom bunks of three: there was a foot and a half of space between me and the bunk above me: a moderate St Bernard would hardly have squeezed into such a kennel. I must confess that I flinched a little at the prospect of long nights spent down there, pondering (soberly) on torpedoes, while not escaping the full effects of any sea-sickness which might occur above me.

The seven majors whom I did not know, plus me, plus impedimenta, being clearly too much for the cubic space of the cabin just then, I made my way back to the lounge. It was now as crowded as a third-class carriage on the way to Epsom on Derby day. Sides, backs, and centres of chairs and sofas were packed tight with military posteriors: officers sat on the piano, on the bridge tables, on the stairs leading to the balcony: they leaned against pillars or just stood, jostling against each other, waiting. And very soon the barking colonel addressed us again. He wished to say a few things about the voyage, h-r-r-umph, pure common-sense, ha-hum. First about accommodation, we should note, h-r-r-umph, that troopship transport was an operation of war, ha, and take the necessary discomforts in the right, hum, spirit. If the ship was hit, h-r-r-umph, the signal to muster would be a continous, cmphm, continuous ringing of the ship's, ha, gongs: an intermittent ringing, cahum, of the gongs would mean, ha, an alert and we stayed, aha, where we were. And some of the officers, h-r-r-umph, would sleep below decks every night: he didn't approve, ha-hum, of men being always on the troop decks and officers above. We should be issued lifebelts: mustn't play with them, h-r-r-cmphm, our lives might depend on them. First thing that happened, ha-hum, when a ship was hit was, aha-r-rah, that the lights went out; there were emergency lights on the stairways which could be unlocked with a key, silly idea, he never could, h'r-r-umph, understand it, very difficult to find keyholes in the dark. If the ship listed, aha, the nets would be put over: great thing was to see the men didn't panic, and they wouldn't, h-r-r-umph, he'd seen 'em, good as gold.

After this enlivening discourse we migrated, *faute de mieux,* on to B deck, from which I now saw myself leaping into an appalling darkness of large black waves with a red torch that didn't work. I chased away this nightmare and endeavoured to take some stock of my fellow-travellers. They mostly looked, I thought, as uncomfortable as I felt. The most striking thing about them was their age. Few were under forty and the majority seemed well on the wrong side of it. Middle-age is not really a good time to go seeking torpedoes, eight in a cabin. Still, men and shipping were short, and there we were. No doubt, I said to myself unconvincingly, we are lucky to have bunks. We might have had hammocks or slept on the decks. What seemed less endurable was the fact, now established, that the ship really was dry. This was generally said to be due to the Americans, though how exactly the Americans came into it, I didn't gather; more likely due, I thought, to Nancy Astor. As I sat down with Croft-Murray to our lunch-with-water, I felt that this temperance was the last straw: for why, if I must eat in a herd and sleep in a kennel prior to drowning in the entanglement of a net or the isolation of a useless torch, must I be deprived of the one thing which would permit me to pass the voyage in a decent haze of tolerance?

Croft-Murray, who was above dependence on liquor and as delighted as any schoolboy with the whole business of leaving, laughed at me and produced, over lunch, a mouth-watering kind of book of photographs of Sicilian art. Though I have given some slices of my life to the study of art and painting, I am one of those unpersevering people who can never become expert in anything and I now learned all over again from Teddy about the beauties of the baroque and in particular the works of Serpotta, to which he was much addicted. We also lit upon the picture of an extremely romantic castle by the sea, belonging, I think, to Baron Bordonaro, and we meditated pleasantly upon the pos-sibility of our ousting the Baron and living there in majesty, magnificence and might. Altogether I became somewhat infected by Teddy's enthusiasm: but not without an uneasy mental glance at the mystery of my own future. To be an expert in Fine Arts, a saver of historic monuments, was straight plain non-belligerent sailing: but for what role should I be cast? I wished that I had given more attention to this detail before I left.

We stayed that night by the quayside. The cabin was hot and smelly, but none of the seven majors snored. Maybe I did: if so, they never told me. In that first scuffle to burrows there seemed little to distinguish one from another: they were all in their forties, one guessed: they were not beautiful: it appeared that none of them had been out of England before: and none spoke a word of Italian. Beyond cursing the cabin and life generally in a hearty way, they did not have much to say. So this was Amgot: these the embryo rulers of ancient Italy. It seemed odd to me.

In the morning we moved slowly upstream, passing the *Queen Mary*, in which, it was said with probable inaccuracy, nineteen thousand men were carried on every voyage by dint of eating and sleeping in a Box and Cox manner. There was a heartening display of warships and aircraft carriers around us, and we hoped – at least I certainly did – that they were all coming along with us. Such monsters seemed unsinkable. A more unpleasant possible prospect was that we should sail, as some ships did, alone.

Our ship, the *Aorangi*, had been built to accommodate 950 souls or bodies. That was roughly the boat accommodation. On this trip we were carrying 3,500 men and 400 officers, sixty-four of whom were destined for Amgot. Interested persons had counted up some sixty rafts in all, and calculated that about twenty persons could hold on to each raft, weather permitting. Thus it was clear that a lot of us would have, in case of emergency, to trust to lifebelts and torches exclusively. This indeed became obvious at the first muster-parade, which wasn't strictly speaking a parade at all, since we were squeezed together in a tight mass on the space of deck allotted to our boat-station. Neither now nor subsequently during the voyage was there any question of boats or boat-drill or even a roll-call: you might as well have tried them on sardines in a tin. If the ship sank we had to get ourselves into the sea, and that was all there was to it. And since deckspace was so restricted, and cabins had to be cleared by 9 a.m., and our only lounge was used during the mornings and afternoons for film shows for the troops, we began to feel that the correct slogan for us was Not Wanted on Voyage.

The *Aorangi* now began to go round and round the *Queen*

Mary. She went round so often, and seemed so confused about her own purposes, that Rumour began. Rumour was potent and active among the Amgoteers. Hardly any of us, I think, knew quite where we were going, what we were going to do, whether we were really wanted, what Amgot really was. Of course, many officers, not including me, had been to the school at Wimbledon to learn about military government, but few seemed very certain about their own role. A Perpetual Personal Uneasiness was evident. On this occasion Rumour had it that our compasses had gone wrong and that as a result we should miss the convoy. I supposed this to be rubbish; actually it was quite correct. Details gathered: a tug drew alongside and hailed the bridge – 'Compass Engineer reporting'. Uneasily we tramped the crowded decks, stared at the grey slopes of Clydeside, ate our large but tasteless meals, drank our water, and shivered. Night fell: the ship remained anchored.

Teddy and I now discovered that we had made a fatal blunder by placing ourselves on the 'second sitting' for meals. We thought that we had been clever, since the second sitting was the grander of the two, reserved for the higher ranks, at civilized hours, and you didn't – a really important point when dressing and shaving were acrobatic feats – have to get up so early for breakfast. But no, this didn't work at all. The first sitting, when replete, rushed up and filled all the available seats, so that the second sitting found none. This was a grave matter after breakfast, when we had two hours of the lounge before the films started and we were hustled out on deck; less grave after lunch, when films started almost immediately, and you had perforce to walk or sleep: but catastrophic after dinner, when you were faced with an immensely long evening without a seat, and the only alternatives were pitch-dark rolling decks or the kennel in which, owing to the dim light, you could not read. As I think very poorly of walking on dark cold decks or lying idly in a kennel, my life rapidly became a game of musical chairs. Once you had got a chair in the lounge, you could not abandon it; and when nature forced you to do so for the purpose of eating or disposing of what you had eaten, the only course was to return and stalk a prey who gave any sign of leaving. I considered the possibility of abandoning dinner altogether, but compromised by eating it in five minutes on the altar of indigestion and rushing upstairs to the lounge before some of the more unwise of the first sitting, who had gone to fetch books from their cabins, could get there. Of course the

Aorangi, as troopships go, was a very good troopship, and nothing, after all, mattered except that our bodies should arrive more or less intact at their destination: but for middle-aged gentlemen like me she wasn't exactly a home from home. And what with one thing and another, our mostly middle-aged company was quickly swept by a plague of influenza; in the cabin eight throats wheezed, and eight noses trumpeted, all through the night.

Ah, if I were King of England, or better, Pope of Rome,
I'd have no fighting men abroad, no weeping maids at home!
All the world should be at peace, and if Kings must show their might,
Then let those that make the quarrels be the only ones to fight!
Ah, let those that make the quarrels be the only ones to fight!

On Sunday morning, October the seventeenth, Rumour was busy as a bee. We had missed the convoy, said Rumour, and were putting back to Glasgow. And sure enough, towards midday, the *Aorangi* got under way and proceeded, not to Glasgow but up the Gairloch. And there, at a deserted quay among encircling silent hills, we tied up. All activity ceased and a blight seemed to fall upon the ship. Nobody told us anything. As a result all through that Sunday, Rumour grew. The War Office had always known that we should miss the convoy. Six ships had been torpedoed just outside the Clyde. The weather was too bad for any ship to get out. We were all going to be sent home again: Amgot had been dissolved. We should have to wait four weeks on board till the next convoy left. And so on. An atmosphere of uneasiness and irritation pervaded the ship. The brass hats no doubt knew but would not tell.

I took the opportunity to quiz my seven bed-fellows. Top bunk of my tier was red-headed, high coloured, loud-voiced Major Gray who swore fluently and often, shook the whole tier every time he climbed up, and required, mentally and physically, a lot of elbow-room. 'Tell you,' he bellowed, 'what the first thing I'm going to do if the ship's torpedoed is —' I looked a polite question. 'Come right down here and load my revolver!' I was puzzled and thought him perhaps madly Germanophobe. 'Why,' I said. 'To have a shot at the submarine?' 'No!' he shouted. 'To shoot the first man that panics!' I flinched at this, feeling that I undoubtedly should be the shotee: and registered a mental note to sequestrate his ammunition. But he was a nice fellow, all the same, and his sixth-form schoolboy attitude to life was admirably effective, later on, in restoring order to shattered Italian towns. But he remained always angry and frustrated, and never got any promotion at all.

Major Green, immediately above me, wasn't really a major at all, and that was his trouble. He was a stoutish man, with bloodshot blue eyes which continually watered, and a long white face like that of a delapidated bloodhound. 'Can't *understand* it.' he kept groaning. 'The War Office *promised* me, absolutely *promised* me, that I'd be a major, and here they go sending me as a *captain*. Can't *understand* it!' We all came to know the details of his trouble – the interviews at the War Office where this and that had been said, the letters which must have miscarried, the grave possibility of mix-ups with other Majors Green. He was a little tiresome.

Top bunk opposite was Major Brown, a very different character. Thin and frail, with a long long nose which looked as though it should drip and was crowned with pince-nez, Major Brown was less military than anyone I have ever seen. He wore his beret perched like a chef's cap on the top of his thinning locks, and his clothes seemed to hang in festoons from his narrow shoulders. The odd thing was that he had a fine three-year record as a colonel in the Home Guard, which shows that you never can tell. He was the gentlest of creatures, meticulous and methodical, getting up very early in the morning and moving like a mouse about the dark cabin, so that his dressing was completed before any of the rest of us had stirred.

Below him was the shining bald head, waxed mustache, and swelling stomach of Major Black. Major Black was a *faux Bonhomme* of the very first water. He was the soul of gusty good fellowship, clapping us all on the back, swearing loudly, and cracking dirty jokes. I put him down at first as an ex-sergeant-major and rather liked him: but soon his humour palled, and one saw that he was a hollow drum of a man, with nothing but a windy boastfulness beneath that glistening cranium. He it was who insisted on covering the cabin walls with pin-ups of the female nude: he it was who told us almost every night through the darkness about the 'little Italian widow' he was going to discover, and what he would do to her, and she to him.

Underneath him, in a kennel similar to mine, was ferret-eyed Major Rose. To him I took instantly and probably unreasonably the strongest possible exception. He was a fusspot, and a murderous one. His shifty little eyes probed like gimlets into everybody else's business. He was, in his own interests, every man's enemy. He talked far too much, in a snarly little voice. In the morning he crawled rapidly from his burrow a few minutes after Major Brown, and proceeded, in spite of a torch flashed in the eye of anyone still attempting to sleep, to knock over and against anything that could be knocked. Crash it went, and 'tut!' said Major Rose in a subdued yet penetrating voice: the torch went out and he was heard fumbling and swishing about the floor: then crash again, and the torch in one's eye. This finally so exasperated me that one morning I extruded myself in the manner of a tortoise from my wooden shell, and with a shout of 'Leave my boots *alone!*' thrust him backwards into his burrow. He never forgave me, and for the rest of the voyage glared balefully at me whenever I entered the cabin.

Major White, top bunk on my right, and in possession of the only spring bed in the cabin, had a large round smooth face which had absolutely no characteristic except a large pair of tortoiseshell spectacles. He *was* the spectacles and the spectacles were him. Through them protuberant blue eyes peered upon the world with unjustified contempt: he was an accountant, and I'm sure a good painstaking one, and clearly he thought that all men without mastery of figures were fools. The only porthole in the cabin was just over his bunk, and he spent much time and trouble in adjusting it, after the light was out, so that the draught blew straight on to my face and not on to him. He also took possession, for his clothes, of what I firmly considered to be my hook: so that hooks being scarce, I had to put my clothes on the always dirty floor. I stood this meekly for some days and then, one evening, madly removed all his possessions to the floor and put mine on the hook: to my infinite surprise he did nothing at all about it.

And below him, last of the seven, lay Major Mauve, who had absolutely no character at all. He was fair and well-favoured: he hardly ever spoke: when he did, it was to utter a pleasant and meaningless banality. Once or twice I tried to draw him out but found nothing to draw. No doubt he must have had some vices or virtues but I never discovered them: and after the voyage I never heard of him again. He was a blank.

Major Gray – to return to my top-bunk schoolboy again – claimed to be a farmer and forester: and he certainly was interesting and genuine on both subjects. His King Charles' head was the flooding of the Sahara Desert by the sea and its consequent fertilization as a result of the evaporation of the salt water which would return as rain: I never really attained to more than an academic interest in this to him absorbing topic. Major Green was an usher at a private school: and I could visualize him saying that he simply couldn't understand it when little boys were naughty, and smacking them with a succulent glint in those watery blue eyes. And if you want to know why he, a captain, was still among the seven majors, the answer is simple: he had simply put a crown on his shouder, but, for some unearthly reason, could not resist telling everybody that he was not entitled to it. Major Brown of the long nose and pince-nez, was a Post-Office Traffic superintendent, a high position I gathered but exactly what he did I never fully grasped. He had a way of telling immensely long-winded stories which wandered further and further from the point, so that after a time one was agonizingly conscious that he had lost the thread and was madly trying to think why he had started: and one's own attention had by then wandered too far for one to be able to help. Some of these stories included flashes of post-office work during the blitz in, I think, Sheffield: and I got a picture of him, perhaps very wrong, sitting up through the small hours over a telephone and trying to locate a lost train of parcels upon which his honour depended. Major Black of the bald head said loudly and constantly that he was a farmer, which he patently wasn't and never could be: one guessed that he had possibly been a commercial traveller in cattle-food or fertilizers. Major Rose was going to Amgot, he informed us, as 'Public Utilities': what that was none of us quite knew, though I angrily put him down as an inspector of drains. He contrived to give the impression that he knew exactly what his job was, which was more than the rest of us did. Major White of the tortoiseshell glasses was, as I have said, a chartered accountant: and the blank Major Mauve was, rather surprisingly, an insurance agent. Perhaps he dealt with funeral insurance, which would explain his taciturnity.

Between me and these seven majors hung a subtle veil of mistrust. I was, although without wealth, a plutocrat: they, probably all richer than I, weren't. I had had forty-seven years of a life in which it was natural to command servants, waiters, taxi-drivers, shopkeepers, travel-agents and other modern serfs: they hadn't. I knew what to do with leisure, because I had been brought up amongst leisured people: they didn't. Above all, and perhaps owing to that now-contemptible thing, a public-school

247

education, I had learned to be fairly deft in small matters with life and people: and they certainly had not. With eight majors of my own circumstances and environment I should, though un-utterably bored, have had the correct coinage of conversation and mutual acquaintance: with eight ordinary soldiers I should have been at ease: but with the class of affluent surburbia I was wholly and in both senses at sea, and no doubt, to protect my shyness, I was supercilious. I am sure that they were exasperated by me and everything about me, from my drawl to the electric razor which I slipped into the only electric light socket. But we were all terribly polite to each other for all the twenty-one nights which we spent together in that dim cell.

For that is what it turned out to be. Throughout that first Monday, Rumour was queen: on Tuesday we were paraded, in the usual scrum on deck, and cautiously informed that we had been delayed: we might be there a little time: we could not leave the ship: we could write letters but must say no word of our circumstances, and the letters would be sent only after our de-parture. This was stupid, and we all knew it: the first thought of most of us was to spare our families unnecessary anxiety: and since buses from Glasgow passed within fifty yards of us every fifteen minutes it was hardly probable that the presence of a 20,000 ton liner in the Gairloch was unknown.

On Wednesday, paraded again, we were informed that we might go for walks but only in parties of fifty under a senior officer: and we must on no account speak to the natives. So, since anything was preferable to permanent confinement on that ship, we set out in pouring rain, crocodiled like a girl's school, and trudged four miles of dreary road, casting envious eyes on red pillar-boxes. To me it was quite outrageous: we could all perfectly well have gone home for ten days, and there was no earthly reason why we should not have written letters to say that we were still detained at a British port. I am only grateful for a much clearer understanding of the feelings of our political prisoners in India: but they had at least a cause and reason for confinement: we did not.

But it must be recorded, and it was no small thing, that during our ten days of English purdah we *drank*. Alcohol in large quan-tities was conveyed aboard, perhaps to stupefy any grudges that we might have felt. Gin cost 4d a glass, a double brandy 1s. Such prices were in any case irresistible, and we had nothing else to spend money on. With nothing to do on a crowded ship, can it be wondered if some, or even most, indulged with scant measure of wisdom? Officers staggered about the decks: the bursting lounge was rent by banged piano and the concerted yell of obscene song, against which bleary but determined bridge players roared their bids at one another, and addicts of housie-housie deafeningly proclaimed their hieroglyphic auctions. Day and night the row went on and on and on: Major Gray was sick in his bunk: Major Brown tishooed and tishooed after over-indulgence to drive out influenza: Major Black's dirty stories got dirtier, louder, and more incoherent: Major Green was maudlin and persistent about his captaincy. At last I understood, and dazzlingly, how infinitely preferable a dry ship might be.

On the morning of Sunday, October 24, we moved majestically into the Clyde. There *was* something majestic about it, because our move coincided with morning service, and the land began to slip away from us to the strains of *Onward Christian Soldiers* sung by thousands of male voices and accompanied by the band of the Irish Guards, which – so rumour inadvisedly had it – Alexander had summoned to Italy for the entry into Rome. Being personally unmoved by religious rites, I sat in the mercifully deserted lounge, and enjoyed a discussion between my emotional associations, which were entangled in the sentimentality of hymn-tunes, and my reason, which stated flatly that it was absurd for people who were off to murder and plunder for the sake of greed to sing about the cross of Jesus.

And now we began to sort ourselves out a bit. A voice in my ear had muttered 'At my age, to sleep in a kennel . . .' and I recognized the voice as friendly. It belonged to Fred Beddington, intelligent and charming and a skilful draughtsman who amused himself by drawing facile and flattering portraits of us all, which we, of course, accepted with alacrity and satisfied vanity. Teddy Croft-Murray remained my chief prop and table companion, and through his intelligent eyes I began to know more of Sicily than I had ever known before. And Sandy, who startled me one evening by remarking, without introduction 'The interior decoration of this salon is not entirely to my taste' made up our quartet for no particular reason, since he was like a large young puppy living entirely for the moment and caring for nothing beyond it. Anyhow, these three friendly faces made life decidedly better.

And then one night we sailed. For some time we had been imagining the throbbing of engines: now at last they really throbbed. The decks began to heave and slide. We were told that we must not undress but lie in our bunks fully clothed. That night we did not know whether we sailed alone or in company. But morning brought revelation of an impressive kind. Around us in exact formation over the dark white-crested sea rode twenty-two great ships, grey ships and black ships and even white ships, ships with one funnel and two funnels and three funnels, with squat funnels and high funnels, ships with high noses and short noses, ships with long lines and stuggy lines, but all ships that somehow looked gallant and purposeful and brave. And beyond them, ahead and astern, to port and to starboard, ran the escorting destroyers like black pencils trailing a feather of foam. It all seemed very silent under the grey sky, very silent and proud and intent. I don't know why there should be anything remarkable about twenty-three ships at sea together, but on that first morning there certainly was. Our forced deck-walking soon made us familiar with the convoy, and we came to note quickly when it was changing direction or when one ship or another changed its place in the staggered ranks.

The sea became rough. The men were sick everywhere and always: the officers scarcely at all. Some of my cabin-mates took to their bunks, but no untoward incident occurred. The lounge and decks were less crowded which was a relief and, apart from a slight nervousness lest I might at any moment have to breast large dark waves in a lifebelt, I hoped that the rough weather would continue. Among other chores it fell to my lot to distribute the famous red torches: I had to show each customer how his torch worked and that it *did* work: and the customers were most particular. Again and again they nervously returned. 'I say, it *did* work all right but it doesn't seem to now,' or 'This thing works *sometimes* but not *always*,' or even 'This one seems to me very *dim*.' There were so many that I got very good at this. 'Tut!' I said to elderly colonels, 'You've been playing with this, you must leave it alone,' and handed them another dud which somebody else had brought back. Truly the torches seemed very temperamental: still, when you considered how many must be issued ... Naturally, I kept the best and brightest for myself, as well as a stock of particularly maddening duds for generals: but no generals appeared. We hung our torches gingerly on our lifebelts, to which they were attached by a long cord, and with this hunchback equipment securely tied on, paced the wet decks. It was extremely cold. Rumour had it that we were somewhere near New York.

And then quite suddenly the sun shone and the seas were blue. We had sailed into another world, a world I hadn't seen for much too long. We came out on to the top decks like flies into the summer and sat about in the boats in the sunshine. Intoxicated by the Mediterranean atmosphere, Teddy and I composed the Amgot anthem, which, to the tune of *Yip-i-addy-i-ay*, went as follows:

Old Samuel Diehard
Loot-Colonel, Retired,
Strolled down Piccadilly one day:
At his club our old Sam got
A message from Amgot,
Which gave him once more active pay;
He said 'Well, by jingo
Must I talk the lingo?'
They said, 'No, your language will do.'
So with rank of full colonel
And vigour eternal,
He sailed on the ocean so blue . . .

Ancient Military Gentlemen!
Off to govern the world!
They have put off domestic cares,
But in their bath-chairs they'll have civil affairs,
Cheltenham, Camberley, Cromwell Road,
Receive their exiguous rents,
Though they're old and they're
To the colours they're called,
Ancient Military Gents!

We thought that this might be an excellent addition to the boringly repetitive ditties howled every night by groups of officers round the piano: but it didn't go at all. Fred Beddington added a neat verse about Wimbledon, but the rest seemed to think it not funny. So we had to be content with humming it to ourselves as we sat in the boats in the sunshine: and one morning when so engaged we watched a submarine attack on the convoy. It was a mild affair. The destroyers wheeled in and out among us, dropping depth-charges, and we, of course, said, 'There she is!' 'No, there, look!' and never saw anything. The convoy sailed on.

It was impossible even to feel nervous among all those ships on that calm blue sea. But we noted later, from the secret telegrams, that our convoy had been attacked at that point: and felt pleased. Indeed, the sinking of just one ship, say, might have been an improvement. In the matter of sinking ships I am the greatest coward un-court-martialled: but a story is a story.

Gradually we drew in to Gibraltar. Land, a faint blur in the morning, narrowed in the afternoon to rocky coasts, south and north: and in one of the most glorious sunsets I have ever seen we passed the Rock. Our convoy had arranged itself into a crocodile: two by two it stretched away over the curving sea, and each pair of proud ships caught the crimson reflection of the sinking sun. And the Rock stood there, sheer, aloof, unconquered. The English have not the faintest right in the Mediterranean, which belongs to much more charming people; still, it was a grand sight.

On the next night at about ten o'clock we had an alert. Very few people had ever obeyed the order to sleep in their clothes: I certainly never, because the kennel in itself was quite enough to try me. On this occassion, when the gongs sounded their most alarming note, I was, I shudder to confess, in the lavatory in my pyjamas and without a lifebelt and a torch. Could anything have been worse? I jumped to the immediate conclusion that we should sink in a minute, saw myself trapped in the lavatory, struggling ... Through officers fully equipped and streaming up the gangways I rushed panting to the deserted cabin, dressed with shaking hands, discovered my torch, put my lifebelt on backwards, and got to the deck only to hear Teddy mutter in my ear 'It's only a practice – I meant to tell you . . .' I said hotly, 'Well, you are a disgusting pig!' and realized that I ought to have been shot by Major Gray.

When the extremely long parade – for it amused the Commandant to walk, heralded by bugles, all over the ship – was over, we discovered the flagship was signalling. Somebody kindly translated the signals, which amounted to the instructions that such-and-such ships would turn in towards Algiers next morning. We were, so to speak, home: and I breathed a sigh of relief as I crawled for the last time into my kennel. I need not have been so optimistic.

On the same morning General Kenyon Joyce was to arrive at Brindisi as Deputy-President of the Allied Control Commission, the establishment of which was to be announced on November

10th, and in which I was destined to play a long, thankless and irritating part. Had I known anything of this, I might have played what cards I held in a very different way: but I knew nothing, I was only a military number, and my future only a military whim. Although the *Aorangi* didn't tie up until a little after ten that morning, one of the habitually idiotic ship's orders had got us all up for breakfast at 6.30: and after that there was nothing to do save sit, if you could get a seat, in the lounge, and play bridge. Through sheets of steady rain Algiers did not appear inviting: and looking down upon the ocean of mud which lay over the docks, I profoundly hoped that a messenger from General Sir Humphrey Gale, Chief Administrative Officer of Algiers, to whom I had constrained a High Authority to write regarding my person, would arrive with a cordial welcome and warm invitation. In that hope, it is scarcely necessary to add, I was disappointed. It is extraordinary, looking back on myself, to note how thoroughly deluded I was into thinking that I had some importance.

Sandy, who had been here before in wartime, seemed to know all about it.

'You'll be stuck at the racecourse if you don't watch out,' he said encouragingly. 'Terrible place. Worst camp in the world, I should think. Nothing'll get *me* there. I'm off to do something about it.'

Amgot was now struggling into its impediments, its greatcoats, its green and brown gascapes. Teddy, as usual, was grinning. 'Bordonaro!' he admonished me, flourishing his stick. 'We are *en route* for Bordonaro!' I said crossly that I was on the direct route to pneumonia. The lorries, it seemed, had arrived. There was just no getting out of the lorries, and the camp.

We scrambled in. It was the Euston Road over again, but colder, wetter, and much more crowded. We bumped and jolted in a sodden mass along cobbled streets, past the dock-sheds, past dilapidated warehouses and dismal barracks, past wrecked ships with the seas breaking over them; stopping every now and then with a jerk which sent us tumbling over one another; always in a sea of traffic, jeeps and trucks and lorries outvying each other in blaring horn and thundering exhaust. After about half-an-hour we came to a halt. A dripping white wall, holed with guichets, proclaimed, in fading letters *'Pelouses'*. We got down.

A red road of shining sticky mud led down to the racecourse, which was little less than a river. On the further bank long lines of brown tents crouched abjectly. We filed across. Somebody, goodness knows who, said 'Thirteen of you in tent 7: twelve in tent 6...' Here was tent 20, tent 19... splosh, splosh, splosh. Tent 7, you could clearly see, had once had a trench round it: now the trench was a trace: the pegs for the side-flaps had vanished and there were no floor-boards. So wind and rain blew merrily through and nothing was likely to stop them. The mud inside the tent seemed deeper and stickier, if anything, than the mud outside. Light? No light. Batmen? No batmen. Our luggage? No luggage. It was chilly, and would soon be growing dark. I suddenly found Major Green drooping beside me.

'Terrible!' he groaned. 'Can't *understand* it.'

'I can, though,' I said. 'In the last war an officer had a batman, and a field officer even had a certain degree of comfort. I was idiotic enough to imagine that these things still held good. But no lack of manpower can kill the old-established game of scrounging; and I am going back to Algiers.'

'But *how?*' wailed Major Green.

'That,' I said, 'we must find out.'

So we made our way to the road again, and held out signalling arms. Instantly an obliging jeep stopped and took us on board. We bowled gaily over the six miles. A telephone call to General Gale was now clearly indicated, and, to my great surprise, General Gale answered.

'Come up and have dinner with me,' he said at once.

Dinner I thought, is all very well; what I want is a bed.

'I'm stuck,' I replied, 'stuck in two senses at your racecourse camp, which is quite horrid.'

'So's war,' said General Gale.

'There isn't any war here that I know of,' I said, nettled, 'and I don't want to spend the whole night trying to find my way back to the racecourse.'

'Send you my car. Speak to my secretary. And shut up about the camp.'

'Anyway,' I said to Major Green, as I put down the telephone, 'even if we've got to sleep in mud, we have a General's car for the evening.'

We found Fred Beddington in the hall. He was a colonel.

'Tried to fix you up with the spare bed in my room,' he said, 'but the Town Major wouldn't hear of it.'

'Majors are dirt,' I agreed. 'So are Town Majors.'

The car arrived. It was very luxurious and swift. Muddy and

dripping, we sank back upon its deep upholstery and tried to think of somewhere to go. But we didn't have anywhere to go. The best thing seemed to be to hunt for our luggage. We drove to the docks: no, the luggage had gone. Well then, the racecourse. We flashed over the shining cobbles, driving against glaring head-lights which, after the years of blacked-out England, seemed in-credibly dazzling. The rain beat down in silver rods, a tropical flood of rain. I had no compunction about the general's car and chauffeur: they took me right up to the entrance of tent 7.

Tent 7 was deserted: it was pitch-black: there was no light: but by striking matches we discerned our baggage, higgledy-piggledy in the mud. The tent-flaps blew hither and thither in the dark-ness: the rain beat in. Not really camping weather.

'Put up our beds, I suppose?' said Major Green's wet voice.

I said: 'I'm going to dine first,' and felt a beast. But hearts must be hardened when you're scrounging, and I left Major Green in the wet and windy night. The general's car spun silkily over the gleaming roads and up the winding Rue Michelet; and very soon indeed I was following a white-coated batman across a white marble hall occupied only by a white grand piano. A door opened and I found myself in an elegant library, warmly lit, wherein sat a smart young gentleman whom I correctly diag-nosed as ADC, and a portly Brigadier covered with ribbons. There was also a convincing array of bottles and glasses and de-canters on a walnut table. I had a sherry and made conversation. The atmosphere was somehow fraught with generals: it smelt of red tape: it exuded convention. Not my sort of place at all, I thought. But it must do for a night. I had been careful to bring toothbrush and razor.

General Gale blew in, living well up to his name. He was very hearty and very large. His coat seemed larger than any coat I had ever seen. His voice reverberated. He knew he was a general. His personality enveloped us all, not necessarily because he had any personality but because he was General Gale at that moment, CAO Algiers. I wondered what kind of a being really inhabited that large body and what it thought about. The General, I had been told, was a keen patron of the arts, and much addicted to music. Very soon, in fact, he asked whether I played the piano, and seemed disappointed when I said no. (Should I try and play for my bed, I wondered?)

'We had Noel Coward here the other night,' he remarked. 'Magnificent.'

The last word I should apply to Noel, I thought.

'Fine fellow!' said the General. 'Done a magnificent tour, all over the damned place, you've no idea – right out into the camps, giving a one-man show. You know him?'

I said that I did, slightly.

'Fine fellow!' said the General. The conversation languished. Hell, I thought, at this rate I'll never get a bed.

'So you don't care about the racecourse?' asked the General.

'I just thought it an abominable disgrace to the Allied authorities,' I said.

'Damn it all,' said the General, 'I'll have to put you under arrest if you talk like that. Damn it, it's *my* camp!'

'Then it's a disgrace to you. Perhaps you don't know about it.'

'How you chaps grumble,' said the General, helping himself to another glass of whisky. 'You're all soft, that's what it is.'

'Soft be damned,' I said. 'If you bring out old wrecks like me to a country which you're supposed to have gallantly taken and can't give them even a dry spot to sleep in, there must be something wrong with your administration. After about a year, too.'

'But, my dear chap,' said the General, leaning back on the silk cushions and waxing confidential, 'don't you realize that that camp is out of use? People like you generally get sent straight to Tizi-ousu or somewhere. It just happened that your boat arrived late.'

'Surely,' I persisted, 'that makes it all the worse. We could have stayed on board, or you could have put us in one of those many trains standing in the station, or, after all, you could have found us a villa like this. But not the racecourse.'

'Hell,' said the General. 'Hey, Robinson, we'd better give the Major a bed. But mark you,' he added to me, 'not for more than one night. I've got a whole posse of generals coming tomorrow.'

The room had meanwhile been filling up with generals. More than half were American, and since I was then blissfully unaware that a star connotes generalship in American, they might have been lieutenants as far as I was concerned. Still, their silver hairs undoubtedly indicated exalted rank. I, the one unexalted but also the one guest, sat at dinner on the General's right, and asked him if he knew the whereabouts of Oliver Baldwin, who had, I knew, a villa in Algiers and whom I had hoped to find there.

'Haven't the foggiest notion,' said the General. 'Took his villa away from him. Had the impudence to complain, the brat. We've had quite enough of Prime Minister's sons here.'

'I should have complained, and loudly,' I said. 'Why should you take it away from him?'

'Why not?' said the General. 'I've no use for him.'

'He's a great friend of mine,' I said.

Definitely, I thought, I am not getting on at all well: and I told myself sharply that I was a soldier, and an insignificant major at that, who must get on well with generals by never crossing them. But then again, myself told me, you are a person of middle age with no stake at all in generals, and all these gentlemen who behave in the manner of schoolboys and are covered with ribbons and stars, are quite possibly, judged in the context of beauty, truth, intelligence, or their passage from the cradle to the grave, insignificant people. Such thoughts, I told myself, get you into trouble, and I began to drink a great deal of the excellent red wine which was served so deftly by white-coated and even white-gloved waiters. Presently I had an enormous headache, and sat on a sofa conversing with this general and that, while the radio blared. And presently I got myself to bed, and, remembering the racecourse, I did bless General Gale for that.

In the morning, at breakfast, nobody spoke. The white-coated white-gloved waiters served us with eggs and bacon and coffee and rolls, and nobody spoke. Everyone had a paper, and nobody spoke. General Gale did not appear. My cue clearly was to vanish, and still without speaking or being spoken to, I got myself out of the house. I had not the vaguest idea of where I was, but after a little walking I came to a high point where there was a balustrade and some steps, and an excellent view of Algiers. The sun was shining in a clear blue sky, and Algiers, a place I have never much liked, looked moderately picturesque from this eminence. I could almost imagine myself a tourist, free. So I sat upon the balustrade and considered my position. I did not care much for it.

Suddenly I saw Teddy on the steps below me, brandishing his stick.

'Bad man!' he panted, coming up. 'Bad man! Where have you been?'

'Sleeping with generals.'

'I guessed as much. Wise man! It was hell down there. Those policemen! Cursing and shouting and trampling over everybody. Haven't the remotest idea how to behave decently. Would you believe it, one of them said to me 'I've spent most of me life managing toughs in Golders Green, and I guess Italy'll be about the same. And those are the people we send to Italy! I hate them!'

Teddy banged his stick on the balustrade. 'And you're not at *all* popular with them, I may tell you,' he added.

'Probably I'll survive it,' I said. 'But I didn't know they knew me.'

'Oh yes! Oh yes! They all cursed you for running off like that and leaving your baggage all over the place. However, I put it in a corner.'

'Thank you,' I said, feeling ashamed. 'What happens to us next, do you suppose?'

'I shall now take you to see the English Church here which used to be a mosque. Very fine. Then we must visit the Kasba. After that we go to Tizi-ousu, I believe. Berners has gone to Palermo.'

'How did he manage that?' I asked. 'And what on earth is Tizi-ousu?'

'Awful, I think,' said Teddy. 'Some sort of school. Nobody knows how long we stay there. I'm going to get out of it if I can. I say, shall we go to GHQ and try to do something? What about your generals?'

'I'm no good at all with generals,' said I, firmly. 'Of course, I might try Maxwell. But it's all rather depressing. I don't know what on earth I'm here for.'

'Why don't you come into Fine Arts? You'd love it, and you'd be just the person for it,' said Teddy, with his usual enthusiasm.

'Unfortunately I don't know the first thing about it. It is being rapidly borne upon me that I don't know the first thing about anything. Fine Arts at one end, drains at the other. And law and education, I suppose, in between. I'm merely a dilettante.'

Teddy quoted some lines from Beddington's verse of the Amgot anthem:

> At Wimbledon College
> They stuffed him with knowledge
> Of Amgot's essential hygiene:
> He took sanitation
> And crops in rotation
> With law and fine arts in between –

'Hey, I mustn't sing in church, I suppose,' he added, breaking off, for we had arrived at the so-called English Church, whose delicate lines and graceful domes seemed oddly a variance with the rows of rush-bottomed chairs and hassocks. 'It is fascinating to see how Saracenic culture –'

'Teddy,' I said, 'why are you a soldier at all?'

'Because I hate the Germans.' Teddy tapped his stick angrily against a column. 'I hate them and I hate them and I hate them. I suppose I oughtn't to say that in church. But I've always hated them.'

'I don't believe it. You don't hate anybody. You'd be giving all Germans cigarettes and chocolates the moment you got into Germany.'

'I shouldn't! I shouldn't! One may respect their art, but –'

'Not even the descendants of your beloved Mozart?'

'We've got to win the war, I suppose,' said Teddy, moodily. He began to hum a phrase from *The Magic Flute*. The mosque had a pleasant echo. How many preachers of various religions had exhorted their congregations in this building to assist them in slaughtering the heretic? Perhaps one should look upon it all as as huge joke: look after oneself and be careful to be on the right side. But then, one couldn't pick one's side: that was decided by the accident of birth. Oneself, then.

'I suppose,' I said, 'we'd better try our luck with GHQ.'

GHQ, as far as Amgot was concerned, proved to be at the top of a great many rickety stairs, and rather a mean place when you got there. But it was full of dignity and bureaucracy. I could not see Colonel Maxwell without an appointment and he was exceedingly busy. We could and did see a very vague Captain Mitchell in a very small office, and he assured us that we should be going to Tizi-ousu the very next day. Italy? Oh, well, perhaps later, when we had been 'assigned'. Transport was very tight. We must have patience. At this point we ran into Sir Leonard Woolley, who was passing through on a rapid visit to Italy, accompanied by a lady secretary dressed as a captain. I had known Sir Leonard slightly for some time, but his views and mine on India had collided violently at the beginning of the war, and I could hope for no help from him. He was, on the other hand, very much up Teddy's street, and said at once that he would help him to get quickly to Italy. The depression which this occasioned in me was only slightly alleviated by the fact that Sir Leonard did not seem to be able to get to Italy himself.

'Deplorable lack of organisation!' he complained. 'Here I am with all the necessary papers, and the Home authorities wanting me back, and day after day I come to this office and there's no transport!'

This was my first introduction to Priority, a most important by-product of war. Priority I was reserved for VIP – Very Important People – and got you anywhere. Priority II was for generals and such, and ensured you a moderately quick passage, provided that transport was available. Priority III was for lesser, but still urgently needed, fry: we might have got it if somebody had urgently needed us, but they seldom did. All other Priorities were scarcely worth having. It must be added that Priorities could be gotten and lost in various peculiar ways. On this occasion Captain Mitchell, after noting that we knew Sir Leonard, whispered to us: 'Who *is* that bird, really?'

Teddy replied quite indignantly that he was a most famous archaeologist and Head of the War Office Department for Fine Arts.

'Well, well,' said Captain Mitchell. 'We know nothing about him here, you know. Perhaps he should have Priority II? I had only given III, which means that he'll never get there.'

We said (noting that Priority III couldn't do for us) that he most certainly ought to have at least II. Captain Mitchell sighed, and with a duster removed the name Woolley from one part of the blackboard which hung above his desk, and chalked it up in another. Teddy and I looked at one another, great minds thinking alike. If, when Mitchell was out of the room, we were to chalk up Croft-Murray and Fielden in the right place . . .

Having nothing more or better to do, we now registered our names with the clerk in charge of mail. In this world of lost identities, that seemed important, and we left the office with the pleasant but wholly mistaken idea that our mail would reach us without undue delay. The day was passing and I began to feel anxious about the camp, the policemen, and the mud. Something had to be done. I steered Teddy down the rue Michelet to the British Officer's Club, a gloomy affair which resembled an enormously over-crowded station buffet. Here, by waiting in a long queue, one could get something to eat. But as I was checking in my cap and overcoat at the cloakroom, a familiar voice said in loud tones: 'So they've got you at last!'

I looked round and saw Oliver leaning against the wall, regarding me with amusement.

'I imagined that you'd be turning up. No escape, you know, however much you wriggle!'

'Oliver!' I exclaimed. 'The answer to my maiden's prayer! A roof, a bed, in mercy's name!'

'Of course,' said Oliver. '179 rue Michelet, at your service.'

Thus I evaded mud. Oliver's flat was grubby, down-at-heel, and in execrable taste. It had, rare in Algiers, a showerbath which actually worked, though spasmodically, shooting a jet of scalding water into the eye while projecting an icy deluge on to the navel. I could sleep on a much-battered divan in the corner of Oliver's bedroom. For these mercies I was not only at the time grateful but shortly afterwards homesick. They were an oasis of comfort and cleanliness in a desert of diminishing delight. And the diminution of delight started on the next evening, when we were ordered to parade at the racecourse for transit to Tizi-ousu.

There was no evading this. Obviously I ought to have been quicker and wiser with Maxwell or the generals, but I had failed. Under the probing eyes of the policemen in uniform, a tough lot, I had to drag my luggage across the racecourse, earnestly wishing that I had refrained from taking with me all the two hundred pounds permitted. Two hundred pounds, when wet with rain and slippery with mud, is a heavyish load for a middle-aged gent. There was also, I felt and feel, a certain loss of dignity in dragging luggage about. I am all against the dignity of labour, except in other people. In some disorder and a bad temper, I managed to land my belongings in the colonels' lorry which had just arrived from Algiers, and seemed less crowded than ours. Also it had no policemen.

We started. Nobody, not even the colonels, had the remotest idea of the distance to Tizi-ousu or of our fate when we got there. We sat on the floor of the lorry, which after a little seemed hard. It began to rain, and it was also extremely cold. An hour passed, and another, and then a third and a fourth. The land around us grew more and more desolate. There were hills in the distance with violet shadows, very picturesque, but small signs of human habitation. At last we trundled into a straggling village and, turning into a deserted lane, came to a standstill. It was very quiet. We got stiffly out, stretching cramped legs. Two or three officers appeared round a corner, and perceiving some of our company, uttered cries of welcome. Old Wimbledonians, I gathered. I wished that somebody would welcome me, or rather I wished passionately that I were somewhere else. If the *Aorangi* were bad, this, my very bones told me, was going to be infinitely worse.

Led by the welcomers, we started to walk up an extremely steep road. At the top appeared gaunt, naked buildings which had the appearance of unfinished schoolhouses. That is what they

were. Our guides, pointing to them, said politely: 'That's London.'
I did not understand, but I wished that it were.

There are certain moments in my life when I am overcome by
a panic so intense as to make me feel that I must instantly
explode, expire, or be translated to a quiet room where regular
meals are served to me by a silent and beautiful nurse who also
places a hot water bottle at my feet. Such moments do not occur
in wars, blitzes, or other similar catastrophes in which my
cowardice is merely cringing, but more at childrens' and grown-
ups' parties, formal meetings, bazaars, funerals, weddings and
family gatherings. They are moments when human sanity, whatever that may be, seems about to leave me, and I feel riding
within me a foaming chattering ape, tearing hair from heads
and spectacles from noses, burrowing under sofas and cracking
craniums with anything handy. Does anybody else ever feel like
this? I shall never know. But one of these moments came to me
very soon after I stepped over the threshold of 'London'.

Tizi-ousu was a Military Government School. That is to say,
is taught, or was supposed to teach, people how to militarily
govern. The school had been located in this village eighty miles
from Algiers because, presumably, the empty half-finished buildings were handy and the officers would be far from mischief,
their hands, be it added, being quite frantically idle. Convenien-
ce or secrecy or the whim of some extra-imaginative commandant had decreed that the scattered buildings should each be
dowered with the name of a city. 'Come down and dine at
Washington,' or 'I must just run over and get my pen from
Manchester,' seemed at first a little queer, but one got used to
it as one gets used to all things. It was a great deal more difficult to get accustomed to the fact that these far from commo-
dious buildings were filled to more than overflowing with four
hundred elderly officers, of whom three hundred and fifty, at
the time of our arrival, were American.

My moment of panic had, however, nothing whatever to do
with Americanism. I was far from noticing the nationality of
the denizens of London. My consciousness registered only the
fact that I had stepped into the exact atmosphere of my private
school, a place which I had loathed so extravagantly that all
my notions of hell, when I have them, are connected with it.
Here in London were the same aggressively bare walls and
tables, the same sense of chill discomfort, the same jostling un-

thinking herd of humanity with its same unwashed smell, the same feeling, above all, of being part of a condemned and imprisoned pack. We were placed on benches at long wooden tables on which gobbets of food lingered, and before us were set earthenware bowls looking none too clean and containing something which, had I known it, was American C rations, doubtless sustaining to the stomach but revolting, as far as I was concerned, to eye and palate alike. No sooner were we seated than the bench which supported three fat majors opposite me collapsed, and with three heavy smacks they landed on the stone floor. Everyone laughed uproariously. The majors took it in very good part. It was all exactly as it would have been at my private school. And at this moment I felt rising within me the urge to escape, to go mad, to run and run and run upon the desolate hills, to do anything, in short, but this. I felt with an absolute rising of the hair on my scalp that I was for ever a prisoner, a prisoner without identity, just another one of these old and bloated colonels and majors stretching away and away down the long bare tables, cackling and rumbling into an eternal void ...

But human sanity being a chain which, for fear of imprisonment by our fellow-men, binds us all more or less, I did, of course, nothing. I registered myself for a billet and meekly put up my camp bed in the freezing little cell which I shared with two other majors, Major Blank and Major Zero. Major Zero had been at Tizi-ousu for three months and had, it seemed, acquired a measure of indifference to it with the help of enormous quantities of poisonously bad cognac which he somehow managed to import from Algiers. He was completely bald, had no teeth and a certain amount of charm. When asleep he made a regular little chirruping noise followed by a long sighing puff, and for these noises I could gladly have killed him. Major Blank had spent, so far, only a fortnight at the school, and was still fighting it: he spoke of his 'assignment' quite hopefully, whereas Major Zero had clearly long ago given up all hope of being assigned anywhere. Major Blank was ruddy and hearty: he snored in a wet gurgling way and almost invariably gave vent to a frightful yell at about 2 a.m.: I once drew his attention to this and he said immediately, in an indifferent sort of way, that he had always done it. Between these two majors I put up, as I have said, my camp bed and at once began to indulge in some painful regrets. The first regret was that I had not in all London been able to obtain a mattress, and camp-beds without mattresses are decidedly chilly: the second was that I had not enough blankets: the third was that I could no longer carry the sleeping draught without which, for the past ten years, I had been eternally wakeful. I slept but ill: and it need scarcely be recorded that my nights were remarkable for one steadfast resolution – to escape, as soon as might be, from Tizi-ousu.

In the morning it was breakfast at 7.30, parade at 8. On notice-boards in the big bare hall we read our names, dismally enrolled in platoons: for a few fortunates there were instructions to proceed to Algiers. It was raining hard, so we assembled muffled in gas-capes on a kind of barrack square which faced the gaunt walls of London. A less military-looking lot can hardly ever have been seen. We were all, it seemed, middle-aged or more than middle-aged; and the years had given to most of us a definite stamp of corpulence or lankiness. A few British veterans there were who still bore the impress of the last war: but among the Americans there was scarcely any attempt at smartness. They were business men dressed up for the occasion and didn't attempt to disguise it. The wonder was, one couldn't help thinking, that they arrived on parade at all.

When we had been shuffled into some kind of order, a Voice descended unto us from above. It was the voice of the British Colonel in charge of training, who stood on a balcony after the fashion of Mussolini, and, with the aid of a loudspeaker, told us our duties for the day. The Colonel had a refined-Oxford voice which was faintly funny even to Englishmen, and must have been fantastic, as well as almost incomprehensible, to the Americans. He patted the air as he spoke, and obviously very much enjoyed his performance. He said:

'Eh'm gled to welcome some newcomers to our midst and Eh feel sure that they will benefit bey this course. Eh'm sorry the weatheh is so bed, but that I cehn't help. Neow this morning there will be the usual Italian classes, and Eh must esk newcomers to faind the appropriate class for themselves. Et ten o'clock all newcomers will parade at Bristol. Et ten thirty there will be a lectchah on the Legal Administration of Administered Territory and et eleven thirty we shell have the pleshah of hearing Colonel Rowell, lately returned from Secily. Gentlemen, thenk you.'

We now went indoors, if it could be called indoors. I cannot remember any doors and there were certainly no windows. A bitter wind blew through the classroom, so that we could not take off our dripping gas-capes. The Italian classes began at once, and were all, it appeared, conducted in the same manner, that is, in the manner of a chorus. Officers sat in rows at the desks, and the instructor, an Italo-American soldier, said 'Buon giorno!' whereat the class repeated, with one very American voice 'Bwahn jah-naw'. We newcomers were meanwhile 'tested' in Italian by a corporal. He exchanged a few words with me, seemed extremely startled by my knowledge, and passed on. Presently I found myself a member of a 'top' class of three, one of whom was a colonel who spoke Italian so much better than I did that I was immediately reduced to silence, while the other, also a colonel, had apparently no reason for joining us since he appeared to understand nothing. The net result of this ill-assorted trio was that Colonel Coke conducted a fluent political discussion with the Italo-American corporal, while Colonel Coal interjected a few idiotic remarks and I remained silent. In any case I was not, in my dripping gas-cape, soaked boots and extreme state of cold, in any mood for conversation.

At ten o'clock we were in a large lecture hall with a stage. We sat about on the benches, for all the world like droopy wet birds on telegraph lines. The colonel who had addressed us from the balcony now spoke from the stage. We must remember, he said, that this was an Allied show. We had to do our best to work in with American officers. Their ways were not always ours nor our ways theirs. And so on. He added a point of illustration. All American officers saluted each other irrespective of rank. That was not in the British tradition. But we must forget the British tradition and do the same. This annoyed me and I wanted to ask why on earth the Americans should not forget American tradition which was after all much younger, but I was too cold and broody to put the question. The result of this fantastic instruction was that while we were at Tizi-ousu we wore out our right arms and the peaks of our caps in frenzied saluting: once we got to Italy, it became the rarest thing on earth for any officer or even soldier to make any pretence of saluting at all. By December 1944, any soldier saluting me in Rome would so startle me as to make me drop at once anything I happened to be carry-ing.

Through the rain we sludged up the hill to London again, saluting right and left, and sat us down once more at the grubby wooden tables to scrape our earthenware bowls. Afterwards we crowded hopefully round the notice-boards. There would be revolver practice and then a 'hike' in the afternoon. Mysterious entities known as 'Region V' and 'Region VII' were being formed. The following officers would be seen tomorrow by the Assignment Board . . . not me. My spirits sank still lower. I looked at the rain and decided that nothing on earth would persuade me to shoot a revolver or walk. On the other hand it was too cold to sit still, there were no books to be had by any means, and although I supposed I could roll myself up on my camp bed and listen to the conversation of Majors Blank and Zero, the prospect had no appeal.

Teddy – whose Woolley had not saved him from Tizi-ousu, and who, as an expert on Fine Arts, was ludicrously out of place there – had become intoxicated as well as irritated by the American accent. Neither he nor I had ever been to the States, and our sudden precipitation into an overwhelming mass of American voices and mannerisms was startling. 'Did you understand a *word* of that?' he would ask me eagerly, after some officer had been explaining the beauties of Ithaca, or Cleveland, Ohio. 'Not a word? Nor did I. Shall we ever?' And he began to talk loudly in an accent which he thought American, shouting 'Marnin' Maijor!' in the street, so that I, who felt that this might be rude, tried to shush him. But of course the addressees must merely have thought that he spoke better English than most mumbling incomprehensible Englishmen. Teddy, however, was also irritated and alarmed. 'Too *many* of them! It's a swarm! It's Bedlam!' he would groan, thumping his stick on the ground. 'No, no, no, it gets me down!'

In the evening before our last scrape of earthenware we were allowed a glass of wine. It was filthy stuff, the first of many litres of horrible near-grape that I was destined to pour down my gullet, and we drank it, standing in the rain-and-wind-swept corridor, out of the halves of bottles roughly broken, on which, if you were not careful, you could prettily gash your lip. While musing over the mixture in my bottle-bottom, I was accosted by a very nice American major, who introduced himself as Randolph Leigh and said that he had been wanting to meet me. He had some regard for a little book I had written which ought, he thought, to be published in the States. I almost embraced him. It was unbelievable that anyone should pick me out of the ruck, should actually know my name. My tail absolutely wagged. Major Leigh asked, without further ado, whether, if he could get my book published in America, I would give him fifty per cent.

266

My tail wagged a bit slower, but I said yes, why not, because after all that book seemed a faint and far away thing now. Leigh then told me that he was waiting for assignment as Public Relations Officer.

This was interesting. I had done Public Relations work in the Ministries of Food and Aircraft Production, and if it came to an Assignment Board, I could claim a sort of *expertise* in that field, to which my years of radio also more or less fitted. I had detested Public Relations work always. The Public Relations Officer is everybody's fool. He is supposed to filter Authority's news to the press, thus collecting dirt from above and execration at the vile filtered mixture from below. If a good story 'breaks', Authority will skip the Public Relations Officer altogether and reap the credit: if a wily correspondent gets away with confidential news, the Public Relations Officer is to blame: if there is no news, the Public Relations Officer is an oaf for not inventing it. 'PR' has in war, perhaps owing to America, grown to huge proportions: its only real use, as far as I could ever see, is to feed, billet and transport correspondents. On the other hand, the Public Relations Officer sees a good deal of the game: and I would, in any case, have seized upon anything that offered the shadow of an excuse to escape from Tizi-ousu. So I learned from Major Leigh all that I could about the Public Relations of Amgot. It appeared that there weren't any. So far, so good.

After two days, along with many others, I got dysentery. I know how to deal with this old enemy from Gallipoli days, but it did not make life more comfortable. The wind seemed colder, the food more revolting, the barren hills more drear. I discovered that very few officers ever went to lectures and indeed there were very few lectures. Mostly people sat about in greatcoats in the classrooms, reading Italian grammars, or sat on their camp beds and drank synthetic cognac, if anyone had it. Regions V and VII were discovered to be Umbria and Tuscany, parts of Italy as yet unconquered. Our armies appeared to be so firmly stuck just north of Naples that the prospects of further conquests were remote. It was even said that Amgot officers were being sent back from Sicily. There was talk of forming Regions IX and X but even if they were formed – that is to say, when a group of officers had been set to study their geography and economics – there would still be far too many officers without a job, it seemed, inTizi-ousu. Something, in fact, had to be done, if one wasn't going to be caught in Tizi-ousu for ever.

But the days dragged on. I grew dirtier and dirtier, in fact extremely dirty. The water that dribbled out of the common taps was almost too cold to wash even the hands, let alone the body. I was encrusted with dirt. In spite of our visit to the clerk at GHQ, no mail arrived for us: and this was to enrage us for weeks to come. For want of something better to do, I wrote some long letters, and for want of something better to say, I remarked in one of them that what chiefly struck me about Americans was their musty superfluity, and that it was high time that the Volsces, or somebody, were in arms. I forgot to 'frank' this letter, which was, perhaps, unfortunate. It was opened by an American censor. But of that, at the time, I knew nothing.

Summoned at long last to the Assignment Board, I waited in some trepidation in the corridor of Washington. I told myself that my fate was about to be decided and I must pull myself together. Fred Beddington was also waiting: he had had dysentery rather badly and looked bedraggled. 'This place,' he remarked, 'is no longer even funny.' When he came out he told me that he had been assigned as Chief Executive Officer of Region IX. That was Emilia. I said that Bologna was a charming place. He said with a sigh that he hardly expected to see it. He was right. I went in. The Assignment Board was nothing more than the mild Colonel Mildeman and another sealyham type of colonel, very small and stupid. At their request I reeled off my Who's Who list, which always sounds impressive when reeled.

'I feel sure that you should be of great value,' said Mildeman.

'Ah-hum, yes, indeed,' muttered the sealyham, shuffling his papers.

Neither of them, of course, meant it. All authorities know by instinct, whatever I or anybody else may tell them, that I am a Dangerous Person, somebody who Won't Do What He's Told, somebody who laughs at the wrong things, probably doesn't believe in God, above all Lacks Respect. They always know and I always know that they know. I told myself now that I must be very careful indeed. Both Sealyham and Mildeman were clearly puzzled. Law, Education, Local Government, Police, Finance, Transport, Education –

'What about Education?' asked Sealyham, who clearly thought that I was a highbrow.

I said that I knew nothing at all about education.

Not Education, then. Public Health, Sanitation, Public Works, Agriculture, Food –

'What about Food? You were in the Ministry of Food, I see.'
I said I had never understood anything about food.

'H'm, Displaced persons, Refugees, Information – what about Information?'

'What sort of information?' I asked.

'Well, – tut – information, I suppose,' said Sealyham. 'But I don't think the Information Section has been formed.'

'You couldn't,' I said hopefully, 'assign me to something that hasn't been formed?'

'Well – tut – no, I suppose not, no. Rather a difficult case. Let's see now – Prisoners of War, Army, Navy, War materials, Disposal, Industry, Commerce, Fine Arts – what about Fine Arts, now?'

I wondered, could I do it? It would be fascinating. No, I felt sure that I didn't know enough. No, I said, I knew nothing about Fine Arts.

'Nothing about Fine Arts?' said Sealyham, looking over his spectacles. 'But what about the BBC and all that, hey? What about the BBC?'

I said firmly that the BBC had nothing whatever to do with Fine Arts.

'Ho!' said Sealyham, 'the BBC ... nothing to do ... Quite a wag, aren't you?'

It seemed that the interview was getting out of hand.

'I think you should put me down for Public Relations,' I suggested.

'Public *Relations?*' said Sealyham, as if this was quite a new idea. '*Public* Relations? I don't thing we have any. Have we?' he added, turning in a puzzled way to Colonel Mildeman.

'I – er – really don't know,' said Mildeman. 'Perhaps there should be.'

'Obviously, there'll have to be' I said.

'I don't think *obviously*,' said Sealyham, nettled. 'That is for the authorities to decide.'

'Of course,' I agreed, cursing my tongue. And with an effort I added: 'I should think for *you* to decide, sir.'

'Hum – well, in a sense, perhaps, yes,' said Sealyham. That had done the trick. I watched him writing slowly 'Recommended for Public Relations' against my name. That has got me, I thought, so far: but damnation take me if I ever do Public Relations work again. Just let me get out of this and into Italy ... What should I do in Italy? That question seemed to grow more and more difficult. I had visualized myself as doing possibly radio work, which with Italians might have been good fun, or merely acting as an interpreter. What I *wanted* to do in Italy had always been a vague and indefinable thing in my mind. I wanted to be there because I felt that the Allies would trample over Italy, and I wished, if I could, to prevent a little of the trampling. But I had never thought of Italy in terms of these jobs, these Laws and Public Works and Sanitation, and I couldn't see myself in such capacities. But why worry? The thing was to get out of Tizi-ousu.

On the next day we were told at breakfast that there were some trucks going to Algiers, and officers could go if they liked, and return that evening. In a hurry and a scrum officers dashed from their earthenware bowls. Not being a hurrier or a scrummer, I arrived almost too late to be able to force my way in to any truck, but on the tail of a truck for eighty miles I sat. Only the compact coating of dust which I received prevented me, I am persuaded, from falling to pieces. But so glad was I to be out, even for a day, of Tizi-ousu, that I should not have minded if my feet had dropped off.

There was only one first, obvious, and essential thing to do in Algiers, and that was to have a bath. Oliver had told me that he was leaving for England and in any case the truck did not go near his flat. So I hurried with the others to the American Red Cross. This was actually the only place in Algiers where officers (below the rank of colonel) could get a bath at all. And each of us had to be introduced by an American. The American officers were kindness itself: they not only introduced us but pressed food and drink and soap and towels upon us: but I felt that the British authorities might have done better. It was the beginning, in me, of that sense of material inferiority which has made, and will make, so many strained relations between Americans and British. The British are so accustomed to dominating things and people that they cannot swallow the idea of being a poor relation: whereas the Americans, who can seldom dominate, resent the British assumption that the British, in fact, still do, and occasionally and naturally remind them that they do so with American permission.

The American Red Cross was – even apart from the dazzling contrast with Tizi-ousu – an exceptionally attractive place. It had a vast reading-room, the walls of which had been covered by the most slick and amusing frescoes of New York that you could wish to see. Perhaps they were more than slick and amusing: they had real beauty, and gave the place a gallant air. There was a prettily furnished snack-bar and a handsome dining-room: flowers everywhere, and plenty of books and magazines. You might have expected a luscious bath: oddly encugh, the only baths consisted of one large room in which twenty showers set close together in the ceiling played upon twenty naked figures set close together on the floor. The effect was rather Michael-Angelesque and amusing, and I revelled in my shower: in any case the 1914 war had destroyed any sense of modesty that I may ever have had. But I observed that the British officers were a little shocked by this, whereas to the Americans it was perfectly natural: and generalising from the particular, I wondered whether Americans wouldn't take very easily to communism.

As soon as I had bathed I flitted up the hill to GHQ. I was determined to see Colonel Maxwell, arbiter of our destinies, and I sent through Colonel Maxwell's office door a persistent thought which told Colonel Maxwell that he would not get out of that office without seeing me. And Colonel Maxwell saw me. He was very polite and very courteous and very distant. 'I am sure,' he said, 'that you can be very useful to us.' I wanted to say 'But have you never *heard* of me? Did nobody in England say they were sending me or why they were sending me?' But I knew that it was useless to say anything, for I knew that Colonel Maxwell was not really arbiter of anybody's destinies. He was another red-tabbed bureaucrat. And I came back thinking to myself, in a fury, that do what I might, I should be immured at Tizi-ousu for the rest of the war. I flung myself into Captain Mitchell's little office and said: 'It's the limit!'

'What's the limit?'

'The way you keep people hanging about!'

'Would you like to write a letter?' said Captain Mitchell, 'There's an air courier going tomorrow.'

'I would,' I said. 'But there's something I'd like better.'

'What's that?'

'To get out of Tizi-ousu.'

'You don't like it?'

'I don't like it.'

'Where would you rather be?'

'Italy, here, anywhere! In a dustbin, for that matter.'

'Here?'

'Better than there.'

271

'Then come here.'

'How?'

'I'll write an order.'

'You mean to say,' I said 'that *you* can write an order to release me from that prison?'

'Why certainly,' said Captain Mitchell.

'*Now?*'

'Now, if you like.'

'Write it,' I said. 'Can you give me a car?'

'Might be done,' said Captain Mitchell.

I got the order and I got the car. I called at Oliver's flat to see if he was still there and found that he was. The driver of my car, a lumpy open American machine known as a Command car, was a bulky singing swearing Yankee who must have driven trucks very fast in peace-time: he covered those eighty miles in two hours and a quarter. I seized my luggage, told Teddy what he must do, deposited my order in the office, and was back on the road again in a quarter of an hour. I pinched myself to see if I was well and truly awake. 'Good-bye, Tizi-ousu!' my rising spirits chanted. A French lorry, refusing for some time to let us pass, followed us doggedly, its headlights blindingly reflected on our windscreen. My driver only fled the faster, screaming round precipitous curves and diving into wells of darkness. It did not matter: nothing mattered. Tizi-ousu was safely behind me, and in Algiers, I felt, all things were possible.

We were flying high across the Mediterranean on a cloudless day. Tunis, a smudge of brown mist on the tilting horizon, lay behind us: ahead and as yet unseen was Sicily. Far below, the silver sea was speckled by a large convoy. Our plane was not the latest word in luxury: running along the sides were tin benches, appropriately dented for posteriors. They were slippery and hard, and most peculiar twists of the neck were necessary if any view was to be obtained from the little portholes behind us. A stink of petrol drifted through the cabin, already blue with the smoke of thirty cigarettes. Thirty men's baggage lay in a heap towards the tail. Everybody was very gay.

Teddy and I were gay, too, but apprehension clung to us. Mentally we poured incessant libations to the gods – the old gods of Sicily, perhaps, whose pilgrimage we were, not without stress and ardour, making. But we still felt nervous about the gods of Africa, those redtape gods who had bound us and held us, and who might yet, who knew, recall us. It was only twenty days since we had stepped ashore from the *Aorangi*, and yet those twenty days seemed a purgatory which might have had no end. From our tin bucket seats we looked down on the lovely sea and prayed.

Algiers had proved, in fact, nearly as bad as Tizi-ousu. True, there were no early parades, no earthenware bowls, no revolver-practice and hiking: but it was a city of nothing-to-do, a station-waiting-room city, where our morning and afternoon trudges up the long hill resulted in nothing except Captain Mitchell's sigh of 'Nothing today, I'm afraid.' And, stupid as it may seem, it had seemed more than easy to get lost and forgotten for ever in Algiers. Nobody cared whether we stayed or went, that was the truth of it; we knew now that the Allied Commission had been formed in Brindisi to supervise the execution of the Armistice terms: we knew that Amgot was busy in Sicily and Calabria: but nobody, it appeared, wanted us. Teddy, I knew, must be wanted eventually: an expert from the British Museum couldn't be indefinitely ignored: but almost anything, I felt, might happen to me. And because of this, perhaps, Teddy was bolder with Captain Mitchell than I was. We came to know, with desolating familiarity, the exact meaning of the various spaces on the Captain's blackboard; and Teddy, jabbing his stick ferociously towards it, would exclaim, 'Now just be a good fellow and put us *there* this morning,' to which Captain Mitchell would wearily reply that it was no good putting us there with Priority III. Teddy thumped his stick and said 'Well, give us Priority II, man!' But Captain Mitchell shook his head; and down the hill, disgusted, we went again.

We roamed the Kasba, tested the mostly horrid little restaurants, ate meals in dingy Transit Messes, and preyed on the goodwill of the American Red Cross: this last matter worried me eventually into writing a letter to a High Personage, suggesting that England still possessed sufficient money, goodwill, ability and pretty women to be able to give British officers some semblance of equality with their American peers. Teddy later advanced, rather vilely, the theory that the main result of this letter was the seizure, to his mortification and disgust, of the Royal Palace of Naples as a canteen for British troops.

It was Teddy, eventually, who had the Bright and Cunning Idea. I had bought, rather expensively – but how, over and over again, was that expense justified! – an enormous Arab rug of white and blue, the kind of thing that you could roll yourself in, and the kind of thing that my chilly limbs had yearned for at Tizi-ousu. And as we passed down the street with this bundle, we came to the shiny doors of MATS – the Mediterranean Air Transport Service. And Teddy, tapping his stick on the window, said, 'now perhaps we ought to do something here?' And I replied 'Well, we might try.' And in we went. And thus the main force of our daily attack shifted from Captain Mitchell to MATS. And MATS, perhaps because it was chiefly American, was more amenable than Mitchell. We had only to get a travel order, they said, and then . . .

Mitchell was unexpectedly stubborn about the travel order. Why should we want a travel order, when we weren't in the right place on the blackboard? We could only mutter that it would be nice to have a travel order, one day we should want a travel order, why not a travel order now? Mitchell objected that he had no orders to give us a travel order: didn't, in fact, really know anything about us. Why on earth, anyway, were we in such a hurry to get to Palermo? We said we really didn't quite know, it seemed to us that we ought to be there, what were we doing here? Mitchell didn't know that either, so we said that we knew that we were being a great nuisance to him, with which he heartily agreed. Then, we suggested, with a travel order we *might* give him no further trouble. But how could that be, he said: nobody could leave without his permission. Oh, we knew *that*, we said hurriedly: but if we found methods about which we could tell him, wouldn't that be a good thing? Think of this office without us, said Teddy, rapping his stick on Captain Mitchell's papers. Captain Mitchell thought: eventually he made out two travel orders. Priority III.

'Priority III?' said MATS. 'Well, well, we'll do our best.' And after a few disappointing mornings, MATS had a paper for us – by A/T to Sicily. We said nothing to Captain Mitchell. We crawled one morning with our luggage into a truck and sped to the aerodrome of Maison Blanche. The aerodrome was almost knee-deep in mud, crowds of officers with mountains of luggage seemed to be everywhere, but the chatter of planes was music in our ears. We presented our papers at the booking-office.

'Priority III?' said the clerk, raising pained eyebrows. 'Not a charnst, I'm afraid, sir, not a charnst. Very full today.'

We had a few glib lies ready, such as 'General Weevil has sent for me immediately,' but this was a British clerk, the Lord be praised. So I said to him 'Do British officers always get left behind?' And he said 'Well, I'll see what I can do, sir.' He went away and we sat and sat and sat. To pass the time away, we had ourselves and our baggage weighed. I, being a lightweight, came off creditably, but Teddy, who was positively bulging with books and other accessories, was about twice the permitted standard. 'Most *essential* papers,' he exclaimed loudly, tapping a bursting suitcase. 'Straight from London, and instantly required in Sicily,' he confided, indicating a collection of prints which he had purchased in Algiers. I fully expected him to say that his stick was essential to Italy: which indeed, now that I come to think of it, it probably was. The weight-adjusting sergeant accepted it all very mildly. And presently our clerk came back to tell us: 'I think I've got you on to the two o'clock plane.'

We waited. A ritual that was to become familiar again. The loudspeakers issued the lists. Plane Number EJQRE leaving for Palermo at fourteen hours – Colonel Bonk – Here! – Colonel Tonk – Here! – Major Maggs – Here ... The list ended. We were not called. 'Sorry, sir,' said the clerk. 'Told you we were full up today.' Teddy groaned, 'I suppose we shall have to go back to Algiers.' I replied 'Not me,' thinking that this time Oliver really had gone back to England. To the clerk I said 'Well, we shall have to sit here till we get a plane.' 'Can't do that, sir,' said he, 'this office closes at five.' I said 'You'll find us here tomorrow morning, or the next, if necessary: you see, we have to get to Palermo.' Teddy sat obediently and very large: I endeavoured to look as aggressive as possible. The clerk looked at us as at a pair of clowns, and presently went away. 'It's no good,' said Teddy. 'Nevertheless,' I replied, 'I shall continue to sit here until a plane takes me away. Back to Algiers I am not going, not, not, not.' I had but little faith in my own determination, and visualized our eventual ignominious expulsion. Two hours slipped by and I had just given up all hope when the clerk returned and, bending over the counter, said: 'There's a special plane going to Tunis. Would that do?'

We said it would. We were not very happy about it, because Rumour had warned us to avoid Tunis at all costs: there, Rumour said, you could easily get stuck longer than at any other known place. But Tunis was not Algiers and in Tunis the long hand of Captain Mitchell might stretch in vain. In Tunis at least there would be a different office, different Transit Messes, a different American Red Cross. And from Tunis it would be more difficult to send us back. Thus reasoning we climbed with joy upon the plane, and fled along the coast. It was growing dusk, and as we looked down on the sea we told ourselves that it was here and here – so we had learned from the telegrams – that our convoy had been attacked after we had left it by torpedo-carrying planes, which had sunk three ships and blown up one of the destroyers: yes, the lovely white ship which had been our constant neighbour had gone down, and the little ship with the high prow, and the grey two-funnelled liner. It all seemed very unlikely on that calm evening.

It was dark in Tunis when we landed. The aerodrome had a deserted and faintly repellent air. All the airsheds were knocked about and burned out, of course, and the usual skeletons of dead aeroplanes lay around. We were told that we should stay at the Kock Hotel and the Kock Hotel, when we got to it in the darkness, was a strange gaunt tenement of a building, black and scarred, with very few and faint lights. Inside there were bare passages crowded to suffocation by Americans. Nothing but Americans. Except for ourselves, there wasn't a British soldier. We were given a ticket and sent into a huge black dormitory, where, under a single dim bulb, were fifty plank beds. Here and there American officers were sitting or lying about. It was immensely depressing: I had a slight feeling of panic. We went downstairs. It was 6 p.m. – not an hour at which it seems suitable to me to eat dinner, but it does so seem to the multitude of Americans. Therefore we waited in a queue, and after a while had C rations out of earthenware bowls.

'*No!*' I said to Teddy. 'I don't care for it. I don't believe it's necessary. And I can't stand all these Americans.'

'I *told* you!' replied Teddy. 'I told you they were a menace! Too *many* of them!'

'Let's get out,' I suggested.

'But where?'

'I don't believe,' I hazarded, 'that this is all of Tunis. In fact I know it isn't. I've been here before.'

Teddy, always willing to oblige, followed me into the darkness. He protested a little, but not much, when I heaved him into a passing lorry, which presently picked up a score of Spanish workmen. They talked volubly and I wondered where on earth we were going, for I certainly had not the faintest idea. However, something that looked like the street of a city did after a time show up, and when I asked the Spaniards for the Majestic Hotel they responded immediately, telling us where to get off and adding details of direction which I didn't understand. Without difficulty however, we found our goal.

Here were bright lights and a marble staircase and even an orchestra playing in the restaurant. No difficulty about getting two rooms which appeared to be clean and civilized. Teddy decided at once that we must start dinner all over again. I flinched at this, two dinners in an evening, even if one is C rations, being more than I can take. But Teddy was adamant: very soon he was on intimate terms with the orchestra, discussing what they could and could not play: and before long they were obliging him with a one-man concert. We went to bed feeling replete and gay, and I then discovered that one counterpane was all that the bed possessed: our baggage, of course, was still at the airport. My night was chilly: and when at last I fell into an uneasy sleep it was only to be awakened, it seemed instantly, by the strangest and slowest, surely, of human feet moving down the passage. Softly my door was opened, and an immense negro with a guttering candle stood before me: he opened his mouth but no sound came: instead, he advanced five fingers and then one, and moving forward advanced them again near my face five fingers and then one –

'Oui, oui,' I almost shouted. 'Oui, j'ai bien compris, six heures!'

Five fingers again, and then one. Slowly, silently, the negro withdrew. I got up, shuddering, and washed my face in icy water. Perhaps I had been altogether foolish to come to Tunis. We must not miss the plane. The bus, the only bus, so they said, was due to leave at seven. Teddy and I waited for it on the sidewalk, but when it arrived it was full and more than full. Officers clung to its bonnet and balanced on its footboards: officers bellied out behind it like the tails of a wind-blown waterproof. 'No room for more!' they shouted. 'We must get on!' we yelled. And scrambling, scraping, pushing, wrestling our way through a jungle of legs, we got on.

'Priority III?' they said at the airport. 'Not a hope, not a hope in hell! Have to wait for a fortnight at least.' But we were little daunted. We felt a new certainty that the thing could be done. We asked who was in charge. Sergeant Rafferty was in charge, it seemed, at that moment. Where was Sergeant Rafferty? In that office? We went in and said 'Sergeant Rafferty, isn't it?' and Sergeant Rafferty was pleased (just as we all are) that somebody knew his name. We said to Sergeant Rafferty that Captain Mitchell of GHQ, whom he was sure to know (and he didn't deny it) had instructed us to see him at Tunis so that we should reach Palermo for a meeting that very day. A most important meeting, we said. It was extraordinary, said Sergeant Rafferty, that we hadn't got higher than Priority III. We agreed warmly that it *was* extraordinary, but the whole thing had been done at such short notice, and Captain Mitchell had been so sure that Sergeant Rafferty would see us through . . .

And now, really, the mountains of Sicily could be discerned, painting their violet lines against the blue.

'Or do you think it's Algiers?' I asked Teddy.

'Get thee behind me, O father of horrors,' said Teddy, with his face twisted round to the porthole. 'The land of Bordonaro lies before us – though we'd better not *count* on it, perhaps, quite yet.'

No counting on it, I agreed: no counting on anything until it was firmly snatched. That, perhaps, was the outstanding difference between the nineteenth and twentieth centuries, the Victorian era and the Bright Young Things of Edward or George or Elizabeth. Would it be true to say that our forefathers looked forward with placid certainty to long orderly lives spent in toil or leisure in one baronial hall or in one cottage, while we of the twentieth century had known nothing save a world that cracked and crumbled with change? Hardly, because the great poverty-stricken majorities of the world could never have felt secure. Nevertheless, the elusive prize of 'security' was an eternally popular aim, perhaps particularly of the British, who so much admired Mr Baldwin's pipe and his slogan of 'safety first'. Should human beings feel secure? Clearly it was contrary to Christianity, which aimed at the sufficiency of the day and the consideration of the lilies of the field. Clearly it was contrary to nature, whose creatures are never secure. Clearly it was destructive, since a secure aristocracy had everywhere deteriorated in three or four generations. Clearly too, it was death to art and science, since the artists and scientists, the poets, painters, musicians and writers, seldom emerge from the ranks of the secure. Yet this war, like all wars, was being fought for security, which from a propagandist point of view meant saving ourselves from Hitler, but basically was the same eternal struggle for the lion's share of land, food, power; the struggle which could not end because nature's uneven distribution of talents to men made the even distribution of world resources impossible. Or was that a fallacy?

It was a fallacy only if human beings adopted the doctrines taught by all the great religious teachers of the world: the doctrines of abnegation. Yet, paradoxically, the doctrine of abnegation was most faithfully pursued by the soldiers and sailors and airmen who gave their comfort, limbs and lives to the unworthy aim of power. The deduction was, perhaps, that human nature possesses an essential nobility which is constantly misdirected. If we desire to stop wars, our problem is to discover an objective which unites men in a common endeavour and produces courage and self-sacrifice to the same extent as does war. We have never found such an objective yet. And until we do, all peace conferences must fail.

Such thoughts are dangerously pacifistic, and in fact I was a pacifist escaping from pacifism in khaki. Maybe most of us were. The struggle to stick to pacifist beliefs, which in time of war seem formless, passive, even cowardly, as well as extremely unpopular, is a much harder struggle than the donning of khaki and the acceptance of orders. Once one is a part of the machine it is easy to concentrate on the cogs and forget the purpose. There is even a warm sense of self-righteousness in being on the side of the big battalions. But the real heroes of mankind are never with the big battalions. The Christs, the Buddhas, the Rousseaus, the Tolstoys, the Kants and the Gauguins, the Jeremiahs and the Dantes, are never with the mass. Their lives are isolated struggles, intense, unswerving, unhappy, unhonoured, against the conventional beliefs, the accepted formulas, the Pharisaical complacencies of mankind.

'You've gone,' shouted Teddy in my ear, 'off into a dream. Trapani! *Trapani*, don't you see?' he exclaimed, jabbing his finger at the porthole. And there, below us, swam through the blue sea a crescent of sunwashed white houses, lavender hillsides and rust red roofs, and a high campanile whose bells, soft across the water, stole to the mental ear. No country in the world has, for me, the breathtaking beauty of Italy.

Teddy peered anxiously at me.

'What were you thinking about? Something *awful?*'

Yes. I was thinking about something awful. I was having a foretaste of what a publisher's reader was to write, two years later, about this diary: 'I have read these chapters with very little interest and a good deal of disgust . . . It is obvious that the author hates war and everything to do with it . . . The book is a study in perversity and you cannot found a book on perversity . . .

Unless later chapters contain something of real value as to the inner workings and high personalities of Amgot, I unhesitatingly recommend its rejection.'

Inner workings and high personalities of institutions, I reflect, as our silver aeroplane glides up the Conca d'Oro towards the blue mountains of Palermo, are not what I write about. Not what any sensible person writes about. One writes of beauty or horror or squalor as memory or imagination divulges them. One writes of experience and not to order. The important thing is that I am flying as a conquering (but rather dull) soldier into an enemy country which I love: and what are my feelings about it and how do I come to do it in this year of grace 1943, in this year of events which may be only dreams, figments of my own imagination in that 'experience' which occurs between truth and death? One peers into the kaleidoscope of memory, and the queer coloured pieces fall into new, meaningless patterns.

Chapter Eight

Kennst du das Land, wo die Zitronen blühn?
Im dunklen Laub die Gold-Orangen glühn,
Ein sanfter Wind vom blauen Himmel weht,
Die Myrte still und hoch der Lorbeer steht –
Kennst du es wohl? Dahin! Dahin!

GOETHE

... what trash is Rome,
what rubbish and what offal, when it serves
For the base matter to illuminate
So vile a thing as Caesar!

JULIUS CAESAR ACT I SCENE III

IN THIS RATHER erratic manner I came at last to Italy in 1943, and, apart from a few brief interludes, I have never left it since. Nor have I for an instant regretted that decision. In another year I shall have lived in it longer than in any other country, the only comparable period being in England up to my eighteenth year. Such expatriation must, I suppose, affect the character. *Inglese italianato, diavolo incarnato?* I shouldn't be surprised. What does surprise me is that everyone in the world doesn't want to live in Italy. No other country offers, in so small a compass, so great a wealth of natural beauty, of man's greatest handiwork, and of human courtesy and kindness. My years in Italy have been the happiest of my life. That does not imply disloyalty to my native England, though it does breed some regret for present Britain. English literature, English poetry, and the pastoral heart of England are unique and unsurpassed: but the nineteenth century conception of Great Britain, Rule Britannia and, to some extent, the British Empire – these, surely, have been mistakes in our history. Kipling, however jingoistic at times, saw it clearly enough in *Recessional*. We have been drunk with power. And, like all great nations, we have been corrupted by it. Thus we are in confusion. We strain at gnats and swallow camels. Every year we kill six thousand innocent people on our roads, and yet contrive to howl if a dozen violent negroes are killed in Africa, or a girl is strangled by a sex maniac. We spend huge sums which we cannot afford upon armaments which will make not the smallest difference to the fate of our little island. And to do this we destroy by taxation every source of our greatness – aristocracy, leisure, freedom of trade and travel, even the last vestige of respect for good architecture. We talk, how we talk, of generosity and equality and fairplay, but with an overgrown population shouting for higher wages, can never afford to lose economic domination over others. The English are a charming people, but the façade of Britain needs pulling down. Somewhere behind it lies the real England, the England of Shakespeare, the England which could produce him.

Palermo, when I came to it in 1943, was a town terribly and most unnecessarily wrecked by Allied bombardment. Looking at the ruined houses along the lovely waterfront, who would not ask what purpose had been served by such barbaric destruction? The Liberation of Italy! The liberation of a rose by a sledge-hammer. The rose would grow again, no doubt. And who could be blamed, after all? Mussolini, mesmerised by Hitler, encouraged by the failure of the Hoare-Laval pact, had failed to realize that Italy can never afford to fight a maritime power.

We were instructed, I cannot now think by whom, to report to Generals Spofford and Gueterbock. They sounded like a brand of champagne, but proved not nearly so invigorating. It should be explained that in the Allied Control Commission, and indeed in all administrative units in the Italian campaign, everything had to be controlled by Anglo-American twins. British colonel, American major: American colonel, British major: and so on. No jealousy, chaps, and fair play for mutual spying. The whole meal of Italy must be eaten with an American knife and a British fork, or vice versa. There were some French spoons too, and long ones: Russian tin-openers also appeared now and then. We found Generals Spofford and Gueterbock (perhaps feeling rather irritably ungeneralish in Amgot) polite but not enthusiastic about us. It took us a long time to see them at all, and when we did, they said that they knew nothing about us, and perhaps we might sometime be of use somewhere, and that was that. With some difficulty (and a lot of stick-tapping by Teddy) we got ourselves billetted in a tiny and very hideous villa, abandoned by its presumably Fascist owners. It was superbly uncomfortable: there was of course no light or water: drawers and cupboards had been flung open, clothes and papers scattered at random. Obviously we could have looted what we liked with impunity: it was an odd feeling. We could not resist looking through letters and papers. 'No, it's awful,' said Teddy. 'We are being disgusting, we mustn't – extremely fascinating, I must admit.' So we went out and looked at churches.

After a few days I landed a quite unofficial job with a Colonel Gayre. He was controlling Education, which meant that he had to sort out teachers and textbooks as quickly as possible, and get the schools going again in a (oh dear) democratic manner. It was a peculiar experience. No teacher, of course, would admit that he or she had ever been Fascist. The school textbooks were a revelation: and I now much regret that I did not keep some of them. At the time such evidence seemed to me better forgotten. I had known a good deal of anti-British feeling in India, but never anything which remotely approached the obscene cartoons of the British which had been provided for Italian children. I marvel today that any Italian who was schooled in those days can look upon an Englishman with aught but horror. Perhaps the period was mercifully brief: in any case, the Italians are not a people to cherish hatreds. But those books dented my mind for ever with the fact that all nationalism is the enemy of peace. All nationalism, white or brown or black or yellow. Nationalism and patriotism are foul perversions of the human spirit.

All of a sudden I was summoned to Gueterbock. There was a perfect hue and cry for me. I felt rather like a small boy who had been sent for by the Headmaster, and found hiding in the bushes. 'Where on earth have you *been*?' said Gueterbock. And he proceeded to tell me that I had written a Most Imprudent Letter about the musty superfluity of Americans, which had been opened by the censor. I opened my mouth to argue about freedom of opinion, but he waved a deprecatory hand. 'Don't do it again. What I have to tell you is that General Joyce requires you urgently. You must get off to Naples this evening.' I was not very clear as to who General Joyce was and what he did: and enquired what I was wanted for. 'Public Relations, I understand,' said Gueterbock. So my chicken had come home to roost. I left that night on a ship which appeared to be full of shells to the very brim, and on them I slept.

General Joyce was no longer young. He was a kind old boy with pince-nez. Rumour had it that he had been Eisenhower's military teacher, and for this reason had been given control of the Allied Commission. (Or perhaps it was still known as Amgot.) With him I flew off from Naples for Brindisi. It was piercingly cold. For some reason which now seems strange, the pilot was unable to get over the mountains. For about an hour we banked terrifyingly above and between snow-covered pinnacles. Then a member of the crew came in and informed the general that we should have to go down by the Gulf of Taranto. Halfway across it, the aeroplane made a tremendous lurch and dive, which scattered us all on the floor: and General Joyce's pince-nez were momentarily lost, but happily discovered intact. The pilot came in and apologised: there was, he said, a messerschmidt above us, which was bombing a ship: he had had to take evasive action. He seemed alarmed, and commented that we were unarmed. General Joyce adjusted his pince-nez, and said: 'I don't think they can possibly know that *I* am aboard' – a lovely example of egotism which did not entirely comfort me.

Brindisi is not, at the best of time, an attractive town. We – the small nucleus of the Allied Control Commission – were grouped in a very squalid little hotel on the dockside. The King, the Crown Prince, and Marshal Badoglio, rump of the Government of Italy, were accommodated in a little castle. It was apparent that nothing much was going on, and that of that nothing much I was expected to do the least possible. General Joyce already had an American Public Relations Officer named Cade: and neither he nor Cade wanted any British interference. I had been imported only to make a British twin, as regulations demanded. I was told nothing and did nothing. For the moment that did not much matter: it was one step better than Tizi-ousu: but I chafed a little. Presently Bari was badly bombed, and General Joyce decided that this was too near for comfort. It was arranged (and we had no choice) that we should all spend every night at Santa Cesarea, which is at the very tip of Italy's heel. It was some sixty-four miles from Brindisi. In a mad procession of jeeps, command cars, and lorries, we made this journey twice a day at breakneck speed, with the sullen and anti-Allied inhabitants of Apulia providing obstacles in the shape of large boulders at various points along the frightful roads.

At Santa Cesarea there was a new but not quite finished hotel, which was clean but freezing. Arriving there at ten or eleven at night, we got our frozen limbs to bed, and arose again at six, to repeat the race to an office in which I, at any rate, did nothing. There was nothing particular to complain of, but you must admit that it was peculiar. The fact was that neither General Joyce nor, I suspect, the Combined Chiefs of Staff, knew what to do about Military Government in a country which was half at peace and half at war, and, which was half occupied by the representatives of four different nations with different ideas. It was too peculiar to last.

And so, one morning, without the smallest warning, General Joyce and all his American staff were gone. They had flitted during the night. We, the British remnant, were left in a sort of politico-military fog. (At least I was: maybe some of the more distinguished, such as Gerald Upjohn KC, knew and would not tell). The fog was dispersed by the bulldog jaw and hunched shoulders of General Sir Noel Mason MacFarlane, straight from the Rock of Gibraltar. I took one look at him, and thought that my number was up. Not at all; for some strange reason he approved of me (At any rate then.) 'Got to get over to Naples at once,' he growled through clenched dentures. 'This Brindisi business absurd. You take over Public Relations. Find a staff. Sack anyone you like. Leave it to you.' We flew off to Naples that day. Mason Mac was a lovable man. Outwardly he was a braggart and a bully: he affected a beret, and, even in a snow-storm, shorts: he put on all the airs of a dictator. Behind the façade there was a nervous, worried soul, not very sure of itself and longing to be loved. He came to regard me, I fear, as a tire-some bore, and I was sorry about that. But much later, after the war, when he was an old man crippled with arthritis, I went to see him often, and he was not only pleased by these visits, but became amiable and told me a lot about himself. He certainly did not have an easy time with the Allied Commission.

It now suddenly became apparent that in the various regions and units of the Allied Commission, scattered over Southern Italy, there were quite a number of Public Relations Officers, and that they were all American, and all tough. To sort them out was not easy. The general idea seemed to be that 'the Bi'ish doan knaw a thing abaht publicity'. Author of that remark was Jack Leacacos of the Cleveland *Plain Dealer*. Jack, who stayed with me until the end of the war, is one of the rudest and angriest men I have ever encountered, but he somehow manages to com-bine this with charm, and is one of the hardest and most conscien-tious workers I have met. We had as Secretary an English sergeant named Cash, a rock in any crisis. And later I managed, after a lot of persuasion, to attract Major Tom Bergin, now Master of

Timothy Dwight College at Yale. He was a great acquisition, and became (as he has remained) a witty, wise, and valued friend. Such were the pillars of my staff. Were any of us necessary? I doubt it. I think the war would have been won without us. A PRO is not much use in any case: we were particularly badly placed because, although there was a quite good story to tell about Allied Military Government, it was always overshadowed by war news. I was, among other things, censor of the theatre, and we sat on an Allied Publications Board which was supposed to control the Italian press. I also had the unenviable job of controlling the Italian Minister of Information, Signor Spataro. The idea, theoretically, was that the Italian Government – nominated by the Allies but not yet, of course, elected – was a collection of naughty little boys who had to be taught democracy by us their masters, though their dignity must not be impaired. It was not a role in which I fancied myself, and I hope that if Signor Spataro (who is a Minister in the Italian Government today) reads these words, he will realize how hard I tried to keep out of his way, though our parallel courses involved a good deal of work. At this time I also started two publications which later landed me in some troubles. One was a précis – which it somehow amused me to do – of the despatches sent by Allied correspondents: and this became very popular. The other was called the Weekly Bulletin, and was a summary of activities in the Allied Commission: Tom Bergin and I found it a tempting opportunity for pulling authoritative legs, and sometimes we went too far. We also ran about Italy, noting the progress made in shattered towns and villages. But perhaps our only really useful function was the nannying of correspondents, who were always wanting information, or a bed, or a car. So pressing did these needs become that I eventually took over the old Manchurian Embassy in Rome as a club where correspondents could find bed and board. That was (thank God) my only experience of running a boarding-house, and I should have run it at a hideous loss had it not been for the bar, which just made the budget balance. All in all, there was quite a lot to do, however pointless it may have been.

That Neapolitan winter was surprisingly cold. I had been in Italy often enough. I had never realized that it was one thing to stay in a warm hotel with the sun shining, and quite another to work in offices and sleep in bare billets when all windows were blown out by air raids. Despite the Bay of Naples, it all tended to be rather squalid and dreary. The tremendous exception was the eruption of Vesuvius which, though not so dangerous as the war, dwarfed it in sound and fury. At that time I was living in a rather ramshackle flat near the docks with Christopher Lumby of *The Times* and Cecil Sprigge of Reuters and *The Manchester Guardian:* Teddy Croft-Murray, when in Naples (he had now become a busy man) made a fourth. At around midnight one evening, I noticed two streaks of red near the crater and pointed them out to Cecil and Christopher. Cecil trotted off at once to cable this bit of news: I thought he was daft, but he was quite right. Next day Vesuvius was belching red-hot boulders to the skies. By evening the spectacle was so grand that everyone in Naples who had a car – and there were plenty – went to have a closer look. The result was pandemonium. The Allied Commission decided to close the roads leading to the crater, and to me, the dogsbody, was assigned what I can only call the task of supervising the eruption, and signing passes for those whose genuine business took them to the villages on the slopes of the mountain. There was already an Italian Professor, with the rather unlikely name of Imbo, 'in charge of Vesuvius'. He was a nice little man, and he had an observatory perched on a crest near the crater. From this vantage-point I was able to watch the furious furnace of nature in action, and the two wide rivers of molten lava which flowed down towards the villages. Imbo was the spirit of caution. 'Will it get worse?' 'It may: perhaps it will not.' 'Will the lava reach the villages?' 'It did in 1890.' Suddenly one day Vesuvius gave a mammoth puff, and up to the sky went swirling a cloud which looked like the pictures of atomic explosion today. 'Is that ash, and will it come down on us?' 'Well, it might be light ash or heavy ash: it might come down or be blown away,' I could get no sense out of Imbo. I took a party of correspondents to Pompeii: ash was raining down, and occasionally a bit of coke gave one a sharp rap: we all had handkerchiefs to our noses. I said to Godfrey Talbot: 'We look exactly the casts in the museum,' and wondered if the same fate would be ours. Presently the whole area was covered with ash, sometimes two feet deep, and dense clouds of sulphurous smoke poured from Vesuvius. It was early spring, and the almond trees were in blossom: one could advance to the lava streams, twelve feet high and forty yards across, and red-hot, moving at a steady twelve feet a minute, and watch the pink blossom mown down. Never had I seen, nor shall I see again, such extraordinary tricks of lights and colour. Soon the villages were menaced. The inhabitants would not believe it. Plaster saints were taken out of the churches and placed along the roads, staring up at the boiling crater. It became obvious that, unless the eruption suddenly stopped, the various villages would be overwhelmed at an exact hour. But we could not persuade the Italians to go: they still believed in a miracle. Then, quite suddenly, they panicked, and long lines of lorries took them – and what furniture they could rescue – away. Attached to me were two American photographers, very reminiscent of Laurel and Hardy, and they had a whale of a time. It was indeed a camera-man's Paradise. The very slow but seemingly inevitable advance of the red-hot river was astonishingly impressive. From a distance of twenty yards or even less, one could watch it pouring into the back of a house: then, very very slowly, the façade would bulge outwards and crack: suddenly, as the lava reached the cellars, barrels of wine would explode in pink fountains: then, hey presto, the house silently collapsed, and the lava was on its way again. It gave one a curious end-of-the-world feeling. And in its way, it was beautiful.

I had a jeep-driver (officers, I cannot imagine why, were strictly forbidden to drive themselves) called James. He hailed from Cardiff and was a perfect example of all that is best – and what a good best it is – in the English private soldier. In these egalitarian days, it is difficult to express appreciation of such people without sounding patronizing. James had an unsophisticated, innocent, yet shrewd view of the world, and very often picked out points of interest which I should never have noticed. I was entranced by his description of a free fight which took place in Rome between British soldiers and French *poilus*, who lived in barracks opposite one another. The French imported tarts every night, and the British took exception to this, and raided them. It was one of the examples of sexual prejudice in occupied Rome. Another was the fact that most British officers went and lived quietly at the Eden hotel, which was assigned to them, while most American officers felt it imperative to set themselves up in a requisitioned flat and keep a mistress. This gave rise to quite considerable anger on both sides. Among the British, there were legends to the effect that the Americans were impotent, and were doing this only for show: and anyway (a common grouse) that they had too much money. The Americans quite often said that the British must indulge in homosexuality or masturbation. The French, of course, indulged in everything: and their coloured troops, the Goums, soon gave us a headache.

They would rush into a village and loot it, raping all the women. As a result, a great many Italians fled at their approach, and blocked the roads. After a lot of quite painful negotiation, the Goums were sent home: what experience I had of these talks made me feel that the French are as cruel and ruthless a nation as any in the world – or perhaps that applies only to the French Army. Certainly in a conquered country, with women at two a penny, odd national differences appear.

In Naples I would occasionally say to James: 'One of these days, James, I shall be able to say "Rome, James".' When I did this he would give me a hostile and contemptuous glance, thinking (quite rightly) that I was making some stale and in-comprehensible joke. The day did in due course arrive, and when we topped the Alban Hills, and looked down at the Eternal City, just fallen, intact and unspoiled, to the Allies, and I said, with a lump in my throat (for it seemed a great moment) 'That is Rome, James,' he replied morosely 'Is it now? An' I wish it were Lunnon' – thus extinguishing my flicker of sentimentality. Nevertheless the shining splendour of Rome, after the squalor of London and the bombed cities of England and Palermo and Naples, seemed almost incredible. Civilization had, after all, survived.

The brilliance of Rome was a little dimmed for me by a personal assignment with tragedy. In the sparkling Egypt of 1918 my cousin, Sir Ian Macleod, had married a lively, intelli-gent and attractive Italian named Isa Brusati. He must have been (I scarcely knew him) a singularly unimaginative man, for he took her off to live in the high dark and hideous house of his mother in the centre of Glasgow. A girl of seventeen, brought up in the sunshine of Italy and Egypt, was thus condemned to live under the thumb of a domineering and tyrannical old woman in the gloomiest city in the world. Isa stood it for ten or twelve years, and then mustered courage to escape to Rome, where she took a very beautiful apartment looking down over the Pincian Gardens and the Trinità dei Monti to St Peters. Ian, her son, grew up into a dazzling blend of the Latin and Anglo-Saxon. He had the charm and flexibility and gaiety of the Italian, and the phlegm, integrity, and perseverance of the Englishman. In 1939 he started to work at the British Embassy in Rome, and, when Italy declared war, departed with the Ambassador to England. Devoted to Isa, he tried to persuade her to go with him: she refused. Perhaps the idea of Glasgow deterred her: perhaps she thought (as anyone might have done at the time) that England would lose the war. Ian never relaxed his efforts to get her away: he arranged a passage for her through Switzerland: she would not budge. Ian meanwhile distinguished himself as a soldier: when we got to Italy, he commanded a group of Partisans which he sent to reconnoitre in enemy territory with useful results. At his funeral, I was deeply impressed by their smartness and intelligence. He died – stupidly it seemed – in Naples from osteomyelitis, contracted from a small bump on the knee in a motor-cycle accident. I sent the news of his death to Isa via the Foreign Office and the Vatican: I could not face the prospect of breaking it myself. When at length I sat in her drawing-room in Rome, she flung open the double doors and stood, draped in mourning and with her fair hair dyed black. Pointing a finger at me, she declaimed: 'Why did you let it happen?' Had I let it happen, I wondered. I had been busy, and for some time had not realized that he was gravely ill. When I did, Mason Mac-Farlane had been unforgettably kind about it: a specialist had been brought down from the line: great quantities of penicillin (then a rarity) had been flown over from North Africa. But the aristocracy of Naples, who knew both Isa and Ian, insisted that the British doctors were no good, and that an Italian doctor could cure him. The British authorities were adamant: no Italian doctor could visit the British military hospital. All this, of course, came back to the ears of Isa. She blamed me, the British doctors, the Allies, and the world. She wished to visit his grave, and when permission was refused (civilians could not travel to Naples) she wept and stormed: 'I, a British mother, may not visit my son's grave!' When his possessions were brought to her she swore that they had been pilfered, and that his Will was missing. There was no doing anything for her. The purpose of her life was gone. Some people recover from such losses, some do not. Isa never did, and never has. Her grief and fury ran like a black thread through my Roman days. It is said that those who mourn are blessed, but she was not comforted.

There was one other cloud in the Roman sky, and that was the behaviour of the Allied troops. When, some weeks earlier, it became clear that Rome would fall, detailed arrangements were made for its occupation. I don't know where these originated – perhaps among the Combined Chiefs of Staff, perhaps with Alexander. The idea was that Rome should be left intact. No Allied troops were to enter it. The Allied Commission was to be billeted in Tivoli, and from that discreet distance watch over law and order in the Eternal City. It was, perhaps, an impossible conception: it broke down at once. General Mark Clark, commanding the Fifth Army, said that his boys deserved a good time, and sent them into the city in batches of fifteen thousand. Other commanders, I suppose, followed suit. Spacious shining Rome became a bedraggled whore of a town. It was as though Vivaldi had suddenly changed to Louis Armstrong. Italian vendors poured on to the pavements with the wares apparently required – terrible sham jewellery, huge cameos, pots painted with the Stars and Stripes, hideous scarves. Pimps multiplied. At night along the Via Veneto Allied soldiers lay in a drunken stupor. It was not pretty. All right, it could be said – do you prefer this tolerant uproar or the Ardeatine massacres and the torture chambers of the Via Tasso? You could only reply, with Matthew Arnold: Madman or slave, *must* man be one?

The Italian press also was bursting with liberation and freedom. Freedom (of course, why not?) to say what it liked about the Allies. So the Allied Publications Board was hurriedly formed. Its Chairman, Ian Munro, was a gentle and tolerant man: other members were not. The proceedings verged on the farcical. Could the King be caricatured? Yes of course, he's a Fascist. No, you can't attack the Monarchy. Anyway they'll have to vote for it – why shouldn't they be informed. Informed? Misled? Pooh, you're a Monarchist. No, but this is going too far. And just look at this about Winston, we can't pass it. Seems to me innocuous. Well, that's a treasonable remark. Well, what do we do? Have the Editor on the carpet? A lot of good *that* will do! Suppress the paper? Heavens, think of the Labour Party! And so on.

General 'Jumbo' Wilson, C-in-C Meditterranean, decided that there must be a Report on German Atrocities in Rome. Dogsbody Fielden got this job, of course. I protested that it was not at all up my street: no good. So I set Jack Leacacos to work on it: between us I think we interviewed 175 people who had been tortured in the Via Tasso. The result was inconclusive. I remember in particular one young man, intelligent, well-spoken, of good family. Had he been tortured? Oh yes. For how long? Oh, about three weeks. What happened? Well, first a bit of beating up in the cellar: four men to knock him about. Badly hurt? Well, no: fainted very quickly. Any scars? No. And then? Oh, well, beating with steel birches. Terrible? No, not really: fainted at once. Any scars? No. And then? Oh well then, fire, you know:

flames in the armpits, under the testicles, and so on. Any scars? No. But you didn't divulge information? Lord, no, never occurred to me. What does one make of all that? Jack sifted every detail of information: never was there such a sifter: but it all added up to nothing. However, about the Ardeatine massacre there was no doubt: the Italians had ambushed a German lorry and killed thirty Germans: the Germans had demanded 300 Italians as a reprisal, and killed them all in the Ardeatine caves. The then Chief of Police in Rome, Caruso, had been instructed to supply fifty from the prisons, and had done so. He, escaping northwards, had been caught by an Allied bomb, and had his hip shattered. He was the first real Fascist prisoner. The Italians must put him on trial – so they were informed.

Moroni, the judge of this trial, took the crazy decision to advertise, in the Italian papers, that all widows of the Ardeatine dead would be welcome in court. As a result, the court was crowded with hysterical women. I was supposed to be looking after the journalists, who were there in force: and, to some extent – though that was never officially conveyed to me – after the whole trial. I took a young American officer of my staff, Atkinson, down to the court, because I was far too busy to attend the whole trial. I did not much like the atmosphere of weeping women, but it did not then occur to me that anything could go seriously wrong. There was a man called Caretta, who had been Deputy Chief of Police to Caruso and who had agreed to give evidence against him. When Caretta entered the court the crowd (who did not know Caruso by sight) started to shout 'That's Caruso!' and there was a movement towards him. I told Atkinson to take him up to the gallery, where the crowd could not reach him. I then rushed away to keep my office appointments. Caretta, unfortunately for him, decided to run out of the court. The crowd ran after him, threw him into the Tiber, saw that he was well and truly drowned, and hung him upside down on the walls of the Regina Coeli prison. Atkinson brought me this news at midday. The trial had to be moved to a less accessible and more guarded court, and I scarcely dared to leave it for the following three weeks. At the end of that time Caruso, as was inevitable, was condemned to death, and Allied journalists had the greatest fun in photographing and filming both him and the judge at the moment of sentence.

Before this trial, and during it, I had come to know two wonderful people. They were named Pollock and Coxhead, one

a major and the other a colonel, but in fact Scotland Yard policemen. They were the perfect answer to all violence. 'Your police
are wonderful!' says the film-star. Well, these two were. A few
days before the fall of Paris to the Allies, a crowd of Romans,
some 5,000 strong, surged into the Piazza Farnese, wishing to
cheer the French Ambassador. Couve de Murville chose to ignore
them, since Paris had not yet fallen. The crowd became restive,
and started to jeer at a Caribiniere station on a corner of the
square. A man from the crowd ran up to the balcony, tore down
the flag of Savoy, and ran up a red one. A Carabiniere rushed
out, tackled him, and threw the red flag into the Square. 'Burn
them out!' shouted the crowd. It was an ugly moment. Then
Pollock and Coxhead, wearing shorts and shirts and quite unarmed, drove into the square in a jeep. Someone threw the red
flag in Coxhead's face. Coxhead gave him a beautiful upper-cut
and sent him twenty yards. The crowd began to laugh. Pollock
and Coxhead proceeded to the balcony, and put up the Savoy
flag with great deliberation. The crowd cheered them. I thought
that maybe I was prejudiced, but it really seemed that the
English, and only the English in the whole wide world, know
how to deal with crowds. Coxhead and Pollock became my
heroes. And they (I think and hope) rather liked me. They
brought me a lot of their problems. The worst of these was the
Regina Coeli prison, in which the Allies (or rather their damnable
Security Services) had immured hundreds of quite innocent
people. Conditions in this star-shaped prison were frightful. To
give only one example, we came upon three old sisters, all in
their eighties, who had been thrown into a crowded cell because
they had been found sewing German uniforms. Coxhead and
Pollock did a great job, but it was uphillwork: the Allied authorities simply did not care. During the Caruso trial, Coxhead and
Pollock were in some way responsible – such responsibilities
were vague – for his custody and treatment. They visited him
daily and came, as I also did, to like him. The accusation against
him was that he had signed the order to hand over fifty prisoners
to the Germans. He did not deny it: his defence was simply that
he was doing what he was instructed by his Government to do.
Had he refused, he would have been shot. It was a nice point.
To understand it, you had to imagine an England dominated by
Russian 'allies' who were hated by the people: and ask yourself
how far, under such circumstances, the Head of Scotland Yard
would have gone. Caruso was executed at Fort Brevetta outside

Rome, and died bravely under the eyes of some fifty Western correspondents. Strapped to a chair with his back to the firing-squad, he threw up his head just before the volley, and in ringing tones shouted: '*Evviva l'Italia!*' Then a dozen correspondents rushed on the body to take nice close-ups for their readers. Caruso, during his last night in the cells, wrote a moving letter to Pollock and Coxhead, thanking them for their kindness to him, saying that he had come to admire and respect them greatly, but that, for his part, he remained convinced that Fascism was the best form of Government ever devised.

It was about this time that I received a telegram announcing my father's death. This was quite unexpected: I had known he was ill, but I had never quite believed that he would die: he was tough. I cannot honestly say that I felt the slightest sorrow: he was a man whom I had never known or liked. I did, however, feel a considerable curiosity as to whether he had (as in 1914 he had threatened) cut me off with a shilling. Some time elapsed – I was not allowed to return to England – before I knew that I was the sole residuary legatee of some £120,000. More time was to elapse before I realized that taxation and other legacies took two-thirds of this, and that no less than seven years were needed to 'settle the estate'. However, I did undoubtedly feel a lift of the heart to think that perhaps I was now free from bosses and the necessity to work. Yet it is an odd experience to inherit money, and, at least to me, not quite the unalloyed pleasure that one would expect. A pay packet for work at the end of each month seems natural and right: but an unearned income seems unreal. I have never got used to it. I am always convinced that it will disappear. I should like it to be under the mattress. I have known quite a few people who, towards the end of their lives, became absolutely convinced that they were penniless, and this seems to me easy to understand. It is possible that the possession of an unearned income automatically makes one more nervous about money – and therefore less generous – than one ever was while earning. That does not mean that I don't like having money – it's great fun – or that I am not everlastingly grateful for the privacy which it gives me. But it does mean that my dreams are haunted by a constant dread that it will disappear before I do. I suspect that, as the years roll on, I grasp every penny with a meaner hand.

In July 1944 Mason MacFarlane resigned on grounds of ill-health, and returned to England. It was, in a way, a forced resignation. When Rome fell, Mason Mac decided that the Southern Italian Government, nominated by the Allies under Badoglio, Sforza and Togliatti, should fly to Rome and there meet the secretly formed government of Bonomi – and freely decide who was to rule. That strange meeting took place in a small room at the Grand Hotel. Mason Mac addressed the politicians, and made, I thought, a good speech, perhaps slightly weighted towards Bonomi. It was translated – to me very badly translated – by an American interpreter called Montfort. The result was that Marshal Badoglio threw in his hand. (Possibly he would have done so anyway: more than once he said to me, laughing: 'Not my job, politics.') Churchill went into a fury over this. He sent Mason Mac a surprisingly rude cable, insisting that Badoglio, who had signed the Armistice terms, should be reinstated as Prime Minister. That was obviously impossble. Mason Mac, who was subject to acute arthritis from an injury to his spine, became ill with worry. His arms were, in fact, partially paralysed from the elbow down. Sitting dejectedly in the Grand Hotel before his last Press Conference, he said to me: 'Am I supposed to act democratically, or not?' (He was so angered by Churchill that he later contested and won a Labour seat.) The American correspondents scented a row, and harried me unmercifully to admit that Churchill had sacked Mason Mac for not being Fascist.

MacFarlane was succeeded by his deputy, an American called Ellery Stone. Ellery Stone held the rank of Captain in the Navy. He was a shrewd business man, but he did not carry enough guns, in rank or personality, for the job: such, at least, was my impression. It may well have been a biased one. Ellery Stone, like General Joyce, wanted an American, not a British, Public Relations Officer. He wanted, quite naturally, to be promoted to Admiral (as he eventually was), and for that purpose it was essential, or so he thought, that his personality should be played up by the American press. But I had no standing with, or knowledge of, that press: and Tom Bergin, though a wise man, was far from being a journalist. It would have been quite reasonable, from Ellery Stone's point of view, to shunt us both: but he had no good reason for doing so. There was nothing against us, and our job, as far as it went, was efficiently done. Ellery Stone, for some reason that I shall never understand, was enamoured of my weekly précis of Allied correspondents' despatches. This, he said, must now appear daily. I protested violently. I tried to explain that in Naples I had had the time to talk with the correspondents and to do the précis with care. It could be a dangerous thing if not carefully handled: and in Rome I no longer had the time to do it personally. He thrust these objections aside. Anybody could do it. I agreed, and thus dug my own grave. I handed over the précis to a young English officer who could write shorthand. I endeavoured to warn him about its dangers. It began to come out every day, and was sent to seventy-three General Officers. Doom was in store for me.

Florence had been captured, and the Allies moved northwards. The aspect of Florence was not encouraging for liberators. With bridges destroyed, buildings in ruins, and rubble-heaped streets, it seemed at first sight a town whose glories had departed. Indeed, when I visit it today, I never cease to marvel that it has so nearly re-assumed its original form. Arriving there after its capture I was billetted with other officers in the Excelsior Hotel, and felt that I must escape from this khaki mass at once. I walked in the twilight to the Ponte Vecchio, with the idea of re-visiting the tower in which I had lived in the twenties. It had been blown up, and not a vestige remained. This trivial incident depressed me. Next morning I walked along the Arno, determined to find some of the Italians I had known. A woman at a window was speaking to a boy on the pavement below: she interrupted herself to say in Italian, looking at me: 'I think that officer looks nice: reminds me of Grandfather: go and speak to him.' I was tickled by this remark, and joined in the conversation: and in this way I met Elle Milani, surely one of the most amusing, unpredictable, irritating women ever born in Florence. She took me there and then to Leland's Bar, where many Florentines were gathered: from there, with the Marchesa Strozzi, we drove up to the famous Tatti, Bernard Berenson's villa at Settignano. There, it seemed as if the war had never taken place: everything was somewhere in 1905: the two charming sisters, Nicky Mariano and Alda von Anrep, moved like duchesses among the guests: the famous BB was, as ever, the soul of wit and courtesy. Suddenly I was caught up into this enchanted little world, swimming it seemed in some dimension untouched by war. And this, though I was unaware of it, decided my future.

In Rome Herbert Matthews, renowned correspondent for *The New York Times*, decided to write an article about the views of the new King, Umberto. This was, of course, a tricky thing to do. The House of Savoy was walking a tightrope. Its future was uncertain, it was – to some eyes – tarred with a Fascist brush, and

Umberto, a pleasant man dragged hither and thither by unkind circumstance, had not quite made his personality felt. Whether Matthews wished to smear or extol the Monarchy, or to do neither, I don't know. What came out was an article in which Umberto, asked by Matthews: 'Why did not you and your father stop Mussolini?' replied (as far as I remember the words); 'Because every Italian would have been against us.' Matthews covered this article by a note to his Editor, saying that the article had been seen and approved by the Prime Minister, Bonomi, and the ex-Prime Minister, Orlando. The article appeared in *The New York Times*, and in due course came back to Italy, where it caused a crisis. Italians were furious with the King. Bonomi, frightened, denied that he had ever seen it. My précis had stated that he had, and Ellery Stone, seizing the opportunity, said that it was all my fault. I could only retort that my précis had gone to him and seventy-three generals a fortnight earlier, and none had objected. Matthews left for America. Ellery Stone now had a case against me. John Boettinger (if that is his name, but he was not a man whose name I should remember) the son-in-law of Roosevelt, came to Italy. My American staff were paralyzed by this alleged VIP, and assured me that my fate depended upon him. I took no trouble with him. Very soon I was informed that Roosevelt had appointed a new Public Relations Officer to the Allied Commission. I should be required to work 'on equal terms with him.' I said that I would do nothing of the kind. The department had run under my supervision for eighteen months, and I would run it or clear out. It was, of course, a childish sort of squabble. And it was quite clear that I should lose the game, and that Ellery Stone would delightedly exile me to the most remote and squalid town of Italy, where (as far as one could see at that time) I might be immured for years. I should not have minded that, but a complicated situation was developing about my father's estate: both lawyers and family were demanding my presence. I did not want to get stuck. So I wrote to the Secretary of State for War, and asked him to recall me, which he obligingly did. It is good to have a friend at court. I was tempted to cock a snook at Ellery Stone.

Social life in occupied Rome has found no place in these random recollections: and perhaps it deserves one. Had I been less tied by office routine, I should have seen more of it. But certainly Rome in 1944-46 was a Paradise for an Allied officer. It may be wrong to conquer countries and occupy them, but the occupier has – at least for a time – an amusing experience, if he so desires. The Allied officer in Rome was run after, petted, flattered, and entertained: and the Roman aristocracy was, after all, an old hand at entertaining magnificently. Moreover, with the nice new bank notes printed by the Allies (and stamped with the Four Freedoms, none of which are in great evidence today), there was a sense of affluence. An Allied officer could, more or less, get away with anything, and that in the world's most beautiful city.

In April 1945 I flew off from Rome, and found myself landed, rather surprisingly, in Cornwall. The war was as good as over, and I told myself, perhaps over-optimistically, that never again (unless reincarnation was a fact) would I become involved in men's massacres of each other. At least, I thought, I should have the money, and the conviction, to run away from them as far and as fast as I could. But the antics of the human race have now made even that proposition doubtful.

Business affairs are boring: for the rest of that summer I was overwhelmed by them. When the debts and legacies and death duties had been paid, the house and its contents sold, my step-mother established elsewhere and thousands (it seemed to me) of dreary lawyers' conferences attended, I returned to the flat in London which I still held on an annual lease. It was a dark pill-box of a place, filthily dirty now, and it stank of war memories: almost one seemed to hear bombs still dropping. I now possessed (or would presumably, when the estate was settled, possess) a gross income of some £2,500 a year, which taxation reduced to £1,200. And I was, of course, free to spend the capital sum of about £40,000 as fast as I liked. It was a quite enviable position. Will you be surprised if I tell you that I felt desperately depressed, extremely lonely, and entirely lost? But that is what I did feel.

I could have entertained people: I had no desire to do so. I could have gone out to parties: the idea revolted me. I sat like a mangy mouse in the dirty little flat, dusting the furniture (I could not find a charwoman) and cooking myself horrid little messes in the doll's kitchen. For thirty years I had been, more or less and often pointlessly, active, and had thought that I hated that thralldom: now the Gods offered me freedom and leisure on a plate, and, believe it or not, I had not the remotest idea what to do with them. I was so idiotically conditioned by social convention that I could not envisage the notion of doing nothing. So I looked carefully through the advertisements for jobs, and eventually answered one which said that the Allied War Crimes Commission needed a Public Relations Officer. I sent in a list of my achievements which now, on paper, looked impressive. In due course I was summoned to an interview in that Headquarters of Vengeance, suitably established at Church House, Westminster.

Selection Boards, as I have said earlier, are futile things. You can seldom hope by interview to judge candidates who are inevitably too nervous to behave normally. But in this particular case the situation was unusual. I was in my fiftieth year and had said good-bye to nervousness. I had a private income, and therefore was indifferent. I did not take to the Selection Board which, under the chairmanship of Lord Wright, was composed of representatives of various victorious nations. (Or perhaps, in some cases, semi-victorious.) There was a curious feeling of arrogance: they seemed to be licking their chops. I was asked questions about my career, and the answers sounded quite good. I was aware that I was making a good impression, and my instinct was to withdraw. I said that I did not quite understand (which was true enough) what the Allied War Crimes Commission was supposed to do: I went further, and insisted that I might be the wrong person for it: I abased myself, and urged them to realize that I knew very little about Public Relations, and had really been a complete failure. Such is human nature that the lower I went, the more they thought of me. When I got to the point of saying that I did not think I wanted the job at all, they were convulsed with laughter and admiration. The next day I received a letter to say that the Board had been unanimous in choosing me. Feeling a perfect fool, I put on my pinstripe suit and went to Church House.

The reality was far worse than my anticipation. God knows what I had expected: perhaps I saw myself interviewing Goering & Co, and getting a kick out of it. I was so confused that any activity seemed preferable to none. The reality which confronted me was a horrendous library of files, recording idiotic 'crimes' against all manner of silly little people. A lift-man in Rome had been rude to the Yugoslavs: to the gallows with him. The Mayor of Rien-sur-Mer had said that he admired Laval: off with his head. A chamber-maid in Brussels had refused to sleep with a Russian: to Justice with her. Unfortunately for me, I was known to a large number of newspaper correspondents, and, as soon as my appointment was announced, they were after me. And they knew their stuff. 'Case number 23052, now if you go ahead with that, we'll make a stink. It's merely a plot to oust Monsieur Rien, Signor Niente, Gospodin Niet, in favour of Fascist or Communist Monsieur Chose.' And so on. What was to be made of all this? I became more uncomfortable. I could not Public-relationize sheer vengeance. It may, perhaps, have been an unlucky moment, or possibly I was in a particularly mulish frame of mind. The cases which came up to be examined as 'worthy of trial' seemed mostly based on slender or biased or phoney evidence: the members of the Commission appeared more intent on hanging people than on seeking a peaceful world. One day, feeling ashamed of myself and an utter fool, I told Lord Wright that I had made a mistake, and that I must leave the AWCC that very day. I had been there for about a fortnight. Lord Wright grunted a bit, and said that he hoped that I should not divulge anything that I had learnt there. It was tempting to reply that I had already arranged for a series of scandalous articles. Perhaps Lord Wright felt this. 'We could have made you sign the Official Secrets Act, you know,' he said. I could only reply, 'But you didn't.' Official secrets about War Crimes! Into what world were we moving, had we moved? As I left the sacred precincts of Church House for ever, a new breeze blew about me. What on earth had I been thinking of. I was utterly unfitted, had always been unfitted, for all bureaucratic jobs. I was also unfitted for anything else. It remained to do nothing. And why not? Nothing spread out delightfully before me. I was an old man with groggy health and a private income: why the hell should I do anything?

This decision made, there was instantly a lot to do. Warm letters had been arriving from Florence, urging me to go and settle there: and I could at least begin with that idea. In November 1945 it was impossible to leave England without a reason. I therefore went to Kingsley Martin, and asked him whether he would let me go as unpaid correspondent in Italy. He kindly agreed, and wrote the necessary letter. The first step thus accomplished, I took an enormous second one: I bought a Rolls-Royce. True, it was a second-hand one of 1937 vintage, and cost me only £1,000: on the other hand, it had belonged exclusively to Mrs Victor Bruce, was in excellent condition, pretty, and of low mileage. This acquisition – maybe I should apologise, in these days, for such bad taste – perhaps gave me more pleasure than any I have ever made. Why? Well, because I wanted to show off. If you write yourself down decisively as a failure in life, you must have something to bolster the ego: behind the wheel of the Rolls I felt that I could spit upon humanity. But I also had to spit successfully on other things, including the Ministry of Information and the French and Italian Embassies. Without their permission I could not start. And the first two were astoundingly reluctant to let me. Various departments of the Ministry of Information blandly assured me that I could not take a car across the Channel, and that even if I did so, I should find no petrol and no food in France: and that, in any case, the car would immediately be stolen. And why on earth, they asked, should I want to go to Italy as a correspondent: there were more than enough there already. The French Embassy repeated most of these warnings, and added that I had better take sufficient food for the whole journey, and a tent to sleep in: I should find neither food nor hotels. (Why I was told these extraordinary lies, I still wonder.) The Italians, as always, were the soul of courtesy: delighted that I should want to go: no difficulty. I extracted the various permits, like so many teeth: then I had to get a *carnet* from the AA. The AA were delightfully comic: they said quite simply, 'But the Continent is *closed!*' I could only reply that I had been on the Continent for two years, and it didn't seem closed to me. After many interviews and the filling-in of countless forms, I got my *carnet*. The doors of the English prison were open.

Having got so far, I grew slightly nervous. Peter Rodd had come round to my flat and told me, in rather dramatic terms, that my journey would be dangerous. He painted an unpleasant picture (which perhaps was in part true) of deserters from every army who would hold up the car and ransack it, of long empty roads where no help would be available and anarchy would rule, of lines of military lorries charging along at fifty miles an hour and caring little for civilian cars. I decided to take with me Peter Forster, a member of the BBC staff who had estates in France which he wanted to see, and who was a stout and bilingual fellow. The Rolls was filled, literally to the roof, with every life-preserving commodity I could think of – blankets, sheets, pillows, tins of food, soap, cigarettes ... I might have been going to the North Pole. At this moment the laughing Gods shot a vile arrow at me, and I was struck down by the most staggering attack of lumbago I have ever experienced. It was the sort of lumbago (which I have never known before or since) which ties you into an immovable knot when you are crossing a street. It had to be cured, and I could not cure it. I ran up and down Harley Street, I went to every possible osteopath. I was poulticed, rolled about, massaged, boiled: all to no purpose. I creaked myself into the Rolls, and set off to Newhaven. There, a Customs Officer looked unbelievingly at the mass of nonsense inside the car, and said 'Have you anything to declare?' in a lost kind of way. I said, yes, ten thousand cigarettes. 'Don't try making fun of me,' he warned. 'How much soap have you?' I said, 'Four dozen.' 'A wag, aren't you?' He chalked the car as passed. It was then lifted on to the ship. The art of lifting cars had been forgotten, and it was bundled unmercifully by the cranes into the hold. By sheer luck, there was no damage. It took four hours to cross from Newhaven to Dieppe. At Dieppe in the twilight the tide was obviously too high, even to my inexperienced eye, to allow the temporary cranes to swing the car clear. The French authorities would not listen to me: the ship must be unloaded at once. So bang, crash, went my beautiful Rolls into the derricks: the windows were shattered, the doors stove in. I argued and shouted till midnight about damages, and who was going to pay them. Useless. We climbed the hill and established ourselves (there were no hotels) in a small brothel. Mercifully the car still functioned: a Rolls always functions. I left it in the garden. My sleep was uneasy: perhaps the Ministry of Information, the French Embassy, and Peter Rodd were right. Perhaps I should return at once. Lumbago haunted my dreams.

Next morning Dieppe provided us with a breakfast such as could not be found in all victorious England. A bank manager, smiling, cashed my enormous cheque immediately. Petrol was available in any quantity. We bowled off southwards on a beautiful straight road. The sun shone. My lumbago vanished. We ate a delicious lunch at Evreux.

And so it went on. Everywhere we found smiling faces, excellent food and wine, admirable hotels, and a great welcome for English travellers – or perhaps for English travellers with a Rolls. Only at Montélimar, where we had planned to stay, did we encounter the aftermath of war. This was at twilight, and we were slightly unnerved – after the various gipsy's warnings – about the long trek to Avignon in the dark. But no: a charming brothel appeared unexpectedly in a village. A cosy Madam: exquisite food, luxurious rooms. In sunshine we trickled on to Monte Carlo. I could not resist the temptation to be as grand as possible. Never before had I driven and never again should I drive, up to the Hotel de Paris in a Rolls. And at the Hotel de

Paris the war of 1939-1945 had not yet been observed. The same expensive ladies sat at the same expensive tables eating the same expensive food served by the same expensive waiters. Delicious! Why wasn't I a subject of Monaco? No: on second thoughts, I couldn't afford it. I did, however, afford to take myself to the tables, where I almost instantly lost almost all my travelling money. We pressed on to Italy. Italy was different. War had hit the Italian Riviera heavily. There were endless diversions where bridges had been blown up. But people were cheerful, and Black Marketeers rushed at us with petrol wherever we stopped. We arrived in Florence without difficulty. As correspondent (unpaid) of *The New Statesman,* I sat down at once and wrote a glowing article about the delights of European travel. I thought that people would be glad to know. *The New Statesman* refused to publish it: Kingsley wrote me a sharp letter, in which he said that everyone in the office was agreed that this horrible description of 'driving a Rolls through ruined Europe' was the most vulgar thing ever submitted to the paper. Vulgar or not, it was true. But one must toe the official line. Occupied France had to be 'ruined' – but, in fact, it was far better off than victorious England.

Chapter Nine

No, Sir, I am not obliged to do any more. No man is
obliged to do as much as he can do. A man is to have a part
of life to himself.   SAMUEL JOHNSON

At Florence I entered upon two years of glorious, irresponsible
life. There were plenty of amusing people: money didn't (as I
then thought) matter: I toyed – that is the word – with the idea
of buying a villa, and, as there were 365 villas for sale, this gave
a lovely excuse for picnics. The rarity of pleasure, and of private
cars, gave me an easy choice of gay delightful company: what
could be more enchanting than to pile into the Rolls and float off
along empty roads, luxuriant with the Italian spring, to spend
timeless days in great neglected gardens, whose owners had fled
or died or lost their money or decided not to return. And these
once-tended gardens were perhaps more beautiful, certainly more
magical, in their neglect than they had ever been in their days of
affluence. Punctuating the landscape, the secular cypress shot
from smooth grey bole its spire of velvet darkness into the blue:
climbing roses, once so carefully imported and pruned, rioted up
to attic windows and rusty roofs: the unconquerable honeysweet
wistaria thrust its choking fingers over arbour and trellis, arch
and wall: spiraea and forsythia and jasmine, grown to the size
of trees, cascaded racemes of white and gold: untended lawns
glowed with white and red and purple anemone, scarlet wild
tulip, and the soft blue of iris stylosa. And, as always in Italy, the
distant prospect, unfolding over Florence or the Appenines or the
silver gleam of the Arno, curling across the plain, had the Peru-
gino quality of misty and mysterious blue. It was good, it was
enough, to be alive in such a world. And the vague, the very
vague, idea that one of these lost villas would be bought and inhabited by me, gave a bright edge to laziness. 'A swimming-pool,
just here, don't you think?' 'Hammocks under these trees, with
the view beyond, what Heaven!' 'One could always eat outside,
in this corner.' 'A rose-garden here?' 'No, no, a smooth lawn, with
perhaps a border.' We kept away from all utilitarian projects: it

was all a Bocaccio dream: Bocaccio fled from the plague, we were fleeing from a world gone mad. The villas themselves, elegant, gaunt and bare, had need of some utilitarian thought: they offered vaulted ceilings of great beauty, spacious rooms irradiated by sunshine, and a scarcity of drains. But drains were no part of a daydream.

In due course, as was inevitable, the number of desirable villas was narrowed down. I had no serious intention to buy any, but circumstances were pushing me in that direction. There was Broncigliano, perched on a spur to the south of Florence, above Scandicci: a tall narrow house of baroque and yet faintly ecclesiastical charm. It had a garden which sloped slightly upwards from the house, so that the pattern of box and cypress was spread out like some ancient coloured map: on its façade was a very decorative sundial, with a nostalgic inscription which I have forgotten. It was in perfect order: the owner, intending to marry, had spent much money on it and had installed, among other wonders, bathrooms with seemed suitable to Marie-Antoinette. Then his fiancée had suddenly died: and he had never come near the place again. It had a wistful melancholy: here one could dream life away in a romantic haze. But it had little land, and I thought (how wrongly) that I needed a lot: and, like all Italian houses of its period, it was bereft of corridors: the rooms led one into another: Italians of the fifteenth and sixteenth centuries must have cared little about the privacy of bedrooms. I had a weakness for Broncigliano, but it was not a practical proposition: later, and perhaps suitably, it became a convent. Then there was Montebello, which belonged to Prince Potenziani. Montebello was a squat toad of a house, superbly situated on the top of a hill, with its own land sloping away from it on all sides. It had four different entrances of different periods, and three secret staircases leading to nowhere. It was a mediaeval mess of a house, with great charm. The views were splendid. It was approached by a road so narrow and tortuous that the Rolls could only just negotiate it at a walking pace, not without considerable danger to wings. I was enamoured of Montebello, and rather regret it: but Prince Potenziani wanted more money than I could spend. And then there was the Villa Savonarola, above Pian dei Giullari. This had a mouth-watering garden, full of ancient cypresses, huge wistarias, planes, sycamores, chestnuts, paulonias and catalpas. The house itself, graceful enough outside, was a mess within: mesmerised by the garden, I employed a German architect, at terrifying expense, to plan a new lay-out of the rooms, which he did very effectively. I became very nearly committed to the Savonarola: in fact, when I eventually decided not to buy it, I think that the owner might well have sued me. But I did not buy it. Over and very much above these three was the famous villa of La Gamberaia. This was in an altogether different category. It is one of the most famous villas of Florence and it is said to have been built by San Gallo. Its view over Florence and the surrounding country is unmatched. Princess Ghika, who had owned it, had renovated and replanned the exquisite gardens with immense taste and ability. Water from the hills above flowed down to it in abundance, and the water-gardens and fountains could have had a glitter almost like that of the Villa d'Este. The Germans, during the war, had used the house as a map store: when the Allies approached, they burnt it to the ground: only the outside walls were left standing, with a mass of rubble within. This could be bought for £15,000, and would have cost quite as much again to put in order: this meant that I should have to sink pretty well the whole of my capital in it – both risky and difficult. The gamble, however, had certain advantages: there were some two hundred acres of land, and the annual income from olive oil alone was around £1,500: again, since the house was listed as a National Monument and was of rare beauty, it would probably always find a purchaser. Bernard Berenson, to whom I listened always with affection and respect, urged me to buy it. 'A fine life's work for you, Lionel.' I did not much care for that word work. Nor did I see myself, after shedding all my capital, living in the Gamberaia exclusively on the products of its acres. Perhaps my caution was wrong: old men should be explorers. Today, as I write, it has been bought, and is in process of renovation, by some immensely wealthy industrialists, and doubtless they will live in it with the splendour which it merits. Beautiful Gamberaia! You must be a commercial plunderer to own such houses today: and perhaps that is true in all ages. Good luck to the commercial plunderers who keep such houses going! I like them much better than dreary curators, leading gaping tourists through lifeless rooms.

Sunlit dreams, however vague, have to be accompanied by people and money. In 1946 the money problem was acute. I have (as I hope that this narrative makes clear) no sense of money. I cannot imagine where it is and what it does, though I love spending it. I had lived quite happily in Italy since 1943, and it did not occur to me, believe it or not, that after the end of a glorious war, and with £40,000, I could not live in it again. The British Treasury had other ideas. I had not got around to those. I simply asked my bank in London what I should do about money, and my bank manager (a rather stupid fellow just then) replied that I should inform him as soon as I had 'taken up residence' in Italy – whatever that might mean – and he would then take the necessary steps to supply me. I duly wrote that I was established in Florence, but no money came. I borrowed right and left, and wrote exasperated letters to the bank. Eventually they replied that they were 'taking the necessary steps with the Bank of England'. This was Greek to me, and I was not in a cautious mood. It seemed natural enough to discuss my problem with a friendly Director of the Swiss Bank. I was at that time blissfully unaware of that new-born monster, Exchange Control. That, in the context of our regimented times, may sound silly: yet why, in the piping peace time of victorious nations, and with the Four Freedoms blaring from every bank note, should one suppose that freedom to spend one's own money was denied? Mr Sweitzer of the Swiss Bank was not only helpful but enthusiastic. I had only to write a cheque. For how much? he asked. I said blithely that I thought £10,000 would do. I wrote the cheque, and the equivalent of £10,000 in lire was handed over to me. It all seemed very straightforward and simple. I now had enough money to buy, not La Gamberaia, but at any rate some sort of villa. The dream could continue.

Among people, Bernard Berenson ranked first. He was about eighty-two at this time, and was generally dubbed 'the uncrowned King of Florence'. Much has been, and doubtless will be, written about him: his achievements do not need to be chronicled here. What chiefly struck me about him was that here was that rarest of creatures – a man who had done exactly what pleased him in an unexplored field of learning, had lived a marvellous and glittering life among the things that he loved, and yet, starting from nothing, had made not only an enormous personal success but also an enormous financial one. Yet, if one writes that down, his quality still escapes words. The same thing might be said of a Beaverbrook or a Bottomley. The odd thing about BB was that he had made culture *pay*. His villa, I Tatti, was not only a shrine for beautiful things, and for a colossal library: it also had a garden which, laid out by him fifty years earlier, seemed pure fourteenth century. Moreover, I Tatti was a magnet for distinguished people from the whole (alleged) Free World, from the

King of Sweden to Walter Lippman and Kenneth Clark (or vice versa, if you prefer a different order.) It was a kind of club on which fresh and interesting personalities were always converging. For some reason, maybe *faute de mieux*, BB took a fancy to me at this time, and insisted that I should take him out alone in the Rolls. I was a little frightened of this responsibility, and much more frightened by BB himself who, perhaps because he had never driven a car, thought that any car could go anywhere. In quest of some forgotten shrine or church – or even, on one occasion, a pine tree with enormous spreading roots – he would urge me along precipitous tracks and over matchstick bridges: and, if I complained, would say: 'Go on, go *on*, what is the matter with you?' But he knew Italy like, as they say, the back of his hand, was a mine of information, and a witty companion whose age did not matter at all. I loved his company.

Elle Milani, whom I had first met at a window on the Lungarno, was a very different pair of shoes. She had the knack or craze or irritating habit (however you like to look at it) of dramatizing everything. A butterfly on a rose, a lizard on a wall, a plate of spaghetti, a drifting cloud, a hurrying ant, a tree in blossom, the smoke of a passing train, a handsome *contadino*, a spider's web – from anything and everthing spouted a twinkling flood of superlatives. She rejoiced in life. You could not call her a gushing woman, for everything was deeply felt – deeply felt for about five seconds. She flitted across life like a bee, taking honey from this flower and that. (She still does.) All one's defences were downed by this spate of enthusiasm. In the end, it could be tiresome. But rather *malgré moi*, she constituted herself my bearleader, and I was too feeble to escape. She would telephone to me every morning at eight sharp. 'Not up *Yet?*' 'No, I am *Not*.' 'But such a lovely morning to be in *bed?*' 'I like bed.' 'And did you sleep *well*,' 'No, I didn't.' 'You had dreams?' 'Yes, I had.' 'What about?' 'I dunno, perhaps water,' '*No!* but how *Wonderful!* I dreamt of water too!' 'Oh, for God's sake!' 'Yes, but doesn't it mean that we should go to the sea today? And bathe, perhaps?' 'Don't want to go to the sea.' 'Oh, but think how lovely, the sparkling waves . . .' To be cross with this was as futile as anger with a bit of mercury which refuses to go into the hole in the puzzle: sometimes one might want to hurl the puzzle at the wall, but in the end one came back to it and tried again.

If Elle positively gave off sparks, her son Micci was, perhaps inevitably, negative. He had to be, for they were seldom apart.

Micci seemed hardly to be there at all. Not that he was in any way peculiar: he looked nice, behaved well, talked sensibly, and was unfailingly good-tempered. But he somehow failed to register: one forgot he was there. I never knew him well, and I don't think anyone did. Sometimes I vaguely wondered if his still waters ran deep: sometimes I thought there was no water at all. Eventually he was destined to surprise us all by suicide. These two certainly banished loneliness and solitude and even privacy as far as I was concerned: they adopted me like a new baby, and sometimes the baby wanted to scream in its cradle. I have never been able to enjoy the close proximity of human beings, however charming, for too long a stretch. Nicky Mariano, the mistress of I Tatti (whose adorable grace, intelligence and beauty I can't even endeavour to pin down with words) once said, laughing, that I resembled the man in the Arabian nights who each evening went down to the caravanserai, invited and entertained a guest chosen at random, and in the morning said 'Good-bye, God-speed, and I hope we never meet again.' It was an observation which came near the truth.

One evening, returning from some foray in the Rolls, I said – unguardedly – that I should buy the Savonarola. Elle at once frothed up in a soufflé of excitement. 'How wonderful,' she exclaimed, 'to think that *we* found it for you!' I flew into a rage: pettishly I swore to myself that I would never inhabit a house which someone else would always claim to have discovered for me. The Fates decreed that next morning, the Countess Pecori-Giraldi, a woman who dabbled in estates and houses, telephoned to me to say that she had seen a house which might suit me. In anti-Savonarola mood, I agreed to go and see it at once. She arrived in an ancient car with two dubious individuals whom I took to be middlemen. We drove to a part of the country, north of Florence, which I had not seen before. When we came to a huge bare-looking house, with an unkempt lawn and great doors from which all paint had peeled, I said at once that it was no good at all, and I did not even want to go inside it. While I was turning away, the great doors were slowly opened by a tiny woman who seemed to have stepped straight from the Middle Ages. Beyond them the sunshine fell on a vast courtyard, surrounded by a shady cloister of delicate soaring arches. It had a stunning quality of peace and beauty, and was entirely unexpected. I stepped in, and saw beyond the cloister a small but exquisitely made doorway. Beyond it again was a formal rosegarden, some thirty-five yards square, bounded by ancient box hedges and grey walls: and this garden seemed to hang suspended above a view of Tuscany, stretching away to the Chianti hills, so romantic, so perfectly arranged, so peaceful, that it seemed unreal. Inside the house, bare as a barracks, were great rooms whose vaulting floated up like clouds, or drifting white smoke, so light it was. Eight huge sitting-rooms, twelve bedrooms, a colossal granary, and one extremely ancient and probably unworkable bathroom. This house I had to have. I asked the middlemen the price. 'Twelve millions.' Too much for me: far, far too much. I said that I would offer the owners five (at that time about £4,000) if I had the reply by the next morning, because (as was true enough) I was already more than half committed to another villa. The reply next morning was in the affirmative. Thus, in a freakish moment, I acquired the idiotically large house, with some fifty acres and three farms, known as Le Tavernule. Oddly enough, my snap decision was right not only aesthetically, but also financially. I lived in it and loved it for six years, and I still think it one of the most beautiful houses in the world. When I had to sell it, which was inevitable with my comparatively slender means, it fell, luckily, into good hands, and is beautifully tended today.

The rescue and redesigning of old houses is a game which attracts some people and frightens others. I have always found it one of the most entrancing, and in every way rewarding, occupations imaginable. Some eight transactions of this kind have fallen to my lot, and each one has been not only a delight, but also a successful financial gamble. People are, as a rule, oddly unimaginative about houses, and, as every architect and interior decorator knows, will pay large sums for designs and alterations which cost little. I am, however, somewhat allergic to architects and interior decorators as tribes. Merely to design a house in which you are not going to live, merely to dress up a room in current taste – these are not enough. You must first believe in a house, then alter and decorate it to suit yourself and nobody else, and then live in it for at least a year, so that you can iron out all its inconveniences and failures. After that you may have something to sell which will please any purchaser. Every house that I have ever sold has pleased its purchaser, and, what is more, in nearly every case the purchaser is still in possession, and happy to be. And, besides having myself lived in these houses for a total span of some fifteen years all told, I have made (and, needless to say, long ago spent) about £15,000 profit from their sales. Nature did not endow me with many talents, but this quirk of ability with houses is something in which I have come to believe: I am fairly confident that, if I outlive my capital, as seems horribly possible now, I could still make a steady thousand pounds a year by the manipulation of houses. Not a fortune, but still enough. And, in case you think that I am bragging, I will add that you can't do this kind of thing without some capital to start with – and therefore perhaps heaps of people without capital could do it just as well as I – and also that it can be described as a sort of confidence trick, because you are using ignorance to boost appearances. Still – that could be said of every advertiser in the world.

The pleasure of playing with houses is usually, in my experience, in inverse ratio to their size. Some people, I daresay, would be thrilled by the job of doing up Buckingham Palace or Chatsworth or Windsor Castle – not I. Acres of walls and floors cannot be treated with affection. The real fun is to be had out of an old barn, or a couple of ruined cottages, with an acre or two of garden. Multiplication cancels love, in all walks of life.

Le Tavernule was, as I was uneasily (though only at times) aware, a very risky proposition. In 1946 large houses were white elephants, and no one could tell whether the wealthy international life of Florence would ever be revived. The house was not obviously attractive, appearing at first sight a box-like fortress of a place, formidably austere in its neglected gardens. It had neither drains nor light nor power nor – as I discovered too late – water. It was a good six miles – too far for rich snobs – from Florence. Its only approach, for the last mile and a half, was a very narrow, dusty, and frightfully bumpy track which, whatever you might do to it, was immediately ruined by ox-carts. Against these unsaleable factors there was the position of the house, which was superb: every window in it commanded a wide and lovely view over the unspoiled Chianti country. There was the cloistered quadrangle, and the hanging garden beyond it. There was complete silence – for those who liked it. (Quite often my visitors would remark, with a haunted expression: 'It's very quiet here!' – and, God knows, most of us are now unaccustomed to silence.) There was also the fact, which to me seemed important, that this house, alone of all those that I had seen, had never been renovated or let to a foreigner, and was in perfect fifteenth century condition. It had a long and well-authenticated history of occupation by one Italian family for three centuries: the old documents still preserved showed that they had been an ecclesiastical lot, very careful of their farm accounts, but giving largely and regularly to hospitals and convents. The little chapel contained their tombs, with some touching references to 'these blessed solitudes' *(questi cari silenzii).* The whole place had a great feeling of peace: I felt that the ghosts, if any, were extremely benign. And the fifty acres were very fertile, giving a considerable yield of corn, wine, and oil. I made up my mind (and this is very necessary if you are going to renovate a house successfully) that I would live in Le Tavernule for the rest of my natural life. That dream, real enough at the time, was shattered eventually by the Inland Revenue and the necessity to buy atom bombs to protect a Britain which I never wanted to see again. Thus are we victimised by the places of our birth. However, if my greatgrandfather had not made a fortune from cotton, I could not have bought Le Tavernule: so perhaps it was quite just that I should lose it again in order to pay money to the wealthy working-classes of Britain. All the same, I rather resent being done in the eye by power-seeking politicians.

A nice financial mess was in fact in the making, even if it was temporarily obscured by my ignorance and by the immediate distractions of the job. A quarter of my resources had been transferred to Italy, and although ten thousand pounds was a large enough sum to me, it was not sufficient to cope with the purchase and renovation of a down-at-heel mansion of some twenty-five large rooms. That it was done at all was due partly to the then high value of the pound (before Cripps had devalued it), and partly to the low cost of Italian labour in 1946. Another and not unimportant factor was that foreign visitors had not yet begun to return to Italy, and shops were anxious to sell, even at low prices. Servants could be had for the equivalent of one pound a month, and labour was correspondingly cheap. Started six months earlier, the job might have been completed within ten thousand pounds. As it was, between the purchase in August 1946 and the partial but necessarily final conclusion of work about a year later, all prices were multiplied, more or less, by ten. Estimates, carefully made, became comic scraps of paper overnight, each week the household bills climbed to dizzier heights: prices of furniture – and even haggling about them – became impossible. By the time that Sir Stafford Cripps had cut off a quarter of my income, I was already in no position to maintain Le Tavernule. In spite of all that I had, for the first eighteen months, a splendid spendthrift time.

Water provided the first and worst crisis. The house had been bought on the spur of the moment, without any surveying advice: and it was lucky that the roofs and structure were in stout good order. But I had accepted all too lightly the owners' assertion that the ancient well in the courtyard, ninety feet deep, was inexhaustible. The water in it was about ten feet deep and produced, with luck, one bath per day. That seemed strange, though perhaps washing had never played a great part in the history of Le Tavernule. The idea of digging it deeper was opposed on the grounds that, if it had ever been inexhaustible, the earthquake of 1896 had probably diverted the underground source, which would not be easy to rediscover. At this point Signor Peruzzi, very fortunately for me, entered my life. He was a builder in a large way, and President of the Builders Trade Union. He must have been getting on for seventy, but every day, in blazing sun or drenching rain, he walked up the steep hill to the villa, and radiated energy, charm, and commonsense. Once, when I asked him how, at his age, he could be so active, he replied: 'No Tea, no Coffee, no Alcohol, no Tobacco.' Signor Peruzzi said that if I really wanted five new bathrooms (and I did) I must sink another well. But where? A number of water-diviners were summoned, ranging from a charming old priest who had been water-diviner to the Italian Army to a tight-lipped young man with a box of coloured chemicals from a firm in Milan. They all gave their widely-differing advice, and there seemed to be no reason to believe any of them. To sink a well at great expense, and then to find no water, was an unpleasant idea. But without water, all my plans would be futile: one might go without baths, but without water one could not begin to make a garden. Eventually I discovered that the *contadini* grew their occasional vegetables in a place which was, by common and ancient consent, the least dry on the estate: and it seemed best to experiment there. So, under Peruzzi's direction, a well eight feet in diameter was begun: and, as always, I admired the ability, tenacity and gaiety of Italian workers. At six feet below the surface we struck rock, and I could hardly believe that manual labour would get through it. At twelve feet water began to come in, at twenty there was a promising flow, but at thirty-five it had not increased and Peruzzi advised me to stop. It was not quite what I had hoped for. It was enough to supply the house, and, moderately, the garden: but it wasn't enough for rain-sprays for the lawn or a swimming pool, both of which were then among my crazy ideas. The well was 400 yards from the house and eighty feet below it: a major trench-digging operation, and a huge expenditure on pipes, to say nothing of an automatic electric pump, were required to get the water up. When it first gushed out in the house I was thrilled: my thrill was chilled by my three tenant-farmers, who asked at once whether I was not going to pipe it to their houses. I wasn't and I couldn't afford to do so: but I felt guilty.

The garden was now going ahead. I planted three thousand roses, and, after dragging out twelve old trees with the help of oxen, laid out a lawn some seventy by thirty yards. Both these bits of work were idiotic: to look after 3,000 roses and a huge lawn without a gardener (which I couldn't afford) was an impossible task, and it kept me in a flurry for the rest of my time at Le Tavernule. But, since I never did enough, the roses got worse and worse, and the lawn, as lawns do in Italy unless they are flooded on every summer day, wilted away. To the inexperienced eye, the garden went on flourishing for some considerable time: to my own it rapidly became an unconquerable tangle of weeds. I don't know that I ever really enjoyed it: it represented TOO MUCH WORK. Too late I realized that the real Florentines – who kept their gardens to cypress hedges, statues, and very few flowers – were much wiser than I was. When you live in Italy, and actually try to cultivate a garden yourself, you soon realize why English people garden so much and so successfully – because it is easy. Tuscan soil and Tuscan summers are guaranteed to drive any English gardener demented: the earth becomes rock, and you can never water it enough: English (or adopted English) flowers such as delphinium, phlox, and lupins – indeed all flowers that love moisture – die on you persistently. The English gardener in Italy has to learn a new vocabulary – tuberoses, camellias, hydrangea, and such creepers as wisteria, bignonia, and the Cambridge-blue plumbago. A very good vocabulary it can be, but gardening habits are difficult to unlearn. For years I continued to try cultivate flowers unsuited to Tuscany.

Inside the house I installed my five bathrooms and gradually collected, at reasonable prices, some excellent furniture. I also had to buy beds and mattresses and curtains and sofas and upholstered chairs – an expense which I resented, because such things do not last. In England, when my *folie de grandeur* had not grown so large, I had stored some 4,000 books (which had been with me to India and back) and enough furniture for one bedroom and sitting-room, which I had thought would be about my mark. But to have these sent to Italy was, in 1947, extremely difficult. The Board of Trade required a permit, and that could only be obtained after they had scanned – and altered – a detailed list. No silver or jewels of course: in fact nothing saleable, because if I were to sell things I might defeat Treasury regulations about my income. They took a poor view even of my books – did I intend to set up a shop? I wanted my books very much, and made a howl about them: I told my solicitors (who were much too grand for me) to badger the Board. Eventually and after a considerable time, the Board gave way, and my solicitors, who had some *folie de grandeur* too, immediately took a complete railway van, and sent my few possessions across Europe. The whole van, perched on a road chassis, duly arrived at Le Tavernule, and knocked down five olive trees and a cypress in its progress up the drive. The bill was £450.

This rake's progress was neatly punctured by a letter from the Bank of England. I was asked to explain why I was trying to buy ten thousand pounds worth of textiles in England. By this time I had come to understand, vaguely, the pains and penalties attached to Exchange Control, and though I still did not understand why I could not spend my own money, I realized that I might have committed a dire offence. I broke into a cold sweat. I had read in the newspapers some of the proceedings taken by Exchange Control against those who got their money out by illicit means, and I now saw myself fined £50,000 and utterly ruined – which was indeed a possibility. I went to the Swiss Bank and asked what had been done with my cheque: they said that it had been sold to a third party, whose name they could not divulge. I wrote a humble letter to the Bank of England, saying exactly what I had done, and suggesting that I could now probably sell the house and return the money (my money) to England. I wrote to my friend Patrick Baggallay, a leading light in the City, who knew all about the transaction, asking him to advise me. The Bank replied tersely that the sale of my house would serve no useful purpose, but that my £10,000 cheque would not, of course, be honoured. Patrick wrote in high glee, saying that the cheque had been presented by an Italian industrialist to a Bradford wool firm, that they had sent it for collection to the Bank of England, that the bank had returned it marked RD, that the Bradford firm had indignantly sent it to him, and that he had immediately burnt it. 'There is, so far as I can see,' he added, 'no written record of this transaction, and your Italian cannot proceed against you, because he has broken his own country's laws. You have therefore got £10,000 for nothing.' That was all very well as a joke: but the fact remained that I had a debt of £10,000 which I could not repay, and that the Bank of England would not view my antics with any pleasure. Worse still, I had spent £12,000 on Le Tavernule: and how could I now ever hope to get the £2,000 which I owed? From this time onwards my scribbled diaries, which had been extremely gay, become peppered with the ominous phrase; 'Must sell this house at once.'

It was a hideous idea, because Le Tavernule was a unique and exquisite house, and, although I had not been able to furnish it more than sparsely – perhaps a mistake on the right side – was comfortable enough. Life on the outskirts of Florence had become very pleasant: there was a small group of friendly and amusing people with houses in the neighbourhood, and the rather casual social life gave a perfect mixture of occasional parties and solitude. And I clung obstinately to the notion that, with the world at peace, everything would improve. But in the meantime (as is not uncommon in these days) money became a Maddening Misery, and soon I could think of nothing else. Into this persistent nightmare stepped a rich Italian industrialist. He was brought up to the villa one day, and I was impressed by this tall grave gentleman who – so I was told – had had all his property confiscated by Mussolini and had been sent to the Lipari Islands: but had since managed to make a huge fortune all over again. He asked if he could be of any assistance to me, and said that he was making, in collaboration with an Englishman, an Anglo-Italian film which would be highly profitable and that if I cared to invest in it, he would be able to pay me my profits in Italian lire. He told me all about the film, which was to be called *Children of Light*, and shot at Ischia. I thought that the story was an excellent one: moreover, the film was heavily backed by the National Provincial Bank and also by the Film Finance Corporation. I met the partner, who seemed agreeable, if vague. Without further ado, I invested £7,000 in him, in England: and received an advance of £1,000 in Italian money, which enabled me to pay some debts. The rest, £6,000, went down the drain and was never heard of again. Despite all my efforts, I have never to this day discovered what happened to the film, or whether it was ever shown. This put *finis* to Le Tavernule. I had spent £11,000 and lost another £6,000. A fool and his money, you may rightly say, are soon parted. But wait.

It is odd to reflect that, in this story, money takes a more and more important place. At the beginning, when there was little of it, it scarcely mattered: in retrospect the moneyless days seem to have been the best. When it was earned it was carelessly spent: it seemed possible and natural to be able to earn more. Even when the power was temporarily lost, the resulting squeeze was of no great concern. But from the moment that money was inherited, it turned into an anxiety. It came like a spectre at night to the bedside, clawing at the mind: it produced an allergy to any visits to the bank ('how much *is* there in my current account?'): it made all bills a threat and a menace: it threw a cloud across the future. Yet two simple remedies always existed. If you haven't enough, earn more. Alternatively, if you have £1,000 a year, live on £800. But it is a quirk of conventionalized human nature that the man with private means, while not necessarily shirking activity or 'work', will try to avoid being bossed about. Again, a man brought up in a certain circle and with friends of a certain way of life, will attempt, whether he can afford it or not, to keep to that circle and that way of life. He will keep up with the Joneses. It may be, indeed it is, stupid: but it is as insidious a habit as smoking and quite as difficult to break. In *The Way of All Flesh*, Samuel Butler wrote: '*Money losses are the hardest to bear of any by those who are old enough to comprehend them. A man can stand being told that he must submit to a severe surgical operation, or that he has some disease which will shortly kill him, or that he will be a cripple or blind for the rest of his life: dreadful as such tidings must be, we do not find that they unnerve the greater number of mankind ... Loss of money indeed is not only the worst pain in itself, but it is the parent of all others. Let a man have been brought up to a moderate competence, and have no speciality: then let his money be suddenly taken from him, and how long is his health likely to survive the change in all his little ways which loss of money will entail? How long again is the esteem and sympathy of friends likely to survive ruin?*' People today may not agree with Butler's opinions, and Chancellors of the Exchequer do not subscribe to it: in my own case it seemed menacing enough.

So, in 1948, I put Le Tavernule in the hands of agents. Many wealthy and distinguished people, including the ex-Queen of Bulgaria and the Duchess of Aosta, came to see it, and I developed a line of patter. But none of them came near buying it. There was no disguising the facts that the approach was bad enough to ruin any car, and that there was neither central heating nor telephone. After a while I became convinced that I should never sell it: and saw myself retiring servantless to live in the kitchen, and allowing the rest of the house to fall down around me. And that, indeed, was one way out of my troubles, and might have been imposed on me. I am not even sure that it would have been particularly unpleasant. But such is the weakness or vanity of human nature that I should have flinched at that confession of poverty.

I had by this time discovered a legal method of repaying £10,000 to my Italian industrialist, and discharched the debt. So I was now £17,000 out of pocket, with some debts still hanging over me.

One day two charming friends of mine, Walter and Lenore Lucas, asked me if I would care to drive over to Lucca with them, to see a small house which they might buy. When we arrived, I was surprised to find myself in front of a villa which I had frequently and greatly admired from the road below. It was beautifully perched on a spur in an isolated valley, with blue mountains rising sharply behind it: the architecture, though unpretentious, had that special Italian harmony of line and colour which seems to make a house grow naturally from its environment: best of all, it was surrounded – and this is rare in Italy – by thick woods of acacia, oak, lime and sycamore. Inside, it had great charm: a spacious hall, one large sitting-room, and four bedrooms. It also had four bathrooms and central heating. It was in a bad state of repair, because bombs and shells had narrowly missed it: but, compared with Le Tavernule, renovation was child's play. I had an immediate yen for it: but, since it was the Lucas's discovery, my hands were tied. In any case, I could hardly flirt with a new house until or unless I sold Le Tavernule. All the same, I did flirt with the idea. And sometimes ideas, if well flirted-with, are realized.

At this time I was still painting. Painting, however poor the talent, is the most wonderful occupation in the world for anyone who has worries. Take your box and your easel and your canvas, and you are lost to all else while the light lasts. I found it an unbeatable remedy for anxiety. I am far from a talented painter, but I had done just enough work to make myself capable of building up a passable picture: and I never failed to convince myself (for the first hour at least) that this was going to be the best thing I had ever done. The result, of course and inevitably, was a horrid disappointment. Nevertheless painting, however badly done, alerts the eye and widens the appreciation of colour and line. But I now felt that it was not enough, and decided to take up music. I bought a Bechstein (the rake's progress was still in full spate) and vamped on it. I had never possessed a piano before, and my father's horror had so influenced me that I had never dared to play on one: so I made some nasty noises, conscious always of my father's ghost near by. I decided that a teacher was necessary. There was in Florence a certain Signor Reali, a musician who seemed engaging and sympathetic: I went to call on him. The maid who answered my ring said: 'Signor Reali died yesterday.' A little daunted by this contretemps, I asked Nicky Mariano, who was an excellent musician, if she could recommend anybody to teach the piano to a fifty-two-year-old. After some thought, she chose Professor X. I went to call on Professor X. The maid who answered my ring said: 'Professor X died this morning.' I concluded that either God or my father did not wish me to have a teacher: and went on vamping.

Presently the Lucases announced that they could not afford the house at Lucca. I at once wrote to the owner, explaining my position and saying that I would buy the house if and when Le Tavernule was sold, but could not do so before. I did not have much hope about this, because owners who wish to sell are not usually inclined to wait, and I knew that Countess Pecori-Giraldi was already angling for the house. But in this case the owner, Lady Norah Smith, was an unusual person. She replied with a most engaging and witty letter, saying that the suitability of the owner was more important to her than the price or date of sale, and was I suitable? She had met my sister, and thought that I might be. I answered, of course, that my suitability was supreme, but that she might have to wait for ten years or so. From this exchange of letters a pen friendship developed rapidly, and blossomed into affection when, later, I met Norah in London. Very soon she was sold on the idea that I alone should have the house: and refused all other offers. I was both delighted and embarrassed, since there still seemed little hope of selling Le Tavernule.

English people who have houses in Italy are (or certainly during the forties and fifties were) subjected to heavy pressure by English visitors. After I had been at Le Tavernule for two or three years, scarcely a day passed without some missive of this kind – 'Perhaps you may remember Mrs Willoughby, whose sister-in-law told me that you very kindly invited her brother to tea last year. Mrs Willoughby urged us to write to you when we were in Florence. Of course, we do not wish to disturb you, but . . .' Even though one didn't remember any Mrs Willoughby or a sister-in-law or a brother, *noblesse oblige* (or a desire to show off) held firm: down one went in the car to Florence: call at the hotel: 'perhaps you'd care to come up to lunch the day after tomorrow?' 'Yes, indeed, how kind . . .' Down with the car again, because they're far too silly to find their way by tram, and travelling allowances don't permit taxis: and up to the villa: and a dreary lunch, and you never want to see them again: back to Florence with them: and, totted up, a considerable expense. Elnyth Capponi, one of the most enchanting women in Florence, told me, when I spoke to her about this constant intrusion, that she put all such letters straight into the waste paper basket. 'They can think,' she said, 'that I'm dead: I simply can't afford to entertain them.' Nor could I: but I did.

One summer evening at about eight o'clock, when I had a bevy of these strangers sitting in the courtyard, drinking cock-tails and waiting for dinner, a huge green Cadillac drew up at the door. In it were three elegantly dressed people, who intro-duced themselves as Mr and Mrs James C. Smoot and Mrs Boehm. They wished to see the villa. Browned off by phoney purchasers, I said curtly that it was too late. They protested that they had driven from Montecatini with the sole idea of seeing Le Tavernule. I offered them five minutes, saying that my guests were waiting. They were rushed through the house, and I forgot my patter, which perhaps was a good thing. Emer-ging with her pekingese, Mrs Smoot threw me a smile and said: 'We are vurry interested in this villa.' I did not believe it. But next morning an agent arrived to say that the Smoots wished to buy the villa immediately, *with all its contents*, and what would be the price? I was staggered. I had never dreamed of selling the whole thing as it stood. They wanted an instant answer. Needs must when the devil drives: I could not turn down any offer. I said, a hundred thousand dollars. The agent said that he thought that they would consider that quite reason-able. They did: and next day came to lunch. I said to Mrs Smoot: 'But surely you don't want all these dusty old books?' 'Oh, yes, I do.' 'The Bechstein?' 'Oh, yes.' 'These bits of white china?' 'Yes, yes.' I nearly asked: 'My grandmother's photograph?' and felt sure that, if I had, the answer would have been yes. When they departed, I put my head in my hands. A hundred thousand dollars was something, but could I be stripped naked of every possession? Obviously I must be.

Fortunately the Smoots had second thoughts. They asked me to lunch on the following day, and Mrs Smoot confided to me that Mr Smoot had another 'proposition' to make. (My heart fell). They had, said Mrs Smoot – who was an elegant and charming woman – several houses already, and Mr Smoot (who remained for the most part silent) did not care to commit himself too far in Yurrup till the Russian problem was solved. So they would like to take my villa for two years, paying me five hundred dollars a month (in advance). I was to continue living in it, and they would maybe come over. At the end of two years, either they would buy it, in which case the rent would be deducted from the price, or they would not, and I should retain the rent. It sounded utterly crazy to me and I said so. I even heard myself arguing against it. But nothing would deflect them. In the afternoon we went to a notary, and the agreement was drawn up and signed. After that, Mr Smoot (I felt that I must be dreaming) paid twelve thousand dollars into my bank. And I never saw, or (personally) heard from them again. They vanished into America and never returned. I have been told that they divorced: I don't know. All I know is that I got twelve thousand dollars that afternoon. And I remain grateful to the Smoots. This story sounds incredible, but it is perfectly true.

With twelve thousand dollars I was, at least for the moment, in clover again. I paid debts and bought Lady Norah's house, for which she asked an absurdly small sum. And very quickly I moved over to Lucca, leaving a maid and the caretakers at Le Tavernule. This was consistent with my agreement with the Smoots, since I left Le Tavernule and its furniture intact and well maintained. I wrote to the Smoots suggesting that they could easily let it, if they did not themselves want it: I felt somewhat guilty about them. And they did eventually let it to a charming couple called (in this sequence strange names pursued me) Mr and Mrs Humphrey Mudd. Meantime I went into stark but carefree residence at Lucca, and started another orgy of reconstruction. And this time I had a house which, although far too isolated to be a business proposition, enchanted me as no other house has ever done. It still does, and, by the skin of my teeth and a vulnerable skin at that, I am still in it. How long I shall remain probably depends on the number of people who read this book.

I must now go back a little. Early in the winter, before the Smoots arrived, I went out one morning and found Lady Berkeley surveying the garden. Molly Berkeley is an engaging and unpredictable person. I asked her what on earth she was doing there. She replied that she had decided to rent my house for the winter. I said that I never let my houses. She was used to having her own way, and offered me a fairly large sum of money. But, poor as I was, the idea did not attract me: in these days, if you are going to be turned out of your own house, you need a colossal sum of money to make up the loss and live comfortably elsewhere. And if you ask, as well you may, what I mean by living comfortably, I mean at least ten pounds a day. If you have not got that, you are better off in your own burrow, with your own books and your own servants. So I did not care for Molly Berkeley's idea. But Molly was not to be beaten. She kept on appearing. Since she had a huge house in Assisi, and another in Rome, I couldn't (and cannot now) imagine what she wanted with Le Tavernule. But she wore me down. At last, one day, she arrived from Assisi in pouring rain, and I said: 'Look how dreary it is: you'd never stand it' – and she produced 500 dollars from her purse. It happened that I had just then been invited to attend the inauguration of the Indian Republic in Delhi. I took the dollars and bought an air ticket. A week later I was in Karachi.

In Karachi Zulfaqar, now Director-General of Radio in Pakistan, gave me a tremendous welcome. Almost instantly he arranged a party of a hundred people, which went on all night. Afterwards I retired to bed with the most thundering attack of malaria I have ever had: and this was very odd, because it was winter, when malaria does not usually occur, and I had never had it since leaving India ten years before. Zulfaqar sat on me while I rattled with fever, and his wife Inayat came and waved cooked crows over my head, to avert the evil eye. The doctors were puzzled by my continuing fever. Eventually I was bundled in blankets to a radiologist, who found, quite correctly, that both lungs were affected by tuberculosis. I was advised to return to England. But, having got so far, I could not miss Delhi: and I eventually got myself into an aeroplane (road and rail traffic between Pakistan and India did not exist) on the day before the celebrations. In darkness we dropped down on a Delhi marvellously illuminated. One saw that, however dull the British garden city was on the ground, it was superb as a sparkling map. Next morning I got up early and went with my grandly gilded cards to the Durbar Hall, where I found Nehru and Amrit Kaur alone, fussing over the seating arrangements. They were enchantingly warm and kind, and took my teasing lightly. I asked Nehru what on earth he was doing with a bodyguard, all standing round like statues and dressed up with lances in correct Viceregal fashion. He said, 'You wouldn't want me to put the poor chaps out of work, would you?' I felt inclined to ask him what he thought about all the poor English chaps who had been put out of work by his nationalism: but the reply was too obvious.

The ceremony that followed was an impressive transformation scene. Only a few brief years before, the Durbar Hall had seen the stiff British swearing-in of a British Viceroy, surrounded by the dull rectitudes of British civil servants and their dowdy wives. Now the whole atmosphere was changed: and one of the most striking changes was the multitude of foreign representatives, whom British India had never had, and whose presence one had unconsciously missed. Here they all were now, from all over the world, dressed with brilliant elegance in all the varied attires of mankind. They made a splendid decoration. (One wondered, all the same, how Gandhi would have viewed it.) Among them were some striking personalities, such as Soekarno of Indonesia and his beautiful wife, and the grave and gentle Abdullah of Kashmir, so soon to go to jail. But to me the most striking of all was Rajagopalachari, the retiring Governor-General. He always was my favourite man in India: and still is: and I still receive his wonderful letters. That day, at the end of the long and glittering procession, he shuffled up to the throne in a *dhoti*, clearly indifferent to the whole business, but nevertheless dominating it. I knew that he was leaving for his Madras home next morning, and felt that I must speak to him at all costs: I was told that it was out of the question, and that his every minute was already booked. In the terrifyingly crowded reception which followed the inaugural ceremony, I pushed wildly around, trying to find him, and for a long time failing to do so. When I did, he was surrounded by a chattering crowd. I hovered, discouraged, on the outskirts. But suddenly he saw me, and opened his arms to me. I whispered; 'I *must* talk to you!' He beckoned to an ADC, and said: 'When I go out, see that Fielden comes with me.' And so, when the trum-

pets shrilled and the great doors were thrown open for the retiring
Governor-General, I was the only one who followed him. That
– though perhaps it was only a boost of my vanity – was a thrilling moment, and compensated for much. I talked to him for an
hour, and did not (I hope), like Omar Khayyam, come out by
that same door as in I went. There was another (for me) emotional
moment. Some twenty people were lunching with Nehru in the
garden of his house. Lunch was set out on a buffet, and we helped
ourselves (Nehru carefully explaining which food was strictly
Indian), and took our plates to five small tables. Nan Pandit said
to the assembled company: 'We are taking Lionel Fielden to our
table, because, you see, he's an honorary citizen of India.' I was
alone with JN, Nan, and Sarojini, Naidu's daughter. I thought it
a splendid occasion to get the lowdown on everything. But Nehru
wasn't having any of that, and talked throughout lunch about
the two baby elephants which he was sending by aeroplane as a
gift to the American President.

In spite of all this, and indeed much more, kindness, I found
India disappointing and depressing. No doubt it was unreasonable
to expect that great changes should have been accomplished in so
short a time. But I did, I think, expect a miracle: or at any rate
a change as great as that in the Durbar Hall. Yet conditions
seemed just as chaotic as they had ever been under the British Raj.
The teeming poverty-stricken millions were as daunting, the
streets as smelly, the faces as apathetic, the whole way of life as
tawdry, as ever before. In the thirties, people like Nehru and
Amrit Kaur and Rajaji and Satyamurthi, had often teased me,
either directly, or (more often) by implication, for living too
luxuriously in poor India. Now, it seemed to me, they were living
rather more luxuriously than the British ever did. They gave
various explanations. 'We must keep up the prestige of India.'
'This furniture, these silks, are Indian-made: we must support
Indian industries.' Of course: quite logical: what had I expected?
Well, what had Gandhi expected? Not quite this, surely? Gandhi,
I thought, would have the Government living in village huts,
dressed in *dhotis*, and would have thought that prestige would
accrue nevertheless. Gandhi would have decentralized industry
into the villages, and in that he may have been far ahead of his
time: for American writers today have argued that it may prove
less costly and more efficient to take machines to the worker than
to transport the workers to factories. Above all, I was struck
by the too towering influence of Nehru: take away this corner-

stone, and maybe the whole house will fall down. Nehru was and is by far the most intelligent and long-sighted politician alive: I don't think that anyone who knows him can doubt that: but what happens to India when he disappears? And India is not yet a country: it is at best an uneasy federation of very different tribes. I have never liked alien occupation, and I still believe that India could be a great stabilizing influence in the world: equally, she could be overrun by Russia or China.

Pakistan was a different problem. Arrogant, provincial, angry but (at any rate in West Pakistan) united. Aesthetically backward, it was tough. Its young nationalism hankered to throw off the English language and English influence; which seemed to me to be a practical mistake. The Pakistanis could be admired but not loved: the Indians could be loved but not admired. Perhaps my thoughts were conditioned by ill-health: I flew off from Karachi in a censorious state of mind. I stopped in Rome, because the flight, like all aeroplane flights nowadays, seemed to me hideously boring, cramped, and dull. If I have got to fly, I want to have a window and see the ground: I don't want to be stuck in a noisy bus at 20,000 feet. That's no way to travel. In Rome Elle Milani met me and whirled me off to the sanctification of some minor Spanish saint in St Peters: I watched Pius XII darting about with vigour, and having a chat in front of the altar with the Spanish Ambassador: and wondered if anything in India was more barbaric and nonsensical. Next day I flew on to London with Cyril Radcliffe and a group of Australian footballers: the Australians got very drunk and rushed up and down the aeroplane: Cyril read Trollope to avoid my arguments about his arrangement of the Indian frontier: and there was dense fog over the Alps, which frightened me considerably. In London I broadcast four talks on India and Pakistan, and wrote some articles for *The New York Times,* at their request. All these seemed to be startlingly successful, and, since the Pakistan Government reprinted my talks in a pamphlet, anyone who is interested can read more than I have put down here. I greatly offended many friends in India: but one is always tempted to offend those whom one loves: the others matter so much less. The net result was that I said good-bye for ever to the non-glamorous East, and never wanted to see it again: and my articles and broadcasts paid for my journey. The inevitable conclusion seemed to be that black and yellow and brown men's countries are not for the white man, nor – and this is of equal importance – are the white men's countries for the black or brown or yellow. There may come a time, and one hopes that it will, when all races will be equal, but it is not yet. It is not a question of better or worse. The origins, habits, and thought processes of Asia and Africa are entirely alien to the white man, and all mixtures will provoke explosions. For the moment at least, the best thing we can all do is to mind our own business. British leftwing journals and British leftwing politicians have evolved a myth which makes the white man an eternal tyrant, the black man an eternal slave. They will learn better before long. All men of whatever colour are about equally kind, and equally cruel. But habits and ways of life die hard. To try to impose Christianity or Communism or Democracy on anyone is about as silly as to attempt to explain respectability to a Zulu, or to ask the Archbishop of Canterbury to wear a *dhoti*. Some there are who, by mental and spiritual suppleness, have learnt to walk happily among all nations without losing their own individuality: perhaps they are the Baptists of a new world of understanding and tolerance: but as yet they are few.

Returning to Lucca I started, once again, to spend money like water, convinced as I then was that the Smoots, in spite of their silence, would eventually buy Le Tavernule. But as the months slipped by, and at last only four of their lease remained to run, I lost hope, and asked the agents to put it into the market again. The money nightmare reappeared, now worse than ever before. With two houses on my hands, I was sunk: and the prospects of selling Le Tavernule, now unlived-in for nearly two years, were far from rosy. But the Gods were still with me. One day a car drove up to the house in Lucca, and out of it stepped a vision of beauty, who introduced herself as the Countess Denise de Perousse de Cars. She was accompanied by a well-known and wealthy Venetian lawyer named Carnelutti. The vision told me, without more ado and with the certainty of a pretty woman, that she *must* have Le Tavernule. I explained that it was still leased to the Smoots, and that its ultimate future depended on them. Nothing daunted, she said that I must there and then sign an agreement that, if the Smoots did not take it, I would sell it to her. I could not get to the table fast enough. It was agreed that she should have it, without furniture, for fifteen thousand pounds: and eventually she did. As soon as I had signed, she went off and was sick in the bathroom: and I reflected then and later (when she had spent colossal sums on Le Tavernule) that I might have stung her for a good bit more. However, there it was: all in all, Le Tavernule had cost me nothing, and the furniture was sheer profit. Houses have always been lucky for me: or perhaps I have been lucky for houses. Le Tavernule, a ruined barrack in 1946, is now one of the most beautifully kept villas in Tuscany, and although I can't bear to go near it, I am glad that it is happy.

The retreat to Lucca changed my life profoundly. Le Tavernule had had a certain isolation, but it was an isolation with plenty of neighbours a quarter of an hour away. Lucca was altogether different. There were no English people – as far as I ever discovered – for forty miles around; the ancient Italian families, in huge villas which they used only in summer, were of a Victorian stodginess and, after I had attended a few of their formal parties, I concluded that I was as much at sea with them as in, say, Warwickshire. The fifty miles to Florence were just enough to put off the casual lunch or dinner guest, and I also found that to drive there for a meal was an effort rather than a pleasure. Fortunately, friends did still come to stay with me from England and elsewhere: but I was inevitably condemned to a considerable dose of solitude. Whether that is a bad or good thing I don't know: perhaps it is as well, towards the end of one's life, to learn to be self-reliant. If sometimes I rail at solitude, I am still aware that I should much more dislike to live permanently with another human being. And I should be an ungrateful dog if I didn't enjoy life in this enchanting house, with (so it seems to me) one of the most varied and beautiful gardens that it is possible to imagine. What more, in one's middle sixties, can one want? But I do, dammit, want more: I want youth back again. So will you, one of these days.

Notes in November

The notice which you have been pleased to take of my labours, had it been early, had been kind: but it has been delayed till I am indifferent, and cannot enjoy it: till I am solitary, and cannot impart it: till I am known, and do not want it. SAMUEL JOHNSON - LETTER TO LORD CHESTERFIELD

END OF STORY: end, very nearly, of self also. *Tu reclamais le Soir: il descend: le voici.* It is oddly unexpected – the backward glance at life vanishing, the forward glance into darkness. Was any of it worth doing, was it even worth living? To me this seems the tale of an irresolute flunkey, as meaningless as a stone dropped into a silent pool. The ripples are gone: they altered nothing.

Anyone who writes a personal story of an undistinguished life risks the label of egocentric bore. And so he may be. Egocentricity, close relative of individuality, is unusually unfashionable today. The emphasis, in our climate of opinion, is placed on the crowd, the mass, the shuffle of gregarious movement. The slogan is objectivity: facts, figures, empires of one sort or another: nothing personal, if you please. The individual, unless closely linked with a party, a fashion, a cause, an ideology, is suspect. The independent candidate is not elected: the small shopkeeper is swallowed by the syndicate: the craftsman is supplanted by the mass production machine: the good politician votes as the Whip directs: the worker obeys his Union. Departures from orthodoxy are considered arrogant. Like piracy, slavery, the application of leeches, a belief in witches, or the regular collapse under the table after two bottles of port, such ideas seem proper enough in their time and place. They are not eternal truths but current myths. Governments today are driven to equate a cut-throat national prosperity with human happiness. Industry must turn out shoddy goods as fast as possible. Advertisement flourishes to create a lust for unnecessary possessions. Transport carries people further and faster with less and less purpose. Newspapers must appeal to instincts of greed, envy, luxury and power. Education must extol nationalism. And the object of the exercise is to persuade or dragoon millions of ignorant souls to vote for their own strangu-

lation by despotism or by bureaucracy. The dictator, the statesman, the trades unionist, the syndicate, and even the crowd itself,
all wish, for their different reasons, to encourage uniformity.
Virtue becomes attached to conceptions such as discipline, loyalty,
reliability, perseverance, common sense (a dull lot), while a
pejorative fungus creeps over such words as rash, queer, wild,
impetuous, capricious, sensitive, and even artistic. That is one
measure of our climate of opinion. Eccentricity, if permitted at
all, must be highly successful. The orderly and prosperous ant-
heap is the goal: and, if we score it, we shall have lost the game.
The candle, if a candle there was two thousand years ago to light
man's way, will be extinguished.

   That is a way of putting it: tendentious of course, as all opinions
must be. The point of my narrative is the pointlessness which may
overtake individuals in certain climates of opinion. Our younger
writers, I think, harp on the theme of pointlessness: the angry
young men are not complaining of poverty or fear or enslave-
ment: they are complaining of sheer boredom and lack of aim.
And this applies also to my portrait. The fellow whom I have
tried to describe is a disappointment to me. I find him unexpectedly
dull and silly. He has ambled through life with small effect. Most
people do: that is no consolation. Must a man go through all the
hoops of birth and death and the maddening maintenance of a
body for seventy years for no apparent purpose? Or is the purpose
merely the *enjoyment* of the seventy years? And, if it is, why do
men so consistently deny it to other men? Or is it, Holy Father,
no more than a preparation for the abysmal boredom of harps
and angels? Heaven, as imagined by man, is oddly repellent and
unconvincing: I cannot feel enthusiastic about waking up with
wings and a nightgown. Yet that proves nothing: the human brain
may be unable to perceive an eternity which it cannot deny: it
can, however, perceive the mess on earth, of which I am a part,
and you also. No half-century in history can show a more hideous
display of massacre, torture, regimentation, stupidity and confusion than the first half of the twentieth century. We have out-
done all past ages in sheer murder. Never has man been so badly
and so madly marshalled to dull apathy and self-destruction.
And, in spite of that, we are quite proud of ourselves! An intelligent lot we think we are! And the process continues. Alter a letter
and call it progress. Progress to what? If my man is a poor stick,
his background is an array of ugly bludgeons. Could he escape
their pressures and menaces?

In the last fifteen years, poverty has been greatly alleviated *in the more prosperous countries:* and much more has been done – quite another thing – to encourage the accumulation of possessions. Alleviation of poverty is a must for humanity, but accumulation of wealth raises two questions. First, should the peoples of the West (or, for that matter, of the Soviet Union) have man-per-head automobiles, television sets, council houses and the rest, while the peoples of the East live at starvation level? Secondly, how far can what is called (though never with precision) the 'standard of life' be raised in prosperous countries without damage to the rest of the world, and perhaps even to the people concerned? Wealth, if not wisely used, becomes meaningless squander. Man is an adaptable creature: as most of us have seen, he can be surprisingly cheerful under conditions of war, bombardment, boredom, frustration, hardship and loss. To link happiness with physical comfort and possessions may be a mistake: Sparta had a word for it. A manual labourer of 1960, put down among the fine flower of Elizabethan aristocracy in 1560, would be revolted by the dirt, the stink, the manners and the general savagery: yet who will dare to say that the Elizabethans were less happy, or less gifted, than we? A quarter of a century ago Mr Rajagopalachari, then Prime Minister of Madras, said to me in an interview which I wrote down at the time: 'The gospel of more and more will ruin the West.' I saw what he meant. But, since then, the gospel of more and more has infected the world. The gospel has its point: like drinking, gambling, or fornication it's fairly harmless when not obsessive. The trouble is that all the forces of government, advertisement, insurance, entertainment, and nationalism are busy turning it into an obsession. You've never had it so good. Jesus wept. Not because Mr Macmillan was wrong, but because man does not, oddly enough, live happily by bread alone.

In his two or three thousand years of what we may, possibly, call intelligent life, man has not yet discovered how to govern himself. Or, to put it in another way, he does not, in the long run, wish to be governed by other men. He wants a god or gods (sometimes taking human shape), and nothing else will do. As a result, all human government tends to break down. Democracy is a good idea, if only because it keeps on, apparently, shuffling the governors: you can't be a god for too long. But it is also a bad idea, because the pack gets dog-eared from continual shuffling. A joker turns up and disrupts the game. Who's at fault? Don't tell me that it's economic conditions or slumps or the high cost of living. It's man. Man creates his own conditions. The gods must double themselves up with laughter at the mess he makes of them. Just look down for a moment, my dear Jupiter, at all those people crammed in cars on the Brighton road, with nothing better to do. They never had it so good.

Our solemn fact-finders can impress us, no doubt. Over-population can be dressed up as a nightmare, and the insistence on cannonfodder in the service of nationalism, or unrestrained breeding sanctified by religion, is neither pretty nor sensible: still, who can tell whether human beings will not contrive to live in mile-high skyscrapers and get food from air or sea? Man, if he wishes to live in crowds and produce endless children, can do so for some time to come. Man's desires create the facts. If men desire nationalism and flag-wagging and the defence of their soil, then of course they cannot solve unemployment, they cannot get rid of high tariffs and backward areas, and they will certainly have war. If men desire power over others, propaganda, subversion and corruption will come along too. If men desire money, plutocracy will be there. If men desire to move in crowds, they will get stultifying bureaucracy or the dictator. If men desire too high a standard of living, they will depress the living standards of others. I don't see how any political sophistry can get over these ineluctable facts. But the desires of men, at this time, may move in a blind circle and automatically, so far as human *prosperity* is concerned, create a zero. You struggle for a rise in salary, get it, and find that prices have risen accordingly. Also you have priced yourself out of the market, and your goods no longer sell. Whether such things have anything to do with human *happiness* is surely questionable.

It is said that it will all be the same in a hundred years or that *plus ça change, plus c'est la même chose.* It might be truer to say that human nature changes very little, if indeed at all in our short period of history: but that the human condition does change drastically, and, in doing so, alters the scale of human values and thus makes history. Religion, art, scholarship, money, power, physical beauty, athletics, sport, nationalism, space-travel, war, peace: such stars glitter in the skies of time, and the human generations passing beneath follow one or another. The Greeks aimed at beauty, intellect, heroism, glamorous gods: the Romans concentrated on power and order and law: Italy of the Renaissance mixed art and religion in a splendid brew. Greed,* said President

* Truman, *Years of Trial and Hope,* p.27.

332

Truman in 1946, seems to be the keynote nowadays. That may be too harsh. We live in an age of bodily comfort, money-worship, speed and sport. They can logically be defended, but, as top values, they exclude others.

The greatest changes which have occurred in my lifetime (in human society, not in science, which is another story) are undoubtedly the growth of crowds, and the growth of interference by the State in the life of the individual: perhaps two sides of the same penny. Not a penny that pleases me. Among other changes, pride of place for the Ugliest Duckling goes to the spread of advertisement, defiling cities and country with its bad taste and lies: close runners-up are universal suffrage, fanatical nationalism, and the loss of religious belief. Might one dare to suggest that advertisement serves no useful purpose at all, and that people would be much happier without it? Could one venture a theory that when illiterate people vote (as they do in India and Africa) for pictures of elephants, bicycles, and sewing-machines, Democracy looks fairly silly, and that even our own voters, choosing one of two faces produced by a party, are not much more literate in the complex business of government? Is it permissible to think that nationalism and patriotism are as dead as last year's raspberries in a world which communications must unite, and that their resurgence anywhere is a danger signal? And as for religion, even if it's no more than the opium of the people (and nobody can prove that), surely a little opium may be good for a universal stomach ache?

But to return to my penny. To interfere has always been a strong urge of human nature. We all interfere: missionaries, politicians, doctors, scientists, reformers, advertisers, imperialists, communists, husbands, wives, parents, teachers: interference passes as a kind of virtue. But is it? The new fact of our times is that the ability to interfere has been strengthened as never before. The conquerors of old interfered with only small bits of humanity: now almost any fool with a microphone can interfere with the lot. No individual today has the privacy or liberty that once were his: you must fill up the income-tax return, the passport, the identity card, the insurance policy: you are safely registered for whatever any Government has a mind to do with you. John Stuart Mill wrote, a hundred years ago: A State which dwarfs its men, in order that they may be more docile instruments in its hands – *even for beneficial purposes* – will find that with small men no great thing can really be accomplished. Men permit interference, because they are foxed by propaganda and crowd emotions, and perhaps above all because they continue to think that the spot on which they happen to be born is more sacred than any other.

Crowds of today's dimensions and ubiquity are also new. Not just crowds in the Sportpalast or the Red Square, in front of St Peter's or at a Cup Tie Final: but crowds on roads, on beaches, in trains, in buses, at beauty-spots, in cities, in shops, in hotels, in streets, in parks, in dance-halls, at exhibitions: everywhere the human tide flowing torrentially, and, like a rising torrent, potentially dangerous. Crowds asphyxiate individuality: crowds are malleable mindless monsters, sometimes a flock of obedient sheep, sometimes a pack of angry wolves. Crowds are the paradise of the interferer. Crowds may be the herd of swine which run violently down a steep place into the sea, and perish. But, when Jesus had the temerity to say so, he was besought by the people to depart out of their coasts: even that small crowd resented it. The almighty mob brooks no argument. But gregarious man is mindless man. Crowds can menace intellect, truth, and beauty. So must Marcus Aurelius have felt, turning away in disgust from the bloodthirsty crowd that filled the Colosseum. So also Hadrian, when he built himself into angry solitude at Tivoli.

It is of course fatally easy to be a sourpuss. If I pick on crowds and interference, it is because they seem to represent a longterm tendency towards the regimented ant-heap, giving to political and military leaders, who are not much wiser than other men, powers of compulsion which the fully free individual would never concede. The essential leaven of individual variety, even of individual kindness and tolerance, may be swept away by mass emotions, conditioned and controlled by the technical power of communications. What individual amongst us, untouched by mass hysteria and patriotic slogans, would have himself deliberately opted for the four-year Kaiser, or six-year Hitler, war? Not one in a thousand. Yet lack of foresight made both inevitable. Are we better off today? We are more frightened: but the armament race continues, because material possessions must be defended: wealth, security of wealth, economic planning for wealth's security, are ultimate aims. Christ had a different view when he said: The Kingdom of God cometh not *with observation*, neither shall they say 'Lo *here*,' or 'Lo *there*.' The Kingdom of God is *within you*. I take that to mean that the individual must work out his own salvation, irrespective of the shouts, appeals, threats or promises addressed to him.

My own experience, which for all I know may be a lying jade, suggests that there is hardly a man or woman alive who does not have a natural bent for *something*. The difficulty is first to discover it and then to follow it. Comparatively few people do either. I myself, as you have seen, dismally failed in spite of great advantages. What small talents I possessed were fitted for small things. I was comically unfitted to be a soldier, an administrator, a reformer, a civil servant, or a member of any hierarchical institution. Social pressures, world events, and my own weakness and ignorance, pushed me into such activities, but, since my enthusiasm was never quite fired, I slid from one to another, not quite discontented yet never dedicated. And therefore, naturally, apt to be quarrelsome. But the man or woman who is dedicated to a congenial activity (or even inactivity, as socially judged) has neither the time nor the desire to quarrel. Strikers who strike for money are striking only to escape from boring jobs. Peace becomes monotonous, and quarrelling attractive, to millions of men, simply because they are condemned to a dull routine. To rush into a cinema or gape at television after a day in the factory is not, whatever anyone may say, a satisfactory way of life.

This, I would think, is the greatest challenge which faces our industrial age. Not only because machines are dull things to work with day by day, but also because automation will release leisure to millions who have been conditioned not to use it. The massive myth that human beings must always be busy dies hard: it survives only because people are afraid of leisure and of the growing terror of nothing to think about. Yet, if people refuse to think, and want even leisure organised for them, we are certainly for the dark. The talks and treaties about peace and disarmament which have been trickling on for forty years now, have had small effect; peace cannot be forcibly imposed from above, it must be built on a foundation of human happiness, intelligence, and toleration. Our world cries out for a clean, a revolutionary, sweep of educational methods: even of the damnable word education. The fusty old ideas of schoolhouses with mobs of bored children marshalled by underpaid teachers to climb ladders of parrot examinations based on biased textbooks are out-of-date. We need instead – perhaps: I am drawing a bow at a venture – some free and lively movement of young, very young, people all over the globe, not herded, not marshalled, linguistically literate as young folk can so easily be, seeing for themselves not one dim parochial corner of 'national' territory, but the whole vast field of man's endeavour, learning to live easily in one world. Some such design, easily accomplished with a tenth of the money we spend on armaments, might free millions to follow their natural bent and do more than any summit conference to make the world secure.

November mists begin to steal across the valley. Here on the *piazzale* in front of my little house, I look over a view as beautiful, I think, as any that our world can offer. At my feet lies Mister, last of a long line of bulldogs, enchanting companions of my life. If Mister could read and laugh, I am sure that he would laugh at these muddy reflections of mine. 'Warmth, food, sleep,' he would say, 'some sex and a little fighting: that's life: why worry about what you don't understand?' The garden, with cypress and pine, mimosa and oleander, tumbles away to the fertile plain, where the river Serchio meanders through lush meadows: beyond rise the craggy majesties of the Apuan Alps. Above them the sky is serene, green-tinted, deep as eternity: the evening star glitters solitary in its vast expanse. The sky has something to say to us, perhaps: men have always connected it with their dreams of gods, of heaven, of immortality. What have the apparently intractable problems of earth's little inhabitants to do with that serenity?

> *A world above man's head, to let him see*
> *How boundless might his soul's horizons be,*
> *How vast, yet of what clear tranparency.*
> *How it were good to sink there, and breathe free.*
> *How fair a lot to fill*
> *Is left to each man still.*

Ripafratta

1958 – 1960

A DREADFUL DESTINY

A DREADFUL
DESTINY

Rosemary Rowe

**SEVERN
HOUSE**

First world edition published in Great Britain and the USA in 2021
by Severn House, an imprint of Canongate Books Ltd,
14 High Street, Edinburgh EH1 1TE.

Trade paperback edition first published in Great Britain and the USA in 2022
by Severn House, an imprint of Canongate Books Ltd.

severnhouse.com

British Library Cataloguing-in-Publication Data
A CIP catalogue record for this title is available from the British Library.

ISBN-13: 978-0-7278-8991-1 (cased)
ISBN-13: 978-1-78029-817-7 (trade paper)
ISBN-13: 978-1-4483-0555-1 (e-book)

All Severn House titles are printed on acid-free paper.

Typeset by Palimpsest Book Production Ltd.,
Falkirk, Stirlingshire, Scotland.
Printed and bound in Great Britain by
TJ Books, Padstow, Cornwall.

FOREWORD

T
he story is set in 194 AD in Glevum (modern Gloucester), at a time when Britannia was the most remote and northerly province of the Roman Empire. It is April, the birthday month of the current Emperor, Septimius Severus, who had seized power just a few months earlier. Emperors' birthdays were traditionally marked by formal celebrations, including a temple sacrifice which all male citizens were required to attend, and although there is no documentary evidence of such rites in Glevum at this time, they almost certainly occurred, not least because Severus was insisting on such public demonstrations of support. His continued grasp on power was by no means certain yet. There were still other powerful candidates with rival claims.

The assassination of the Emperor Pertinax (a previous Governor of Britannia, and the supposed friend of the fictional Marcus in this story) by his own Praetorian guard, had precipitated a political crisis. In the absence of any obvious heir, the Empire had effectively been auctioned off, to whoever promised the same guard the highest sum for their support. The winner, Didius Julianus, was officially acclaimed but he found to his dismay that – as Pertinax had said – there really was not sufficient money in the Imperial Purse to pay the bribe. He would not survive for long.

Meanwhile there were three other claimants to the purple, all of them with legions loyal to their cause. Pescennius Niger (a man of African descent, as the name implies) would probably have been the general choice, but Severus, being geographically the closest, seized his chance and shockingly marched his troops to the very walls of Rome. Didius attempted to negotiate, but – abandoned by the Senate and the guard – he was executed and Severus duly proclaimed as Emperor.

The other two pretenders did not capitulate at once. Pescennius, who had already been acclaimed as Emperor in the Eastern Provinces (and indeed is still described as such in many texts) set up a rival court, issuing coinage in his own name and – at the time of this story – actively leading an armed struggle against the 'upstart' Severus. He would not be defeated for another year and Severus continued to be merciless to anyone suspected of supporting this dangerous rival in what was effectively an ongoing civil war.

Meanwhile, in order to avoid a battle on two fronts, Severus had reached an uneasy settlement with the other claimant, buying him off with the courtesy title 'Emperor of the West' and a (worthless) promise that he would be next in line. This was Clodius Albinus, the current Governor of Britannia, whose supporters (including the local legions, naturally) were rightly doubtful of the awkward compromise and so were regarded with suspicion by the new regime. It made for an atmosphere buzzing with division and distrust.

There was cause to be alarmed. Public figures around the Empire were being denounced (often anonymously), accused of treasonable anti-Severan sympathies, stripped of goods and office, and either exiled or killed. Meanwhile the new Empress, Julia Domna, was rapidly emerging as a powerful influence, to the extent that the Senate was alarmed. However, to displease her was very dangerous.

She may have been resented as an incomer, in part. Her father sprang from a priestly dynasty of Baal – rather than of the Roman pantheon – and her mother may have been descended from the disgraced Mark Anthony (both families from what we should now call the Middle East). Although a woman, she came to wield considerable power. Several of Severus's edicts were rumoured to have been issued at his wife's behest, and later coinage shows her profile as well as his. (Interestingly, though Pescennius is sometimes called 'the first black Emperor', Severus too was probably dark-skinned, as portraits on coins appear to testify.)

Julia Domna was unusual. Although individual women might inherit large estates, they were excluded from public office, could not make commercial contracts, and a woman of any age was deemed a child in law, under the official tutelage of first her father, then her husband (if she had one), or – if these failed – some other male relative or willing family friend. If necessary one could be appointed by the state. The only exception was for a widow with three children still alive (who was considered to have rendered service to the state by providing citizens, and was therefore entitled to conduct her own financial – though not legal and contractual – affairs). Until and unless she remarried, naturally.

Being a wife and mother was the expected role. Respectable wives and daughters of Roman citizens did not work outside the home (and often not much in it, apart from genteel 'spinning,' since she was likely to have slaves). The man under whose 'protection' (or 'potestas') she was, was expected to choose a spouse for her, usually for reasons unrelated to romance, though an indulgent father might permit a choice.

Theoretically the bride had the power to refuse, but this was clearly problematic, since if her wishes were ignored she could not appeal to a court herself, and the male who had arranged the match was her legal representative. It does appear that if this guardian was not a relative by blood (for instance an in-law or official appointee) she could appeal against his tutelage, provided she could prove that her physical safety was at stake, and find someone else to protect and speak for her. (Rather as a slave at this time might appeal to a magistrate or priest against a brutal master – in the hope that a new one might be found.) This is the presumed grounds for Druscilla Livia's appeal to Marcus in this tale, though successful transfers (like the slaves' again) seem to have been rare.

It was a great deal easier to divorce – especially for men – though quite how easy might depend upon what form the marriage took. The oldest, most complex and most binding form – the 'manus marriage' – was now vanishingly rare, confined to priests (who were permitted to marry, but only in this form) and a few top members of the patrician tribes, like Druscilla and her first husband in the tale. Such a marriage was virtually indissoluble except on the grounds of the woman's infidelity or infertility (though not the man's, of course). Much more common was the 'usus' marriage which was easily dissolved (especially if the wife could prove that she had slept elsewhere for at least four nights a year, which many women seem to have achieved by returning to their parents, although the legal position was probably derived from presumed adultery).

However, another form of marriage was still current at this time, and fashionably favoured by the highest born. Called 'co-emptio' it involved, among other rituals, the sharing of bread (the 'co-eating' from which the ceremony takes its name) and the symbolic 'purchase' of the bride from her current representative, making her notionally her husband's property. It was therefore difficult to escape. This is the kind of marriage proposed by Hortius.

All this, of course, related only to the wives and daughters of Roman citizens, who were thus officially of that rank themselves (though without the civic privileges afforded to the males). Most freeborn women, however, were not citizens at all. Marriage for them was a more casual affair, and might have been conducted by ancient tribal ritual. Tradesmen's women worked beside their men, and in the poorest households everybody toiled. There were even a few traditional 'female' trades – like the wet nurse, midwife and herb-woman mentioned in the text.

These roles were respected, even by the rich. In a society where girls might legally be married off at twelve, and maternal mortality was high, a successful birth attendant could command good fees. Self-respecting Roman matrons did not generally breastfeed their young, and either farmed them out to a local wet nurse or retained one in the house – sometimes for many years. (Humble mothers with abundant milk could also sell the surplus in the marketplace, where it might provide a welcome supplement to family funds.) And though every household would probably concoct a few of the most common remedies – and even cultivate some plants on purpose for this use – almost everyone needed a skilled herb-woman now and then. (Except perhaps for army personnel, who had the services of the army doctor who would be fairly skilled – though there is some evidence to suggest that even a commander's wife might occasionally purchase a peasant's 'healing draught'.)

Such remedies were all that many households had. The very rich, like Marcus, might have a private Greek-trained doctor to attend the house – though this was expensive, and such were rare. (Even Marcus does not have one at this date.) Battlefield experience had resulted in good army surgery (for the period) and nearby Corinium was famous throughout the Empire for treatments of the eye, but other medicine might be of variable quality. Glevum, like other important towns, had a public 'medicus' – available to anyone who could afford his services – but there was no official training, far less an exam. One accompanied an experienced colleague for a year or two, then copied his prescriptions and procedures – which varied from the probably effective to the questionable at best. (Willow-bark, a source of aspirin, might be prescribed for pain, but carriage-rides were recommended for both 'lunacy' and what was clearly cancer. The cabbage-leaf diet mentioned in the text was a real, and popular, nostrum for all ills.) Home remedies might often be preferred – even to the lancing of a wound, especially (as here) in an emergency, when professional assistance might be miles away.

The Britannia these folk inhabited was the most far-flung of all the Roman Provinces, still occupied by Roman legions, criss-crossed by Roman roads, subject to Roman laws and still administered – precariously – by the Provincial Governor. Latin was the language of the educated, people were adopting Roman dress and habits, and citizenship, with the precious legal and social rights which it conferred, was still the aspiration of almost everyone.

Almost everyone. At the perimeters there remained small groups of dissidents who refused to yield to Rome, and – in the north and far south-west – there were areas still outside of Roman Governance, although the Celtic tribes which held them were widely traded with (largely for precious metals, timber, fur and tin).

Glevum itself was an important town and river port, built as a colonia for retiring veterans, which gave it certain privileges. For one thing, it enjoyed a degree of self-governance under an elected town council or curia. In the story, Libertus is now a member of this, holding the rank of duumvir (from the Latin for 'two' and 'man', meaning that it is a joint position shared with another man). This was originally a very prestigious appointment in Rome, but in the provinces the system appears to have been used to fill quite junior and unglamorous posts – as here – by halving the duties and inevitable expense, since all councillors were unpaid. All freemen born within the walls of a colonia were citizens by right. Most inhabitants, however, did not qualify. Many were freemen, born outside the walls, scratching a more or less precarious living from a trade. Hundreds more were slaves – mere chattels of their master, to be bought and sold (as described within this book) with no more rights or status than any domestic animal. (Servants of either sex were available for use in any way their owner chose, the offspring of such pairings being either raised and sold for a profit when they were old enough or – since Romans considered that newborn infants did not yet have souls – simply disposed of at birth.) Some slaves led pitiable lives, but others were highly regarded by their owners and might be treated well. A slave in a kindly household – with shelter, food and raiment guaranteed – might have a more enviable lot than many a poor freeman struggling to eke out an existence in a squalid hut.

The Romano-British background to this book has been derived from a variety of (sometimes contradictory) pictorial and written sources, as well as artefacts. However, although I have done my best to create an accurate picture, this remains a work of fiction, and there is no claim to total academic authenticity. Septimius Severus and happenings in Rome, as well as the events surrounding Clodius, are historically attested, as is the existence and basic geography of Glevum. (Several new fine pavements have recently been found during excavations around the bus station, suggesting an area of wealthy housing which is not accounted for in my description – but this was not known about when I began and the series must be consistent with itself.) The rest is the product of my imagination.

Relato refero. Ne Iupiter quidem ominibus placet. I only tell you what I heard. Jupiter himself can't please everybody.

PROLOGUE

Rome
Autumn 193 AD

Hortius Lollius Valens, the Senator, was furious. Not, for once, about the fatuity of politics in Rome; he knew enough to say very little in the Senate, nod a lot and – if voting was essential – vote the way the brand-new Emperor Severus would like. It was a technique which had enabled him to survive the reign of several emperors in the last few years.

This matter was even more maddening, if that were possible. It concerned the second marriage he'd contracted for. He'd had such plans – delicious plans, and profitable too. But now he suspected that the lady had heard rumours of his tastes – most likely from his previous wife who hadn't liked the way he took his pleasure, but whose reluctance made it all the more delectable. He should have been more careful about whom he let her see, while she had lasted. But he had learned from that – just as he had learned that it was possible to cause a little too much of that exquisite pain. He would know better next time. He liked them writhing; he didn't like them dead.

If there was a next time! He was getting older, he'd lost his looks and hair, and wealthy families were getting so particular these days. Respectable well-bred virgins could take their pick of handsome boys. Of course, one could buy one's pleasure, but where was the fun in that? He'd had his share of slave-girls and prostitutes of course – handsomely rewarded to ensure they held their tongues – but they weren't really satisfactory. The humiliation and outrage was at least half the thrill.

The woman he had selected would have been ideal. Spirited, so she would be a pleasure to subdue. Not exactly pretty, but still voluptuous – which was almost a prerequisite – and recently widowed, which might have been a fault (since she

would clearly not be wholly innocent), but she was available
and one must be realistic at his age. Besides, she was child-
less and he would quite like an heir; she was probably still
young enough for that, and her husband had willed her a
fairly large estate, which came to her fully if she ever had
a child. The money – though not essential – would have been
agreeable. Most of all she was related to the Empress Julia,
distantly but close enough to boast of in a wife, and potentially
enough to merit favours here and there. The new Empress
was said to have a lot of influence with her spouse.

That alone would have outweighed most disadvantages. His
own familial connections – to one of the unsuccessful
pretenders to the Imperial purple – though remote, were quite
potentially dangerous, these days. But a marriage link with
the Empress would counterbalance that, and possibly even
bring preferment at the Imperial court – provided the new wife
did not gossip about their private life, as he suspected that his
foolish former one had done.

How could that have happened? He'd circumscribed her
movements – hadn't let her go out visiting or join the feast
when he invited acquaintances to dine. Confided in her family,
probably – he'd known it was a risk, but not to have asked
her kinfolk to the house might have raised questions and he
hadn't wanted that. A man in his position must be seen to do
what is socially required. So there had been family banquets
now and then – and lavish ones as well – and of course she'd
entertained the female visitors. But he'd never left her on her
own without a watching slave who would report to him, and
tell him exactly whom she was talking to and what she said
and did. And he'd made sure that she knew that – and what
she could expect if she tried to prattle about their private life!

It had never occurred to him that she might smuggle written
messages – like many women, she was barely literate – but
he now concluded that she must have done. Why else would
his new selected bride, her distant cousin, have attempted to
refuse? The match was in her interests (in appearance anyway)
at least as much as his. It would give her status and protection
and a guardian in law, the possibility of children, even yet, and
the respect that matronhood officially enjoyed, together with

the expectation of a comfortable old age. She should have been flattered to be asked.

Her family had been willing, too, which should have been enough. Her younger brother, in whose care she had been left, was positively anxious to see her wed again. 'I should be glad to see her settled, at her age,' he had said. 'Especially to someone of such distinguished rank.' Not to mention that she was a threat – her dead husband had sided with Pescennius Niger in his battles for the throne (a misjudgement he had answered with his life), but his association implicated her, and potentially her family as well. It was only her connection with the Empress that had protected her. No wonder that her brother had been keen to have her married to somebody politically sound.

Even the woman herself had not at first demurred. But on the night when the betrothal contract was to be affirmed, and they brought her in to tell her, her face was horrified. Disgusted, almost. Though when he bade her raise her head and look at him, her eyes were full of fear. It was that which thrilled him to his loins and sealed his choice, in fact. She'd raved and ranted – even stamped her foot – so much that her brother had been afraid that the prospective groom would change his mind.

'I fear that she is wilful, Hortius.'

But Hortius did not mind a touch of fire – it quite excited him (all the more fun to subdue her later on) – and it did not alter her connections at the court, so he waved it off as 'natural modesty . . . or commendable loyalty to her former spouse, perhaps?'

So they'd sealed the bargain with a cup or two of best Falernian wine. There were even discussions about propitious dates on which to hold the wedding rites. The bride had seemed resigned, if terrified, and he'd gone home full of private, exhilarating plans.

Only to find, today, that she had disappeared. Allowed to leave the city for a day or two on a 'prenuptial visit to aged relatives', she'd taken a couple of her most loyal slaves, together with some gold – most of the money her husband left to her – and fled. When she was his, Hortius told himself, she'd never have private attendants of her own, again. Or be allowed to visit anyone alone.

But that was for later. First she must be found. Nobody knew where or even in which direction she had gone. She had taken her brother's carriage from his villa, as arranged, and simply not arrived where she was due – and no one admitted to having seen them on the road, though questions had been asked on every crossing-point within a dozen miles.

The brother was incandescent and swore he'd drag her back. Already he'd sent parties of searchers after her. Only the assurance that the wedding could still take place (albeit privately) had persuaded him to promise not to have her flogged on her return. That was a pleasure the groom was saving for himself.

He himself would see that she was 'properly chastised'. Anger would give it an especial edge. She would learn what it was to insult his noble name, and how to plead for mercy through her sobs.

As soon as he found her.

As he proposed to do.

(Of course, we here in Britannia could not know anything about this at the time. I learned it many moons afterwards from one of his ex-slaves – of whom, more later in the narrative. And it would have taken a rune-reader to guess at the terrible consequences it would have for me and mine.)

ONE

When I awoke, on that cold morning in Aprilis, I had no idea what lay in store. My immediate concerns were of another kind.

It was the smell that first roused me – an overpowering, sour-green smell, like every kind of dye-stuff and vegetable leaf all boiled up at once. I blinked myself awake. I was not dreaming, and the roundhouse was not afire – though the already smoky air was hanging thick with pungent steam. My wife Gwellia was obviously awake, cooking something unaccustomed on the central fire. I rolled over on my bed of reeds, ready to complain that it was scarcely dawn, though – since it was the Emperor's birthday and my presence was required at the Glevum rites – I would obviously have to be moving very soon.

Then in the firelight I saw her huddled shape. She was sitting on a stool beside the hearth holding her leg and obviously in pain. Something was seriously wrong.

'Gwellia! What is it? Are you feeling ill?' I did not immediately guess the cause. Foolishly, because I should have done.

She had trodden on a fragment of metal in the lane some days before – probably a lost hobnail or some loose fastening fallen from a cart – though whatever it was it must have been extremely sharp, since it had gone straight through her sandal-sole and right into her foot. But she had treated it and bound it by the time that I came home, and waved away my expressions of concern. She is generally clever in the use of healing herbs and had made light of this, so at the time I had not worried over-much. I clearly should have done.

In my defence, I had not seen the foot. I was not in the roundhouse when she hobbled home. And up to yesterday, apart from the inevitable limp, she'd seemed more or less her normal self. Even now there was the tang of burning oatcakes in among the steam, suggesting she'd been attempting her customary tasks. But I should have known my wife.

Like me, she had spent many years in servitude, but her master (unlike mine) was not a kindly one and she'd learned – the hard way – to endure all things silently, for fear of earning worse. It was something about which I had chided her before – as her husband I had a right to know if she was suffering – but some habits are too painfully acquired and deeply ingrained to break. I might have guessed that she would not complain about a wound, however bad.

But it was very rare for Gwellia to overcook her cakes – a sign that today she was distracted by genuine distress.

'Gwellia!' I said again, more urgently.

She heard me this time and tried to scramble to her feet. 'It is nothing, husband! I . . .' But her voice was not entirely her own, and she broke off with an involuntary gasp as she put her weight onto the bandaged foot. And I realized – finally – that matters were far worse than she'd encouraged me to think.

I threw off the furs and woollen covers from the bed and went across to her, straightening my sleeping tunic as I came. 'It's that foot you injured, isn't it? It cannot be healing properly.' There was no candle lit, but I pulled up a second stool and patted the one that she'd been using. 'Sit down by the fire and let me have a look. You can rest your leg on my lap, so that I can see.'

She was not keen to show me, even then, but – when she reluctantly complied and let me ease the bloodied binding off – I was appalled at what the flickering firelight revealed. The metal had clearly penetrated right up between her toes. The wound had sealed over, but the area around it was tight and yellowish, while the entire remainder of her foot was swollen, red and purpling.

'Wife, you should not be walking on that foot! It's twice its normal size. There's some evil humour in it.' Concern caused me to speak more sharply than I meant.

'I should not have shown you. It will heal in time,' she

muttered, trying feebly to take the rag from me, to wrap the foot again.

I held it out of reach. 'You'll need clean binding on it,' I said, and made her scowl. I tried to cajole her with a little levity. 'It looks like that pig's bladder that Marcus's slaves inflated to make a plaything for his little son.'

But even the notion of my patron – one of the most important men in all Britannia – unfashionably doting on his family, could not raise a smile today. 'I'm making a poultice for it, as you can observe,' she said, defensively. 'I've sent Minimus and Tenuis out to gather more medicinal leaves.'

'In the dark?'

'Half-light, husband. Dawn is breaking and I sent them with a lighted taper each. It's not ideal, I know, but I could not sleep with this, though I'd used up all our poppy juice to no avail. And I'd run out of sufficient leaves to make the poultice-mix. I could not go myself, but they'll manage, I am sure. Tenuis is nimble-fingered and Minimus is eagle-eyed and knows which leaves to pick . . .' She moved her leg a little and I saw her wince with pain.

'A pity that I did not see this earlier,' I muttered, guiltily. 'I will send a slave with a message to the town to say that I will not attend the festival today.'

Gwellia sat upright and snatched her foot away. 'And have yourself arrested and arraigned?' She was trembling and there was a quaver in her voice.

I took it for emotion but when I put out a hand to comfort her I realized that – though shivering – she was, in fact, unnaturally hot. 'You are feverish,' I chided. 'I'll get the kitchen-slave to mix a cooling linctus for you. Where is he anyway? I know it is early, but he should be tending you, if the other two aren't here. And never mind my duty to the state. I can't go into town and leave you here like this.'

'And how will it help me, if you're dragged away and exiled for showing disrespect to Emperor Severus?' She shook her head and I saw that her eyes were wet with tears. 'Or executed, like those protestors in the capitol? And don't pretend it couldn't happen here.'

She was quite right, of course. Even my great patron, Marcus

Septimus Aurelius had recently begun to live in fear. His once-fabled connection to the old Imperial House had suddenly become a liability. Septimius Severus saw rivals everywhere, and was quietly and efficiently disposing of them all.

Gwellia had not finished. 'You told me yourself there was to be an important visitor to the rites this year. From Rome, I think you said? That makes it more important. Anybody from the capital is probably a spy.'

She had a point, but I dismissed it with a shrug. 'Some relative of the Governor of Britannia, that's all. Not an official ambassador. And it's not as if the Governor himself is popular with Rome.' I meant it: Clodius Albinus may have been proclaimed official heir to Severus and given the token title 'Caesar of the West' to stop him temporarily from pressing his own (and equally legitimate) claim to the Imperial throne but anyone could see that it did not mean a thing. 'Severus has living children,' I went on. 'Between ourselves, I think the Governor will be lucky to survive.'

'All the more reason to be careful then. His relatives will be reporting everything to Rome, simply to prove their personal loyalty.' Her voice was quavering but the argument was firm. 'You know what Severus does with those who do not show him proper deference. And if the Governor himself may be at risk – don't suppose your new-found rank will rescue you! The contrary, in fact. What could be more public as an act of disrespect than a member of the curia failing to attend the Imperial birthday rites? It's one of the few rituals which are compulsory.'

All this was true, again. I knew the risks when I suggested it. All the same I made a deprecating face. 'But I'm a humble tradesman, not a man of Roman birth. I'll send a letter saying I am ill, express my desolation and agree to pay the fine. A mosaic pavement-maker is not likely to be missed.'

'Tradesman you may be, husband, but these days you are a duumvir as well, and your absence will be marked. And claims of illness would hardly be believed – you presided at a hearing only yesterday, and very actively, from your account of it. And don't argue that even that would give you time catch the plague,' she went on, guessing correctly what I was about to say. 'There is no plague about. Those rumours of it in that hilltop farm were proved to be no more than poisoned water in a well, caused by the decaying body of a dog. You told me so yourself.' She tired suddenly and seemed to be struggling to pronounce the words. 'You know the law. All male Roman citizens must attend the sacrifice! Of course you must go, and be seen to take your part.'

'And leave you here alone?'

She made a little noise, halfway between a sob and an exasperated 'humph'. 'I shall hardly be alone. I shall have the kitchen-slave. He's only gone out now to fetch clean water from the spring, while the other two . . .' She tailed off, exhausted by the need for argument. Not like her usual self at all, in fact.

I made a swift decision. Worry about me would cause her additional distress. 'Then I'll go. But I'll leave all three slaves at home with you, today.' Normally Minimus escorts me into town and helps me change into my curial attire, and often Tenuis comes as well, to take care of Arlina, my mule, and run any errands wanted in the town. But this was clearly an emergency. 'Junio will be attending the feast in any case, so I can walk to town with him, and one of the slaves from the apartment can escort me at the rites.'

She could hardly argue with me there. Junio, my adopted son, lives right next door to us, with his wife and family, in another roundhouse whose grounds adjoin our own. His duty as a Roman citizen obviously requires that he, too, should attend the birthday rites. So we could journey in together, as we did on any working day. He would expect no less. And once in Glevum there would be no problem about slaves. I had some, at the flat.

Technically, a councillor should always have at least one slave escorting him when he's togate in the town (though this regulation is not generally enforced) but it is obligatory on civic occasions like today. When Marcus had proposed me as a duumvir, he'd not only ensured that I met the property qualifications for the post (by 'gifting' me a town apartment of the appropriate size, on condition that it should revert to him when my civic duties ceased), but had also seen that it was 'basically equipped' – which naturally meant some house-hold slaves as well as furniture. Gwellia often grumbled about the cost of keeping them, but it meant I'd have my requisite attendant at the birthday rites.

She tried to argue about it even then. 'Leave all the servants with me, husband? What about Arlina? Why don't you just take Minimus and leave Tenuis with me?'

Because Minimus would not be afraid to send for me if there was need of it. Tenuis was eager, but too small and insecure. But I did not tell her that.

I said, 'You may be glad of Minimus's strength – he's very near as tall as I am now, and twice as muscular. If you were to fall faint – which Jove prevent – the other two together could hardly pick you up. Besides, I'd like to leave you with several pairs of willing legs, so if things worsen you can send for me and also call that wise woman who lives out in the woods. No one knows more about the use of herbs – you've said as much yourself.'

To my surprise, she gave a grudging nod. 'Well, perhaps you're right. I own that I'd be glad of extra help today.' Admissions of weakness don't come easily from her, but her next words startled me. 'I would not like to let the fire go out. I almost did so, yesterday.' She shook her head, apologetically. Keeping something burning on the hearth is one of the first duties of a housekeeper. 'I lay down for a moment to try and rest my foot, and I fear I fell asleep. If Kurso had not come in from collecting up the eggs—' She broke off as the boy himself appeared, struggling with a water bucket almost half his size.

Kurso realized that we'd been discussing him. He assumed the worst at once. 'Have I offended, mistress?' He looked beseechingly at us. 'I had to leave the taper when it blew out at the spring. It was almost spent in any case and I could not carry both.' He gestured to the pail.

The poor lad had been so showered in blows by his former owner that – when he first came to us – he could move fastest backwards. He had blossomed somewhat since and grown in confidence, but he was still as skinny as a reed and terrified of having unwittingly done wrong.

I got up from my stool and smiled encouragement. 'On the contrary. Your mistress says that yesterday you kept the fire alight, which she could not have done without you.'

He flashed a grateful grin and nodded speechlessly. Kurso never did have very much to say. He put the bucket down.

'And,' I told him, going across to him, 'we are going to rely on you again today. I am obliged to go into the town – official business which I can't escape.' I put my hand upon his shoulder. 'I'm leaving you and Minimus to run the household here, and Tenuis can stay and help as well. Your mistress is to rest – her foot is very bad. She'll supervise and tell you what tasks to do, of course. But if she's any worse, you are to send for me at once. Minimus can run to town and fetch me home. Those are my orders, do you understand? Whatever your mistress tells you to the contrary.'

Kurso shot an uneasy glance at Gwellia. This would not be easy for him, I was sure. In my absence my good wife was unlikely to submit very readily to idleness and the poor little slave could hardly force her to sit down. Neither, in general, could he order the other slaves about, so – if Gwellia told them not to send for me – they might have had conflicting loyalties. But the master's word is always paramount, and by saying this, I'd made my orders clear. And Gwellia knew it. I could see her scowl.

I tried to soften this by murmuring to her, 'Promise me you'll rest that foot till I come back.' A slow reluctant nod. 'Then that is settled. I will agree to go, but won't stay for the feast or celebration games – I'll simply take part in the ritual and come straight back home. There's no legal obligation to do more than that. I'll speak to Marcus: he'll make apologies for me if they're required. But if you feel you need the wise woman, meanwhile, I would like to know – it could only be because that foot is worse. So send and tell me, is that understood?' I nodded at Kurso, who was grinning like a fish, proud of being entrusted with a role.

'If you command it, master!' he replied. 'If there's any problem, we'll send Minimus at once.' I smiled at the 'we'. Kurso was taking his new responsibilities very seriously.

Gwellia gave a dismissive little snort. 'I can't imagine what the wise woman could do, that I could not,' she grumbled, with a flash of her old self. 'Plantain poultices and draughts of willow-bark are what's required. And I'm already doing that!' She gestured to the pot of leaves and water bubbling on the fire, as she raised her swollen multicoloured foot again to rest it on my stool. 'Without the need to pay for her advice! I'm sure the poison will escape if I . . .' She abandoned the attempt to speak, which was through gritted teeth, and surely could not sound convincing even to herself.

'I wish that I could help,' I told her, soberly. 'But I simply don't know how.' Herbs and potions were Gwellia's field, not mine. My competence was limited to simple things, like removing splinters or wrapping spiders' webs around a wound. 'I only wish that Marcus still kept a medicus these days. We could ask him for advice.' Marcus, like many wealthy Romans, had once kept a private doctor in his household – a skilled man of some intelligence who had been trained in Greece – but it had ended badly and the man had gone.

'I don't want the public medicus from Glevum,' Gwellia found the energy to snap. 'Even if Marcus were offering to pay.'

'That would have to be a very last resort,' I said. I'd had dealings with that public medicus before, and – like Gwellia – I had no faith in his abilities. (His remedy for everything appears to be confined to either letting blood or prescribing cabbage soup, for which services he charges an enormous fee.) 'We could try leeches if the wound was weeping still, though . . .' I had a sudden thought. 'There'll be a midwife at the villa, I suppose, since my patron's wife is likely to give birth again within a day or two. And perhaps a wet nurse too. I don't suppose that either of them would be of help? Julia would be happy to lend one, for an hour or two – she would not be needing both of them at once.'

'My foot is swollen but I do not think that it can be with child! What possible use could a birth-attendant ever be to me? Or a wet nurse either?' She was close to tears again.

I cursed myself for having mentioned it. It was a disappointment to us both that we'd never had a child – we had been reunited far too late for that. I had adopted Junio, of course – but for Gwellia our childlessness was a double tragedy.

She never spoke of it, but I'm sure that she'd borne children to her owners in the past. Gwellia – when young – was very beautiful, and a master is free to use his slaves in any way he likes. (Any resultant children would be killed at birth or sold as soon as they were old enough to fetch a decent price.)

I was still cursing my thoughtless tongue when I became aware of Kurso hesitantly plucking at my sleeve. 'What is it, Kurso?'

'Master,' he whispered, 'with your permission . . .?' He seemed more tentative than usual. 'About that injured foot . . .'

I frowned. It was rare for Kurso to venture anything. 'You know someone we could go to for advice?'

He shook his head. 'Not that,' he murmured. 'But there's something we could try. I held the lantern once while it was done. My former master's land-steward, it was. He had a metal splinter in his hand which swelled up just like that. He caught a fever from it and was close to death, but he was worth a lot of money so they called a doctor from the garrison. You know your hunting knife . . .?'

'What about it?' I was really frowning now.

He gestured me to bend so he could whisper in my ear and Gwellia couldn't hear – indeed, he dropped his voice so low that I could hardly hear myself. But what he was saying startled me so much that I actually recoiled.

'I could not do that!'

'It saved the land-slave's life,' my slave declared. 'Unless the evil humours had come out, he would have taken a fever and died in agony. That is what the army doctor said. And the same thing might save my mistress, now. I think it could be done. But you would have to do it, master. I would not dare to try.'

TWO

I found myself now faced with an appalling choice. I could take a knife-blade to poor Gwellia's foot, as Kurso suggested – certainly hurting her and possibly making bad things

worse – or I could follow her instinct and trust to herbs
and rest. And have her 'take a fever and die in agony'?

Put that way, there was only one decision I could make.

I do not generally take instruction from my slaves – and
Gwellia would normally no doubt have told me so. But she was
already shivering and clutching at her leg and I, too, knew of
people who had died from wounds like this. If there were any
chance of saving her, I would have to try.

'Light me a taper here so that I can see, then take one
yourself and fetch that hunting knife – it's out in the dye-house
with my axe and scythe,' I murmured, and Kurso hurried to
obey.

It was always called my 'hunting knife', though it had never
been used for hunting anything. It was more like a dagger,
with a point and single edge, but carrying a dagger is forbidden
nowadays unless one is a soldier of the Emperor, so 'hunting
knife' it had officially become. I had bought it from a peddler
in Glevum years ago: most of his merchandise had proved
worthless in the end, but this was splendid: one of those rare
knives that one could sharpen to an edge which cut through
anything. I'd used it more than once for quartering a sheep,
but its sharpness was never more important than today.

I went over to my wife. She was whiter than a toga and
breathing heavily. For a moment I thought that this was caused
by fear, but I quickly realized that she was only half-awake.
I was alarmed to find her slipping in and out of consciousness
– it had happened so quickly – but it strengthened my resolve.

I crouched beside her. 'Can you hear me, Gwellia?' I
enquired, and told her gently what I proposed to do. She
opened her eyes, and summoned the energy to speak. I expected
her to protest and insist her herbs would help, but she did not.

'I suppose it must be done,' she murmured. I was just
thinking sadly that her complaisance conveyed – more
eloquently than any direct words could do – how suddenly
urgent the matter had become, when she added, with a ghost
of her usual forcefulness, 'But only if you swear by all the
gods to go straight to Glevum afterwards and join the birthday
rites.'

I forced myself to smile. 'I promise,' I told her, getting to my feet. 'Provided, in return, you will agree to rest.' I waited for her reluctant nod, then added in an inner whisper to the gods, 'And on condition, deities, that this humour-letting doesn't make her worse.'

I feared that the painful process would be too much for her, and if she was clearly suffering afterwards I would stay right where I was – relatives of the Governor or not.

My promise seemed to satisfy her and she sank back on the stool – though when Kurso came back with the knife she paled and I saw perspiration break out on her brow. But she was still my Gwellia, and more courageous than I could believe.

'Help me to walk over to the bed, and fetch me a belt to bite on, to stop me crying out. Something solid I can clench in both my hands.' The words were rational, but the tone was far from calm and her voice seemed to be coming from somewhere far away.

I was glad to recognize these signs of her resolve, though it was not like her to ask for help to walk. But – like the planned procedure – she seemed resigned to it, allowing me and Kurso to assist her to the bed.

'Kurso had better hold me down so I don't jump up without intending to, and make you slash me somewhere else by accident,' she murmured, without a touch of her familiar fire. 'But do it quickly, husband, if that's what you propose. You can't be late to town and miss the rituals.'

There was no danger of that yet, since it was scarcely after dawn, but I understood. She wanted the ordeal over as soon as possible. Kurso meanwhile had found a pair of rush-holders and, having set the tapers down upon the floor so I could see, he fetched my leather belt.

I flexed it in my hands. It seemed inadequate as a method of controlling pain. 'Don't we have a little valerian somewhere?' I enquired. Gwellia sometimes brewed a sleeping cordial of it. It was not as good as poppy juice, of course – but we had none left of that – and if I could find any way of dulling this torment for her, I would. 'There was a jar of it somewhere, I believe. She was going to take it to Julia as a post-natal gift, to strengthen her and soothe the discomforts of the birth.'

Kurso was about to take a candle and go and look for it, but Gwellia shook her head. 'It isn't fully ready yet,' she murmured feebly. 'It needs more time to steep. My foot was so painful in the night, I tried a draught of it – but it did not help.' She gave a woeful smile. 'Besides, valerian needs time to take effect, so it would be useless in this case anyway. You must get to Glevum, with the Governor's kinsman there, or I shall not rest all day. Just pierce it, husband, and have it over.' She crammed the middle of the belt into her mouth and clenched her teeth on it, clutching the ends in either hand as she closed her eyes.

I flinched, appalled at the idea of hurting her. But she was right, as usual. If this was to be done at all, it should be done at once. I told myself to think that I was digging splinters out and, still unwillingly, picked up the hunting knife.

In passing, I dipped the blade into the boiling herbs – not so much to clean it (I had already polished it) as with some idea of getting a little of the potion in the wound. Then I glanced at Kurso, who took this as a sign. He approached his mistress gingerly, then – with a single action – threw his weight across her upper legs and nodded encouragingly at me. 'Now, master. Quick is merciful.'

I stepped forward, raised the knife and – with a muttered prayer to all the ancient gods – brought the point down into the poor swollen foot. Even then, at the last minute, I felt myself draw back – fearing to be too hard, and cause a greater wound, or too tentative and not cut through the skin. But I need not have worried, I had made the merest nick yet the effect was instantaneous. My wife bucked upwards and gave a strangled cry, and a fountain of blood and yellow matter shot into the air.

I stepped back, shocked, but Kurso was grinning up at me in obvious relief.

'You've let most of the fiery humour out, master,' he said. 'You can feel the heat of it.' He had seized the discarded bandage-cloth, and was busy mopping up the discharge as he spoke. 'If you press around the cut,' he went on, 'you might dispel some more. That's what the army doctor did.'

I was unwilling to cause further pain to Gwellia, but his

earlier suggestion had obviously worked, so I gently did as he advised. More of the 'fiery humour' dribbled out.

To my relief, at the same time, the patient roused herself. The belt fell from her fingers and after a moment she actually sat up. She prodded at the area herself, more firmly than I'd dared, and produced another spurt, this time streaked with blood – together with a little flake of something solid, thin and dark. It was small and tapered to a vicious point, and might have been a little piece of rust.

The cause of all the trouble, I surmised. So perhaps it was a kind of splinter after all. Certainly the tightness in the foot was gone, and much of the tension had drained from Gwellia's face.

'Better?' I asked and she nodded speechlessly. I went on quickly before she found her tongue, 'Now remember what you promised. You are to stay in bed – even if you feel a great deal better later on. The servants can take care of you today. In the meantime, you had better bind that foot – or get the slaves to do it.'

'I'll wait until I've put that poultice on,' she told me, with a suspicion of her usual decisiveness. 'I think I hear the other boys returning with the herbs, so I can boil the mixture up.' She seemed to read my thoughts. 'Or they can, since you insist. And don't say you'll wait to see it done – I'll have to let it cool before it is applied so it can counteract the heat. But that should help, and by tonight I shall be on my feet again . . .' She broke off as my two other young slave-boys hurried in, each carrying a shallow basket full of fresh-plucked leaves.

'The herbs that you required. With the dew still on them, mistress.' Gangling, red-haired Minimus was the oldest of my slaves, and – though he was scarcely fully-grown himself – generally overseer and spokesman for the rest. He breezed in cheerfully. But as his eyes became accustomed to the smoky candlelight and he took in the scene – his mistress half-dressed and lying on the bed, and me standing over her with the hunting knife – his face grew grave.

'Master, is everything all right?' Now it was skinny little Tenuis who spoke, hurrying forward with his offering of herbs.

'Your mistress is a little better now, I think,' I answered, and Gwellia assented with a nod. 'Though perhaps you should add those herb-leaves to the pot. Your mistress says she'll want a poultice presently.'

Minimus glanced at the still misshapen foot and nodded doubtfully.

'Kurso and I have been attending to the wound.' (It seemed only fair to include the kitchen-slave in this, and he was clearly proud I had.) 'But your mistress needs to rest, and he can't do everything. So I want you and Tenuis to stay and help today. Kurso has my orders. He will explain to you. You are to send to me at once if that is what's required – birthday rites or no.' I saw that Gwellia was about to remonstrate, so I added quickly, 'But if I'm to go to Glevum, I will have to get prepared. It is long past dawn and I've neither washed nor dressed.'

'Nor eaten, husband.' Gwellia had gestured Tenuis across and was already pointing out the herbs that she preferred, and the quantity to use. She gave me a wan smile. 'There are oatcakes if you want them, but I fear they will be burnt. I'd forgotten all about them.' The effort clearly tired her and she slumped back on the bed – though as the slave-boy stirred the new leaves into the pot, she tried a feeble jest. 'Don't try eating that concoction though – or we shall be holding solemn rites here of our own.'

'If Kurso scrapes the bottoms off, they will be edible,' I said, as the boy blew the embers off the baking tray and – winding a tunic round his hand – removed the lid to show the blackened cakes. 'I will have one of these before I leave – you four can eat the rest. But I will need some water from that pail – first of all, a cup of it to drink, then Minimus can help me wash and dress, while Tenuis goes to saddle up the mule. And we'd best be quick about it – Junio will soon be waiting for me at the gate. I suppose there were signs that he and his family were awake, when you went out to the spring?'

I was thinking of candles glimmering from within, or smoke and sparks arising from the chimney-space, but Minimus surprised me. 'Indeed so, master. We met his slave-boy going for water, when we were coming back. He was grumbling that their household had been awake for hours – one of the children was crying with new teeth. I was to tell you that your son would be ready very soon. I'm sorry, master, when I saw my mistress, I forgot.'

I was as quick as it was possible to be, but by the time I hurried out to the enclosure gate – wearing a clean tunic underneath my cloak – not only was Tenuis there to meet me with the mule, but Junio was already waiting in the lane.

THREE

Junio's first enquiry was for Gwellia's foot, of course – though when he heard what I had tried to do, he was inclined to reproach me.

'Why did you not call on my wife, Cilla, to assist? She would have come at any hour. She may not quite have Mother's skill with herbs, but she's not far behind.' (Both Junio and his wife had been my slaves until I freed them and adopted him – thus allowing them to marry – and they still felt they should be taking care of me.)

'Cilla is busy with the children,' I replied (not mentioning that, in my panic, calling her had not occurred to me). 'The youngest one is teething, I believe?'

'All the more reason to call her – we are awake in any case. But Tenuis can take a message now, asking her to keep a watch on Gwellia today. And perhaps to take some soup to her a little later on.'

I confess I was relieved – our slaves are not generally required to cook. It is a task that Gwellia prefers to do herself, so Cilla's care would mean an easier day for everyone. But Junio waved my thanks away and – once Tenuis had hurried off to do as he was told – we two travelled companionably into town, myself on Arlina and Junio walking briskly at my side.

The sun was up by now and the spring day cold and bright, so we made quick progress along the ancient track and soon reached the southern gate, from where it was normally only a short walk to my town 'residence'. This morning, though, the streets were already filled with noisy crowds, so it took us twice as long as usual. I was beginning to worry that I should, after all, be late – reprehensible for anyone, but especially for a councillor with an official role to play – and I could not help remembering what Gwellia had said about the need for special vigilance.

So I was in some haste when we finally arrived at the apartment block. I rushed upstairs, dispensed with the usual welcome ritual – refusing house-slippers and a warming drink – and sent one of my two townhouse slaves off at once to take Arlina to her usual stall and grazing place, at a hiring stables just outside the walls. Meanwhile the other servant, Rastus – a slender boy with big ears, protruding teeth and beaming smile – hurried us two citizens into our awkward Roman robes.

I insisted that Junio should be assisted first, since his needs were obviously simpler than my own. He, too, had left his newly fullered toga in the flat in preparation for today's events (a sensible precaution, since it is not a garment in which to walk very far, much less to trail for miles down muddy forest lanes) and in a few moments he was fully dressed. He took a couple of exaggerated steps to make sure the folds did not unwind, looking distinguished in his freshly laundered white; every inch a Roman citizen. No one would ever guess that he was once a slave. He looked up and caught my eye. 'I always feel encumbered by this wretched thing,' he grumbled, sheepishly.

I made a noncommittal noise since, in my role as duumvir, I was now being still more awkwardly attired: a clean white tunic first (over the one that I already wore) and, on top of that again, my formal curial toga complete with purple stripe – albeit the narrowest one the weaver could achieve. Both garments were constructed of the finest wool, cost a fortune, were difficult to clean, and – naturally – showed up every dirty mark. But the fuller had done his (expensive) best with them and – with a final check that my own folds were pinned securely with the silver shoulder-brooch – I looked presentable.

'We'll take Rastus with us,' I said to Junio. 'He can wait outside, so if anyone is minded to report to Severus I can claim to have been properly escorted by a slave. But when we get into the temple steps, of course, I will have to leave you and join in the rite.'

This was not something I had done before, and I was not looking forward to it very much – joining in procession with the other councillors, from the central altar in the temple court (where a thanksgiving sacrifice would be made to Jupiter) to the Emperor's shrine in the Imperial Grove. As one of the lesser magistrates I had no speaking role – no intoning prayers or little speeches extolling Severus. But I would be expected to prance along behind, waving a hoop of flowers or – worse – banging a beribboned tambourine, expressing joy at this auspicious day. With the whole of Glevum – not to mention well-connected visitors – watching my discomfiture!

And it was no light matter. The slightest deviation – tripping on the step, or accidentally leading with the wrong foot first – would be a dreadful omen, earning the displeasure of both gods and men, and the whole procedure would have to start again.

It was no good looking to my son for sympathy; he was in cheerful mood. He had nothing to do but stand among the crowd and wave a palm-frond now and then (available at no great cost from stalls as one went in).

'But I'll see you afterwards?' he said. 'Although perhaps you mean to go back to Gwellia at once, rather than going on to the birthday games? In which case, you can take the mule, of course. Rastus can fetch her while the rite is taking place, and have her waiting for you afterwards. I can find my own way home, once I have taken off these robes. And I won't need an escort, either, if you want to take the slave – I've walked to and from the roundhouse many times alone. I'm not a councillor, so no one bothers about me.'

I shook my head. 'I won't stay for the games, but you can have Arlina – and the slave as well. Best to be seen abiding by the rules today. I'll hire a litter home and pay the fee when I arrive. That way I won't need to change before I go, or need attendants either – I'll have the bearer-boys. But thank you for the thought.'

'Then rather than going to fetch the mule, Rastus could find a litter for you, while the rite is on and have it standing by when you emerge. They will be rarer than an emperor's visit on a day like this. And expensive too.'

That was certain to be true. Prices rise like bread-dough with increased demand – especially on a festal occasion like today when everybody wants to keep his toga clean. But I did not grudge the cost. Litter-bearers would get me quickly home and having a slave to 'mind' the chair while I was at the rites would ensure that no one made a better offer and set off with it meanwhile. And for once there was plenty of money hidden at my home, thanks to a recent contract for a mosaic entrance floor.

'Once I've gone, get Rastus to escort you to the games,' I said. 'You can take him in with you – there is no entry charge today – and perhaps he could find my patron, in the official box, and tell him where I've gone. The games should be exciting, they have been paid for by some wealthy councillor – an anonymous birthday offering to the whole colonia – so the lad might enjoy the spectacle.' I glanced at Rastus, whose face was split by an enormous grin.

My other slave-boy, who had just returned, was facing a much less entertaining day. He was to stay there in the flat, in case of messages. I rather felt for him, but one cannot always treat slaves equally, and Servus was too well-trained to show dismay. He even held the door politely for the rest of us, as we set off together for the Capitoline shrine.

The crowds were thicker than ever by this time and, as we neared the forum, we found ourselves surrounded by an increasing throng – not only citizens and their servants hastening to the rites, but the whole array of street vendors, entertainers, beggars and general spectators who always crowd the town on festive days.

I elbowed past a snake charmer in multicoloured robes, juggling his so-called vipers for a small excited crowd, but was immediately pestered by a clamouring throng – hawkers of every kind of merchandise, from hot pies and scented unguents to crude wooden carvings of the Emperor and Empress (largely indistinguishable apart from beard and hair). I was in a hurry and had not wished to leave my wife, but even I was drawn into the spirit of the thing.

I was especially tempted by one swarthy man, smelling of perfume and strange spice, who was selling bottles of 'little snake-cure pills: a panacea for all ills', with stories of miraculous recoveries. I was thinking of Gwellia, but she would not approve, and anyway in my formal clothes I had nowhere to store the tablets nor cash to pay for them. So I shook my head and we struggled along the centre of the road – there was no room on the pavement – into the forum square.

Close to the temple it was even worse. There was a noisy mob of citizens, clamouring at the stalls: fighting for palm-fronds to take inside and wave – 'straight from the Arabian provinces', or live doves for private sacrifice at the Imperial shrine. (Though, naturally, not so private that this act of piety would go unnoticed by fellow citizens.)

All these jostling togas might have caused delay but Rastus, proud of his role as escort and recognizing that I was anxious about time, showed unexpected initiative by stepping out in front of us and shouting boldly, 'Make way for the duumvir,' and many people did. Enough, at any rate, for me to elbow through and scurry up the steps.

I lost sight of Junio, almost instantly, but I had arrived in just sufficient time to be escorted through into the inner court and join the procession of councillors. To my relief I got a Fulvial hoop (and not a tambourine) and I contrived to march and wave it without incident throughout the rite, which seemed to last for absolutely hours – at least to me, with Gwellia on my mind.

At last it was over and I hurried out again, glad that I had done my duty and could reasonably leave – though my absence at the games would be remarked, of course, especially by those of my colleagues who did not much approve of having a Celtic ex-slave as a councillor at all. And no doubt the Governor's kinsman would soon be told of that! But that was a problem for another day. For the moment my concern was for my wife.

I hastened down the steps – they were almost empty now, since most of the vendors had packed up and left, and we in the procession had emerged before the crowd. Junio, for instance, had not yet appeared, but Rastus was waiting at the corner with the chair, so I scurried over and was in the process of climbing into it when from behind me came a familiar voice.

'Libertus, old friend. Are you leaving us so soon?'

I turned my head, my old heart sinking to my sandal-soles. It was Marcus, my patron, in full regalia – his purple stripe as wide as mine was thin, and the whiteness of his toga putting mine to shame – as befitted one of the most important men in all Britannia. (For the moment anyway – it was to be hoped that local opponents of the current Emperor did not speak too openly of 'the restoration of the old Imperial line' where any visitor from Rome was liable to hear.)

He was accompanied, as usual, by a pair of matching slaves. There was still a festal wreath atop his curly hair, which served to emphasize the streaks of grey among the gold, and around his neck he wore a handsome torc. He had been called upon to make a speech, of course, as senior magistrate, and had done it very well, and in his right hand – heavy with gold rings – he still carried the small scroll from which he'd read. However, he was out of breath and it was clear that he'd been hurrying to catch up with me.

'Excellence,' I murmured. I had one leg in the litter but I withdrew it hastily and tried to turn the movement into an awkward bow.

Marcus held out his hand so I could kiss the ring. 'I'm glad to find you here. I thought you might have gone. I was delayed a little by the Valerii.'

'Complaining about the latest land-levy?' I asked. Cyrus Valerius and his brother Decimus were wealthy councillors, famous for grumbling about the need to pay the tax – which, unlike some of us, they could well afford.

My patron grinned. 'Threatening a petition to the Governor, this time. But mostly, I think, they'd seen me brought a message, earlier, and they were curious. They see themselves as very well-informed – want to be the first to know of any news, and first to pass it on. I did not tell them anything, of course. But I wanted your advice. Perhaps we could discuss it at the games.'

I gestured to the litter. 'I was about to leave.'

'You are not staying, then, old friend? I know you do not

wholly care for them, but on a birthday feast? It will be quite a spectacle.'

I stiffened, warily. Marcus had twice addressed me as 'old friend', something he never did unless he wanted something done – usually something which would keep me from my trade and family: a consideration which would not occur to him. And with Gwellia unwell, I wanted to be home as much as possible. But Marcus is a person of considerable power, and – though he does not have quite the influence he did, when his friend Pertinax was Emperor – offending him is still not very wise.

'Gwellia has hurt her foot,' I said, doing my best to signal my unease. 'I fear it's serious and I want to hurry home. Hence the litter . . .'

He clapped me firmly on the shoulder-brooch – so firmly that I feared it would unclasp and free my toga to unwind in loops around my feet. 'Then, Libertus, you must travel home with me. As I say, I'd like a word with you. I have my gig outside the gates awaiting me. I too am worried for the welfare of my wife and I was already thinking of not staying to the games.'

I stared at him, amazed. My absence from the birthday spectacle would cause enough remark, but his would be noticed by everybody there – and in the current state of politics, that might be dangerous. Of course his wife, Julia, had not been seen in public for several moons, so the child would soon be born – it was perhaps no wonder that Marcus was concerned. But no one dared show Severus disrespect, and Marcus was no mere spectator at the birthday games.

In the absence of the Emperor himself, or some official representative, he was the one to signal that proceedings should begin – by standing in the Imperial box, holding up a white napkin so that everyone could see, then dramatically allowing it to drop.

'But Excellence . . .' I faltered. 'Is that not perhaps . . .?' I dared not say 'unwise'.

Marcus shook his head. 'I have sufficient reason to absent myself today. That message I received concerns me very much. I'm minded to go back and see my wife at once. Even the

Emperor would understand, I think. Certainly his wife would – which, perhaps, is more significant.'

I understood, or I supposed I did. 'The lady Julia,' I murmured. 'She has been brought to bed?' One did not speak of 'childbirth' in polite society.

'Not yet, I think. I spoke to her before I left today and she was in good health, if a little bit uncomfortable now. But that is not the problem. If the child were merely imminent, I would stay in town, of course – in such events a man is better somewhere else – and pray that the gods are merciful and both of them survive. I would even be content if it were a girl again, if that meant less risk to Julia.' He broke off, perhaps embarrassed at such un-Roman sentiments. A single daughter may be useful, later on, if she can be married advantageously, but a second is generally regarded as a curse. 'There is another matter, of immediate concern. We are to have another visitor from the capital.'

'Another?' I was startled, and a little anxious too. There had already been two emissaries in the last six months from the Imperial court, one of them avowedly a spy – and, on the last occasion, with unfortunate results. There had been no repercussions – until now at least – and with the perpetrator dead, I had thought the matter satisfactorily resolved. But it seemed that I was wrong.

'So Severus still has Glevum under scrutiny?' I said. How many informers were among the crowd today, apparently mingling innocently with the revellers, yet secretly watching for any indiscreet behaviour or remark, ready to report it directly back to Rome? 'As a result of that last unpleasant business?'

Marcus shook his head so hard his wreath dislodged itself. It would have fallen to the ground (a dreadful omen!) if he had not contrived to catch it, though his hands still held the scroll. 'Nothing to do with that, as far as I can tell. This is not an official visitor – in the usual sense at least. A distant relative of Julia's – of whose existence I had never heard before. But there's a complication . . .' He glanced around as if aware he might be overheard. 'Travel home with me and I'll tell you on the way. Never mind the litter, I will take it now and be waiting for you at the gate.'

'But, Excellence . . .' I attempted to protest, but Marcus was not listening.

He had gestured to one of his attendant slaves and was murmuring something in his ear. The pageboy nodded, bowed and went hastening off at once. Marcus, beaming, turned to me again. 'So that is all arranged. I've sent a message to the games.' He was getting into my litter as he spoke. 'Old Tertillius will be happy to officiate, I know – he has been angling to do so all his life.'

'You could hardly call upon the Governor's relative, I suppose?' It was ill-advised of me. Marcus does not like his judgement questioned. I awaited a rebuke.

This time he merely laughed. 'Better to have asked him from the outset, if at all. Suggesting he was second choice would seem like disrespect. Tertillius, on the other hand, will be flattered to be asked. I was talking to him, just before the rites, and I hear his widowed sister has just come to live with him and chides him for not making his influence more felt – so he will be particularly happy to be thrust into the role.'

'But, Junio . . .' I began. 'I must—'

'Tell him where you've gone? Of course! I will leave my other slave to walk you to the gate – then you can leave your own attendant here to explain things to your son.' He leaned forward on the cushions, beckoning me close. 'By the way, don't worry, my old friend. No one can accuse me of disrespect by not being at the games. I was the one who paid for them this year, and I've just made sure that this will be announced. If anything, my absence will be seen as modesty.'

He gave me a sly grin as he pulled the curtains shut, and the litter-bearers raised the chair and trotted off with it. If they were disappointed of the larger fare – out to my roundhouse – they would not dare complain.

Any more than I could, I thought resignedly.

I reconciled myself to trailing my best toga through the dust and allowed myself to be escorted to the gate – even bidding a cheerful goodbye to Rastus as I went.

And still there was no warning from the gods.

FOUR

I could only move ponderously in my curial best, so I was not quick getting to the gate. I expected Marcus to be irritated by the wait. However, though I could see him in the gig as I arrived, he was deep in conversation with a legionary from the fort, shaking his head and frowning in a way I recognized – Marcus at his most imposing magisterial best – but before I could approach the soldier gave a brisk salute and moved away.

My patron said nothing as I was helped up to my place, but when I was beside him on the narrow seat he turned to me. 'That was from the camp commander, asking for advice. That relative of the Governor's has stirred up quite a row. Asked for a girl last night, apparently, so the commander – being keen to please – provided one from the local *lupinaria* and paid the fee himself. But the girl has gone back in such a state she'll be no use for weeks – if she recovers fully, which is currently in doubt – and her owner is threatening to sue the garrison.'

I looked at him. Was he seeking my opinion? It was possible. As duumvir, I often dealt with market law. I said, tactfully, 'So what did you advise? That where there is no formal contract, stating otherwise – as I don't suppose there was – the man who pays remains responsible, in law, for damage to the goods? In this case, the commandant, in fact?'

'Exactly, though he may recover losses if he can prove the fault. Very awkward in these circumstances, as the commander says, so I advised him to offer the owner a few denarii as a gesture of goodwill. I don't imagine the matter would really come to court – the brothel needs the goodwill of the garrison. And vice versa. Ah, but here's my slave at last.'

The freckled pageboy who had walked me to the gate had been freeing the horses from the hitching post, but now he climbed aboard to crouch between our feet, squashed on the floor in what little space remained.

My patron gave the signal, the driver flicked the reins and a moment later we were on our way. Bone-juddering, of course, as such journeys always are, but infinitely faster than the litter would have been, even though – with fragile wheels – we had to take the longer, military route.

For the first half-mile or so we were slowed to walking pace, first through a crush of gigs and carriages – now empty apart from their bored driver-slaves – and beyond them a gaggle of brightly painted carts, presumably those that had brought in the palms and birthday souvenirs.

Once clear of this confusion, there was little on the road and we were soon moving at an alarming pace. I was expecting my patron to tell me what he had sought me for, but even he was forced to concentrate and we were already turning to the little unpaved lane that led to our respective houses and the scattered farms beyond, before he raised his voice above the wind.

'That matter that I wanted to discuss with you . . .?'

The noise and rattle of our progress made conversation hard, and I was clutching the gig seat with both my hands as the lurching motion flung us all about. In the end, I was reduced to hollering, through teeth that chattered with every imperfection in the road. 'You want to wait . . . until we are in private . . . Excellence, perhaps?'

I nodded towards the servant at our feet. Marcus often forgets that slaves have ears and eyes. As an ex-slave myself, I have often had occasion to warn him about this, especially now when times were perilous. But perhaps today there was not really any risk. The driver – whom I'd met before, and to whom I owe my freedom, and possibly my life – could hardly overhear, and the pageboy was in no condition to be listening at all. His eyes were shut and he was looking deathly pale. Obviously the motion, which was hard enough for me, was still more difficult for him. He had nothing to hold onto and was wholly occupied with trying not to fall – or disgrace himself by vomiting.

Marcus, alone, seemed untroubled by the jolts. I don't know what training patricians must receive to enable them to keep their dignity while bouncing to and fro, but Marcus managed it, although his voice came out in little breathless bursts as mine had done. 'Never mind the slave . . . This won't be a secret in my household . . . very long. But it's a puzzle . . . my old friend. I simply don't . . . know what to make of it . . . or how I should respond. Druscilla Livia. Some widowed female . . . relative of Julia's . . . throwing herself upon my potestas.'

There was no warning thunderclap or shower of falling frogs. Nothing to alert me to what might lie ahead. I merely looked at him in mild surprise. 'But surely . . . she already has a legal guardian?' That would be true of any female, however old she was.

Marcus nodded. 'She does. Her younger brother . . . since her father is now dead . . . But he arranged . . . a wedding for her with a man she does not like.'

'But doesn't she . . . have the right . . . to turn him down?'

Marcus gave me a wry sideways look. 'In principle at least . . . she's entitled to refuse . . .' Then, as the driver pulled over to one grassy verge to let a horseman past – a haughty-looking fellow in an expensive cloak and hood galloping madly in the direction of the town – my patron continued in his normal tone of voice, 'If she can prove the groom-to-be is either far below her rank or a man of ill repute. Yet that can scarcely be said to be the case. The suitor's old, apparently, but he's not merely wealthy, he's a senator.'

'In the Senate? A patrician then?'

'One, moreover, who was famously devoted to his wife. Mocked for it, in fact, till he became a widower!' He spoke with feeling. Marcus was unfashionably uxorious, himself – most Romans thought of marriage as a business contract, in which emotion played little part at all. 'Kept her beside him at all times,' my patron went on. 'Treated her family splendidly and showered her with jewels. Hardly grounds for anyone not accepting him.'

'Does she fear, perhaps, that she could never . . . take the place of someone so beloved?' I managed as we lurched away again. 'Or is she still mourning her own loss too much? In the old days a "one-man-woman" was much admired.'

'Hardly important, when her life may be at stake.'

I stared at him. 'How so?'

'Her former husband died an enemy of the Emperor – literally fighting for Pescennius Niger it appears – so a second marriage to someone who is loyal to the court might quite literally save her – and the brother, too. Quite a long life, in both cases, I believe. I understand she's not too old to have a child – one of the reasons that the bridegroom wanted her.' Marcus was sounding more coherent now. We had caught up with a farmer and his lumbering cart and – since the lane was narrow – we were forced to walking pace. 'It's more than ten months since her husband died.'

I knew what that meant. Ten months was sufficient for a bridegroom to be sure that any child the woman bore was rightfully his own!

'I can understand her brother's eagerness,' I said. 'But if she cannot be persuaded to the match, can he coerce her into it?' I may be a civic magistrate, but I have never dealt with family law – I am better on sewage rights and water licences. 'I thought a widow of independent means did have a legal option to refuse. A dowager is "under her own jurisdiction", isn't she?'

Marcus made a doubtful face. 'Technically, I suppose that is the case. Hers was a "manus marriage" of the old-fashioned kind – to show both parties were from ancient patrician families – which meant that she passed to her husband's potestas. But, according to her husband's will, control was transferred back to her family when he died – along with a sum of money, to be hers if she produced a child. I presume that the husband was thinking of his own!'

'I can see that might be difficult,' I said. With the slower pace, I could collect my wits. 'And the brother could argue, if it ever came to court, that he was acting within his rights as guardian.'

'Exactly. But he is no blood relative of hers. He was adopted recently, it seems, shortly before the lady's father died, because the old man had no male heirs of his own and wished the family vineyards to escape the auctioneers. So, when this selected suitor displeased Druscilla Livia so much, she attempted to repudiate her brother's claims to make the choice. It's created quite a fuss.'

'Unusual enough to be the talk of Rome? I presume you heard this from your family there—?' I broke off as we jolted through a rut.

'Actually, it was Tertillius who told me most of it. He'd known Druscilla's family when he was young in Rome. There was a huge public scandal when she ran away, of course, and an ancient kinswoman wrote to him with the details, then. It was he who told me what I'm telling you.'

And earned his reward by being favoured at the games, I thought. But all I said was, 'He is an expert on the law, what does he think of this?'

'That with a good advocate, Druscilla might have persuaded a judge to find for her. But he points out that it's unlikely it would ever come to trial. Litigation isn't easy when a woman is living in her guardian's house and he has been left the management of her affairs. Especially when her suitor is a magistrate himself! Besides, the man is said to be both rich and generous. Her brother is clearly trying to do his best for her. And she's under fifty and has never had a child, so there will be tax to pay on her estate if she does not remarry within a year or so. Another argument in favour of the match!'

I nodded. I knew about the tax, though – having found and married Gwellia again – I'd not attracted it myself. The Emperor Augustus had instituted it, when he discovered that the birth rate had dropped alarmingly, threatening Rome's future legionary strength. All fit and able citizens of marriage-able age were liable to a tax if they did not marry (or remarry) within a certain time, though a mother of three children was formally exempt. (There had been much resentment, then as now, but it had never been repealed – it made a useful source of income for the state.)

'So, if this wedding is desirable, I presume you'll send her back?' I muttered, wondering why he'd bothered to consult me about this. 'Or do you fear the lady Julia will be accused of lack of family feeling, if you do?' Roman custom more or less required that a wealthy household should offer hospitality to any relative who asked for it.

'Family feeling?' Marcus gave a short impatient grunt. 'I've never heard this woman mentioned in my life before – I had to ask around when the messenger arrived, to see if one of the other councillors could tell me anything. Fortunately old Tertillius was able to assist – although I didn't mention why I asked, of course. Let him think I'd simply heard the gossip, too.'

'And you've had no chance to speak about it to your wife. She might know more about Druscilla, possibly . . .?'

'I frankly doubt my wife has ever heard of her. Certainly, she never mentioned her to me!'

'But . . .'

But Marcus was no longer listening to me. He was suddenly rapping his scroll on the shoulder of the little crouching slave. 'The lane gets wider here. Wake up and run ahead. Tell that farmer to pull onto the verge and let his betters past.' Then, as the pageboy looked up ashen-faced, he added graciously, 'And if you wish, you can run on home from here, provided you are at the door to help us down.'

We were crawling now and the worst of the violent juddering had ceased, so the boy was more than willing to obey. We saw him stumbling up towards the cart ahead, and saw the driver turn his head to look at us, then – audibly grumbling – start to move his wagon to one side.

'I've a mind to have that farmer flogged for insolence!' My patron was incensed. 'Not even a citizen, and he dares protest.'

I was about to say, 'But he might be a lowly one?' when I realized he could not. Any citizen would be in Glevum at the rites. Clearly the farmer had assumed the same. I saw the look of panic cross his face when he saw two togas pass, and he quickly bowed his head and raised a gnarled hand in salute.

Marcus was mollified by this show of deference. 'Now about this woman,' he resumed, as we picked up speed again. 'She's not just looking for hospitality. She wants to transfer into my potestas. She's claiming sanctuary.'

'Sanctuary? As a slave might do? Does she have the right?'

'She may do, if there's actual danger to her life.'

'But surely there is not?' We were approaching the cross-roads now, where my roundhouse lies. I was shocked by what my patron had just said, and I was anxious to end the conversation and get back to Gwellia. But the carriage did not slow.

We jolted straight on past my gate. I could see I'd have to walk back from the villa, by and by.

Marcus was entirely concerned with finishing his tale. 'She seems to think there is. Suggests that he ill-treated his first wife – or even caused her death – but that does not seem to be the general view. Tertillius says she was a gentle soul, who died quite unexpectedly – lost an early baby, his informant seems to think – and left her husband heartbroken. Whereas Druscilla was spoiled and troublesome, even as a child. Not the sort of woman one wishes to adopt.' He paused as the gig drew up outside his villa gate.

'Then where is the problem? Can't you just decline?'

The gates were opened from within and Marcus tapped the driver on the shoulder with his scroll as a signal to drive in. 'That is where I want your judgement, my old friend,' he said, as we swept on towards the villa door. 'The wretched woman also writes that on her mother's side, she is related to the Emperor's wife. That makes her potentially dangerous to offend.'

I gulped. This gave the matter quite a different slant. The present Empress was becoming known as a very powerful personage indeed. 'But what does Julia Domna think of this escape? Isn't it likely that she strongly disapproves?' The gig had rumbled to a halt and I was able to relax my cramped fingers from the seat.

'That is exactly what I do not know, my friend.' My patron was smoothing down his toga-folds, and rescuing his crumpled wreath from underneath his seat. 'She is from Syria, of course, from a priestly family, and therefore has enemies on the Senate, it is said. It is possible that this would-be groom is one of them. Or he may be a supporter. I simply do not know. Though Severus has argued, in a recent speech, that a guardian should not have the right to force his ward towed – and it's thought that Julia Domna was behind the sentiment.'

'But also suggests that it is not written into law?'

'Not yet, at any rate.' He raised his brows at me. 'Hence my dilemma. Here, let us go inside and you can read the note yourself.' He stood up in the carriage as he spoke, just in time for the freckled pageboy to come panting up, red-faced, to take the wreath and scroll from him and help him to the ground.

I slid down in my turn, cursing the heavy garment which impeded me, and we all three went together to the house, where the door was already opening at our approach.

FIVE

We were greeted on the threshold, not by the usual slave-boy, but by a female I had never seen before: a stout, grey-haired woman of uncertain years, with a ruddy pleasant face and well-developed arms. She was dressed in a faded, short-sleeved tunic which just reached below her knees, but she wore expensive sandals and there was no slave-disc or brand that I could see, so for a moment I wondered if this could be the runaway, as she made a deep obeisance at my patron's feet.

Another matching pair of pageboys (Marcus had a weakness for this extravagance) had appeared from the direction of the servants' waiting-room and were hovering nearby, waiting to escort their master through the house, but the woman ignored them and did not cede her place. If this was indeed the missing bride, I thought, she was not easily abashed.

Her opening words dispelled my error instantly. The Latin was fluent and the accent clear, but these were not the cultured cadences of Rome. 'My humble greetings, Excellence. I hope you weren't disturbed. You come most speedily. The news seems good to you, I hope? The new arrivals are lusty and quite strong, so with a little assistance from the gods they might all yet survive – with your permission, Excellence, of course. Do you wish to come and see your wife? She is weakened, naturally, but bathed and sitting up. Propped on pillows, well enough to talk.'

My patron stared at the woman in dismay. 'My wife? I hope there's been no problem, woman. She was as fit and well as usual when I left here today.'

Her round face broke into an enormous smile. 'No problem, master, beyond the fact that there are two of them. Not as large as normal babes, of course, but easier for the mother, possibly. As I say, she is awaiting your return. I think that she is hoping you will take up both of them, but the girl is the weaker, thanks be to the gods, so – between ourselves – if there should a choice . . .'

Marcus signalled her to cease her chattering. 'Do I understand what you are telling me? Julia has been brought to bed and the child – or children – are already born?' He ran his free hand through his dishevelled curls.

'Did you not get the message, Excellence?' The wide brow was furrowed in a frown. 'I sent one straight away. There was a horseman called here, while this was happening, bringing a letter to the house, but you were not here and of course the lady Julia was in no state to read or answer it. So rather than have him simply waiting in the court, I took the opportunity of sending him to you – assuming that he'd find you in the town. Though you came so quickly I supposed he must have met you on the way.'

'We did see a horseman,' I reminded him. 'But I suppose he did not recognize the gig. Especially since you had a passenger. The courier would not, of course, have been expecting that.'

Marcus was looking at me as though I'd lost my wits. 'Then he's had a wasted journey into town. He'll have to come straight back.' He turned back to the midwife – as she evidently was. 'But you say the birth has happened? I can't believe that this is possible. I've only been away from here since dawn and there was no hint of travail then!'

The woman gave him an expressive look. 'If you do not believe me, Excellence, come and see the evidence yourself. I should in any case be getting back to her. They're very new, of course. They've barely been washed and swaddled in clean cloth. I hope that I've done aright. Your wife insists that it is not the custom of this house to bath a newborn boy in cold water and strap him to a plank, but if you wish I could do so even yet.'

My patron shook his head impatiently.

'Well, as you wish, of course. Though it does help to toughen and make a man of them. However – it appears your wife was right about what you would wish. She told me simply to rinse them both in warmed water and lay them on a rug. I did stretch out the legs and wrap them tight, to make them straight and strong. On both the children, I assume you wanted that.'

Marcus looked apologetically at me. 'Libertus old friend, this has come as a surprise. I had better go and see. In the meantime, read this for yourself.' He reached into his toga-folds and brought out a delicate hinged writing-block – a lovely thing, the outside covers inlaid with ivory and tied together with a piece of silver cord. 'From Druscilla. I won't be very long. When I come back, tell me what you think.'

And off he went, accompanied by the woman and the pair of matching slaves.

For a moment I stared after him, impatient and appalled. I had been hoping to get home to Gwellia – but there was now no chance of that. Though I was still likely to see her sooner than I would have done if I'd hired a litter, as I first proposed. If I'd done so, I would scarcely be even halfway home.

I sighed and turned back to the atrium, where I found myself alone, except for the freckled pageboy who had travelled home with us. I was uneasy now, but – having no inkling of the arrows of fire about to rain on me – my fretting was entirely of a social kind.

Not that I was surprised to be abandoned here – as a male and an unrelated one at that, it would be most improper for me to visit Julia in bed. (In a Celtic household there might be dozens of hearty callers bearing gifts, but in a Roman one no man – except her husband – would ever call until the naming day, when all the purifying rites had been performed and she had returned into society. One might invite ill-fortune otherwise.)

Nor could I even send a message, decently. Congratulations were due to Marcus, if to anyone. So there was nothing for it but to stand and wait – however anxious I might feel about my wife. It would be unthinkable to leave when my patron had declared a wish to talk to me.

The slave-boy seemed to sense my agitation. He shuffled

round in front of me and bowed. 'Can I be of assistance, citizen?' He was almost recovered from his breathlessness (and presumably his queasiness as well) but he appeared alarmed to have been left to look after me alone.

I tried to put him at his ease by asking him his name and apologizing that my presence in the gig had made him travel on the floor, but that only seemed to terrify him more.

He turned scarlet to his little shell-like ears and blurted that his slave name was Lentigines – meaning 'freckles' – and that usually there were two slaves in the gig, so they had to crouch on either side of Marcus anyway. He seemed embarrassed by this confidence, and hastened onto more familiar ground, by offering me some honeyed figs and wine. 'While you are waiting, Councillor.'

Secretly, I would rather have refused – I was too edgy about Gwellia to feel like eating anything, and in any case I am not partial to either of those things – but I did not have the heart to disappoint him of his task.

So after a few minutes staring at the mosaic on the floor (a clumsy one, depicting a lopsided Neptune in a pond – none of my handiwork, I am glad to say!) I was duly furnished with a jug of no doubt splendid watered wine and a plate of very sticky figs, for which I murmured unconvincing thanks. I was grateful, though, for the folding stool that the boy had brought for me, and I sent him off to wait against the wall, while I sat down at one of the onyx tables by the door and carefully opened the little writing-block.

The message was written in a bold but spiky hand, fairly grammatical though sometimes badly spelt, suggesting that the lady had scratched it on the wax herself, rather than using an amanuensis for the task. (It was also short, which was another clue – commercial letter-writers charge according to the length, which they generally contrive to make as great as possible.)

The capacity to write at all was evidence that she'd had an education of a kind, but – no doubt because letter-writing was not habitual to her – the missive did not conform to social norms. Even the opening was blunt, with none of the expected flattery. 'To Marcus Septimus from Druscilla Livia, a kinswoman of his wife.' That was all. No honorifics – Marcus was not even addressed as 'Excellence' – no good wishes for his health, and the tone of the remainder of the message was the same. None of the usual conventions was observed.

The effect was positively rude. The import, though, was exactly as my patron had described. She was coming. She had discovered where he lived and was already on her way, and she claimed his protection since she was related to his wife. And to the Empress – she emphasized that point.

I was just wondering why, in that case, she had not appealed directly to the Imperial court, but then I came to the lengthy final paragraph. There was no mistaking the genuine anguish in the words.

> I appeal to you because I am afraid. I'm to be forced into marriage with a man I fear. When my cousin Marcia was his wife, I could see she was completely cowed – though she was such a feeble creature she was scared of everyone, and he always seemed to dote on her. So I guardedly agreed in principle. But on the day of the betrothal, when he came to seal the date, I changed my mind. I did not like the way he looked at me. Of course, I'd never fully met his eyes before, but there was something in them which turned me cold with fear. I remembered how Marcia had died so unexpectedly, and I was alarmed enough to try to turn him down. But they would not hear of my refusing, so I have run away.

So her decision had been a very sudden one, I thought, after arrangements were already underway. On reflection, I should have guessed as much. A betrothal of this kind would not have been announced without many days of careful negotiation first – what was to be the dowry, and what date was most propitious for the marriage day. She had even given notional consent. No wonder that her brother had been so embarrassed and irate. And all – for what? A feeling, little more. Certainly nothing that she could plead against her suitor in a court.

I was rereading her extraordinary words, when Marcus came bustling back, accompanied by the slaves – one of whom carried a pile of kindling, while the other held a little silver tray.

Marcus was looking proud, but sheepish, and his toga was awry. I was already rising to my feet while Freckle-face produced a second, more elaborate folding chair. But my patron motioned me to wait.

'I'll just light the fire of preservation to the gods,' he said, moving to the household altar-niche, where his slave was setting the kindling into place. 'It is unfortunate, at this moment, but it must be done.' Marcus pulled one of his toga-folds around his head to form a hood – an indication that this was a serious event – and gestured that the boy should pass him both the wine jug and the lighted taper from the sconce.

Taking the jug, he poured a little liquid on the shrine, saying loudly, 'Behold, I make libation to Juno, queen of heaven, in gratitude for Julia's safe delivery and now . . .' He set the flame to the kindling, which flared up at once. 'I dedicate this flame to the gods of crib and cradle. To them, too, I offer appropriate sacrifice, craving their preservation of the children which are born.'

The slave passed him the salver, which held a little scoop, a tiny honey pot and a small dish of what looked like grains of spelt. Marcus took the spoon and scattered a little of each onto the fire, murmuring something which I could not hear. Looking back, I wish I'd offered a petition for myself, just in case his gods were listening – but I simply kept my head bowed, deferentially.

When he had finished he pushed back his hood, told the slaves to bring another cup for him and came across to settle himself beside me on his stool.

'That deals with the expected rituals for now,' he told me, with a self-contented sigh. 'I've already formally picked the infants from the floor, to accept that they are mine and welcome them into the family. All that remains is to keep that fire alight until the naming day – although I suppose before then I shall have to think of names.' He motioned to the slave to fill the cup with wine for him. 'Dear Jupiter! As if I did not have enough to worry me, just now. But I'll have to do it, soon, so I can register the births with the tax authorities.'

I nodded, raising my own drink in a salute. As a citizen with grandchildren myself, I understood the regulations perfectly.

'The boy we might call Julius – for Julia's family, since Marcellinus is already named for me.' He picked up the plumpest fig – not at all to my surprise – but did not swallow it, simply turning it between his fingers and saying fretfully, 'Though one has to be so careful, nowadays. With the new Emperor having such slender claims himself, perhaps it isn't wise to emphasize any connection with the old Imperial House. So perhaps not Julius – the first Caesar's name. Such things are often misinterpreted.'

'Then what about Septimius, perhaps?' I was pleased with my suggestion. 'An open tribute to the current Emperor? There would be several arguments for that. For instance that today's his birthday too – and the fact you are Septimus yourself?'

Marcus slapped his knee and glanced admiringly at me. 'A very clever notion, my old friend.' He popped the fig into his mouth, and took another one. 'With the cognomen Germanicus, perhaps, because he is a twin? Marcus Septimius Aurelius Germanicus. That has a certain ring. I'll tell Julia what we have decided on.' There was a moment's pause while another sweetmeat disappeared, and then he added, 'Though that still leaves the girl. Second daughters are always difficult. Marcella Aurelia, like her sister, I suppose, but we'll have to add Seconda or something similar.'

'Or Domnita, for the Empress, possibly?' I ventured, then wished that I had not. I generally knew better than to keep suggesting things.

But Marcus appeared to be considering the idea. 'In which case I should send to my family in Rome, to make sure that Julia Domna gets to hear of it – no point in flattery if it does not reach the proper ears. But we have days to think of that, and the girl may not survive – in which case we won't have to worry about her.' My patron paused in his consumption of the figs to sip his wine with a judicial air.

This time I did not nod. We Celts prefer to have a son, of course, but I have never quite been able to accept the Roman view that newborn children do not yet have souls, and are

therefore merely little animals, who – until the naming day
– can be disposed of in any way their paterfamilias thinks fit.
Especially second daughters of uncertain health. I sincerely
hoped the little girl was going to live that long.

Marcus selected the last remaining fig. 'So that is that.
Always assuming that Severus isn't meantime overthrown, and
we find Pescennius Niger on the throne and have to think
again.' He sighed. 'Meanwhile, I have sent out to the dovecote
for a bird, to make a proper burnt offering to the household
gods – and the land-slaves are already sorting out a flawless
pig and ram for the lustratio sacrifice on the naming day.'

'You'll time that occasion for the boy, I suppose?' Girls
usually have their ritual one day earlier.

He licked his fingertips. 'Of course – but we'll offer another
dove on the appropriate date, for her. That should make sure
that any evil spirits that they trailed with them from the
otherworld are banished, from them both. And speaking of
cleansing . . .' He waggled his sticky fingers at the slaves,
who came hurrying over with a finger bowl and cloth.

I watched as he extended his ringed hands to have them
wiped – glad that I'd had the writing-block as an excuse to
keep my fingers clean. 'One cannot be too careful to placate
the gods,' I said.

'Or to placate one's colleagues, either,' he remarked. 'With
matters as they stand. I'd better hold a public banquet, too, to
celebrate the births, and a thanksgiving sacrifice for the safety
of my wife.' But it was clear that Marcus was not in expansive
mood.

'And see that the Governor's kinsman is invited to the
feast?'

He did not rebuke me for impertinence. 'Of course. Not the
fort commandant, perhaps, but all the curia. Yourself included,
if you care to come. And a sacrifice, something spectacular at
the Capitoline shrine – just as soon as these things can be
arranged, what with the birthday rites and then the Ides . . .'
He broke off, 'But forgive me – all this fatherhood has made
me tedious. About that message, what did you think of it?'
He held out a hand for the little writing-block.

I gave it to him, open as it was. 'It tells us a little about the writer, Excellence.' I proudly outlined the conclusions I had drawn. 'Clearly a lady of some spirit, too – not many women of her class would be content to journey around the Empire alone, with only a handful of slaves for company.'

'Meaning she shows a lack of proper *modestas*?' he said.

In fact, that was not what I meant at all – I almost admired the spirit she had shown – but my patron obviously would not agree. Modestas is a female virtue prized by Romans in all their womenfolk – and generally required in any bride. However, I merely made a noncommittal noise. There were slaves about and – since Druscilla might soon be visiting – I did not wish it to be rumoured that I'd insulted her.

Marcus had no such inhibitions. 'You're right, of course,' he said. 'This prospective bridegroom must be genuinely keen – her behaviour would deter the average citizen. And Jove alone knows where she must have been staying on the way from Rome. She could hardly send ahead to reputable inns, for fear of being traced.'

That was a point I hadn't thought about. Most ordinary taverns are (famously) no place for anyone, let alone a lady of patrician birth. They never change the mattresses (and rarely coverings), one never knows with whom one will be forced to share a room, and there is a good chance of being robbed (or worse) while one's asleep. And as a woman, with no letter of conduct from her family, she'd have no access to the military inns – where the facilities, though often basic, are generally clean, and sometimes excellent.

I went on, still guilelessly pleased to demonstrate my powers of reasoning, 'I doubt this Druscilla ever used the inns at all. I imagine that she's travelling in disguise, most likely under a different name, and seeking accommodation at farmsteads on the way – places where people would be glad to give her paid lodging overnight.' I saw his doubtful look. 'That would make her more difficult to trace. One cannot ask questions at every single farm.'

My patron looked doubtful. 'Even so, it must have been a risk. No wonder she is anxious to be back under male protection.' He stared at the message as though it might yield some new information. 'And by this time she may be running out of funds. Perhaps that's why she suddenly decided to come here.'

'That's possible,' I said. (Dealing with Marcus it is never wise to contradict.) 'Although I suspect that she planned to do this all along – how could she 'discover where you lived' except from friends and family in Rome? And, though she left the capital a moon or two ago, she could hardly have got here any earlier.'

That was self-evident, of course. She had left Rome at a season when travel by land is difficult enough, as mountain routes become impassable, and when most sea captains will not venture out of port at all for fear of winter storms and gales. At least without official orders, or a hefty bribe.

Marcus shot a look at me. 'Of course! It would have taken several moons to get as far as Gaul. And – unlike that visiting relative of the Governor's – she wouldn't have a travel warrant to ensure a boat to carry her. She'd have to wait until the Ides of Mars were past, for normal trading to begin again.' He paused a moment. 'Though she might have tried a bribe.'

'And draw yet more unwelcome attention to herself? As a well-bred woman travelling alone she would already be remarkable enough – even if she has a slave or two with her – and the last thing that she'd want is for someone to suspect that she was a fugitive. She's no doubt invented some plausible account of where she's going and why. Visiting distant family, I expect – which, if the letter is to be believed, she could quite truly claim.'

'But how can we know this is genuinely from her? It is not even sealed – though a woman she may not own a signet ring, of course.'

'There are initials on the outside of the writing-block,' I said. 'There can't be two of those.'

Marcus snapped the tablet shut, to examine the ivory letters inlaid on the frame. 'D.L. Druscilla Livia. You're right, as usual. That would correspond. So we presume it's genuine. But this writing-tablet is a memorable thing, which any courier would instantly recall. Would it not draw attention to her whereabouts? Unless, having reached Britannia, she feels reasonably safe.'

'But surely it was one of her own slaves she sent ahead?'

Marcus looked at me in some surprise, as if the implication had just occurred to him. 'Not at all. And as a woman she could not apply to use an army courier – which would have betrayed her whereabouts in any case. It was a hired messenger who found me in the town – I had to pay the fee.'

(That, at least, was no surprise at all, since obviously she would not pay it in advance. With a public courier, no one ever does – otherwise there is no guarantee that one's message will actually arrive.)

'A public courier? That was clearly not ideal, if she is afraid of being found.'

'He did not know much about her. She sought him out at the port at Rutupiae, so the fellow said. Having learned that he was coming to Glevum anyway. Gave him the message and made it clear that she was not expecting a reply. That was days ago, and that was all he knew – beyond the fact that she was in Britannia, and mostly likely on her way.'

'Supposing that is actually what she means to do.' I had been struck by an alarming thought. 'This whole message may be a deceit, intended to mislead, in case there is anyone pursuing her.'

'If so, it's disrespectful, especially at this time – she must have known we would prepare to house a guest. What makes you think of that? There's nothing to suggest it.'

'Except, perhaps, the second messenger?'

SIX

My patron looked at me as though I were insane. 'What second messenger?'

'The one who came here to the house while you were out? I assume he came from this Druscilla person, too? In which case, he might be bearing different news. The first message was delivered in a very public place – in Glevum forum at the birthday rites, where it was sure to cause remark

– while the second one was sent discreetly here and seems not to have been written. There's no sign of any note.'

'Great Jupiter,' Marcus said, slowly, 'We had forgotten him.'

I ignored the 'we', and just inclined my head. 'And according to the midwife that courier was awaiting a reply . . .'

'Though, with Julia safely delivered of the twins, he was sent off into town instead to look for me.' He nodded. 'So let's hope that our deductions are correct and this was also from Druscilla, telling me what she genuinely plans to do! If she does not really hope to come, I will not be faced with problems as to how to deal with her. I wonder if her courier gave the household any clue?' He beckoned to one of the paired slaves who had met us at the door. 'The messenger who came here, earlier. You saw him, I suppose?'

The slave-boy bowed. 'Indeed so, master. The doorman let him in, but – since you were out, the mistress indisposed, and chief steward temporarily unavailable – we showed him in here, to the atrium, to wait.'

Marcus frowned. 'Where was the steward, then?'

'Gone to the storehouse to assemble the items for the sacrificial fire. The midwife had told him that the birth was imminent.'

His owner greeted this with an impatient grunt. 'I see. So the courier could not give his message after all.'

'Oh, he did so, master. It was a written one. A proper letter, in a special little case, all sealed and everything. He was waving it though it were a talisman. To prove the sender was important, I suppose – as he kept on telling us. Though we might have guessed that by his own embroidered uniform.'

Marcus glanced at me. 'So, it seems that you were right, Libertus, my old friend. A second letter, sealed and brought by private messenger to ensure it was not intercepted on the way. Clearly this Druscilla Livia is more resourceful than we thought. I begin to regret that I shall not be meeting her.' He turned back to the slave. 'Where is the letter now? He did not take it with him, I suppose?'

The slave-boy looked embarrassed. 'I suppose it's with the mistress – we took it into her – or tried to, since you were not here yourself. But when we reached the sleeping room where she'd retired, the midwife-woman would not let us speak to her. She took the message from us, but sent us both away. The mistress was too busy to deal with anything just then, and the messenger would simply have to wait till you came home – though later on she seemed to change her mind. I heard her send him into Glevum after you.'

Marcus ignored that. 'But she kept the letter?' He was indignant now. Any moment, someone might easily be flogged.

The slave-boy was abject in his apologies. 'Forgive me, master, but I do not know. I presume she has it still.' Then he added, perhaps in the hope of deflecting Marcus's anger with a helpful thought – since it was not usual for His Excellence's slaves to venture information unless directed to – 'although, with your permission, Excellence, I'm sure it was not from this lady, Druscilla Livia, of whom I heard you speak. The courier kept on saying that his owner was a man – indeed, that he was a most important one.'

Marcus glowered at him. 'You are quite sure of this?'

'Quite certain, Excellence. He said so several times. No less a person than a senator from Rome. He uttered threats in fact – that you and your household would very soon regret keeping his courier waiting with such casual disrespect.' The boy seemed to realize that he might have made things worse, and turned as scarlet as his tunic. 'I am very sorry, master, but that is what he said.'

'Great Jupiter!' Marcus by contrast, had turned absolutely white. 'I do not care for this. Libertus. Let's pray to all the gods that this is not that wretched kinsman of the Governor. He's the only Roman Senator I know of locally. What could he want with me? Nothing to my profit, I would wager that. He's staying with the commander of the garrison, who is no friend of mine.'

He was right to be concerned. The previous commandant had been – if not a friend – at least a close acquaintance of my patron's – and had been a guest here at the villa several times. He was a man of some intelligence, much loved by his troops, and I too, had grown to like him very much. But recent upheavals in the Empire – especially his known support for the Emperor Pertinax – had seen him abruptly relieved of his

command and summoned back to Rome, though he'd had the
wisdom to disappear to Gaul instead. But Marcus had been
Pertinax's close friend and protégé and – though Severus was
rumoured to have lifted the 'opprobrium' and reinstated
Pertinax to the Imperial pantheon – times were still uncertain
for his followers. I agreed with Marcus. The omens were not
good.

I tried to comfort him. 'The new commander is not altogether
an enemy, these days. After a bad beginning, things are more
cordial now.'

Marcus sighed. 'All the same, I do not trust him very much.
He would testify against me, if it profited himself – and I've
defied convention by not staying to the games. Especially with
this senator attending them.'

I forbore to say that I had warned him about this, but a new
idea had just occurred to me. 'You don't suppose this letter
might be from the would-be groom? Tertillius said the suitor
was a senator, I think?'

Marcus shook his head. 'It is hard to imagine that he would
come so far! He would have to have the Emperor's sanction
to have left the capital for long. Or the Empress's, I suppose.
Although if he has somehow worked out that Druscilla Livia
intended to appeal to me for sanctuary, I suppose he might
have done.' He tailed off. 'Dear Mars, Libertus, you do not
suppose that the two might be the same, and the bridegroom
is actually the Governor's relative?'

I said nothing, since that was exactly what I meant.

'Merciful Minerva, what am I to do? If that is the case
there'll be all kinds of problems for this house! Jove only
knows what he'd accuse me of – not only disrespect to Severus,
but disrespect to him – interference with his wedding plans,
attempting to usurp her brother's potestas, and who knows
what other crimes against his dignity. Punishable in law, since
the man's a senator! Dear Mars! Although this letter may yet
be unrelated to the girl.' He looked at me for comfort. 'We
have no reason to think otherwise.'

'As yet,' I murmured. Offering false comfort can be
dangerous. Then honesty – and hubris – compelled me to add,
'Though it's hard to know why, otherwise, he'd send to you

today. He must have expected you'd be at the birthday rites – like every other Roman citizen, and as he was himself. I saw him at the temple, I believe.'

Marcus nodded. 'So did I. He even bowed to me.'

'Then he must have known that you had made a speech, and so were likely to be opening the games. And that messenger was here not long before us, as we know, so he can't have left Glevum much ahead of us – though a rider is obviously faster than a gig. So, his master intended to send while you were out, perhaps hoping to find the girl in residence – or proof, at least, that she was expected here.'

'In which case he will be disappointed!' Marcus said. 'No one here could have the least idea.'

'Exactly. Which may be why the courier, finding nothing to report, was suddenly happy to go back to town.'

Marcus puffed his cheeks in an exaggerated sigh. 'You may be right, old friend. In which case trouble is averted, for now at any rate. Though much depends on what the letter says. I almost fear to read it – though I suppose I must.' He turned back to the slave-boy. 'You say the midwife has the scroll? Then fetch her here! At once!'

The slave was looking terrified at having started this, but he bowed himself away and we heard his sandals hurrying down the covered passageway, round the courtyard garden, to where Julia's chamber lay. A pause – in which neither of us said a single word – and then we heard him scurrying back accompanied, this time, by the midwife's heavier steps. She did not wait to be announced, but strode in, smiling, not at all abashed.

'You wished to see me, Excellence?' She bobbed her head in a token gesture of respect, but there was nothing subservient in her attitude.

Marcus looked back at her, his face as stony as a statue of the gods. 'I understand you have a message for me?'

She beamed. 'How did you hear of that?' She hitched her ample bosom on her arms, and – without waiting for an answer – launched into a lengthy diatribe. 'The fact is that when your wife had given birth, I sent for the wet nurse that you had arranged. She came – just a moment after you had left us, by

the back slave-entrance, naturally – and I introduced her to the
babes. They suckled very briefly and are both asleep, dear lambs
– and for the moment that is good enough. But the woman is
still feeding her own infant, too, and your boy's a sturdy lad.
I'm concerned that in a week or two there won't be enough.'

My patron was frowning and manifestly displeased. He held
up a hand for silence, but she ploughed on earnestly.

'I know it's possible to buy the extra breast milk from the
marketplace in town, but by the time it gets here it will not
be fresh. Besides, that's very inconvenient, and one cannot be
sure exactly how much will be required—'

Marcus cut her off, at last, with an exasperated snarl.
'Silence, woman! Why exactly, are you telling me this now?'

The midwife looked startled. 'Because, that was the message,
Excellence. Should you wish to hire an additional wet nurse
for the boy, I know of one that I could recommend.' My patron
was still staring at her like a basilisk, and she added with a
frown, 'I hoped you would approve of my suggestion, so that
I could send for her at once – before she is engaged by someone
else.'

My patron was visibly nonplussed. It was clear – to everyone
but the midwife – that this was not what he had wished to
hear. He said, impatiently, 'Don't worry me with trivia, at a
time like this. Whatever you decide. Or better, ask my wife.
I know nothing at all about such things. I wanted to hear about
the message, that is all.'

'Thank you, Excellence,' The beaming smile was back. 'I'm
sure it's for the best. And I am quite certain that your lady
will agree, since you would hardly expect her to feed the babes
herself? And now, if you'll excuse me, I should get back to
her. It is too soon to leave her – there is still a risk of flux.'
She dipped another genuflection and seemed prepared to leave.

I could see that Marcus was about to roar at her, so I intervened (though it was strictly not my place). 'Madam, I don't
think you understand. You were not sent for to deliver this
message of your own, however pressing you might feel it to
be. His Excellence was speaking of the letter that the courier
brought today. I understand you took possession of that, at the
time?'

'By all the immortal goddesses! So I did!' For the first time a look of apprehension crossed her face. 'Oh, Excellence, I must apologize. Of course! I meant to show it to the mistress, when I could. But with the birth so imminent I did not get a chance and with all the excitement of finding there were twins, afterwards I quite forgot about the scroll.'

'A scroll?' Marcus and I exclaimed in unison. We had heard that the letter was protected in a case, but I had not expected that.

A proper writing scroll is an expensive thing, rarely used by private individuals, other than for business of the most important kind – and then only to demonstrate the standing of the person sending it. So this letter was either an official document, or it was a communication intended to impress.

We were still exchanging startled glances at the news, when the midwife shocked us once again, by hitching up her faded tunic skirt to reveal – slung between it and a still more faded tunic underneath – a drawstring hanging pocket of some size. No doubt it was intended for discreetly carrying items of her trade, but from it she now took a handsome scroll-case, ribbon-tied and sealed, and handed it to Marcus with a bow. She alone was wholly unembarrassed, it appeared.

'Here it is, Excellence – with the seal unbroken, as you see, exactly as it came. Not that I could have read it anyway. I never learned to cipher, though I can scratch my name.'

Idle talk about herself was almost as inappropriate as the lifting of her skirts, and Marcus shot her a disapproving look as he struggled with the seal – but far from persuading her to hold her tongue, this only encouraged her to gabble on the more.

'I should have known it was important – the courier told me so, though they always say that, don't they? He wasn't pleased when I asked him to take my message into town, though he agreed to do it when he discovered what it was, and if you ask me, he was glad enough to go. He was obviously superstitious about being here at all, once he discovered there had been a birth – especially of twins. Probably a Greek – you know what they are like about these things.'

I didn't, though I might have guessed, I suppose. Roman

beliefs about a house of birth are strong enough, themselves. Marcus however, said impatiently, 'What makes you think so?' He was still picking at the wax-seal.

She looked surprised. 'Well, he went, although he claims his master is apt to be displeased, and would be impatiently awaiting your reply.'

'He did not ask who else was in the house?' I said.

'He might have done so, citizen, though I would not have heard. I only spoke to him to ask him to carry news to you. He was so self-important he could scarcely deign to speak – to me or anyone he thought of lesser rank.'

'But he took your message?'

'That is what I mean. You would expect a pompous idiot like that to decline outright to carry messages on behalf of anyone like me, and instead demand refreshment and a place to wait. But once he knew about the babies he could not wait to leave. He was clearly really frightened of his master's wrath if he went back without an answer, but – with the mistress in childbed – he still decided he would rather not be here.' She seemed to realize, at last, that she was talking out of turn. 'Which reminds me, Excellence, I must get back to her. Now that I have given you the scroll, do I have your permission to return?'

'Oh go, woman, in the name of Jove!' Marcus looked up from his efforts with the knot, and briefly spared a hand to gesture her away.

SEVEN

T he ribbon yielded, the wax-seal broke away and Marcus was able to extract the document.

'Fresh vellum, written on one side only, and not crossed,' he said, raising his eyebrows expressively at me – meaning that this was a very expensive document indeed. (Parchment is so costly it is commonly reused, either by writing on the back of an earlier message, or sideways across it as a palimpsest.) 'The writer wants to signal he's a man of consequence. Well, let us learn the worst!'

He passed the empty scroll-case to the waiting slave then, holding the letter in his right hand, he unrolled it with his left and began to read aloud. 'To his most esteemed Excellence Marcus Septimus Aurelius, chief magistrate of Glevum, from Hortius Lollius Valens, Senator of Rome. Greetings in the name of the glorious Emperor. I trust that this epistle finds you in good health . . .'

There were several more paragraphs in a similar vein.

This letter was everything the other one was not. Carefully courteous and beautifully phrased. Hortius Valens was indeed in Glevum, staying at the fortress as he wrote but, claiming acquaintance with my patron's family, he craved accommodation for the remainder of what he planned to be a slightly longer visit to the town.

'Immortal Jupiter!' Marcus had been mumbling through this up to now, but suddenly he raised his voice again. 'He's in Britannia, he says, to show support for his kinsman, now that Clodius Albinus has been named Imperial heir, and – just listen to this – "as a known supporter of the immortal Pertinax, I am sure that you would wish me to convey your own congratulations to the Governor as well".' He let the vellum snap back into a roll. 'Now what am I to do? It could be fatal to send messages like that – everybody knows that Severus will not keep his word! That reference to Pertinax is practically a threat. And just look at that final paragraph!' He thrust the scroll at me.

I unrolled it and read the words aloud, as he clearly meant me to. '"I also have private business in this area, a delicate affair, which I have reason to believe may affect your family. It involves a lady, as you may already know. As a fellow magistrate I am hopeful that you can assist me to resolve it speedily. So greetings and farewell".' I paused, 'At least that sounds quite courteous – to my unRoman ears, at least!'

My patron snatched the roll from me. 'Courteous? This is outright blackmail or very nearly so! Libertus, I wanted your counsel earlier. Now I am even more in need of it.'

For a moment I thought that Marcus wanted me to offer

him the use of 'my' town apartment for this guest – as I had done (with unfortunate results) during a recent visit of his cousin, an avowed Imperial spy. I would have to volunteer it, though – since, naturally, as he had gifted it to me, it would be unthinkable for him to ask for it outright. I obediently mumbled, 'There is my apartment, Excellence . . .'

He waved the thought away. 'Thank you, but that would hardly be appropriate this time. For one thing bad omens now surround your flat, since several deaths occurred there – a fact which he would be certain to hear of very soon, and which he is likely to take exception to. One cannot offer a senator a residence of evil augury. Especially with the present Empress in authority. She is descended from the priesthood of an Eastern cult, so the court has to be more than usually alert, lest they take back perceived potential for ill-luck.'

'But, Excellence, the place was purified—'

He shook his head to interrupt. 'There are rumours of swingeing penalties, these days, for those accused of careless-ness in this. Besides, this is no ordinary man. This is a kinsman of the Governor, no less – and he invites himself specifically to me.'

'And most men in Glevum would be flattered, I suppose, by his condescension in suggesting such a thing.' I raised my brows at him. 'As you yourself would be at any other time? But as it is, this woman's coming here, and you are obliged to have him, too?'

Marcus nodded glumly. 'In practice, that's the case. Hortius has already weighted all the dice. He claims acquaintance with my family in Rome, and makes it clear he's here on private business, too, so it would be quite extraordinary for me to refuse – an insult of a calculated kind.' He sighed. 'He's holding me between two spears, as well – support for Clodius suggests potential disloyalty to Rome, while anything else is failure to support the rightful Governor. It's blackmail, as I say. As things stand, I cannot even ask them to keep him at the fort – though generally a military inn might seem a fitting place for him to stay. Hortius would clearly be a dangerous man to thwart. And he'll have lictors – or at least armed guards – to accommodate as well. Do you think that he likes demonstrating power, or do you think he simply plans to ruin me?'

'Perhaps not so much to ruin you, as to make certain that you cannot keep this girl from him,' I said. 'Since he seems to know, somehow, that she's appealed to you for help. Perhaps he hopes his presence will prevent you sheltering her. Though . . .'

I must have sounded hopeful, for he pounced on it at once. 'You have some idea?' He brightened. 'She could use that apartment that you were offering, perhaps?'

'That hardly offers the protection that she seeks,' I said, privately glad of the excuse. If there was trouble with a senator, I did not want her in my flat. 'It would be too easy for him to seize her there, and she could not claim your aegis – while mine would not suffice. My thoughts were running on a different route – what you said about the need for him to take account of evil auguries.'

My patron was frowning at the scroll again. 'But what has that to do with anything?'

'You might use that to advantage, possibly. Since Julia is in childbed – as the midwife said. It frightened off the courier. Something about the Greeks?'

Marcus glowered at me. 'I believe the Grecians argue that any man who is not a relative, who visits a house where a birth has newly taken place, contaminates himself and cannot enter a temple for forty days – and then only after a purification ritual. But we are Romans, surely?'

I detected real panic behind this curt remark, but I genuinely believed that my idea was quite a clever one. 'But does not high society in Rome vie to have Greek physicians in the house? And their opinions have spread throughout the Empire.'

Marcus nodded, absently. 'No doubt of it. Especially at court. My family write that . . .' He broke off and stared at me. 'Go on, Libertus, you begin to interest me.'

'What's more, your wife has given birth to twins – there are those who count that as a blessing, as you do yourself, but I have heard it murmured – and by Romans, in this case – that such unusual events are some kind of warning from the gods. And that any newborn children, fresh from the other world, may trail evil spirits in their wake?'

'You mean this house is inauspicious?'

'That's exactly what I mean. And for some days at least – more if you prefer the Grecian rule. So I think you might with dignity decline to have him here. You could even phrase it as concern to shield him from bad luck'

He nodded, thoughtfully. 'Perhaps I might, indeed, though it may not stop him taking grave offence.'

I had not finished with my smug advice. 'You might, though, put him in your town apartment for a while, especially if you stay there with him – which it might be wise to do.'

'But I must visit Julia, and attend the naming ceremony – for the boy, at least – and be here to put his bulla on.'

'Of course. As the father you are not yourself at risk – although you cannot be seen to trail the bad luck after you. So be sure to purify yourself before and after every visit here – a temple sacrifice would be appropriate – so that even you are technically pure. But a woman, unless she is a virgin – and Druscilla Livia was married, so she obviously is not – can't be entirely free of contamination once her monthly courses start, not without continuous propitiatory sacrifice, like the priestesses at the Vestal shrine.'

Marcus was looking at me with a dawning comprehension in his eyes. 'So she might stay here the villa, where a man may not?'

'And as a relative of Julia's she could be said to offer familial support.'

He actually smiled. 'Of course! I should have thought of that myself. No doubt I would have, given time – but all the same I'm glad I asked for your advice.'

He passed the scroll, which he'd been holding all this time, to little Freckle-face, then – perhaps as a sign of his relief – picked up his empty goblet, frowning into it as though surprised to find no wine. The gesture was enough. The older slaves seized up the jug and empty fig-plate respectively and glided off with them.

Marcus turned to me. 'I am glad to have this settled, Libertus my old friend. Could I keep the two parties from each other, do you think? Perhaps neither need actually know the other one was there.'

I actually laughed. 'I hardly think that would be possible – and it would probably be dangerous to try. But if you treat this woman as a guest of Julia's, for the first few days at least – it is not surprising that a kinswoman should come at such a time – rather than agreeing to take her into your potestas, it would give you time to work out what to do. Arranging a reconciliation would be best. Though if you do agree to offer her protection, that might endanger you, given her former husband's history. You might have to arrange a different advantageous match.'

'But who would be equal to a Roman senator?' Marcus muttered bitterly. 'I'd need the eldest son of some ancient family of enormous wealth. Preferably from Egypt, or some province such as that, as far away from here – and Rome – as possible—' He broke off as the matching slaves returned, carrying a second plate of honeyed figs and another jug of watered wine.

Marcus signalled that the jug-bearer should fill his cup but – at the risk of seeming impolite – I respectfully declined. 'I would love to stay and revel in your hospitality, patron, but you will remember that my own wife is unwell. So if you can spare me, now – and there is nothing else that I can do – I should get back to her.'

My patron nodded, but his mouth was full of figs so it was a moment before he was able to reply. 'Of course. I have already delayed you far too long. And since you are still wearing your formal council-wear it will take a little while to walk. If you care to take it off, I'll send it after you. Or, better, lend a slave to carry it – unless you would like me to provide you with the gig?'

This was an offer which I was, of course, expected to refuse, but I surprised my host. 'I would be grateful for a slave to walk me home, but I think that you should in any case have the gig prepared and send it into town as soon as possible. The lady Druscilla may be arriving soon, and it is clear – from how her message found you – that she is likely to look for you in town. The gates should be alerted to direct her here.

You also need to send a message, not only to your flat – warning them to expect a visitor – but to the garrison, to tell the Senator that you accede to his request. Though no doubt his own messenger will come back here quite soon.'

'And I should send his master a courteous reply, inviting him to use my apartment while he's here and saying that I'll shortly join him there?' Marcus acknowledged my suggestion with a smile. 'An excellent notion. I'll instruct the slaves at once. And I'll have the gig prepared. Would you care to wait for it?'

I shook my head. 'Thank you, Excellence, but I'd prefer to leave at once!' and murmuring best wishes for Julia's health and that of her young babes, I bowed myself away, to hurry as fast as possible back to my own poor wounded wife.

EIGHT

Lentigines was detailed to accompany me home, though I fear I shocked the freckled little fellow several times. First, when I took my curial toga off and gave it to him to carry down the lane (this made walking much easier for me, but I knew that offering justification to a slave would only demean me further, in his eyes) and more still, when we arrived outside my gate. Accustomed to the Roman world of lofty rooms and formal courts in which he was a slave, he was visibly aghast to realize that this gaggle of one-roomed Celtic huts and storehouses was mine. I could almost hear him thinking, 'And you a duumvir!'

He was saved the necessity of venturing inside my enclosure, though, because Minimus (who had clearly been watching for me to arrive) came running out to greet me with a smile. I was ready to invite our visitor to a snack of salted peas (any self-respecting citizen would offer refreshment to a borrowed slave) but Lentigines took one quick look at the three-fold picket fence, the straggling geese and chickens pecking round the path, and the cooking-smoke arising through my humble reed-thatched roof – and babbled an excuse. He thrust my toga at me and ran quickly off.

'How is your mistress now, Minimus?' I said – quickly, to preclude remark – as we hurried past the dye-hut towards the roundhouse door.

The slave-boy adopted a serious tone, at once. 'Sleeping, master, I am glad to say. Mistress Cilla brought a jug of poppy juice that she had made herself, gave her a draught of it, and now is keeping watch.'

'Good of her,' I murmured. 'She has babes at home.'

'She has left them with their slave, and been here almost ever since you left. Between us we have changed the dressing more than once, and she managed everything so that the mistress did not have to move at all. She even brought a pot of stew with her, and there is some left for you.'

Bizarrely, after having had no appetite for Marcus's fine treats, I found that I was hungry suddenly – and very tired. Inside the roundhouse, things were as the slave had said. Cilla was stirring something splendid-smelling on the fire, and my wife was lying on the blankets, deep asleep – though I was disturbed to see Tenuis crouched beside the bed, fanning her face with a little fan of woven leaves.

'Still feverish?' I asked, bundling my best toga onto the wall-shelf I had made.

Cilla was reassuring. 'Much cooler now – although the fan's still comforting. You and Kurso saved her life, I think.'

Kurso, who had been shelling hazelnuts on the floor nearby, was already on his feet. He went pink with pleasure at this praise and pulled up a stool for me beside the fire.

'Goat's meat and turnip stew,' my daughter-in-law announced, ladling some into a bowl for me. 'There should be plenty for today and even some to spare. But now, since you are home and Kurso seems to have finished with those nuts, I'll take them home and grind them for some bread. I'll bring a loaf tomorrow, when I call again.'

I tried to thank her, but she waved my words away and was already pulling on her cloak of homespun plaid. 'You know that my husband looked in, earlier? He left early from the games and was coming to report. Apparently there was a

disturbance at the start. Old Tertillius thought he had been
asked to drop the handkerchief, but when he stood up to do
so, he was pushed aside by some visiting senator from Rome,
who insisted that it was his right. Did not even wait to be
announced – which might have given Tertillius a role and so
placated him a bit – just laughed at him, and made him look
a fool. The man was not here on official business, either, Junio
says. It appears he simply turned up at the fort a day or two
ago.'

I nodded an agreement that I did not feel. 'So I heard. But
a relative of the Governor, apparently. One might guess that
he would think it was his place to give the signal.'

'Well, he certainly offended poor Tertillius. Humiliated in
front of all the elders of the town – to say nothing of the
sniggering electorate as well! He went off swearing he would
have revenge and muttering about having a curse tablet nailed
up at the shrine. And he was not the only one upset. The visitor
offended almost everybody there by continually signalling that
all losers be despatched.'

'Really?' I was genuinely shocked. Fights in Glevum are
rarely to the death. Though I knew that various recent Emperors
(Commodus in particular) relished such events, so perhaps the
custom was more commonplace in Rome. 'That won't please
Marcus very much,' I added. 'He was sponsoring the games.
Trained gladiators are expensive things, and no doubt he'll be
responsible for replacing those that die.'

Cilla made a face. 'Poor Marcus. Junio thought it was
discourteous, as well, both to the sponsor and also the town,
because it suggested the visitor was not pleased with the
display. And everyone was grumbling, apparently, because
there was no recognition of agility or skill. However hard
the people cheered a valiant defence, the outcome was the
same – and often the winner of one fight was loser in
the next. No justice, Junio said – so at the earliest opportunity
he slipped away himself. He was expecting to find you here,
of course – since you'd left him the mule. Said you'd planned
to take a litter.'

I recognized the question which she had not liked to ask.
'Marcus offered me transport in his gig, but he took me to the

villa first. I was delayed because we found that the lady Julia had – rather unexpectedly – given birth to twins while he was out.'

Cilla paused in the act of fastening her cloak to echo, with a grin, 'Twins? He will not be entirely delighted with that, either, I suppose – since it is likely to cause him even more expense.'

There was more than money to worry Marcus now. Hortius Valens did not seem to care whom he upset. If he was really as imperious and high-handed as he seemed, my patron had reason to be actively alarmed – and I began to feel some sympathy for the reluctant bride.

Cilla was still chattering on, as usual. 'Now that you're here, Father, I will take my leave. The children are of an age where they need watching all the time, though Junio's there now and he is good with them, and I have chores to do – including nuts to grind. If Mother wakes, try to get her to eat a little if you can – earlier she could not stomach anything.' She embraced me – which was not usual at all – and a moment later she was gone.

In the ensuing silence, I set about my stew. 'You and Mistress Cilla used up all that poultice, then?' I said to Kurso when I had polished clean my plate. 'I see that it has gone. I hope it soothed the wound?'

'It seemed to, master, though there's a little left, in case we need some more.'

I looked about for it, but Minimus chimed in, 'We put it in the dye-house, with the potion for the rats. Mistress Cilla says we'll have to purify the pot – put it in the stream or something before it's used again – or it will make us very ill.'

'We'll cleanse it carefully, before it's used again. But there's no hurry about that. Cilla will be cooking for us for a day or two. Which reminds me, I should have sent a message home with her, to ask Junio to mind the workshop tomorrow. It's the day before the Ides so there's no curia to attend, and I'll be staying home to see your mistress gets some rest, You can take a message to him later, if he does not call again – though I expect he will, if only to tell me all about the birthday games.'

If he did, I did not see him come. I was so exhausted by

the stress and worry of the day, that – while Kurso cleared away – I permitted Minimus to undo my sandal straps and lay down on the blankets by my wife. My original intention was to take over from Tenuis with the fan, but in that I fear I failed, and it was well after dawn before I shook myself, guiltily, awake.

Fortunately, my help had not been missed. Cilla had been better than her word and the household was already busy about its morning chores – fetching reeds and water, sweeping floors and chopping wood. The air was full of the scent of fresh nut-loaf and there to my delight, was Gwellia herself, sitting by the fire, wrapped up in an ancient shawl and nibbling at a slice of the new bread. She saw me stirring and flashed me a shaky smile – there was even a trace of colour in her cheeks.

'You are waking, husband? I am better, as you see. I'm sure I could manage, if you wished to go—'

I shook my head. 'Not while I am here to help!' I said. 'Junio can cope . . .'

'And has already left for town!' I turned to find Cilla herself, standing at the door. She grinned at my surprise at seeing her. 'But now that you are waking, Father, I will leave this house to you and get back to managing my own. Call me if you want me, you know where I am. I'll come back later with some broth in any case. Enjoy your nut-bread!'

It was my intention to employ the day doing little tasks around the house: the slave-hut roof had sprung a leak, and I began with that – though I broke off from my thatching now and then to ensure that Gwellia was not attempting to get up and work. She tried, of course, but – though Tenuis was assisting me – the other slaves were able to report and in the end she reluctantly agreed a compromise. She would sit down on the bedding and spin some wool she'd dyed, a task which she enjoyed – though not without complaining that there was insufficient drop to make the spindle work efficiently!

I had almost finished thatching when the interruption came – it must have been a little after noon, judging by the angle of the watery April sun. I was on my homemade ladder tying in the final straws, when I heard a scuffle at the foot of it and Minimus saying, 'Master, a messenger for you!'

I frowned down at him. 'Messenger?' I had been so engrossed in my task that I had not noticed anyone come in through the gate.

Minimus looked up, nodding. 'From the lady Julia. She says that it is private, so she has written it.'

It must be something of importance then. Julia did not write without a cause – especially when she was already in diminished health. She could read fluently enough, but her script and spelling very clearly showed that her education had (like most other Roman girls) placed more emphasis on comportment and household management than on literary skills. She was rather charmingly embarrassed by this fact and never attempted a written message where a spoken one would do.

I wiped my sticky fingers on my tunic to get the straw strands off, then backed down my homemade ladder as quickly as I could. 'You've no idea what the message is about?'

'Only that she obviously hopes that you will come,' Minimus said as he helped me to the ground. 'The pageboy says he was told to wait for you – and only you will do.' He jerked his head towards the roundhouse and added with a grin, 'He's in there now, though he's clearly ill at ease.'

I took the rag that he was proffering and tried to improve the condition of my hands, but I was still adorned with adhering wisps of thatch. I only hoped the courier wasn't Lentigines, or I would lose whatever dignity I still retained with him.

But it was Freckle-face of course, resplendent in his scarlet uniform, and looking as out of place in my smoky roundhouse as he obviously felt. He had entered – just (it would have been discourteous to do otherwise) – but had stationed himself immediately inside the door, as near to the outside world as possible. I had to pass him to get in at all, and I saw his eyes widen in disbelief when he caught sight of me.

His bow, however, was exemplary. 'Greetings from my mistress, duumvir. She has written you a note.' He produced with a flourish, from underneath his cloak, one of Julia's distinctive writing-blocks. 'My master's gone to Glevum, at your suggestion, I believe, and my mistress says that therefore she hopes you can assist.' He handed me the message, gingerly, as though he feared contamination from my work-stained hands.

I wiped my fingers on my tunic skirts again before I attempted to undo the cords, which Julia – lacking a signet ring and wax – had tied very tightly in a complicated knot.

'I hope there's been no complication with her health,' my wife remarked, as my large hands struggled with the tie to free an end. 'Two children at one time must put a strain on anyone. As soon as I am able, I must go and visit her – there is a strengthening mixture I could take, which she would appreciate.' She caught my glance, and added, doggedly, 'When she had the last child she was glad of it, she said.'

'Then I will see that it is sent to her,' I said, more severely than I'd meant. 'She'd be appalled if she thought you felt obliged to go, when you are injured as you are.' I'd managed to get the knot undone by now and released the writing-block. The note was scratched in Julia's inimitable style.

> To Libertus greeting. Kindly come at once. Unexpected visit from Roman personage, very self-important, demanding interview. Marcus not here your advice and I must stay in bed. Need somebody of rank but just can think of you. Marcus says trust no one. Important be discreet. Sorry at inconvenient.

'Not her health,' I said to Gwellia. 'But I will have to go, I think.' I turned back to the slave. 'Lentigines, run and tell your mistress I am on my way.'

My wife was looking troubled as we watched him go. 'What trouble, husband?'

'It seems she's had a visit from that obnoxious man that Cilla was telling us about,' I said. 'The Governor's relative. At the villa now, it seems. He was threatening to come – though I thought we'd managed to prevent that yesterday.'

'Threatening? But surely a visit would be a compliment?' Her puzzled look reminded me that this was news to her. She'd been asleep when I came home – and today I'd been preoccupied with getting her to rest.

I tried to make amends. 'There is a problem. He has come

from Rome because his bride has run away and—' I broke off, realizing that my slaves were goggling and this was not a matter to be publicly discussed. 'It's a complicated tale. I'll explain when I get back. Now, I cannot keep him waiting – he is a senator. But if I am to meet him, Minimus had better help me wash and change; I suppose I'll have to put my curial toga on again. It's the only one that I have got at home – and it may impress him more than one without a stripe. The plain one's at the fuller's anyway.'

NINE

Not half an hour later I was at the villa door, cleansed of mud and straw and dressed in my toga – having been hastily pinned into it in the gatekeeper's small room by Minimus, who had escorted me. Lentigines was awaiting us in the vestibule.

'You are expected, Councillor,' he said, as I tried to look as curial as possible. But – to my surprise – instead of going ahead to announce me formally, he ushered me straight into the atrium. Faintly alarming, since senators are famous sticklers for social niceties! And Minimus was not whisked away to kick his heels in the servants' waiting-room, but was permitted to accompany me.

We were greeted, not by the Senator at all, but by the midwife and the chief steward of the house (a lofty slave in Grecian dress whom I had met before, and had always treated me with a sort of condescending courtesy – marking me as a guest of Marcus's, but not otherwise entitled to respect).

Today, however, he rushed across to shake me by the arm, in Roman style, as though I were a friend – then blushed in horror at his own lapse of protocol. 'Forgive me, Councillor, I forget my place. But we're sincerely glad to see you. About this visitation – I believe that you have heard? Without the master here, we don't know what to do.'

I glanced around. 'Where is he?' I would have expected

that the Senator would be here, if anywhere. The atrium was the normal place for visitors to wait – although Hortius Valens seemed to be a man who ignored polite convention and did exactly as he pleased. Perhaps he had chosen to walk around the grounds. Even he, surely, would not call on Julia in bed? He seemed to have agitated everyone enough for even that to be a possibility.

'Gone to Glevum, citizen, as I thought you knew?' That was the midwife, sounding as puzzled as I felt. 'That is why we have this problem with Julia's relative.'

I realized then that I had been misled. Grammatically so. Julia's note had spoken of a 'personage'. I had registered the careful choice of word. (*Persona* also means an actor's mask, so it carries suggestions of strutting self-regard – and pretended dignity, since actors are socially the lowest of the low. But they are also – in Glevum anyway – generally male. Yet the Latin noun is feminine, of course. As – in this case, clearly – was the 'personage'.)

'So it is Druscilla Livia who has arrived today?'

'There!' The steward looked triumphant. 'I told you he would know.' He turned to me. 'The mistress says she's never heard of her. But she claims to be some sort of distant relative, throwing herself upon the master's potestas – and furthermore swears he should be aware of her.'

'He is,' I answered, surprised that the household did not seem to be. 'He received a letter from her yesterday, but obviously other things have intervened. He intends, I believe, that she should be accommodated here, but – for the meantime – purely as a guest. He is yet not offering the protection of his name.'

'And why would that be, citizen?' The voice came from the doorway. This was clearly Druscilla Livia herself, though she was nothing like the picture that my mind had drawn of her.

I had expected a dowdy widow of uncertain years, but this woman was quite young – perhaps no more than twenty years of age, though I'm no judge of such affairs. She was certainly much younger than either her exploits or her reputation had led me to believe, and clearly also a person of some wealth, which – like her other assets – she seemed inclined to flaunt.

Her tunic and stola, in a brighter blue than befitted widow-hood, were trimmed with jet and silver at the hem, and girdled with a silver silken sash which showed off her figure in a not-quite-seemly way. She did wear the modest veil that propriety demands of Roman matrons – especially in the presence of unrelated men – but it was thrown back across her plaited hair to reveal a pair of indignant, flashing eyes, a determined Roman nose and a mouth that was set in a resentful moue.

'Druscilla Livia?' I sketched a curial bow. 'Welcome to Glevum – or to the surrounding district, anyway.'

She fixed the angry, tawny eyes on me. 'And what a dismal place it is! I am surprised my kinswoman can endure the place. So cold and wet and muddy – and hardly a household comfort to speak of anywhere!'

I was just wondering how Marcus would react to such a description of his home – quite the most splendid in the area – but she had not finished yet . . .

'And such a neighbourhood! I saw a clutch of native dwellings down the lane – they must be Julia's nearest neighbours. I will speak to her. Surely it is possible to have them moved? I hear you are a duumvir, could you not see to it?'

I was tempted to tell her that it was my own abode, but it was clear that this would simply have destroyed whatever authority I might have with her. So I simply bowed (though, behind me, I could sense that Minimus was bristling). 'After Rome,' I murmured suavely, 'I imagine any province might seem rather dull.'

'Dull? If I were not in danger, I think I'd rather die – though, I suppose, it will have to be endured. And this husband of Julia's must be forced to change his mind. You seem to know him – send to him and tell him he must take me under his protection, instantly. And does he not have a townhouse, where I could at least enjoy the public baths – and whatever entertainment this god-forsaken province might provide?'

'I will see that he is apprised of your arrival, lady, and meanwhile you have the protection which a host affords a guest. What more he may choose to offer is not for me to guess – still less to command.'

Or you either, if you have any sense, I thought. Marcus does not relish being told what he 'must' do – though it would serve her right if he took her to his flat, with Hortius staying there! But it was not my place to tell her about that. Julia had requested that I be discreet.

Instead, I gave a deprecating laugh, and proffered as much of a warning as I dared. 'If I gave orders to His Excellency, it would probably produce the opposite effect. He does not have a townhouse in Glevum, anyway – just a flat above a wine shop, which might not be agreeable for you – and there he already has a guest. He has a townhouse in Corinium – a half-day's ride from here – but as that was let, quite recently, it's not available.'

She tossed her dark braids in a gesture of contempt. 'Then I don't know why you've been sent for, or what use you are to me – although Julia refuses to speak to me herself. I don't believe she realizes how desperate things are. I only asked to be admitted to her room for half a beat – after I had travelled half the Empire to arrive – but no doubt she was too interested in those babes of hers to take any notice of my predicament. I would exhaust her, so the midwife said.'

I could imagine that. She was exhausting me. I was surprised that Hortius was so keen to marry her – Romans tend to like their women meek and biddable. 'You lost a husband recently, I think?' I said, wondering how that unfortunate had fared.

She tossed her head again. 'Poor Lucius? Indeed. Too weak and useless to do anything for years – but then he must start plotting and get himself run through, supporting Pescennius Niger's claim to be the Emperor! Absolutely foolish – though he was fond of me. And I of him, in a peculiar way. Certainly, I could generally manage him, by stealth – until that one last reckless enterprise. Hortius Valens is an altogether different sort of man. But even he – I hope – will never find me here. At least till Marcus has adopted me, when it will be too late.'

What would she do, I wondered, if she discovered the grim truth – that Hortius Valens was already here and seeking her? Rush in to Julia, ranting and demanding to be heard – disturbing the poor woman in her bed? Exactly what I had been brought here to avoid! And Druscilla Livia was unpredictable – her actions up to now were proof of that. So I chose my words with care,

'And if Hortius found you earlier than that? Could you not fight the matter in the courts – if Marcus would provide you with a spokesman-advocate?'

Though of course I realized that it was not possible. Tertillius had said so, and he was clearly right. A senator is a senator, and no magistrate with any sense would find against him in a marriage case, anywhere within the Empire – as clearly Druscilla recognized, because she shook her head.

But I was not prepared for how she answered me. She looked at me, boldly – as no well-bred matron should – fully in the face with those gold-brown flashing eyes. 'In that case, Councillor, I would sooner kill myself.'

It was tempting to retort that, since there were so many things that she would rather die than do, perhaps she had better consider doing that – but wiser counsel held. This woman was a guest of Julia's and I'd been called upon to help. 'Surely, madam, there are other ways—?'

I had spoken as suavely as I could, but she interrupted me. 'Meaning that perhaps I would do better to kill him?' I was about to protest that I had not meant that at all, but she gave a bitter laugh. 'Preferable, perhaps, and for a man it might be possible, but where would a woman find the opportunity? Though don't suppose I could not kill myself. I have the wherewithal. I took the precaution of bringing it from Rome – and I am resolved to drink it, too, if he does catch up with me and there is no other way. Perhaps then my brother will be sorry, too – it will not please him if the rumour spreads that he has driven me to suicide. And I've left a letter with a friend, only to be opened if I die of poisoning – so I can be certain that the story would be circulated round the capitol.'

'Then I hope for your sake, madam,' I said soberly, 'that you have done the near-impossible and found a draught that's not too terrible to taste – one that will not burn your throat and cause you bulging eyes, and bring on agonized convulsions as you die?'

I was hoping to sober her with reality, but she cut me off, again. 'Well, this one qualifies, or so I am assured. It's made

from aconite, I understand – growing monkshood has been
banned in Rome, but at a price one can buy anything – and
it's guaranteed to take effect at once.'

'Not instant,' I observed. Gwellia keeps something similar
to poison rats.

'But very fast, and I can vouch for that. I tried it on a s . . .'
She saw my face and stopped.

'A slave?' I was certain that was what she'd been about to
say, and I could not keep the icy censure from my voice. Apart
from my own feelings – as an ex-slave myself – I am reasonably sure that even in Rome, the city of excess, such experiments
are illegal, nowadays – unless one is the Emperor, of course.
Even Minimus gave a little squeal, which he hastily suppressed,
and I sensed the steward stiffening with shock.

'A dog,' she countered. 'A starving dog that I found whining
in the street, I was about to say.' She flashed me a pert smile.
'I'm not entirely a fool.'

'Meaning that I must accept your explanation?' I enquired.

'Meaning that I would not simply take the draught, untried
– and the wretched creature would have died in any case. I
did it a service, almost, because it died – without a whimper
– shortly after eating what I put out for it. And in the meantime, at least it had a meal.' She gave me that defiant smile
again. 'So, perhaps you'll now believe that I am serious. And
since I'm forced to stay here in this house – as it seems I
must, for now at any rate – perhaps I could be taken to my
rooms. Unless you have any other questions, Councillor? My
handmaid is waiting somewhere with my luggage, I believe?'

The steward threw an anguished glance at me. 'There is a
woman with her, with a lot of sacking bags. Do you suppose
the master would allow . . . ?'

'I am absolutely certain that is what he planned. The guest
apartments, I am sure. If he were here he'd no doubt tell you
so, himself.'

'Thank you, Councillor, you have put my mind at rest.' The
steward bowed and led Druscilla off while Freckle-face was
dispatched to fetch the maidservant. I saw her from the inner
door a moment afterwards, hurrying after her mistress down
the court: an ancient woman with wispy hair, bowed under

the weight of an enormous sack. Druscilla did not so much as glance at her, but simply harangued the steward all the way.

'Thank you, duumvir, I'll report to Julia. It is time that I tended her in any case. The babes will want their wash.' The midwife dipped her dimpled knees at me, folded her plump arms to hoist up her ample chest and strode off in the direction of the eastern wing.

I turned to Freckle-face who had returned to see me out. 'Of course, his Excellence must be informed,' I said. 'See that the steward sends to him, at once. A spoken message, not a written one, lest Hortius somehow manages to lay hands on it. I presume the house can find a slave-boy who can ride?'

Freckle-face beamed triumphantly at me. 'I could do it, Councillor. Very quickly, if I leave at once.'

'Very well. Though, perhaps, on second thoughts it would be better for us all if the messenger did not appear to come from here. The servants at the flat would be sure to recognize you – and the Se . . .' I checked myself. 'Marcus's guest might want to know what it contained. Better, perhaps, to take it to my town apartment first – almost anyone will tell you where it is – and have my slave Rastus take the message round on foot. Tell him to say simply that it came from me, and it is for Marcus and for no one else. The message is that the expected consignment has arrived – and I await instruction as to what to do with it. That should not raise questions with the visitor, but will give a private signal to His Excellence. Stress to Rastus the need to be discreet.'

'I will do that, citizen. And I have the words by heart,' He repeated them to me then went off, scurrying – leaving me alone with Minimus.

'Have we finished, master?'

'I believe we have.'

Though really the problems had only just begun, I told myself, as Minimus and I walked – unaccompanied – to the gate. For what had I achieved? I had answered the steward truthfully enough – and kept secret about Hortius as I'd been advised – but I couldn't help wondering whether Marcus would be pleased. It is one thing to offer sanctuary to a distant relative, taking pity on a matron in distress – quite another to unwittingly admit an untamed young lioness to your family home. And what trouble lay in store when Hortius heard of it?

If only that had been the worst we had to fear!

TEN

I paused at the gatehouse once again, to strip off my toga and so speed my journey home, but even as I did so I heard the sound of hooves and looked out to see a beaming Freckle-face gallop off, proud of his new role of courier. He was quickly out of sight but on my journey I was much delayed, first by a farmer with a wayward flock of sheep and then by a group of soldiers on foraging fatigues, who took up all the road, and whose marching ranks and lumbering cart took precedence. By the time I got back to my house the day was well advanced.

I was still hoping to complete my thatching before dark – there was a patch on the dye-house that needed some repair – but I was aware that Gwellia would be keen to be allowed to move around and try a little light activity. In that case, I thought, indulgently, I would please her by permitting some undemanding task – some actual weaving, perhaps – and would stay inside myself to keep a watchful eye.

She was ahead of me. I found her, not merely already on her feet, but actively attempting to rewarm a pot of stew that Cilla must have brought while I was out. Nor was my wife the least abashed at my rebuke.

'But I knew that you'd be hungry, husband. You've not eaten since that nut-bread shortly after dawn! And do not blame the slave-boys,' she added, putting herself in front of Tenuis, as though to screen him from my wrath. 'I know you left instructions, but they are not at fault. I am their mistress, and they were obeying me. I am feeling better by the hour and – as I said to them – if I'm to restore myself to health and strength I must try to do a little when I can. And don't frown at me like that! I do have some understanding about cures.'

Tenuis and Kurso were both cowering by now, but only Tenuis was brave enough to speak. 'We did try to tell her master, but . . .' He gave a helpless shrug. 'The mistress insisted. She said she would make matters right with you when you came home.'

Which she obviously felt that she had done – at the same time undermining my authority. In my own household too! Now what was I to do? If I chastised the slave-boys it would be unfair. They had been given conflicting orders, hers and mine, so only one of us could be obeyed. And Gwellia, by her forceful presence and rational argument, had seen to it that I was the person disobliged. Furthermore, it was quite deliberate – relying on my usual tolerance.

I was unreasonably angry – perhaps because of the pressures of the day. Yet there was nobody on whom my fury could rationally be turned. Gwellia was unwell – and everyone knows that a person's judgement can be affected by poison in the blood. Yet the boys were not to blame. I felt like a gladiator backed against the gates, outmanoeuvred and deprived of sword and shield. Well, I would show them that I was not to be ignored.

I don't beat slaves, or wives, but I picked up my walking staff. Everybody stiffened with alarm as I raised it fiercely high. Then I brought it down across the nearby stool with such a force that I almost shattered both, and was perversely gratified to see that the faces round me had all paled with shock.

'Well, now I'm home,' I barked, 'and I give orders here. Wife, get yourself to bed, if you cannot sit in peace. Tenuis, you can help her, and Kurso stir the stew. Minimus, put those wretched robes away, and then I'll sit and eat. The rest of you can do so afterwards.' This was not the general custom of the house: our slaves are generally free to eat as soon as we are served. They looked so chagrined I began to feel ashamed. However, I could not admit to that, so I added stiffly, 'I will forgo the further thatching I had planned, and oversee the evening chores, tonight. Clearly my household can't be trusted unless I supervise.'

All this was not like me and a silence fell, which even

Gwellia did not dare to break. Indeed, she did as instructed and meekly went to bed, where I was relieved to see that she was very soon asleep – thus removing the necessity of an apology (and rather improving my sense of being justified – showing that she had overtired herself).

Meanwhile, Kurso, having ladled out my soup, obediently removed the remainder from the fire and went glumly out to feed the animals and shoo the poultry under cover for the night – visibly glad of an opportunity to leave. He was hardly gone a moment, though, before hurrying back again.

'Master, there is a horseman at the gate. A message for you – very urgent, so the courier declares – and to be trusted only to yourself. He begs your indulgence, but he will not come inside – he has to gallop back to town tonight and it is already starting to be dusk.' Kurso was so fearful in his telling of this tale that I felt guilty for my previous forcefulness.

I tried to reassure him by ruffling his hair, but as I raised my hand he ducked instinctively aside, as if to dodge a blow – as he used to do, when he had first arrived. I felt every inch a bully, as I rose to follow him.

'What sort of courier is this, to call at this late hour? It can't be someone wanting to discuss a licence for the drains! A message from His Excellency, perhaps?'

I was irritated and muttering mostly to myself, but Kurso took it as an instruction to explain. He looked up nervously. 'Master, I did not recognize the man, but he seems to be a private slave – I saw the slave-disc round his neck. Clearly belonging to a wealthy man. There is a crest embroidered on his cloak, and both it and his tunic are of scarlet cloth.'

'Ah!' That was a description that I recognized – the rider who had so rudely rushed past myself and Marcus in the gig had been wearing exactly such a uniform. 'And obviously he feels that he's important, too, since he demands that I must go to him! But nonetheless, he'll have to wait for me to get my cloak.' I paused at the dye-house to retrieve the big plaid one I'd hung in there to dry. 'And you need not be impatient,' I went on, as I wrapped it round me and set off slowly down the path. 'I am too old to run at the command of passing messengers!'

I meant to be sardonic but Kurso took this, again, as a complaint against himself.

'Master, I am truly sorry that you've been disturbed, but that is all the message he would give. I don't think he believed that he has come to the right place – even when I assured him that I was your slave. He kept saying that his errand was with a duumvir, and he could not credit . . .' He tailed in dismay.

'That one lived in such a place?' This time I did achieve an ironic tone. 'Then he's not the only one – others have indicated much the same today.' We were well along the path towards the gate by now, but I paused to murmur, in a jesting voice, 'But if this person is who I think he is, then he's the servant of that visiting Roman senator, and he was just as scathing about my patron's house. Made rude remarks and couldn't wait to get away.'

I did not normally confide such gossip to my kitchen-slave and Kurso recognized it as a signal that I was no longer cross. 'The messenger is rather like his master, then?' he whispered back, at the same time flashing me a nervous grin. 'He's been upsetting everyone that breathes – from what the lady Cilla says, at least.'

'So perhaps he's now upset the horse?' I joked. 'And is afraid that if he does dismount the animal will bolt and leave him stranded out here in the dark?'

I was murmuring this nonsense to make young Kurso smile, but only as we neared the palisade did I realize quite how nonsensical it was. No man could have been more clearly in control of any animal than the courier sitting all but motion-less awaiting me – quite a contrast from the last time I'd seen him, galloping down this very lane as if the hound of Hades were snapping at his heels. However, it was very clearly the same man, who had insulted Marcus (and myself) before, by just ignoring us.

But this time as I came out through the gate he did acknow-ledge me. He did not speak or move a muscle in his face, but raised one hand in languid greeting, while with the other he continued to control his uneasy steed, with effortless assur-ance. Impressive, as it was almost certainly an unfamiliar horse – borrowed from the garrison perhaps. It was clearly not the one which he'd been riding yesterday – that had been a much larger black one, doubtless still being rested after that long and frenzied dash.

I raised my eyes to meet his dark ones, hard and piercing as a pair of javelins. 'You are looking for the Duumvir Libertus, I believe?'

'Indeed. Do I have the honour of addressing him?' The voice was cool and cultured, with the crisp accents of educated Rome (suggesting that this was a very costly slave indeed). There was just sufficient stress on 'honour' to impart the merest touch of irony, as his eyes flicked across my Celtic clothing and enclosure with contempt. 'I was expecting . . .' He let the words tail off.

Nettled, I returned his scrutiny as coolly as I dared, given who had sent him. He was tall and bronzed and muscular – and hairy, too, though the thick light-brown curls had been fiercely trimmed to just above his ears. He might have been handsome, in a haughty sort of way, but his cheeks had been barbered fairly recently – there were fresh scrape marks where the sharpened blade had caught the skin – and there was already a shadow of fast-returning beard. Yet the ministrations of the *tonsor* did not extend elsewhere. His chin and upper lip both sported tawny growth, and beneath the ties of that flamboyant cloak, a mist of fine and curly hairs sprouted from the gap. The backs of his hands, the arms beneath the leather arm-guards and all that could be seen of legs and feet were furred with the same gold.

I wondered if it was a fashion to keep hairy slaves like this in Rome – perhaps to make them look more aggressively masculine. Most owners in Britannia would have had that body hair removed – singed, scraped or tweezered, like their own – giving their courier a more polished look.

He'd begun to shift a little under my inspection, now, and I decided that I'd kept him waiting long enough. 'I am Longinus Flavius Libertus,' I said, stressing the dignity of my full three Latin names. 'A freeborn Celtic nobleman, now Roman citizen and duly elected member of the Glevum curia. So, I am indeed the duumvir. You find me at my country residence.' I gestured to the roundhouse. 'You have a message for me?'

At this he slithered smoothly from his mount and – without relinquishing the reins – afforded me a bow. 'Indeed so, Councillor. From my master, Hortius Valens, Senator of Rome. I am Dasypyges, his courier. Could we speak alone? He was adamant that this should be for no one else's ears.' He jerked his chin at Kurso as he spoke.

Greek then, judging from the name, and therefore even more expensive than I had supposed! I was about to retort that my slave was trustworthy and that anything that could be said to me would be quite safe with him, but then I remembered that my patron's secret might be involved in this. Kurso had anyway backed obediently away, to loiter out of earshot just inside the gate, so I demanded brusquely, 'Well?'

The dark eyes faltered slightly. 'The truth is, Councillor, something rather unfortunate has occurred. I fear that there has been an accident.'

'Accident?' That was the last thing I'd expected, and it shocked me into being indiscreet. 'Not to your master? No one could possibly have pois . . .!' I tailed off in horror, but the word was almost out – like a sling-stone from a sling – before I managed to correct myself. 'No one could possibly have predicted that. And it must be serious, to bring you in search of me at this late hour of day.'

It was a clumsy effort to cover my mistake. My first horrified reaction had been, of course, to think that Druscilla had somehow succeeded in her threat – and at Marcus's town apartment, too – with who-knows-what dreadful consequences for us all. And messengers are trained to listen and memorize each word. I looked at the elegant horseman in alarm.

But it seemed he had not noticed anything amiss. There was a look of blank astonishment on the arrogant young face. 'An accident to my master? Naturally not! He's far too well guarded, even by the gods. What gives you such a notion? And why, in that case, would he think to send to you?'

A reasonable question – though a presumptuous thing for a slave to ask a duumvir. But Dasypyges was likely to report my every word and how in Dis was I to answer him? There were so many things that I was not supposed to know – and for Marcus's sake I must be careful, or I would betray his trust! I had already almost made a bad mistake.

I tried to think it through. It was obviously important to disguise from Hortius that his lady had arrived and was staying at the villa even as we spoke! Marcus, presumably, would know of that by now. That message that I'd sent to town with Freckle-face had been designed to apprise him of events, while concealing them from everybody else. But I'd distanced myself from it as far as possible. So why had Hortius sent a messenger to me?

I glanced towards Dasypyges, but he said no more, simply stood waiting for me to reply.

I took a long deep breath. At least my worst fears were unfounded, it appeared. There'd been no accident to the wretched Senator! So I decided to mutter something about supposing that – if Hortius had sustained a fall on civic property – Marcus might have suggested sending out for me, in my capacity as duumvir. But I only got as far as, 'Did Marcus Septimus . . .?' when I tailed off – aware that I had almost made the same mistake again. Why, if I were not his special confidant, should Marcus single me out – when there were other councillors more conveniently close? Many of them had fine houses in the town (including my fellow duumvir, in fact) and very rarely slept elsewhere.

But the courier was saying, in his smoothest tone, 'I fear not, Councillor. His Excellence was not involved in this – he was absent at the time, arranging for some special family sacrifice to Jove. Indeed, my master would be obligated if this matter could be peaceably resolved without reference to Marcus Septimus at all. It is a mere commercial matter – concerning property. A slave called with a message – and he was yours, I think?'

The way that he phrased this, and the tone of voice he used, were different and far more polished, suddenly. It occurred to me (as it should have done before) that what I was now hearing was not a mere report, but the exact words which his master had chosen to dictate. (It is a skill to which all messengers aspire, and this one was demonstrating that he was good at it.)

I swallowed hard. I must be careful here. In the message which I had indirectly sent, I'd talked of a 'consignment' – deliberately suggesting a commercial one. I had even thought it rather clever at the time. It was intended for Marcus, but Marcus wasn't there – and I could hardly pretend to total ignorance. Had Hortius Valens worked out what that 'consignment' really was? And if so, what was the consequence for me?

I thought quickly. 'I have slaves, certainly – and one may have brought a message, I suppose – asking His Excellence for his advice, perhaps? Since I was not myself in Glevum at the time.'

'So I am told. Unlike most of the other councillors, I understand that you did not attend the games?'

Was that it, I wondered? Was I merely being warned that my absence had been marked, or did the Senator suppose that I'd not been at the birthday rites themselves? That, of course, was a serious offence. I essayed a little smile.

'I left immediately after the temple sacrifice. I was part of the procession – you might have seen me with a Fulvial hoop.' (He could not have done, of course, he was riding to and from the villa at the time – but I wanted to pretend that I was not aware of that!) 'Unfortunately, I could not linger to enjoy the spectacle. My wife is suffering from a badly poisoned foot. I hurried home because I feared there was some danger to her life and for the same reason I have not returned to town today.'

Dasypyges said nothing. No conventional remark of sympathy, but equally no mention of a senatorial fine for non-attendance at the games – nor even a bribe to avoid attracting one. I saw from the blank expression that I had not hit upon the reason for this visit yet. Then I remembered. 'An accident, you said?' Perhaps this was not about me, after all.

His face cleared and he nodded. 'A trifling matter, really, and easily resolved. But I understand some compensation may be due – supposing that the slave was yours, in fact.'

'Ah!' I understood now, or I thought I did. My clumsy messenger had managed to damage or destroy something of value of the Senator's (a travelling shrine, perhaps?) and I, as his master, was required to pay for it. Or something of

Marcus's, more likely, which the Senator had been investigating while his host was out – which would explain why this was to be 'peaceably resolved' without reference to His Excellence.

However, I was hardly in a position to object. 'What happened? He did some serious damage, I assume?'

A grave nod. 'It appears so. He knocked a marble table when he tripped and fell.'

I sighed. I could guess, now, what this related to. There were only two marble tables in the flat, on either side of the entrance vestibule – where, of course, a messenger would wait. Each held a large and handsome onyx vase, with surface carvings of such quality that I've noticed wealthy visitors surreptitiously examining them before. Either vase would cost a fortune to replace. Yet on the polished surface they would be easy to dislodge – especially if one was interrupted while inspecting them. Though naturally the Senator could not have been to blame – responsibility would lie entirely at my servant's door! I gave another sigh. 'Are we speaking of a large amount?'

The courier made a doubtful face. 'I don't know what the replacement cost would be, here in Britannia, though my master is investigating, as we speak. In any case, it was not deliberate – no doubt your servant's feet were slippery.'

That was magnanimous, at least, I thought – there are schedules of fines for damaged property, the size of which may vary according to intent (three times the value was otherwise the norm). Even so, this was likely to be a large expense, which I could ill afford, even in my new role as duumvir (which did – surprisingly – attract its own rewards, as traders positively vied to shower samples of their goods on you). But those vases were another class of thing.

I might have to approach the dreaded money-lenders for a loan – though, at least as a member of the curia, they were unlikely to charge me their full illegal rates. Or – better – I might apply to Marcus privately, to forgive me a little of the cost. Discreetly, of course, and after the Senator had gone.

I brightened. 'I could see how it could happen, especially with winter hobnails in his soles.' I said, still hoping to mitigate the cost. 'The streets of Glevum can play havoc with wet shoes.' That was true enough: the rims of military chariots carve ooze-filled ruts into the paving stones, and the pavement near my patron's flat was sticky with lime-ash at the moment from nearby building work. (Not to mention the usual lumps of rotting vegetables and animal manure around the market-place, and stinking, slippery household middens down every alleyway.) 'And His Excellence's floors are always polished to a treacherous shine.'

The courier acknowledged this with a sardonic smile. 'Indeed. Your servant simply slipped.'

'You are sure that he is mine?'

'We believe so, Councillor. Youngish, skinny, tawny hair. Protruding ears and teeth?'

Rastus, clearly. 'That sounds like one of ours. But did he not identify himself – before he gave his message?' I was suddenly alarmed.

'He would not give his message, duumvir. That was what caused the fall. He defied my master – refused to speak to anyone but Marcus Septimus – so my owner struck him, and he fell and hit his head.'

'Great Minerva! So Rastus hurt himself, as well?'

'As well?' Dasypyges was politely puzzled now. 'There was no other injury, only to the boy. I fear that he is dead. That is what I came to tell you, Councillor.'

ELEVEN

I stared at him, unable to believe what I'd just heard, but he went on – in the same neutral tone of unconcern, 'My master sends you his apologies for the damage to your property.' He paused, as if waiting for acknowledgement.

I was still reeling from the shocking news, but through a mist I heard myself enquire, 'So why is His Excellence not to be informed about something that happened on his property?'

Dasypyges seemed a bit nonplussed – presumably he had

no instructions as to what to say to that – but finally he blurted, 'It is socially embarrassing for my master, I suppose. He'd no idea the owner was a citizen of rank. But the household made it clear that our host would be displeased, because you are His Excellency's special protégé.'

I should have heard the sound of warning trumpets in those words, but I was still thinking about my poor dead slave. 'Great Jove!' I muttered. 'What an appalling thing.'

He misinterpreted. 'Exactly, duumvir. My master said he'd never heard such impudence – it was a marvel that he did not strike them too. Fortunately, his anger was enough to silence them, and after that they scurried to do as he required.' He was speaking in a much less stilted way, and there was almost the smug vestige of a smile. 'The corpse was moved at once, the place was purified, and the rest of the mess was being dealt with as I left. His Excellency will not be discommoded in the least, when he returns. There was a lot of blood, but luckily the fine rugs escaped.'

I was struck by a sudden painful thought. 'Rastus is dead, and you've disposed of him? Before I was informed?'

'Unfortunately so. At the time, we did not know that he was yours. But I come to offer *compensatio*. My master will be pleased to replace him instantly. He was at first inclined to offer one of his – he has escorts with him – but he decided otherwise. The boy was neither beautiful nor particularly strong and had no special skills, I understand. Replacing him should not be difficult.' The condescension was dripping from his voice. 'I believe there is a regular slave-market in the town. So would you prefer us to shop on your behalf – or would you rather select the substitute yourself?'

I am not by nature a very violent man and years of slavery had taught me – like my wife – to bear things silently. But for a moment, listening to these words, I was seized with a suffocating rage. If I'd been carrying my walking staff, I might have smashed it across that smugly smiling face. As it was, I roared and took an unwise step, raising my hands as though to grasp him by throat and shake him till he rattled – until little Kurso, who had been watching this, came rushing out to pull me backwards by the cloak.

'Master, what's the matter?'

I looked down at him in some surprise. I had quite forgotten him. 'It's Rastus,' I managed. 'He's been . . . killed' – I almost said 'murdered' – 'by the master of this man.'

Kurso was frowning. 'Killed? Rastus?' There was genuine sorrow on the little face, although their paths had hardly crossed. 'How did it happen?'

The courier said frostily, 'An accident.'

It was said so swiftly that Kurso looked at me to see if I agreed.

I did so grudgingly. 'If you can call it that! Killed by knocking him over with a blow so violent that he hit his head and died.' But I had dropped my hands, which was as well for me.

I have thought about that moment many times. If Dasypyges had chosen to defend himself, there is not much doubt who would have suffered most. (Though it is likely he would merely have tried to parry me – it is a serious offence for a slave to strike a citizen, even if self-preservation can be proved.) And I might have earned myself a hefty fine – there are laws about deliberate damage done to property, especially that of a Roman senator.

As Kurso was at this moment just reminding me. 'But master, for all that, you must not strike this man. He is the servant of a kinsman of the Governor – you told me so your-self! And the death of Rastus was not *his* doing – from what you say of it.'

He had made me pause, but I was still furious. 'But it's the way that Rastus is being spoken of, as if he were no more important than a broken pot, to be replaced with something more or less equivalent. As though a few denarii . . .'

'But' – Kurso was still tugging at my arm – 'what more could you expect? Is that not exactly what the law requires?'

It was, of course, which merely added to my helpless rage. For a moment I did not trust myself to speak.

Dasypyges did it for me. 'Exactly, slave. That is what I was attempting to explain. It was an accident – his shoes were slippery, as your owner himself seemed happy to accept – and the merest blow was enough to send him staggering. No one could have guessed the boy would hit his head against the marble table-edge, or – even if he did – that it would cause him much more than a bruise. But so the Fates decreed. My master was appalled when he learned what he had done – he had no idea that the owner was a citizen, far less a councillor.'

'Did Rastus not say that he belonged to me?' I found my tongue again.

'He said his master was a tradesman of some kind – a pavement-maker, I believe it was. In fact, that was the only thing he would vouchsafe – that's what made my master furious.'

I said nothing, suddenly envisaging the scene. Obedient young Rastus, refusing to disclose his message to anyone but Marcus, because that was what he had been told to do. Refusing to be bullied into disobeying me – and dying for his obstinate fidelity. I blinked away some most unRoman tears.

Dasypyges was not looking at me, anyway. He had turned to Kurso, who had found the courage from somewhere to respond, unasked.

'And Rastus spoke the truth. Our master is a mosaic-maker in the town, and famous for his work – although he's now a councillor.'

'So we discovered, when it was far too late!' Dasypyges directed his reply to me. 'When we did, I was sent at once to make amends. I was actually quicker than I might have been, because I would have sought you first in town, but His Excellence's gig-driver, who was waiting to be called upon, was able to advise me where you were. With his directions, I came directly here. And now I should return. Should I tell my master that you wish to come yourself, to the slave-market the next time it is held? If a suitable replacement can be found I am sure my master would be more than generous.'

I was about to tell him, in no uncertain terms, what he could tell his master, but I was interrupted by a cheerful shout. 'Father! I was about to come and call on you.'

I swung round to see Junio hurrying down the ancient track. He had Arlina with him on the rein and was evidently just returning from a long day in town. He panted up to us. 'Good

news. I've obtained another contract for a bathhouse floor . . .'
He tailed off, looking from Dasypyges to me. 'But Father, I
see you have a messenger. And you look stricken. Is there
something wrong?'

I was ready to murmur that this was my son, and therefore
also a Roman citizen, but the courier had already worked this
out.

He gave the faintest inclination of his head. 'You are
perceptive, citizen. I am indeed the servant of somebody of
rank – no less a man than Hortius Valens, Senator of Rome.
I bring sad tidings of an accident . . .' He recounted the event,
word for word as he'd related it to me.

Junio shot me a disturbed and searching look. 'So it was
Rastus, was it? I am sorry about that. I'd heard that a slave
had been unfortunately killed, belonging to a member of the
curia. I had no idea that it was one of yours.'

Dasypyges was frowning at him in astonishment. 'You
heard? From whom?'

Junio raised ironic brows at me. 'I heard it from the tanner-
woman from the shop next door to ours – though not quite in
the form that you reported it.'

I nodded. I could have guessed as much. 'The woman is
famous for knowing all the news, and delights to pass it on.
But she can't have known the slave was mine – she'd have
told you that, for sure.'

'What I do not understand . . .' Dasypyges had turned pale.
'Is how she heard at all. It was only the household slaves who
witnessed the event, and my master was threatening to beat
them half to death, if any of them dared to breath a single
word—' He broke off, as Junio quelled him with a glance.

'Then perhaps he should have threatened the funeral guild
as well,' my son replied. 'I understand he brought the slave
guild in? Surely he could see that they were bound to talk –
when he was offering to pay the dues himself, if it could not
be proved that they were up to date.'

Trust the tanner's wife to have all the titillating details, I
thought. But this was at least a glimmer of good news. Poor
Rastus would have a decent funeral. 'I paid his guild dues
faithfully,' I said, with some relief. 'That will be on record, I

am sure. I'll go and claim him back, so we can lament, ourselves – and will gladly pay the extra for a private pyre and mourning women to accompany the bier.'

Junio shook a mournful head at me. 'Father, I am sorry. It's too late for that. The guildsman, from whom the woman heard the tale, was apparently boasting all around the town that the Senator had paid them double what they asked provided that the body was disposed of straight away and put on their pyre tonight.'

'Tonight?' I muttered – though I should not have been surprised. Tomorrow was the Ides – a festal day sacred to Jupiter, and it was unlucky to leave a corpse unburied on that date. 'Then I cannot hope to be there. A man would need the swiftest horse and even then he'd be riding halfway in the dark.' I glanced at Dasypyges – who appeared unmoved, although he would have to do exactly that, himself.

Junio realized how distressed I was at not even being able to attend the funeral. He took me to one side and spoke in a low voice. 'Clearly it is now impossible – for either you or me. But I think that you should be at the slave-market yourself. Tomorrow is a public festival so it will not be held. But there should be one the next day – and you could be there, since there's never a curial meeting on the *postridie*.'

I nodded, vaguely. The day after any public festival is partially ill-starred, so judicial courts and civil assemblies don't convene, although ordinary citizens can do anything they please (unlike the holy day itself when everything shuts down). This Emperor's official birthday date fell awkwardly this month, meaning that the council would not meet for several days.

'You ought to be there at first light, though,' Junio went on, 'to find the best of what's on offer at the slave-market. You know what Marcus says: you have to be there early to get the pick of them, before the other purchasers have skimmed the cream.'

He was quite right, of course. The stallholder was famous for his willingness to take early 'private bids', reserving his best wares for favoured customers. 'Better go in tomorrow, then, you think?' I said. I did not care a whit about replacement slaves, but I could see that Junio was trying to do his best for me. 'Later in the day, perhaps, when the festive rites are done.'

'We'll go in together, if you like – and stay at your apartment, if you can find room for me. Then it would be easy to set out from there at dawn. Cilla can spare me, for one night, I'm sure.' He looked enquiringly at me. 'I assume you'd like me to accompany you?'

'The flat will not be crowded,' I agreed, thinking how much I would miss the gangly Rastus and his toothy smile.

'Then that is our answer,' Junio declared, turning dramatically to the courier. 'I suggest that you take it to the Senator. My father accepts the offer of *compensatio*, acknowledges the cremation of his slave at Hortius's expense, and – together with myself – will meet him at the slave-market at first light, the day after tomorrow. We'll select a replacement, for which your owner undertakes to pay. Can you remember that?'

'Of course!' Dasypyges returned, and to prove it repeated the message word for word.

'Then go at once before the daylight fails,' my son replied.

The messenger leapt up into the saddle like an acrobat, raised a straight arm in salute, wheeled his horse and cantered off the way that he had come.

'Perhaps I'll you see you at the slave-market,' he called, over his shoulder, as he disappeared. It was impudence, of course, speaking as though he were of equal rank with us, and my son and I exchanged a wry glance at his words – but none of us guessed quite how prophetic they would prove to be.

TWELVE

When the dust of the departing hooves had settled, I turned to Junio. 'I suppose that I should think it fortunate that Hortius Valens does not recognize that Rastus is only nominally my slave, and that really it's my patron he should compensate.'

'But surely Marcus gifted him to you?'

'And so he did. Along with the apartment and all that it contains. But if Hortius found out that I did not really qualify for election to the council, and that it would all revert to my patron afterwards, what would he tell the Governor about the pair of us? Or the Emperor, indeed?'

'You think that Hortius might report it back to Rome? Would it matter if he did? An Emperor once declared his horse a senator.'

'Severus has a different cast of mind. You must have heard what he recently decreed, regarding those improperly holding public offices! I should be lucky to escape with just humiliation and a swingeing fine. And as for Marcus . . . I dare not think of it.'

'Then he's unlikely to tell Hortius that Rastus was effectively on loan,' Junio said. 'Even if he finds out that he's been killed. He's involved as much as you.'

'I suppose so,' I agreed. 'But you had some other news for me, I think? Something about a contract, I believe you said. I would be glad of cheerful tidings, after these last few days. Will you come in and have a cup of hot spiced mead?'

He clapped my shoulder. 'Just for a moment, then – I am already late and Cilla will have the dinner on the fire.'

I managed a wan smile. 'And very good you'll find it! She brought some in to us. Which reminds me, Kurso, you run in and get the drinks prepared – and then you and the other slaves can reheat your food and eat. Your mistress, too, if she's awake again by now.' The little slave at once sped off obediently. 'I am afraid I was a little severe with them before,' I murmured to my son. 'I'd had a trying day – though this news is so much worse, I blush at having shouted at my slaves. If I had roared at Rastus, the last time that we met, I should regret it all my life.'

Junio gave me a sympathetic grin. 'Well, turn your anger on that courier instead! He was very nearly insolent – and so self-important you would think that he was a duumvir himself.'

I paused inside the gateway. 'He takes his manner from his master, I suspect,' I said grimly. 'Speaking of whom – you said you'd heard a different version of that unhappy accident which killed my slave?'

He flashed me an uncomfortable glance. 'Probably all lies – you know what gossip's like. Anyway, it makes no difference, now. Poor young Rastus is just as surely dead.'

He was about to move away into the house, but I took him by the shoulder and forced him to look me squarely in the eyes. 'It makes a difference – to me,' I said. 'I feel responsible. He was only at my patron's flat at all, because of me. He was on an errand which I had organized – trying to warn Marcus of another visitor, but in a coded way so that Hortius would not know, and with strict instructions not to give the message to anybody but His Excellence. He died because he was obeying me.' I was ashamed to find my voice was quavering.

Junio affected not to notice. 'I wondered, when I learned that it was him, what he was doing at your patron's flat. But how could you have sent him? You were not even in the town!'

'I sent a message to my own apartment by one of Marcus's young slaves,' I explained, glad for a moment to deal in simple facts. 'Which reminds me – Great Minerva. I wonder where he is? If he's waiting at my flat for Rastus to return he must be almost frantic with worry by this time. And he won't have heard the rumours – unless either he or Servus went out into the street . . .' I broke off, because my next thought was even worse. 'Let's just hope, by all the ancient gods, that he did not get so worried that he went to Marcus's apartment to enquire!'

'Would that be so dreadful?'

'It would undo everything. The whole idea of sending Rastus there was to disguise the fact that the villa was in any way involved.'

'Father, don't distress yourself so much. The boy is much more likely to stay where he was told. In any case there is nothing you can do, from here.' He began to lead the way along the path back to the house, but before we reached the dye-house he paused again to say, 'But who is this other visitor of Marcus's, and why is it so important that Hortius does not know?'

I told him – though I made him swear to be discreet. I knew he would be. I would trust him with my life.

'This is between ourselves, then – in the meantime, anyway.

Though I cannot see how your patron can keep the two apart for very long.'

'He's playing on the superstitions of the capital – citing the bad auspices connected with a birth to keep the fastidious Senator from the villa, temporarily. My suggestion, I'm afraid. And it will not help for long. The time of purification will be over very soon. In eight more days there will be the bulla feast.'

'And Hortius will be insulted if he's not invited to attend!' Junio made a sympathetic face. 'Marcus is really torn between two horses, here. If he offends the Senator, then he offends the Governor . . . But if he betrays this woman who has thrust herself on him – and if her claims about her links to the Empress are true – then the offence is to Julia Domna!'

'And nobody has more influence with the Emperor than his wife.'

Junio whistled. 'Poor Marcus! What is he to do? For once I am thankful that I don't wear his sandals, however rich he is.' He frowned at me. 'But if Rastus has not reached him, after all, Marcus will not know yet that Druscilla's here – or the extent of the danger he is in. But how come Rastus did not find him at the flat?'

I shook my head despondently. 'He'd gone to organize this sacrifice for Julia's safe deliverance, according to that pompous courier. Wanted to get it all arranged today, I expect, because the temple will be busy tomorrow with the Ides. So he was out when Rastus got there – with terrible results. Which reminds me – about him, what is it that you heard?'

Junio sighed. 'I suppose that you will hear from someone, in the end. The tanner's wife, if from no other source, So perhaps, I should tell you . . .' But he hesitated still.

'Tell me what?' I demanded. 'What did the slave guild say?'

'Only that they could not tell whose slave he was . . .'

'Because Hortius did not know?'

'Because they could not recognize the face.'

I gazed at him, aghast. 'It was so badly damaged by the fall?' I let out a sharp breath. 'Jove – it must have been a massive blow to make him crash into the marble edge as hard as that. Unless you mean it was hardly an accident at all?' I could see that Junio was embarrassed and upset. 'More like a systematic beating? That's what you deduce?'

Junio looked more uncomfortable still. 'Something of the kind. But, as I say, it's rumour – and what difference does it make? They'll already be preparing to take him to the pyre. Except that technically, perhaps, if this is true you might have a case against Hortius in the courts for wilful damage to your property.'

'If I dared to bring one – which of course I never could. Who would find for me against a man like that?' I muttered savagely. 'It makes me understand how that Druscilla woman feels. And besides, there were no witnesses except Marcus's town slaves, who would just be tortured to ensure they "spoke the truth".' I shook my head. 'More unnecessary suffering. It is unthinkable.'

Junio assented with a sigh. 'I'm sure that you are wise. Even if you won, all you could expect is an order for compensation – which he is already offering – so there's nothing to be gained. Beyond making a very dangerous enemy, that is.'

'So what am I to do?' I asked him, bitterly. 'Just let it pass, I suppose? Or nail up a curse tablet, as Tertillius said he would?'

Junio made a wry face. 'You heard about that, did you?'

'Though I don't suppose he'll really do it – in case Hortius found out. From what I hear he sounds a man who'd seek revenge.'

Junio made that rueful face again. 'But he knows already. Poor old Tertillius was made to look a fool – in front of everyone, and of his sister in particular. He muttered the threat aloud before he stopped himself and Hortius overheard. Tertillius stormed out of the games before more harm was done, but I fear there yet may be trouble over it. Hortius was almost spluttering with rage and – as you say – I doubt he would forget an injury. So don't be tempted to cross the man yourself. Better to "act the Roman" and accept what can't be changed. Though I'm sadder about Rastus that I could ever say.' He touched my arm again. 'Now, are we going inside to have this drink of mead? Otherwise it will be too late for me to stay.'

We went inside and drank, but there was little joy in it –
though I was glad of Junio's company. It was a concession on
his part, anyway, since he prefers a glass of wine. Minimus
and Tenuis had warmed the mead and poured it out for us,
but then retreated to the shadows, where they sat, subdued –
obviously Kurso had told them the news about their fellow
slave.

Gwellia meanwhile was still – mercifully – asleep, and Junio
was reduced to telling me about his contract in an undertone.
I congratulated him – sincerely, it was lucrative and prestigious
– but I knew my tone was flat. It would take more than
successful busines to lift my mood tonight. All I could see in
the flickering fire was Rastus's young face, his eager smile
and those protruding ears.

Junio sensed what I was feeling. 'So,' he said, getting slowly
to his feet and putting that filial hand upon my shoulder once
again. 'I will come for you tomorrow – shortly after noon?
So we avoid the Ides procession? If you're quite sure that's
what you would prefer?'

I shook my head. 'I wasn't thinking clearly. I'll have to go
early, at our usual time – supposing that your mother is well
enough to leave. Marcus won't have had my message, will
he, as you say? So he still won't know Druscilla has arrived.
I'll have to go and warn him – in person this time, to be sure
it reaches him. Also, of course, I should let Lentigines come
home – supposing that he hasn't gone to Marcus's by now,
and told them everything . . .' I broke off in despair. The same
ideas were chasing round and round my head – like chariots
at the circus – and always ending with the thought that Rastus
died in vain.

'Which might implicate you in the whole affair.' Junio
squeezed my shoulder. 'But courage, Father. You have done
nothing wrong. You were obliging Marcus – nothing more –
when a kinsman of Julia's happened to arrive. That is all you
need to say. How could you guess that Hortius would care?
And I'll be there to say the same thing, should the need arise.
Now, don't get up,' he added as I tried to do so. 'You stay
and have another beaker of that mead. And when you've
finished, try to get some sleep. You've had a nasty shock. Have

a little of Cilla's poppy juice and I'll see you in the morning, shortly after dawn. And don't worry about Mother, my wife will tend to her and see that she does not do more than she can manage with that foot.'

I find it hard to credit that I slept at all, my mind was so busy with a thousand thoughts and fears, but I suppose I must have done, because when I opened my unwilling eyes it was to find Tenuis standing by my side, holding out my working tunic.

'You will need this, master, if you wish to go to town. And I've wrapped your curial toga in a bag, so you can wear it to your patron's flat. We sponged the hems last night, and it is nearly dry.'

I propped myself up on my shoulder. The fire was full alight, and my wife was sitting by it, wrapped up in a shawl, and there was a smell of baking in the air.

She saw me looking. 'Ah, husband, I was loth to wake you but the sun is almost up, and Junio will be waiting. Cilla brought this new-baked bread, so you can eat before you leave. So never fear, I have not been on my feet – though when she comes back later, she is going to help me try to do a little. With your consent, of course.'

She was alluding to my outburst of the night before, and I felt duly guilty. 'Then I suppose I must give it,' I muttered gracelessly as I got up and allowed myself to be helped into my clothes. 'Just be sure you do not overtax yourself.' I glanced through the open doorway. 'Now Junio is here – but where is Minimus?'

'Gone to saddle up Arlina.'

'Then I must go, and I'll be staying overnight. I have business to attend to.'

I was tempted not to tell her about Rastus, but I did – merely that he'd an accident and died, not implicating Hortius at all – and even that upset her, as I knew it would. But better that she heard about the incident from me than have the slaves hear gossip at the spring.

I affected briskness. 'I'll leave Minimus with you. Tenuis can attend me, for today. But if Junio's waiting I will have to set off now. I'll take my breakfast with me.' I broke off a piece of loaf. 'Tenuis, you can carry my toga-bag and lead the mule. Pick up your own cloak and help me on with mine.' I was already striding to the entrance as I spoke.

Junio was waiting. 'Ready, Father?' He looked strangely ashen-faced, I thought.

I climbed onto the mule and we were on our way, though Junio still seemed singularly grim. I taxed him with it as we turned off the lane and started up the muddy ancient track.

He sighed. 'I'm going to have to tell you, I suppose. You are bound to find out once you get to town. The Valerii brothers will have heard the tale by now, so the whole curia will know.'

I turned as cold as if I'd been immersed in snow. 'What tale?' I slid down from my mount. 'I will not take another step until I know.'

Junio motioned Tenuis to take Arlina and go ahead of us, then waited till the boy was out of sight. 'There is no easy way of saying this. I should have told you yesterday – but there was no point in giving you any more distress. It would only have kept you awake all night, and there was nothing anyone could do.'

'This is about Rastus, I assume? The blows were worse than I imagined? He had broken bones?'

'I don't believe that he was killed by a blow of any kind.'

'But you told me—?' I broke off, as I realized that he'd not really told me anything at all. I had made a suggestion and he'd said 'something of the kind'. 'You are trying to spare me. It was something worse?'

'Much worse.' Junio looked at me with intense compassion in his eyes. 'The tanner's wife told me that his tongue had been cut out.'

THIRTEEN

There was a silence, while I tried to catch my wits.

'Father?' Junio's voice appeared to come from far away. I realized that I was goggling – literally goggling – staring open-eyed and slack-jawed with disbelief.

'Father?' The words were sharp with evident concern, but for a moment I could not answer him. This was a horror beyond imagining.

Such barbarous punishment is not unknown, of course. There are famous stories of it being used in Rome, to punish traitors or sometimes slaves convicted of a lie. The Emperor Commodus was even rumoured to have ordered it performed for the entertainment of his dinner guests – but it is not listed as an official penalty, even for those who speak against the Emperor.

In my long life I have seen it only once, and that was many, many years ago – inflicted by the pirates who captured me and sold me into slavery, and it was done to one of my fellow captives who complained too long and loud. What struck me most about that terrible event was the huge amount of blood – no wonder that Dasypyges had mentioned 'lots of it'.

It is not invariably a death sentence, of course, which may be why the Roman system does not favour it. A few survive to be unhappy mutes. But most die, either from drowning in their own blood at once, or – like my hold-companion – linger for several agonizing days, and starve to death because they lack the means of swallowing. At least my poor slave's fate was mercifully quick.

I did not share these frightful memories with my son – in fact, I could not have done so if I tried. The image of what must had happened to my unhappy slave was so appalling that – like him – I was deprived of speech, unable to contemplate such wanton cruelty.

'Father?' Junio's voice was getting urgent now. 'I knew this news would shock you – but should I call back Tenuis and use the mule to take you home? You have turned so pale . . .'

I forced myself to speak. 'Why did you not tell me yesterday?' It was all that I could manage to articulate, although I knew the answer before he uttered it.

'I thought to spare you. I knew that the knowledge would only cost you sleep – and there was nothing whatever you could do, by then. The body was already on its way to be cremated on the pyre – so no proof is possible. And without it, this remains mere rumour – as the Senator would certainly point out. And who could contradict his version of events?

The funeral guild will doubtless have been silenced by this time – if Hortius has not bribed them into feigning ignorance, he will have terrified them into it. And Marcus's household dare not speak – at least while Hortius is in Britannia – for fear of bringing the same fate on themselves.'

'But you believe the story?' I cleared my throat and managed to go on. 'It is so extreme it seems . . . improbable.'

'I'm afraid I do. Why would the undertaker's guild invent a thing like that? And it explains why Hortius was so keen to have the cremation straight away, whatever the expense. I don't imagine for a moment that he genuinely feared he would attract bad luck by a delay. If Rastus was going to haunt him afterwards, it's likely to be for ordering his death, rather than for leaving his corpse unburied on the Ides! Yet Hortius does not seem to have been troubled about that.'

'Though it's said that he's superstitious,' I put in. 'Marcus is rather depending on that fact to keep him from the villa – at least until Julia and the babes are purified.'

Junio snorted. 'Hortius would doubtless see that differently. Patrician birth, especially of twins, may be of some interest to the Fates – the death of a mere domestic tool would hardly trouble them. That is what my earliest master would certainly have thought. I'm not sure Hortius believes that slaves have souls at all. Besides, it is "the hand that strikes the murderous blow that draws the haunting ghost" – and I doubt that Hortius did the deed himself.' He gave a mirthless grin. 'You saw the escort he had with him at the birthday rites?'

I had. Great hulking fellows armed with clubs and knives. Presumably most were still quartered in the military inn, though some – at least – must have accompanied Hortius to my patron's flat. I wondered how Marcus could accommodate these brutes. On mats beside their master's bed, no doubt – there was little extra space in the servants' sleeping room.

'Such men would not be squeamish,' Junio went on. 'And would no doubt do anything he asked – dispensing "justice" at his lightest whim. In Rome he would have lictors to do exactly that—' He broke off as little Tenuis came panting back towards us down the path.

I raised an eyebrow and tried to raise a smile. 'What is it, Tenuis?'

'Master, I was getting worried. You have been so long. I've tied Arlina to a tree . . .' He looked uncertainly from me to Junio and back.

'Just discussing matters. We are coming now.' I forced a grin and waved him back along the track again. He looked reluctant, but he went dutifully away.

As we followed him slowly – the path was particularly steep and stony here – I turned to Junio. 'Speaking of discussions, I suppose we should decide what we are going to do when we arrive in town. For one thing, I suggest we do not tell the other servants what you have just told me. It would disturb their dreams.'

'Much better not to,' Junio agreed, 'and if they should hear the story on the street, we assure them it is rumour – which is strictly true. And wisest – I think – to pretend you have not heard yourself, when you speak to Hortius. It is enough to know he "accidentally" killed your slave. As it is, he's put himself into an awkwardness – for which he will find it hard to forgive you, I expect.'

I had picked up a fallen branch (I generally do when I am forced to walk) to form a makeshift staff but I found myself switching with it at the verge. 'I wish I weren't compelled to meet him,' I said savagely. 'But if am to call on Marcus, I suppose I must!' I decapitated several fronds of fern, wishing they were Hortius.

'Then why visit Marcus?'

I paused in my vicarious execution of the plants to stare at him, surprised. 'To tell him that Druscilla has arrived, of course – supposing that Lentigines has not got there first.'

'I understand that, Father,' he said patiently. 'What I meant was, why do that yourself? Why not let me take the message to his flat? That way you are not obliged to meet the Senator until tomorrow at the slave-market! And, incidentally, no one can see you walking through the town to Marcus's and then question your absence from the procession for the Ides. I assume that you weren't planning to attend?'

I said, still flaying at the foliage, 'I've had enough of

processions to last a moon or more. And I'm certainly not anxious to parade for miles today, just to accompany a sacrificial lamb, however white and spotless it might be. But if I'm in town, I suppose I'd better go – or Hortius will denounce me for lack of piety. It would please him to have something to accuse me of.'

Juno shook his head. 'Not if he's not aware that you're in town. Everyone on the curia will know by now that you did not stay for the birthday games because your wife is suffering with a badly poisoned wound. Decimus Valerius will have seen to that – he actually tried to tell me, yesterday. And it is not obligatory to turn up at the Ides. So you won't be expected at the ritual today, unless you're seen walking in a public place. The forum, for instance.'

'Which I would have to cross, to call on Marcus. You are right, of course,' I said with some relief, 'So I'll leave that to you. You know what to tell him but try to be discreet – he'll want it kept from Hortius, for the moment, anyway.'

'Obviously, Father!' It was almost a rebuke.

'I wish it was possible to see Tertillius,' I said. 'I'd like to hear his version of what happened at the games. But as it is,' I added with a sigh, 'I cannot spare a slave. You had better take Tenuis with you. It is not fitting for a togate citizen to walk around unattended on a festal day like this – and you'll have to wear your toga if you are visiting His Excellency.'

The drawback with all this was that it pinned me to the flat. I could hardly send Servus out to find Tertillius, or someone might arrive and find me there without a slave at all! And, with Hortius ready to report, I could not walk about the streets myself – even with a servant in attendance – unless I was proposing to process!

Junio appeared to read my thoughts. 'You'll have Lentigines.'

'They will be anxious for his safety at the villa by this time. I must send him home. So let's catch up with Tenuis, and tell him of our plans, and we'll drop Arlina at the stables as we pass. Then I suppose I'll simply have to sit in idleness.'

I spoke of idleness but when we reached my apartment there was a task awaiting me – a thankless one, at that. Servus and Freckle-face had to be informed that Rastus had been killed. I gave them an edited account of where and when. 'I'm told it was an accident,' I concluded – truthfully – although I almost choked upon the word.

The pair were so genuinely horrified that I was reassured. Their shock could not be feigned. Of course, they told me, they'd been worried when the lad did not return, but they concluded that he had been sent on some further errand by His Excellence – possibly even to the roundhouse and to me – and had been overtaken by the dark. But, like the obedient servants that they were, they'd stayed where they were told.

'We expected that he'd come back today. Indeed, when we heard your footsteps at the door we thought he was with you,' Lentigines's little freckled face was smudged with tears. 'I can't believe what's happened! Though we were beginning to conclude that something was amiss. I was almost ready to set off—'

I was about to say that I was glad he had not, when Servus – my remaining slave – broke in. He was not weeping, but his face was ashen white. 'So what's happened to the body – when is the funeral?'

So there was more bad news to tell them. Lentigines looked aghast and I saw the tears well up in Servus now, but Junio had been listening and he took command.

'We could not leave the body unburied on the Ides,' he said briskly, and they nodded grudgingly. 'So you can undo that bundle, Tenuis, and drape my toga on – and my father's plain one in case of visitors – then you and I will pay a visit to His Excellence. Lentigines, the steward at the villa will be wondering where you are. You'd best set off at once. Servus, you will attend my father. Make up some hot spiced mead. This death has shaken him and he is not intending to process, or leave the flat today.'

I commended this with the briefest of nods. Keeping busy is Gwellia's recipe for combating despair.

It was well judged. The boys were clearly glad to have duties to perform. Lentigines was into his cloak and gone a moment after my son had left himself, while Servus busied himself in looking after me. No Roman senator could have been more indulged. He brought my soft house-slippers and propped them by the glowing brazier to warm while he rinsed the dust from my feet – in scented water, too – before fitting them gently onto me, and proudly bringing a piping mug of hot, spiced mead. It was a little stronger than it often was, but I was very glad of that, as I sat down at the table and settled in for my long day of idleness.

I could hear the people passing in the street – the shouts of vendors and the hastening feet – but I dared not even look out through the window-space. The town was full of spies. Somebody might see me standing there and report my presence to the Senator. I sighed and turned my attention to the mead.

FOURTEEN

I had barely taken half a dozen sips when there was a sudden hammering at the door. Servus came running from an inner room. 'Should I, master . . .?'

I was almost tempted to tell him not to answer it, and so pretend that there was no one here, but I thought better of it. This might be a message from His Excellency. I nodded wearily.

Servus went to admit the visitor as I brushed my toga down, and I heard the caller say, 'I understand the Duumvir Libertus is in town. Will you announce me?'

But I had already recognized the voice – cultured but a little quavering – and by this time I was on my feet. 'My dear Tertillius,' I cried. 'You are most welcome. I had been hoping that I could speak to you.'

'So Junio told me! I met him in the street.' I could see Tertillius now, as he came into the room. He was tall and birdlike and – though he clearly saw himself as bold and masterful – his quavery voice and uncertain walk (supported by a stick) did nothing to assist. Tertillius could not be much older than I am myself – few men in Glevum are – but I flatter myself that I could be taken for his son. His skin was pale as vellum and stretched thin across his skull and bony limbs, his greying locks were sparse and even his curial toga – the broad-ness of whose purple stripe put mine to shame – had an aged fading look.

He did not wait for me to speak again, but hobbled over to the table where I stood, gave his walking cane to his attendant slave – a frightened-looking, skinny child of no more than eight years old, already struggling with a heavy sack – then seizing both my forearms, to my great surprise, shook them up and down in as warm a Roman handshake as I have ever known. Flattering, of course, but puzzling as well. Up to now we had been distant colleagues, nothing more – Tertillius was too conscious of the difference in our ranks.

There was not a hint of any of that now. 'My fellow coun-cillor, I can't convey how pleased I am to find you here,' he croaked, in that phantom of a voice. 'But I forget my manners. How fares your poor dear wife? I understand that she has been unwell.' The pale blue eyes were rheumy, but there was still sharpness in the gaze.

It was a relief to have him sit beside me on the bench and tell him all about the poisoned foot, while Servus led away the frightened infant slave (whose timid smile showed the absence of his two front teeth) then hurried back to bring refreshment for my guest, albeit a humble plate of cheese and bread. I was embarrassed to remember that I had no wine to offer him. I usually keep a small amount in store, in case of visitors (my personal preference is for spiced or honeyed mead) but my last caller had quaffed the last of it and, with Gwellia ill, I had neglected to arrange for more. All I could offer was a goblet of my own favourite beverage.

Tertillius looked doubtful. 'Only a very little, if you please. Have to be careful with that stuff, my dear chap – goes to my head and affects my thinking, I'm afraid. Raised to Roman customs, I suppose.'

I smiled. 'I have the same the problem with unaccustomed wine.'

'Pity. I have some – quite a fine one as it happens – in that sack my slave brought in. If you liked wine I might have offered it to you. The intended recipient has turned it down. One of the things I hoped to talk to you about.'

I hoped that this was not intended as a hint that I should hastily retract, and accept the gift so I could offer some to him. Most likely it was not. That would be implying that he'd suggested it, and it is more than simply rude to ask for the return of something one has given – it is regarded as bad luck. Besides, he had not been very polite about my mead. So I said, mildly, 'So why not simply keep it for yourself. Is that not why you originally purchased it?'

He shook his thinning curls. 'Meant it for Hortius – peace offering sort of thing. My sister was urging that I ought to make a move. He heard me threatening to nail up that curse, and she says he could make trouble, if he chose. Not just for me, for all of Glevum – everybody knows the town did not support the current Emperor. So I heeded her advice. Picked out the very best wine that I could find – bought the lot, then took one amphora of it and went to call on him. Went to the fort, first, but he wasn't there. He's staying with your patron now . . .' He paused and looked enquiringly at me. 'Though you knew that, I suppose?'

I met his gaze. 'Indeed. He wrote to Marcus from the garrison and more or less demanded his hospitality.'

Tertillius tapped the table as if I'd solved a mystery. 'I wondered why your patron had invited him. Not the sort of fellow I should wish to entertain. You heard, I suppose, how he mistreated me? Almost pushed me over, and insulted me – in front of everyone – when he took over at the birthday games? In full view of everybody, and my sister, too.'

I was about to urge him to go on – I was keen to hear as much about Hortius as I could, and the old man seemed ready to denounce him openly. But – remembering that even Tertillius might be a spy – I felt it wise to be discreet.

'I only heard rumours about what happened at the games. I was not there myself. I have not met this Hortius at all, in fact – only saw him at a distance at the birthday sacrifice. But I find I'm going to have to deal with him quite soon – on my own account as well as Marcus's. So anything you can tell me that might guide my—' I broke off as Servus came in with our beakers of warmed mead.

I was anxious not to have the servants overhear, so I signalled that the talk should wait until my slave retired back to the servants' room. However, the interruption had disturbed the flow, and my guest said nothing when we were alone again.

'Junio told me you had been displaced as starter of the games. Though I believe that Marcus asked you to officiate?' I offered a sympathetic smile.

That was all the prompting Tertillius required. 'Quite an honour, as you might suppose, being asked to deputise.' He spoke proudly, even now. 'Short notice, certainly. But unavoidable. His Excellence was called away – wife brought to childbed early, it transpires. One hopes she gave him another strapping son.'

'Twins. A girl and boy,' I murmured and earned myself a frown.

'Of course, you'd know that, since you're his protégé. But – like the remainder of the curia – I did not find out till afterwards why Marcus needed to select a deputy.' Tertillius spoke with some acerbity. 'Though, as donor of the games he must have been aware that I provided the bull for the birthday sacrifice. Officially anonymous, of course,' he added, preempting the tactless question which was on my lips.

I understood entirely – he'd mentioned it to people like the two Valerii, who would pass on the news and enhance his reputation with the electorate. I nodded.

'Marcus had clearly heard of it for one. And the bull was excellent – completely flawless, as the rite required. I noticed at the time. It must have been a very large expense. Suppliers always ask a premium for a perfect animal, when it is wanted for a public sacrifice. It must have been doubly galling to be rudely brushed aside!'

'Galling? I should think so! When I was sitting in the central seat, too, all eyes upon me, with my sister at my side! I'd just picked up the handkerchief and bowed to everyone – to make sure they could see it when it dropped.'

Or rather, to ensure that everyone would notice who was opening the games. Visiting sisters in particular. Poor Tertillius, what a moment to be pushed aside!

'How inconsiderate!' I said. I was more or less convinced now that my caller was no spy, but all the same I added prudently, 'Though of course the fellow is a senator. And a relation of the Provincial Governor. I suppose he felt he had the right by rank.'

The look the old man shot me was almost venomous. 'D'you suppose he would have done the same if it had been your patron in the central seat?'

It was not a question which needed a reply. 'Perhaps he'd heard that Marcus was unable to attend and needed somebody to deputize . . .?'

'Does that excuse his pushing me aside? Physically pushing me with both his hands? So violently that I almost slipped and fell – with everybody watching?' He took a rather doubtful sip of mead. 'I was in my ceremonial toga, and that made it worse – because when I stumbled the outer folds untucked, and my servant had to hold it to stop it winding off in coils.'

The picture might have been comic at any other time, but it was shocking too – that push was an outright flouting of the civil law. Causing 'loss of magisterial dignity' is a fineable offence – and the higher-ranking the official, the heavier the fine. Except, of course, when a well-connected senator is concerned! No wonder that Tertillius was so furious.

I took a deep breath and dared a frank remark. 'Nothing I have learned about Hortius recommends him very much. It seems to me you might have grounds to bring a case.'

'I'd do so, if I thought that there was any chance I'd win!' Tertillius was so incensed that he took a deep draught of his remaining mead. It made him splutter, but it seemed to lubricate his tongue. 'And it would not be an ordinary claim for loss of dignity. Not only did he lay his hands upon me in a violent way, when I was engaged in an official role, he did it in a public place when half the town was there. That makes it *iniuria atrox*! Injury of the most atrocious kind.'

I nodded, to show that – as a member of the curia myself – I understood the law regarding magistrates.

Tertillius glared into his empty cup. 'If he were anybody else I would have taken him to law.' He slammed the goblet down. 'You know what happened to the last man who insulted me?'

I did. The damages awarded had been huge. It had been the

talk of Glevum, though Tertillius's success had been predictable. He was not the quickest-thinking individual, but he was diligent and had devoted himself for years to study of the law. Hence, he not only knew all the proper forms of words – the slightest deviation from which meant that the cause was lost and could not be brought again – but he also knew the finest advocate in west Britannia, and had made good use of him. And could no doubt do the same again.

'But you can hardly sue the Governor's representative?'

'Sue him? I'm tempted to punch him on the nose. Almost did. Fortunately, my sister tugged my sleeve and I restrained myself.'

'From what I saw of Hortius's escort at the birthday rites, you would have been lucky to escape them without injury, if you'd assaulted him.' I drank the last sip of my own delicious mead.

Tertillius used a feeble fist to thump the tabletop. 'I hardly escaped unscathed, in any case. Didn't your informant tell you about that?'

I shook my head.

'Laughed aloud at my predicament, and then declaimed – so that everyone in the surrounding seats could hear – "The old fool is so feeble that he cannot stand upright. I think his wits have deserted him as well! Look at him staring at me like an idiot!" That was because I was speechless at him pushing me like that! Then – if you would believe it, Libertus, my old friend – he actually said, "He isn't fit to be a magistrate. I shall tell Albinus so." I did not hit him, but I stormed away – foolishly muttering that remark about a curse.'

'I'm not surprised that you were angry,' I exclaimed. 'If Hortius made good that threat, it could be very serious for you.'

If petitioned, the Governor has the right to remove from office any magistrate within his governance. If this is on the grounds of 'incapacity', it is tantamount to ruling him insane, which also deprives him of his rights as a citizen. (An idiot cannot vote, make a contract or a will, borrow money or hold any kind of post, but is placed in tutelage, as a woman is. Even his purchases must be agreed by an official 'guardian' – even supposing he's allowed to leave the house.)

'In your sandals I would feel aggrieved,' I added. 'Even the threat is a technical affront.'

Tertillius looked down at his brown-spotted wrinkled hands. 'But so was my promise that I would have him cursed. It was ill-advised of me – I do acknowledge that – and my sister has been reproaching me for it ever since. She keeps reminding me how I shall be ruined if he carries out his threat. Yet I dare not bring a counter-claim. I would be bound to lose. No one would dare to find against the Governor's relative.'

'Hortius may not mean it – it may be just a threat. But he does not seem a man who would forget a slight,' I said.

'So my sister tells me, constantly. That is why, at her urging, I put aside my pride – you will understand that it took quite an effort to do that – and went to call on him today to offer him a gift.'

I began to understand. 'A wine of very special vintage, I believe?' Meaning, no doubt, it was a very pricey one.

'More than that, I invited him to dine. A banquet, nothing less. I'd called and made arrangements to hire the vintners' hall in two days' time – the first auspicious date that was available. But when I called to ask him, he refused outright. Would not even come to speak to me – not in person – simply sent his slave. A most unpleasant haughty sort of servant too. Treated me with arrogant disdain. Deliberately kept me waiting in the vestibule – Marcus's doorkeeper was looking quite aghast.'

I could imagine that. Marcus always insists on courtesy – even to plebians, if they are forced to call. 'And the Senator would not accept the wine?' I was amazed at that – however much Hortius wished to snub Tertillius. Most Romans would have snatched at such a handsome gift, even if they meant to rebuff the donor afterwards. 'It makes me wonder if he real-ized what it was.'

'He realized, all right. I had it taken in to him when I first arrived – with a most grovelling apology – but he just sent it back. Claimed to fear I might have poisoned it.' He gazed gloomily into his empty cup. 'If I'd known how he would treat me, I might have done so, too!'

'But he would not have drunk it, would he?' The absurdity

of the proposition made me smile – the first time I had done so since I'd learned of Rastus's fate.

Tertillius misinterpreted. His thin hand clutched my arm. 'You will not report me – and tell him what I said? Citizen, I was talking wildly . . .'

I shook gently him off. 'Don't worry about that. I have no cause to love him, either. You heard about my slave?'

'Your slave?' I saw comprehension dawn behind his eyes. '*Your* slave? Decimus was telling me a story but he didn't mention that the boy was yours. Though, whoever he belonged to, it was a frightful act.' He looked at me shrewdly. 'At least if rumour is to be believed?' He pointed to his tongue.

I raised a warning finger to my lips. 'I'm almost sure it is. But I'm trying to keep the story from my remaining sl—'

Another rapping sounded at the outer door and I broke off instantly.

Just in time, as Servus tiptoed in. 'Master, it seems you have a second visitor. Should I answer that?' He nodded towards the entrance – the rapping had become peremptory by now. 'And should I let the caller in? Or do you not wish to have it known that Councillor Tertillius is here?'

The old man had that haunted look again. 'They'll know that anyway. I left my litter waiting on the street.' He turned to me as Servus hurried to the door. 'Oh, Mercury, Libertus, why am I such a fool? Why did I not send the chair away and send my slave to find another one when I'm about to leave? Though it's so hard to find one when you need one – and I'm too frail to walk. But if I've brought you trouble, I will not forgive myself. If that should be the Senator . . .?'

It wasn't. It was my patron, and he was already striding in – though it was clear from the outset that something was amiss. He entered without waiting to be announced – which in itself was unusual for him – and there was no sign of his usual cheerful smile. His face was darker than a thundercloud and he made only the faintest acknowledgement of me.

I wondered if there'd been some sort of tragedy. He was not dressed in festal finery, as I would have expected him to be on an occasion like the Ides, but in a plain dark cloak over a faded toga – almost penitential garb, if he had been wearing

dust and ashes on his face and hair and his garment had not
had that purple stripe. He was, for the moment, unaccompanied
too – though I glimpsed a pretty pageboy (whom I faintly
recognized as a member of the household at his flat) now left
to kick his heels in the corridor outside.

'Libertus!' Marcus gave me the briefest of curt nods, then
passed his cloak to Servus. 'And Tertillius, too!' He went
across and grasped my ancient guest – who had struggled to
his feet – by both his forearms and pumped them up and down.
'Your litter-bearers said that you were here. Though I was
surprised to hear that, I confess!' He indicated that Tertillius
should resume his seat, and sat down himself – on the bench
that I'd vacated, spreading himself so that I had to squeeze
onto a narrow stool nearby. I wondered how I had offended
as, ignoring me, he spoke to Tertillius again, 'Not at the Ides
procession, this year, then?'

'Decided not to,' the old man said, with more vigour than
before. My patron's marked attention clearly flattered him. 'If
I were to happen to meet your houseguest, Excellence, I fear
my thoughts might not be pleasing to the gods.'

Marcus did not throw back his curly head and laugh as I
expected, but started fiddling with the seal-ring on his hand
– a sure sign that he was under strain. 'Indeed! I heard that
you had visited the flat when I was out. I am sorry if he
treated you with disrespect.'

'He seems to make a habit of arrogance,' I said, succeeding
merely in creating an uncomfortable pause. 'Delights in
slighting everyone he meets.'

'He's fairly civil towards me, his host,' Marcus said stiffly,
and refused to meet my gaze.

Tertillius turned his watery eyes on him. 'You know what
happened when I came to call?'

Marcus turned the seal-ring till I thought that it would break.
'Not entirely. My servants seem afraid to tell me anything,
and he dismisses all enquiry. I'm sorry if you feel he has
insulted you, again. And a pity I was out – I might have saved
you that. I was at the temple making a little offering.'

'Ah,' I murmured. 'Hence the penitential dress? I expected
you to be dressed for the procession later on.'

'I am not proposing to attend.' I had forced an answer from him, but he did not look at me. 'You see, Tertillius, thanks to the advice of my old friend and client here' – he waved a hand at me – 'I have been persuaded to declare that I lack purity enough, because of being in close contact with my wife. Childbirth, Councillor, as I expect you know.'

Tertillius beamed assent. 'Not merely childbirth, but the birth of twins, including, as I understand, a second son.' He seemed anxious to show that he was well-informed – though the report had clearly come from me. 'Permit me, Excellence, to offer you congratulations on that. And perhaps, a little gift? My servant is waiting in the anteroom. He happens to be carrying a small amphora of fine wine. May I propose that we three open it? A celebration that you have a newborn boy? Libertus here could offer a little libation to the gods as well – to thank them that your wife and babes have all come safely through?'

Marcus looked at me as though he wished he could decline. The gift of wine was commonplace enough, especially to a person of his rank. But offering to drink it in someone else's house is – to put it mildly – a touch unusual. However, I was only too happy to agree.

This way, I reasoned, there were benefits for all: my patron would be honoured by the gift, a drink of good Falernian might help to lift his mood; Tertillius was doing this so he could have some wine himself, while my own dwindling stock of mead was spared.

'A generous suggestion,' I said heartily. 'Servus, go and see that it is done.'

The slave-boy hurried off, and for a moment we talked civilities, though Marcus still seemed remarkably on edge. After a little my servant reappeared, bearing a tray, on which were my three best (and only) silver cups. He was accompanied by Tertillius's slave, carrying a jugful of the wine. (Now watered, naturally. No self-respecting Roman would drink it undiluted. One hopes the deities prefer it that way too.)

The two boys put their burdens down before the altar-niche, while I pulled up my toga-fold to make a hood. I felt clumsy and ridiculous – this was not something that I often did – but as the officiating owner of the house it fell to me.

I did not know what formal prayer to use, but I muttered something half-appropriate, and saw to it that my libation used very little of the wine. I trust that I did not offend the gods. My mortal companions seemed satisfied enough, especially when the remainder of the jugful was poured out into the cups.

'Splendid stuff this, Tertillius.' Marcus showed his appreciation by raising high his goblet and making little smackings of the lips. 'Fully aged, I think? Where did you find it?'

Tertillius, clearly flattered, named a wine merchant.

'Strange.' Marcus had begun to frown again. 'Only yesterday I called in there myself. I asked for his best wine, but he didn't offer me anything that was a match for this.'

'That would be because he'd sold it all to me.' Tertillius seemed revivified by a sip or two – though I was wondering how I could dispose of what was in my cup without attracting attention to myself. The unaccustomed beverage goes directly to my head (a problem I've had at civic banquets several times, since becoming duumvir) and I had already drunk two brimming cups of mead. It might not have mattered, since I was here all day, but Marcus was clearly in a most unhappy mood with me – perhaps the strain of entertaining the unpleasant Senator. I felt I might need my wits about me very soon.

He was still addressing all remarks to Tertillius. 'It seems the Fates are thwarting me at every turn. I am hoping to arrange a civic banquet for my guest – and of course to celebrate the births. But first there was no really high-class wine, and then I find I cannot even hire the vintners' hall. It's the only place that's big enough to hold a feast like that, but it was not available – at any price.'

'But surely they'd not refuse your booking, Excellence . . .?'

I was silenced by a scowl.

'I wanted it, of course, on the first well-augured day. The Senator is very superstitious, as you, Libertus, guessed.' He gave me that peculiar look again and turned back to his fellow guest. 'You don't know anything about that, Tertillius, I suppose?'

The old man cleared his throat. 'I fear that may be my fault, also, Excellence. The day after tomorrow is already booked to me. And for the self-same purpose. But after all, it seems it will not be required.' He told the sorry tale. 'It's Hortius's loss. He's missed the chance of a very handsome feast. He would have accepted your invitation, I've no doubt.'

Marcus said nothing, and I realized that he'd known the answer all along. So I made the suggestion he was clearly waiting for. 'But you two might come to some arrangement, don't you think? If Marcus will pay you what you gave the vintners for their hall, you can formally transfer the hire of it to him and I can be the witness to the deal.'

My patron said, 'I suppose that would be strictly possible.'

'The Senator would get his civic banquet,' I went on. 'And – if Tertillius would sell it to you – you could even serve that wine. I understand the councillor has more of it at home.'

Tertillius laughed. 'Enough for the top three couches anyway – and you can wait till Hortius admires it before you tell him where it's from!' I chuckled, but Marcus did not even smile. The aged councillor went on earnestly, 'You could even borrow a few slaves from me by then, I think, though you'd have to hire, or borrow, a few more as well. The vintners can never supply enough themselves for any big affair.'

'I take it that they made you pay in full?'

Tertillius had brightened. 'They did.' He named a sum.

'Then you were cheated!' Marcus made a lofty face. 'They quoted me much less. But perhaps, all things considered . . .' He looked at me again.

He was signalling something – I did not know what. Perhaps he did not wish me to hear them haggling, so I rose and left them to it. In fact, I contrived to edge away sufficiently to add a little extra libation at the shrine, and hope the gods were not insulted by the gift.

By the time that I'd edged back again Marcus and Tertillius had agreed the deal. They shook hands in my presence and exchanged the proper formula, so the bargain was formally confirmed.

My patron was still twiddling his seal-ring. 'You shall attend the banquet, Tertillius, of course – and you too, Libertus, if you would care to come. I'm sure that Hortius would be glad to have you there.'

He said that with a savagery that I did not understand. 'I doubt it, Excellence. But it is kind of you to ask, and I accept of course. Though you sound as if you are not entirely happy with your guest?' As soon as I had uttered them, I wished those words unsaid.

Marcus seemed angrier than I have ever known, though he did not raise his voice. For a moment his face grew very red, then he leapt up and clapped me on the shoulder – a rare event, and not as friendly as it might appear. His grasp was painful. 'Libertus – old friend – what can I say to that?' He left his hand there, digging into me. 'You would not expect me to criticize my guest? Especially in front of distinguished councillors?'

Tertillius recognized the cue to take his leave. He stumbled to his feet. 'You two must have lots of matters to discuss. So I shall say farewell. Libertus, thank you for your hospitality. If you are at the marketplace tomorrow, I might see you there – my sister is insisting I acquire some different slaves.'

'You too?' I said politely.

I had encouraged him. 'I have an ancient steward and that boy you saw today, and – apart from a few garden and cleaning slaves – that's been enough for me. But she thinks otherwise – a man in my position needs a staff to match, she says. The boy is ugly and the steward is too old and I should replace them both, and buy a pair of maidservants to wait on her, as well. She's a forceful woman, but she seems to think gold pieces grow on trees.' He gave a wheezing laugh. 'Meantime, I'll see you at the banquet, Excellence. Just let me know when you want your slaves to come and get the wine. I will tell the vintners of the change of plan when they open tomorrow – you can leave all that to me. Ossius!' He clapped his hands.

The boy-slave sidled in, carrying the sack, which from the inevitable stains obviously contained the half-full amphora. 'Master,' he murmured, 'what should I do with this?'

'That is a present to his Excellence,' Tertillius declared.

Marcus acknowledged this fiction with a bow. 'Give it to

my slave-boy. He is waiting just outside.' And as Servus
showed Tertillius to the door, no doubt Ossius did so – with
relief! Amphorae are heavy – even smaller ones – and not
designed to stand upright without support. Especially when
the contents have been broached!

The idle thought had made me smile, but as the door shut
behind my aged visitor, I turned around to see Marcus now
regarding me with what looked like open anger and contempt.

FIFTEEN

'Patron, have I offended you, somehow?' I ventured, when
Servus had withdrawn.

Marcus gave me another scathing look. 'You mean,
apart from sharing secrets with Hortius, behind my back? And
don't look so surprised. Junio let the information out.'

I gaped at him. I was absolutely stunned. 'E-excellence,' I
stammered, 'the Senator must have threatened him with some
dreadful punishment – to make him break a confidence.'
Marcus's expression did not thaw one bit. 'Patron, I cannot
apologize enough – he was explicitly instructed not to tell
anyone but you that Druscilla had—'

Marcus waved my words impatiently aside. 'That is not at
issue. We had already heard. Hortius's guard brought us the
news when they arrived this morning from the garrison.'

I was struggling to make sense of this. And then a thought
occurred to me. 'Most of them are still billeted there, I expect?
So the lady came to the gates of Glevum – as I feared she
might – and was the source of gossip afterwards! I am surprised
that a single traveller caused so much remark – except that
she asked directions to your villa, I suppose.'

My patron leant back on the narrow bench, folded his arms
across his chest and let out an exasperated sigh. 'Spoke to the
sentry on duty, it appears – and in such a rude, imperious way
that it's become the talk of the garrison. The bodyguards must
have heard last night and brought the news to Hortius as soon

as possible. It seems that he had offered a reward to whoever brought him the first news of her – though he has found a reason not to pay, since they had not discovered anything themselves. So be warned, Libertus!' He slammed the goblet on the tabletop. 'Do not trust the man.'

I did not answer; I was too perplexed. Trust him about what? What could it be that Junio had said? Described exactly where the villa was perhaps? 'It's to be hoped he does not go over to your house, and get his bodyguards to drag her out to him. It's not impossible. Your gates and gatekeeper could not oppose them long. And,' I added, slyly, 'that courier knows the way.'

Marcus gave me an unfriendly look. 'Exactly so, Libertus. And on that subject, we need to talk, I think.'

I was beginning to wish I hadn't jettisoned my wine. 'The messenger? I do not understand.'

'Oh, I think you do.' Marcus was gazing into his empty cup, as though it fascinated him. (If this was a signal that he wanted some more wine, it was in his own hands, I was power-less to help.) 'Hortius seemed to think the courier should have told him that Druscilla had arrived, though how he could have known that was a mystery to me.' He looked up, but refused to meet my eyes. 'Though not, perhaps, to you?'

It was clearly a rebuke, but I could not see the force of it. 'Of course he could not possibly have known. Druscilla did not come till yesterday, when you weren't there yourself. That is why the villa sent to me. And I will swear that – before the gods, if that is what the Senator requires. The courier came the day before, and even then he did not speak to you – by the time that we arrived, the nurse had already sent him back to town, to tell you that the twins were safely born – which, come to think of it, he never tried to do. Though, if you remember, we passed him on the road, galloping at full speed the other way.'

'I see your recollection matches mine,' Marcus said, giving me that peculiar look again. 'I tried to explain all this to Hortius, but he paid no attention, just went on bellowing at the wretched messenger and threatening to send him to the mines for failing see what was in front of him. In the end I left them to it and went to the temple to perform my cleansing rites. And on my return, there was Junio at the door.' He pressed his two forefingers together into a pinnacle and looked at me across the top of them. 'That is the story, as far as I'm aware. Is there anything that you would like to add?'

It was such a strange enquiry that I did not know how to respond. 'Excellence, did Junio cause you some embarrassment?'

'Rather the reverse, as the Fates would have it.' He gave me a thin smile. 'His message proved I did not know the wretched woman had arrived. I was anxious all the time that I was out, that Hortius would decide that, after all, I must have known. But when I found that Junio had called, specifically to bring me that very piece of news, I brought him in and asked him to repeat it in front of everyone.'

'And he said something that was unfortunate?'

'Not for me, at any rate.' Marcus was still fascinated by his cup. 'He did it with the greatest tact and skill. Explained that provision had been made for her, at your behest, pending any different instructions from myself. He even apologized for the delay in telling me – something about a slave who'd met an accident. Even Hortius was visibly convinced.'

As of course he would be, I thought bitterly. Yet there was clearly something else. And equally clearly, Marcus was not going to tell me what it was. I struggled for a clue. 'Did the Senator ask for information which Junio did not have?' I'd given my son only the briefest of accounts – and I could imagine Hortius being furious if he asked questions and did not get what he considered an adequate reply.

'He questioned Junio, of course. When did he learn that Drusilla had arrived? And Junio said that he only heard last night, when he got back from town.' He waited in that pointed way, again.

'That's right,' I acknowledged.

'So Hortius asked why – in that case – a messenger had not been sent to us – at that point – with the news. A reasonable question, would you not agree?'

I was about to point out that I had sent a slave – the wretched Rastus, with terrible results – but my patron raised a hand to silence me.

'Junio replied that by then the day was too advanced. It was getting dusk. There was nothing to be gained.' He looked at me at last. 'Then Hortius said something which I thought peculiar – why hadn't Junio told *his* courier at the time?' My patron took a deep breath and leaned back on his bench. 'Libertus, if you are not forthcoming on your own account, I see that I must question you outright. Do I understand that Hortius sent a messenger to you?'

I gaped. I had forgotten that Marcus would not have learned of that – Hortius had not wanted him to know about the murdered slave. 'I'm afraid so, Excellence. For a complicated reason unconnected with all this. But tell me about Junio, how did he reply?'

'Feigned surprise and asked, with the greatest possible respect, why anybody would expect you to do that? Why should it be of interest to Hortius to know that a kinswoman of Julia's had come to stay and attend her lying-in?'

'Clever!' I murmured, approving my son's speed of reasoning.

'Perhaps. Hortius was rather annoyed at the remark, and asked, why, since you knew that the courier was reporting to the flat, you had not sent the message then and there to me.' He gazed into the empty cup again. 'But it was Junio's reply which interested me more. He said – and these were his very words – "Because you, Senator, had made it clear that your courier's visit should not be mentioned to his Excellence." And Hortius suddenly stopped the questioning. Suggestive, don't you think? So what's going on, Libertus? Are you being recruited to spy on me?'

For a moment I could not believe my ears. I was about to demand how he could think such a thing of me, when I suddenly recalled my own inane suspicions of Tertillius. 'Absolutely nothing of the kind – if Hortius had tried it, I would have told you so at once.'

'Then why was he sending secret messages to you?'

'Only one message, to say my slave was dead. Hortius killed him, though he called it an accident. I think you mentioned it yourself.'

Marcus looked at me with dawning horror on his face. 'Your slave? Junio did say something . . . So that is really all?' He shook his head. 'I heard there'd been some sort of accident.

is in town – I told the household that she was not to be informed, unless and until you instructed otherwise.'

'Better to keep it that way, as long as possible. I wish I knew some way of making her agree to talk to him, at least. Though perhaps the banquet – I could invite her then?'

'If she knew that he was there she would refuse to go.'

'But if we kept it from her? She might even be flattered to be asked – if she supposed the feast to be in honour of the birth – which it partly is. She's female, so she's not affected by the curse – only a simple cleansing ritual would be required before she came. And at a public gathering she could not make a scene . . .'

I made a little face. 'Excellence, I should not be too confident of that. And it would not be fitting to invite the wives of councillors, when your own is unable to attend. Though perhaps if Druscilla could be entertained elsewhere – in a private house with one of the other ladies, possibly – they could join us for the entertainments afterwards. Not Julia, of course.'

'She would not have fulfilled the purification period, or be strong enough,' His Excellence agreed. 'But Gwellia might . . .?'

'Not Gwellia,' I said. 'She has been ill herself. But you heard what Tertillius said – his widowed sister has come to live with him? Perhaps she could be invited to be the chaperone. It might give Tertillius the opportunity he seeks to be obliging to the Senator. It would be most convenient of all if Druscilla could stay there overnight, before and after the projected feast. That would make it easy for her to attend – his house is very close to the vintners' banquet hall. And it's too far for her to take a litter to the villa afterwards – there is always danger in the woods at night. Besides, if she is with Tertillius, and Hortius does not know, it would prevent him trying to seize her between now and then.'

'But can't you . . .?' Marcus let the question linger in the air.

'Excellence, do not look hopefully at me, I cannot with propriety invite her to stay here – an attractive widow who is no kin of mine! – without at least my wife as chaperone. And it's surely wiser if I'm not associated with her, more than I can help – Hortius is already displeased enough with me. I imagine Tertillius will be flattered to be asked. And did you not tell me that he'd known her family in Rome? That would make it entirely appropriate.'

'Libertus, old friend' – the hand which clasped my shoulder was warm and gentle now – 'I can only thank you for you counsel, wise as usual. I will approach Tertillius at once – supposing the old man is up to it. Anyone can see he's paid too much for the hall hire and the wine. Perhaps Hortius is right in calling him a fool.'

'Nothing excuses that public insult at the games! You heard about the incident, I suppose?'

'From Hortius himself! He seems to think it an enormous joke, and what he says about Tertillius is unrepeatable. He's so contemptuous of everything he finds that I worry for Glevum – and my part in it – when he writes to the Provincial Governor.' He sighed.

'Which he intends to do?'

'A letter by official messenger within a day or two, he says. If he gives an unfavourable account, it could affect the whole colonia.' He looked at me. 'That's what made me so uneasy, I suppose. Libertus, I am sorry that I doubted you. And I'm sorry about Rastus, I genuinely am. Thank you for your help. Give my thanks to Junio, as well. He has proved a worthy son to you today. If you weren't here, I almost think I'd offer my patronage to him.'

'I'm flattered, Excellence,' I murmured, since something was evidently required. But even as I spoke there was a rapping by someone at the door, that proved – when Servus answered it – to be none other than Junio himself.

SIXTEEN

He did not wait to be announced, but darted in, accompanied by Tenuis, and signalled to Servus to quickly shut the door.

The newcomers were looking a little damp and cold. Clearly they had been caught out in the rain – which was evidently falling, though I had not noticed it – and I thought for a moment that this explained the breathless haste. So as Junio allowed his attendant to remove his cloak, and I rose to greet my son, I instructed Servus to poke our brazier into life.

'Then light the one next door,' I said. 'Tenuis can dry off the wet cloaks and sandals over it – and himself as well.'

I turned to Junio, but he was wholly occupied with the ringed hand which Marcus had extended for him to kiss.

'Citizen!' my patron said, as he bowed over it. (If I were wearing a stripeless toga, like my son's, I would have had to grovel to my knees!) Marcus indicated the stool which I'd been using earlier.

It was an invitation which Junio – amazingly – ignored. 'Your pardon, Excellence,' he said, sidling towards the open window-space. 'But I must make sure . . .' He did not complete the sentence but peered into the street – taking care that he could not be seen by anyone outside.

Marcus was looking disapproving, and I was not surprised. No one declines an invitation to sit down with him. 'I thought you had gone with Hortius to celebrate the Ides?'

Junio answered, without moving from his vantage point. 'I did. At least, I followed the procession and watched the sacrifice, but it began to rain so – since it is not obligatory today – I did not wait to partake in the offering.'

There was some sense in this. The sacrificial animal is offered on the altar fire, and when the deities are deemed to have had sufficient of the smoke, the priests first have a ritual sample of the flesh, and then the rest of it is portioned out among the worshippers. (Not always well-cooked, either, in my experience.) If Junio was able to withdraw with dignity, I could understand why he had chosen to decline.

'Bu what about the Senator?' I asked. 'Since you were there with him? I hope he was not offended when you left?'

Junio was still peering out into the street. 'He could hardly object to my abandoning the sacrifice. He did the same himself.' Whatever he had been looking out at, he now seemed reassured and turned back to us.

'You left together?' Marcus and I spoke in unison, like the chorus at a play.

Junio shook his head. 'I was hardly with him. I accompanied him to the start of the procession for the Ides – I thought he might report me for impiety otherwise. But he insisted on taking a leading place in the parade, prancing along immediately behind the haruspex – where I could hardly go – and at the temple steps I lost him in the crowd. But when I was attempting to slip away unseen, I noticed him do likewise.'

Marcus raised a brow in my direction. 'Very odd behaviour for someone of his rank, especially when he'd made himself conspicuous.' He turned to Junio. 'You did not follow him?'

'On the contrary – rather the reverse.' He nodded in the direction that he'd been looking at. 'I rather feared he might have followed me.'

Marcus was astonished. 'But why would he do that?'

'I can't imagine,' Junio replied. 'But it seemed to be the case. When I came out I passed his escort waiting for him on the temple steps. I thought nothing of it and began to walk back here, but when I chanced to look behind, I realized they were there, and I cannot think of anything that might bring them this way. I hurried on and tried to lose them, but there are no crowds today – I'm sure they must have seen which way I'd gone. Ah, and there they are . . .' He nodded in the direction of the street.

I walked across to the window-space myself. The streets were fairly empty, as he said – the shops were shut in any case in honour of the day, and wet weather always drives most casual pedestrians indoors. There was only a skinny street vendor, with a tray of half-congealing pies, huddling under a portico nearby – even the hot-soup counter at the corner of the road had got his shutters down. And, of course, the group that Junio had been talking of.

I saw the escort first. They were dressed to be noticed, in scarlet uniforms and gold-embroidered cloaks – like those Dasypyges had been wearing yesterday, though on these hulking brutes it was somehow sinister. Each man held a cudgel – one hand on the handle, the other cradling its weight – ready to use on any person ill-advised enough to step into their master's way.

Not quite lictors (which the Senator would be surrounded by in Rome) but the next best thing. Dasypyges too, was there. And in the middle of the group was Hortius himself.

He was shorter than I remembered, from my brief glimpse at the birthday sacrifice. But he had the swagger of the fabled elephant – and (just as the elephant is said to be) he seemed impervious to rain. His clothing was expensive: his cloak was indigo (a most costly dye) and the hood (which he had raised, so I could not see his face) was trimmed with sable fur. The purple stripe around his toga-hem was of impressive size, and even from here I could make out the gold with which he was adorned – anklet, bracelets, and no doubt rings as well. Not a man who was afraid of thieves.

As I watched, the little party paused. They looked around as if uncertain where they were, then after a moment they moved off again and disappeared from sight. Junio emitted a great sigh of relief.

'Gone to the fortress, or to the baths perhaps?' That was Marcus, who – to my surprise – had come to stand behind us, though I had not noticed him. 'With guards like that to watch his clothes he need not fear to leave them while he takes a plunge.'

'Certainly not the direction of your flat, which was where I had expected they would go,' my son replied, as we all three trailed back to where the table was. 'I own I am relieved. I thought they'd followed me. He has a sort of grievance against me and Father, now – having been made to look foolish over what he'd said about his courier – I was afraid I might have led them here.'

'But you came here anyway?' I said.

'I tried to lose them, first, as I explained. But then I decided, if they were coming here, they only had to ask – anyone in town could tell them where the Duumvir Libertus had his flat – and it would be better if there were two of us. Besides, I thought you would be anxiously awaiting my return – though of course I had imagined that you were alone. And someone else has been as well, I see.' He gestured to the silver cups still on the tabletop.

'Tertillius called,' I told him. 'Which saved me the necessity

of seeking him. He gave me his account of what happened at
the games, and was generally fuming about Hortius – who,
incidentally, has insulted him again.' I explained about the
offer of the banquet and the wine – and how we had come to
all be drinking it.

'I'm afraid I have none to offer you,' I apologized. (Junio,
unlike me, is rather fond of wine.) 'The rest of that amphora is
Marcus's of course, and it is waiting for him at the door. Perhaps
you'd like some mead? Though I fear, by now, there's not a
great deal left of that! I should have sent out to the vintners
yesterday, before the merchants shut down for the Ides.'

Junio grinned. 'Don't worry, Father. We shall not go thirsty
overnight. I have some in the workshop – I always keep some
watered wine in store, in case a wealthy customer should call
in person, instead of sending in a slave. And I always keep a
jug of mead as well, in case you happen to call by. Tenuis
can go and fetch them, when he has washed my feet.' He
gestured to the slave-boy who had just appeared – barefoot
himself – with slippers and a bowl. 'You can't believe how
muddy the pavements are today!' He sighed with pleasure as
the sandals were eased off and Tenuis splashed warmed water
on his toes.

I wondered – belatedly – if I should have offered Marcus
this attention too, but my patron chose this moment to declare,
'Then I will leave you and go back to my flat. I should try to
get there before Hortius arrives.' He rose, majestically. 'Who
knows what I might find him doing otherwise? Let's pray he
hasn't lost his temper and killed someone else's slave!'

This was apparently intended as a jest, and I forced a smile
as I pressed my lips to the extended ring. Junio scrambled to
his feet and sketched a bow. Servus must have been on the
watch as usual, because he came out with my patron's cloak
and – very deftly – helped him into it.

'I'll meet you at the slave-market, tomorrow, duumvir!'
Marcus permitted my servant to escort him to the entranceway,
where his own slave was jumping quickly to his feet and trying
to pretend that he had not been sitting on the ground. He
picked up the amphora, which was leaning on the wall, and I
watched them as they moved towards the stairs.

'He'll find a litter somewhere, despite the damp, no doubt,' I said as Servus shut the door and hurried back. 'Marcus would be given preference.'

Junio laughed. 'He already has one loitering nearby! I saw it waiting in the alley when I came. And I see the rain has stopped. So now the slaves can go and fetch the drinks. Better send them both – the jugs are heavy and we do not want them spilled! And while they are about it, they can bring the little bag that is hanging up behind the door. Brown linen with a drawstring, you will see the one.' He grinned at the two boys and then at me. 'Nothing too exciting, you'll see when it arrives!'

The slaves set off at once – Servus wearing his own cloak, and Tenuis draped in Rastus's spare one (which was too large for him, but which at least was dry – unlike his sandals which still squelched with every step). When they were out of earshot, I turned to Junio.

'So your trip to Marcus was a waste of time! And I made poor Rastus suffer all that agony, in vain.'

Junio's answer took me by surprise. 'My visit was not a waste of time at all. Quite the contrary. I think I may have saved that courier from the mines. Hortius was inclined to blame him for the whole affair – but I prevented that. Not wise, perhaps, because it made his owner fall into a trap.'

'Marcus explained,' I told him. 'But surely, no one would commit a valuable slave to such a fate on such a slim excuse.'

Junio stretched out his slippered feet and gave me a strange look. 'Hortius Valens might. I've never met a man who roused more fear in me. Reminds me of the image of Nero that one used to see on coins – fat face, thick neck, and discontented lips – though with much less hair, if you can imagine that. Though Hortius has no athlete's body, as we're told that Nero did. He has somewhat skinny arms and legs. Eyes as flinty as a statue's, too. But he dresses splendidly, and is doused in costly oils.'

'No wonder Druscilla does not care for him.'

Junio wrinkled an expressive nose. 'I would not, in her shoes. There's a kind of violent petulance about him when he's crossed – even in trivial matters – that makes him dangerous. One of Marcus's young slaves offended him today, by spilling a few drops of watered wine on him, and from the roar he uttered one would have thought he'd been scalded by a vat of boiling oil. He fetched the lad a blow that knocked him off his feet and spilt the whole remainder of the jug – then insisted that he lick the floor clean with his tongue.'

'Marcus must have been delighted.'

'Marcus was not there. He'd gone downstairs into the court-yard garden by that time, dealing with some brothel-keeper who'd arrived, wanting compensation from the garrison. Something about a girl they'd hired who was now no further use. Marcus had given the garrison advice which hadn't worked – a token payment was insulting, the brothel-keeper said. It took your patron quite a time to pacify the man. The wine was all licked up by the time that he got back and – amazingly – no one so much as mentioned it. Everyone was much too frightened to say anything – including me.'

'I wonder that you were still there at all by then,' I said. 'You had given your message to Marcus, after all.'

'I was just standing helplessly about – I hadn't been dismissed and I could hardly go till Marcus gave me leave. But the brothel-keeper came and made such a fuss – threat-ening petitions to the Emperor – that Marcus had to take him outside to calm him down.'

'If this is the problem that I heard about before, then that was Hortius's doing too,' I said.

'That would explain the atmosphere when Marcus did return. Less warm than a fish that has been dead a week: I've never been so pleased to get away from anywhere, even if it was only to join the procession for the Ides! Frankly, Father, the sooner Marcus gives the man his bride and lets the pair of them get back to Rome, the better it will be for everyone. Speaking of which, you've met her, haven't you? What is it that the bully finds so irresistible?'

'I really can't imagine,' I replied. 'Shapely, I suppose, but she would not appeal to me. Forceful – as you might suppose from what she's done, and hugely critical of everything she finds.'

'She has one thing in common with her would-be bride-groom then! I was only in his company for less than half an hour and he must have found at least a dozen things to criticize. Glevum is so cold, so damp, so small and insignificant, compared to Rome. Our streets are narrow and the food is terrible. Even the statues in the forum are inferior – in size, in quality of marble and in workmanship.'

'Hardly polite, when he's the self-invited guest—' I broke off as Servus and Tenuis tumbled in, each carrying a brimming, heavy jug.

I changed the subject quickly. 'So,' I said, 'let's warm a little mead, and have some bread and cheese. Later tonight we'll send out for some soup, perhaps.' (Lighting a cooking-fire in an apartment-block like ours is prohibited by law – though people do, of course, and not infrequently cause inconvenient fires. Everyone who can afford it pays a subscription to the incendiary guild – and sends out for food, unless like Marcus, one has a separate kitchen in the inner court, outside.)

'What about a game of Tali, meanwhile,' Junio said. 'To help pass the time?' He signalled to Servus. 'Let me have the little bag.' He opened it, revealing a set of polished knucklebones.

I sighed. Junio has always enjoyed a round of balance-stones, which he calls a 'game of chance' – though from the way he manages to make the pieces fall, it appears no accident. I learned long ago to wager only tokens, never coins. But it was raining again, and there was little else to do. So I agreed to play.

I got so engrossed that I forgot my worries for a while – probably what Junio had intended all along. So that's what I was doing when Gwellia disappeared.

SEVENTEEN

We did not hear about that until the next day, of course, and then not until after we had purchased the new slave. Minimus – who had run all the way to Glevum to find me at first light – had either not known where I was due to be, or (more likely) had forgotten my appointment in his acute alarm.

It is strange now, looking back, to remember how important the visit to the slave-market then seemed. For one thing, I was anticipating meeting Hortius Valens for the first time, face to face, and the prospect filled me with alarm. I was not sure that I could summon Junio's speed of wit if the Senator decided to ask me awkward questions about his elusive bride – and if my fumbling answers caused trouble, it would not be just for me. I was likely to implicate my patron and my son as well.

So I slept very badly, despite the Roman goatskin bed – one of the luxurious furnishings included with the flat – and I was up and stirring long before the sun. Last night's taper had gone out long ago, and as I got up in the gloom I blundered into little Tenuis, who – in the absence of Minimus – had been snoring on the mat. He leapt up instantly and fumbled for the latch. But opening the bedroom door did little to dispel the dark.

'Master?' He had felt his way to the window-shutters now but removing them admitted only the faintest extra light. 'You are up very early. Is everything all right?'

And – all unknowing – I murmured that it was. 'Light a taper from the brazier-embers in the outer room, then bring it here and help me wash and dress. I have an early appointment at the slave-market with Marcus and his guest and I have promised to be there by dawn. We are to meet the dealer for a private view before he puts his wares on general display.'

I heard him groping along the passageway. A moment later there was a distant glow of flame and he reappeared, triumphant, with a lighted taper in his hand.

'Master, I have brought the silver oil-lamp, too.' He put the little object on the clothes-chest as he spoke and touched the candle-flame against the wick. He must have primed it, for it flared to life at once: vague shadows became objects with colour, form and shape and the room took on its usual comfortable look.

Tenuis rubbed his still-reluctant eyes, but he was keen to please. 'Shall I fetch your washing-water now? It will be very cold.'

'No matter. And if there is any bread and fruit, I will have that as well. And a drink of milk, if it has not gone sour. Otherwise some water from the fountain will suffice, though it's not as pleasant as what we get at home.'

He grinned. 'But it does not require a long trek to the spring!' He set off with the taper to fetch what I required.

We had been speaking softly, but we had managed to rouse Junio all the same. He had been asleep in the second bedchamber next door, but he came out – in his undertunic and bare feet – announcing his intention of accompanying me. 'If Marcus is with you, you'll be glad of my support – otherwise he'll simply choose the most good-looking slave. And as for Hortius . . .' He left the rest unsaid.

'Then you'll have to bring Servus to attend you,' I replied – not at all unwilling to have his company. 'You dare not go unaccompanied if the Senator is there – you'll be in the forum in your toga, and he's certain to rebuke you otherwise. And speaking of togas, it will have to be my curial one, I suppose – though that's a nuisance, after all the rain. Tenuis will simply have to walk behind me lifting up my hems.'

And so it was, a little later, we set off from the flat, leaving it empty (which was most unusual, and called for the greatest care in leaving a brazier unattended but alight – so as not to have to kindle it afresh on our return). Servus was entrusted with locking up the door, and it was he who carried the heavy key on a thong around his neck, and held the blazing torch aloft to light our way. There were no litters plying at that early hour and Tenuis was entirely occupied with managing my hems.

It was not actually raining now, but the morning air was damp and cold and I was glad when we reached the forum marketplace. Despite the early hour there was already bustle here. The first farmers were beginning to arrive – driving their poultry or livestock to the butchers' stalls, while their wives bound bunches of kindling wood for sale or struggled with crates of turnips, leeks and cabbages. The licence-holders were setting forth their wares – horn combs, brooms, used armour, cooking-pots – everything from lengths of cloth to ointment-cures for dandruff and bad feet. The permanent fish-market was half-open, all its lamps were lit, and its slaves were busy putting pails of squirming eels on display outside the door. And there, beside the steps to the basilica, the slave-dealer had erected his temporary stage, ready to display his merchandise – but neither he nor they were currently in evidence.

Neither, for the moment, could I see either my patron, or the Senator, though as we made our way across the square, I located Marcus. He was standing near the money-changer's niche, where an enterprising fried-bean seller had brought in a brazier on a hand-cart, and was dispensing snacks – and a crowd were huddling round it, as much for warmth and light as for the expensive salty treat. His Excellence was heading up the queue (he would have taken precedence, in any case), though he seemed out of place in his patrician clothes, and accompanied as he was by a couple of his smartly tunicked slaves.

He must have been watching out for me, because he raised a hand in greeting as he waited for his food – a handsome helping – for which, I noted, he did not have to pay (doubtless because his presence was a great advertisement). Then he came sauntering across, carrying the brimming bark-cone carefully.

'Excellence!' I said as he approached. I did not kneel – I was not dressed for grovelling in the mud – but I bowed and kissed the ring, and so did Junio. 'There is no sign of Hortius, as yet?'

Marcus gave me a strange look, and there was laughter in his voice. 'Nor will there be, today.' He took a palmful of the salty roasted beans. 'He sends apologies, but he is indisposed.'

'Ill?' I spoke sharply, thinking idiotically of Druscilla's poison threats.

'Shaken rather. He has had a fall. No serious damage, I don't think, excepting to his pride.' He lifted his hand and let the hot beans trickle down into his mouth – clearly enjoying his plebeian snack – then held his fingers out to have them wiped clean by his slave. 'I should not say this, but I find myself amused. He has been bragging since he got here of his prowess on a horse, and yesterday – after the procession

for the Ides – he took it on himself to hire one for a ride, with
two of his escort and that courier of his.'

Junio gave a sideways glance at me – that clearly was where
Hortius and his men had been headed yesterday, when we had
seen them from the window-space. 'Lucky to get one, on a
festal day. Unless, perhaps, he had arranged it earlier?'

'I doubt that,' Marcus said. 'He scarcely had the chance. Got
the fort to do it, I shouldn't be surprised – they have the right
to requisition anything – and it was a horse they'd had before,
specially requested by the courier, it seems. He'd had it when
his own was being fed, and had found it good to ride.'

'But it proved frisky, unexpectedly?'

'So it would appear – though Hortius decided that it was
deliberate, and was furious, of course. This time he really did
consign the courier to the mines.'

'Dasypyges?'

'That's the very man. Though his name will not be important
any more – not that it was very flattering anyway. Hairy
buttocks, if you translate the Greek. Anyway, he had commended
the horse to Hortius as particularly swift and easy to control.
So Hortius hired it – only for an hour – to inspect the territorium, he says, though I'm inclined to doubt that. Why the
army farm should interest him, I cannot see. I thought it more
likely, when I heard of it – which was not till afterwards – that
he'd gone out to the villa to try to claim his bride, but he
clearly didn't. They would have sent me word at once. Perhaps
he really had been asked to report to Clodius on the
territorium,'

'More likely just a pretext to get the fort involved, so they'd
arrange a horse,' I said. 'And the farm is in the same direction
as your house. The courier knows exactly where that is, of
course, and could have led him there.'

'You may be right, old friend.' Marcus seemed surprisingly
unperturbed. He shook a few more beans into his palm.
'Perhaps his real intention was to ride that way and demand
to see this wretched girl of his, if only through the gates.' He
shook the remaining beans at me, inviting me to share, which
– since they were greasy – I respectfully declined. 'I would
not put it past him to have forced his way inside – if it were

not for a superstitious terror of calling down the curse. His fear of that is as strong as you supposed.'

'But, whatever his intention, he did not succeed?'

Marcus gave me that peculiar smile again. 'I don't believe he even reached the villa walls. While our *expert* rider,' he emphasized the word, 'was exhibiting his skill – galloping far too fast by all accounts – the horse reared up at something in the road, and threw him to the ground.'

'A nasty tumble, I believe you said?'

Marcus gave a very unsympathetic laugh. 'Hurt his leg, his back, his seat and most of all his pride. But bad enough, at first. His escort had to scoop him up, lie him face-down across the horse, and walk him gently home – including through the streets of Glevum, which must have created quite a spectacle! With all his fine clothing spattered in the mud, Most ignominious.'

'But he is not badly hurt?'

'Nothing broken, I could tell that at once – though he made sufficient fuss. Most of the damage was to his dignity – though of course he swore that it was someone else's fault.'

'The courier, in fact?'

'Of course. Hortius declared it was a plot to have him thrown and killed, and – when they met an army detachment on the road – ordered that Hairy-buttocks should be taken to the fort, and consigned to the commander as labour for the mines. As the owner, and a senator, he could do that, of course.'

I made a face. 'But what a fate to wish on anyone! Though – from past experience – anything might be better than incurring punishment from Hortius himself.'

'Who was well enough to give the order, though he had been thrown?' my son enquired. 'I thought, from your description of how they brought him home, that he'd lost consciousness.'

Marcus grinned. 'I don't believe he really did at all – though he pretended to have done, to minimize disgrace. He seems to have been giving orders perfectly, when there was nobody about to witness it. Though, when he got back to the flat, I called the medicus and had him bled at once. He cannot say that I did not attend his needs.'

'Good of the medicus to come out on the Ides'. If I had

tried to call on him on such a day, I doubt he would have seen me – duumvir or not. 'No doubt he has prescribed his usual cabbage soup?' I joked.

My patron shook his head and gave another grin. 'We were able to call on the army surgeon from the fort. Hortius's men were going there anyway – to return the horse – and the Legate was content to lend his services. The man was very good, looked Hortius over and decided right away that what was wanted was hot yarrow poultices. Boiled up with turnip in equal quantities, and applied between hot cloths, four times a day until the stiffness goes.' He was grinning widely now. 'Makes Hortius squeal – which, I'm inclined to think, was half of the intent. But certainly effective. He's out of bed today.'

'Hot poultices are painful, as I have cause to know,' I answered with a smile. 'Gwellia sets much store by them for colds. They'd make a Stoic groan.'

Marcus chuckled. 'So would the penalty that Hortius had to pay when they returned the horse – two hours late and on a festal day. All the fault of Dasypyges again and further proof that he deserved his fate! I can almost feel sorry for the courier, though I disliked him thoroughly. For Hortius I feel no sympathy at all. Serves him right for being discourteous enough to set off riding out of town without so much as mentioning it to me. And I can't be sorry if it hurts his purse as well.'

I thought I understood where this was leading. 'So, he now feels unable to replace my slave?'

Marcus tipped his bean-cone upside down and shook the few remaining shards into his hand, then put those in his mouth and rubbed his fingers clean of salt. 'On the contrary,' he said. 'I pointed out that he had promised that in front of Junio, who is a citizen – which makes the offer legally enforceable. I thought for a moment that he might refuse – inviting you to sue – but he's given me some gold. Not a fortune, but enough to purchase something quite agreeable. And now's your opportunity. Here comes the dealer now.'

I turned and saw the arrivals for myself. The slave-trader was a man I recognized – I'd had vague dealings with him once before. He was thin and swarthy, with tawny hair and a bushy beard to match – giving him a scruffy, but energetic air.

He wore a long cloak of handwoven Celtic plaid, open at the front to display an ochre tunic reaching to his knees, and a thick rope belt tied twice around his waist – in case it was needed to subdue or bind his wares. He was accompanied by a team of hefty servants of his own, straining – like oxen – at a sort of cage on wheels, in which could be glimpsed a portion of the morning's merchandise.

There might have been perhaps a dozen people in the cart: everything from aging maidservants to skinny, frightened boys, all in shackles and all completely nude, the better to permit a purchaser to view before he paid, and check for any infirmity or obvious disease. (Clothes could be purchased later, at a premium, if required – though the second-hand tunic stall would do a lively trade.) The second cage, which was now being wheeled in behind, clearly held goods of higher calibre: two young, strong and healthy-looking men, and several pretty girls – all equally unclothed – at whose appearance the crowd began to hoot and whistle in appreciative mode.

'Come!' Marcus took my elbow to guide me to where the platform was, but Junio was tugging at my arm the other side.

'Father!' he murmured. 'Have you seen who's just arrived?'

It was Tertillius, looking highly satisfied, accompanied by an aged manservant – his steward, I presumed. And shuffling behind them with his legs in chains – half-draped in an old cloak and nothing else, his hands still roped together – was a despondent slave, who'd clearly just been bought. We were early at the market, but Tertillius had obviously been earlier still.

The purchased servant was an odd anomaly. He was well-built and youngish but completely bald, with eyebrows of a startling but uneven shade of black – as though they had been painted on with squid ink – and his near-naked body was scratched and nicked from head to foot as if he had been mercilessly barbered recently. His hairless head was bowed and his eyes were on the ground. Then the steward jerked the leading chain and the slave looked sharply up.

I saw the faintest shadow of a returning beard and, with a shock, I realized who it was. The distinctive curls and body hair had gone – the man was scraped and razored everywhere – but it was Dasypyges, the pompous courier.

He was not looking very pompous now.

EIGHTEEN

'By all the gods! That's Dasypyges!' I exclaimed. Marcus followed the direction of my pointing hand. 'I do believe you're right – although I would hardly have recognized the man. So he really has been sold. But not, apparently, consigned to labour in the mines.'

'That's surprising,' Junio put in. I had almost forgotten he was standing at my shoulder. 'They are always looking for more labour than they get merely by people being sentenced in the courts. Didn't you say that he was taken to the garrison? That would seem to make it certain. The army runs the slave-force and controls the mines.'

'Perhaps the dealer found out he was there and somehow persuaded the commandant to part with him – knowing that he could get more for him elsewhere. Which gives me an idea.' Marcus was looking animated now. 'Has Tertillius already bought him, do you think?'

'It rather looks like it,' I said. 'He must have been here even earlier than you – obviously the dealer would otherwise have given you first choice.'

'Then would he take an offer? That man is highly trained and – if he's been sold with a bad character – could only have fetched a fraction of his proper price. I would be happy to find a post for him.'

To say nothing of irritating Hortius, I thought, but all I said was, 'For your own establishment perhaps? Not really a replacement for my Rastus, though – for one thing, I don't need a courier. And for another, I did not like the man. Nor would he be happy to be a slave of mine, I think. It would be a painful reminder of how low he'd come. Have him for your-self by all means, Excellence, but I've seen a little fellow sitting in that cage who quite appeals to me. Very small and skinny, but he'll be keen to please.'

Marcus looked disbelievingly at me. 'Not the little blond one who's missing his front teeth? He can't be more than eight or nine years old. He'll have no skills at all. Or stamina! His legs are thinner than a pair of sticks. And he bears a brand, so he's been a slave before – his previous owner clearly did not think much of him.'

'Oh, his master was satisfied enough – it was his new mistress who complained.' I smiled to see Marcus looking mystified at this. 'I have seen the boy before – and so have you. Tertillius brought him to my apartment yesterday – though obviously he's now part-traded him for something that his sister would approve. But the boy is willing, and he'll soon gain strength with food. I think I heard his name is Ossius – which fits. It means the bony one.'

Marcus sighed. 'I didn't notice. I don't look at other people's slaves. But I could buy you two of him, I think, with the purse that I was given. Do you not think that Hortius deserves to feel the sting?'

I shrugged. 'Nothing will bring Rastus back, in any case,' I said. 'But perhaps we could purchase some clothes for Ossius, too? I'm sure I could rely on you to drive shrewd bargains there.'

That was not necessarily the case – people set high prices for anyone of rank – but Marcus is susceptible to flattery. He immediately adopted an efficient air. 'Beginning with the slave-dealer,' he said, pulling his cloak around him and making as if to move in that direction instantly. But then he paused. 'You are quite certain that you want that puny lad? Personally . . .' He let the sentence hang.

I knew what he was hinting at. This was delicate. The slaves at the apartment, like the flat itself, were only by a convenient fiction mine at all. So Marcus, clearly, had every right to choose. But the last thing I wanted was that pompous courier.

Junio caught my eye and found exactly the right remark to make. 'If you do not want to keep that slave-boy in a year or two, Excellence,' he said, 'Father will have trained and fed him and he'll be coming to his prime. You should be able to get a splendid price for him.'

My patron brightened. 'Well said! I should have thought of that. Very well. Wait here, you two, and I'll see what I can do.' And he set off striding towards the slave-dealer – who was overseeing the unlocking of the cages now, and flicking his whip to urge his wares into a straggling line.

We – four of us, in fact, but Marcus didn't count the slaves – watched my patron and his pages as they walked across the square.

The slave-trader was clearly flattered to see him approach. He relinquished his herding to his assistant slaves and turned at once to welcome Marcus with a smile. There was a brief discussion – very brief indeed – during which the dealer looked very much surprised, and then the boy was indicated, unshackled from the line and led away to have his brand-new leg-irons struck away again, at the ironsmith's workshop close nearby – kept for this very purpose. One of the attendants followed with a cloak, which Marcus had selected from the pile – obviously it had been included in the price.

I turned to Tenuis. 'Well,' I teased, 'do you approve my choice?'

Tenuis looked up at me, but did not smile. 'He will be frightened, now, but when you get him home and he has settled in, I think he will be tearful with relief and gratitude. Anyone could have bought him, and used him fearfully.'

'I am relying on you, Servus, to ensure he'll have no time for tears,' I said, embarrassed by this show of sentiment. 'You will have to train him, since I'll often not be there. You can start by going to rummage on that used tunic stall, and see if you can find him something that would fit. And sandals too, if there are any to be had. I see that Marcus has already purchased him a cloak.' Though that would have been much cheaper on the used-clothes stall, too, I added inwardly.

Servus grinned and set off on his errand at a trot while Junio and I strolled over to take possession of our newest slave. I tried to give him a reassuring smile, but his eyes were fixed on Marcus, counting out the coins.

The slave-dealer stuffed them quickly in his purse, anxious to get back to auctioning his wares. Prospective purchasers were already walking round, prodding them and examining their teeth – and, in the case of the women, their other attributes. Tertillius was among them – clearly preparing to bid for a pair of pretty girls.

'I hope you're right in wanting this one,' my patron said, pushing the boy towards me. 'I can hardly persuade him to speak a syllable, beyond his name, but he says you know that anyway. Say hello to your new master, Ossius.'

'Greetings, master.' Ossius was obedient but scared. He bowed, his mumbled answer so subdued that I could hardly make it out.

I nodded. 'I've sent my other servant to select some clothes – with your permission, Excellence?'

Marcus counted out a few denarii and handed them to Tenuis who scampered off to Servus and the used-clothes stall.

'You are generous, Excellence,' I said.

Marcus laughed. 'You could afford to buy a silver necklace for him, if you choose. But you've Hortius to thank. He is travelling with a strongbox full of gold and makes no secret of the fact. He says for expenses – but no doubt bribes as well – to make his journey here as swift as possible.'

'It's a wonder that he was not killed and robbed by someone on the way!' I said.

'Without his escort, perhaps he would have been! In any case, he'd shown me, and could not claim poverty. I insisted on enough to buy a fairly high-class slave though—' He broke off, frowning. 'But speaking of slaves! Isn't that your little Minimus coming into the forum, over there? What is he doing here?'

'Looking for me!' That much was evident. The boy had got up on an empty upturned crate and was standing tip-toe, craning side to side, and scanning the crowd with obvious anxiety. 'There must be some problem.' I was anxious now, myself.

'Is this about Druscilla, do you think?' my patron said. Worry is contagious. 'You said she might be difficult to please. Or, worse, a problem with Julia and the babes?'

'They would have sent a servant from the villa to look for you, in that case, wouldn't they? I fear it's much more likely to be Gwellia's foot.' I was waving both hands above my head in a most unRoman way, and Minimus had finally caught sight of me. He came towards me, fighting through the crowd, and

I went to meet him (easier for me, as – seeing my curial toga – people stood aside to let me pass).

'Master!' he panted. He grasped my hand and held it to his lips, speechless with sudden weeping.

I was really worried now. 'What is it?' No answer, merely sobs that wracked his frame. 'Your mistress, I suppose? Is it her wound again? She's tried to do too much?'

There was a nod this time, and then – perplexingly – a shaken head. Minimus raised his tearful eyes to mine. 'I think so, master, but I really do not know. That is the trouble. She set off yesterday—'

'Set off?' I was disbelieving. 'To where, by all the gods?'

'To your patron's villa. To the lady Julia. She had a preparation which she wanted to present, that after-childbirth cordial to build up strength again . . .'

Marcus said sharply, 'Why should she do that? Did she think my wife in sudden need of it?'

Minimus gazed unhappily at me. 'She'd promised it, you see.' He gulped. 'We were outside the enclosure earlier – the mistress wanted some mallow-root to make a dye . . .' He glanced nervously at me. 'I know, master, that you wanted her to rest but she'd made up her mind that she must be about her normal tasks.'

'Go on,' I said, grimly. 'This promise?'

'One of the villa serving-girls went by.' Minimus's voice was breaking as he spoke. 'The mistress called to her, asking how the lady Julia was, and was told that she was rallying but still very weak. The midwife had sent the girl to find the herb-woman, who lives out in the woods, and ask for a reviving cordial. And . . .' He paused, rubbing his cloaked arm across his tear-stained cheeks.

'And your mistress said that she had a preparation of her own?' Marcus said while I was still considering this news. 'Julia would have preferred that – I am sure. Gwellia's potions helped her once before. But she would never have countenanced the idea of Gwellia walking to the villa with a poisoned foot when a slave could easily have been sent for it.'

Minimus was failing to blink back his tears, and sounded desperate. 'I volunteered to take it, but the mistress insisted she would go herself. She wanted to see the mother and admire the babes.' He looked at me. 'We should not have let her leave the roundhouse, you will say – but how could we prevent her? We are only slaves. She took us with her, for the first half mile at least, but we'd not gone very far before she realized that we'd brought the wrong container. Kurso had picked up the phial which held the poultice mix.'

'She did not give that to Julia? Or drink from it herself?' I knew that I was sounding very sharp, and Ossius – who had just been marched across, proud as an Emperor in a yellow tunic at least a foot too long – winced as though I'd struck him, but I was too upset to care.

Minimus was still clinging to my hand with both his own. He shook his head. 'She didn't drink it. I am quite sure of that. She sent Kurso back to change it – she did not go herself, I think, because her foot was hurting her too much. She'd set off walking well enough at first, but by then she'd started limping heavily. She seemed relieved to have a chance to stop – though she would never have admitted that to us. There's a fallen tree-stump – I think you know the one – and she sat down on it. She said that she would rest there till Kurso brought the jug, and I was to run on to the villa and let them know that she was on her way. But . . .'

'But . . .?' I managed to disengage my hand. 'What? Did she take a sudden turn? Did that foot of hers erupt again?'

Minimus startled me by letting out a wail. 'I don't know, master, that's what I'm telling you. I went on to the villa but she did not come. I waited and I waited – till in the end the steward got concerned and sent that freckled slave-boy out to look for her. I told him where I'd left her – but she wasn't there.'

Marcus muttered, 'Useless!' but the slave-boy shook his head.

'He did find Kurso, who had come back to the spot – with the right concoction – and was wondering what to do. He'd waited a little (in case she'd had a call of nature or something of the kind) and was just deciding that she must have gone on after all when Lentigines arrived. I don't think anyone had really panicked until then.'

'So where is she? Tell me!' I found I'd grabbed him by both shoulders and was shaking him.

Junio restrained me with a gentle hand. 'Don't worry, Minimus, no one's blaming you – my father is just naturally upset. But the worst thing is not knowing. However terrible the news, imagination's worse. So tell us, is she badly hurt? Or has she – the gods send it isn't true – had a return of fever and collapsed and died?'

Minimus shook his tousled head again. 'I've been trying to explain that we don't know. She can't be found. The villa sent a party out at once to look for her, and we searched the roads and ditches. I even went out to the herb-woman, in case she'd gone that way. The woman had not seen her, but she frightened me. Says there may have been a fever to the brain – it sometimes happens with a poisoned wound – in which case the mistress may have lost her mind and simply wandered off into the woods.'

'You looked for tracks – or broken twigs? The tracks of animals?' Junio asked the question which my tongue refused to shape. I seemed to have lost all power of speech, with shock.

'We searched with lanterns, after it was dark, and called and called – but there was no reply. We searched until there was no light to see, then one of the villa slave-boys tripped and hurt himself, so we were forced to stop. They were starting again this morning, as soon as it grew light – but I was sent to find you and tell you she was lost. I don't know if a bear or wolf has taken her – we heard them in the woods – but we can't find the slightest trace of her.'

NINETEEN

Marcus recovered his wits before the rest of us. 'Libertus, old friend,' he said with a seriousness and sympathy rarely seen in him, 'You must get back at once. You'll want to join the search. But it will take too long to walk. Come to my apartment – I was going to suggest you did in any case, so that Hortius could witness that you had your slave – my driver-slave is waiting, and you and I will ride back in the gig. You too, Junio, if you choose to, though it would be quite a squash.'

Junio was looking as stricken as I felt, but he said, 'Thank you, Excellence, but I think I must decline. We brought the mule to town, I had better ride her back – though of course I'll be as quick as possible. Better if Minimus rides with you – he can crouch between you on the floor. He has already run to town. It will be very wearying if he has to run straight back.'

'I'll come home with you, then, Master Junio.' Tenuis was so eager to assist that he spoke uninvited. 'I can trot as quickly as the mule – and then I can take care of her when we arrive.'

Junio looked at me and I assented gratefully. 'Ossius can go with Servus to the flat – he'll have to learn his duties anyway.' I turned to Marcus. 'Unless you think that Hortius will want to look at him?' (This was not a possibility which had occurred to me till now. I could see that the Senator would not approve my choice – though that was the least of my problems at the moment and I really did not care.)

'I don't think that is necessary now,' my patron said, to my relief. 'Later, perhaps, when your wife has been discovered safe and sound, we'll make a point of it – meantime, Servus can try to train and fatten him a bit. But enough of chatter, we are wasting time – and if the herb-woman should turn out to be right, who knows how far Gwellia might have strayed by now. Junio, we will see you at the villa later on.'

My son and Tenuis turned to go, then Junio whirled round. 'Does Cilla know that Mother's missing?'

Minimus had stopped weeping, but seemed likely to begin again at this. 'She's known as long as I have – almost. I called in there at once. We wondered if she had seen the mistress wandering past, but she had not. She was the one who suggested that we try the herb-woman, but when I reported failure there, she was very much alarmed. She left the children with your slave and joined the search herself. She's done the same this morning.'

'Then I must hurry home,' Junio exclaimed, and set off at

a pace which little Tenuis, despite his boasting, found it hard to match.

Marcus meanwhile had sent his servants off to find a double litter to take us to the flat and they returned to say that one was waiting for us at the forum entrance now. In my working clothes I could have outstripped the bearers easily – double litters are designed to take a master and his wife (Marcus used to have one, for a year or two, before his growing family made it inappropriate) and even with lusty bearers they are inevitably slow – the more so when the second passenger is not a dainty girl, but a hefty tradesman in a curial tunic and a heavy cloak. But such official garments prevent the wearer hurrying, and I was glad to ride today. Marcus drew the curtains round us, but we found nothing much to say, and after what seemed a lifetime we arrived outside the door of his apartment block to find the usual crowd of people jostling on the stairs.

Marcus's apartment is a very spacious one, occupying the entirety of the floor above the street, but it is built over a wine store and a barber's shop and the upper floors are given over to more humble flats – progressively smaller with every flight of stairs. It brings him a handsome income, I believe, but at any time of day or night one is likely to encounter other residents, to say nothing of people playing illicit games of dice – and so it was today. I chafed at the delay. But Marcus's servants cleared a path for us (making the gamblers gather up their coins and try to pretend they were simply gossiping) then hammered at the door of the apartment so that it was opened just in time for our approach.

Even then we could not simply instruct the gig-driver and go. The doorkeeper, a hulking giant who filled the passage-space, ushered us inside, and murmured urgently to Marcus. 'Excellence, thank Jupiter you're back. The staff are in an uproar, and don't know what to do. Your illustrious visitor has been quite difficult to please. Every dish they bring him he finds inferior – and says it is insulting to offer him such things.'

Marcus made a wry face at me which meant, 'I'm sorry, but you see what kind of visitor he is!' But all he said was, 'You had better leave Minimus outside the door to wait. Like you, he has enough to bear today.' And with that he followed his little matching slaves, through the spacious entrance foyer (past the marble tables where Rastus met his fate) into the luxurious reception room beyond.

By this time we had been announced, but the Senator, who was sitting on a comfortable folding chair (with arms) – surrounded by cushions and with his foot up on a stool – scarcely glanced towards his host. He was waving away an appetising plate of fresh bread, cheese and figs, while two of his escort stood behind him, near the wall.

I had glimpsed Hortius at a distance once or twice before, of course, but this was the first time that I'd met him face to face. My son had prepared me for the thin limbs and Roman nose – but I had not imagined how the receding chin, the thin hair, downturned lips and fleshy neck would give him the appearance of a discontented frog. The grey eyes which now flicked up at us were as cold as an amphibian's, too, as Marcus introduced me.

'The duumvir Libertus, Senator.'

'I am honoured, Eminence.' I stepped forward, prepared to bow and kiss the proffered ring, but Hortius barely gave me the curtest of brief nods.

'You found him a slave then?' he enquired – of Marcus, as though I were not capable of speech. 'Good. Then perhaps you could turn your attention to your own. The breakfast they brought me was inedible – coarse bread and peasant's cheese. Do they intend to be insulting?'

'They brought you nothing that I do not eat myself,' my patron answered, in a courteous tone. I wondered at his patience – Marcus is not noted for that attribute – until I realized that he was clenching and unclenching both his fists, and that his fury was only just contained.

'I see.' Hortius's thin lips curved in a contemptuous smile. 'Is there nothing better in this benighted isle? I do not ask for exotic luxuries – spiced dormouse or fresh cherries steeped in wine – a simple fine-wheat pancake with honeyed dates would serve, and perhaps some goat's cheese and a goose's egg or two?'

'I will see that some are furnished for you in the morning,' Marcus said – as though these things were not expensive luxuries themselves. 'How are your injuries? You seem a little better, and I hope you are as I am planning a banquet in your honour – in just a day or two.'

'I have already refused a civic feast,' the Senator replied. 'And that was before I had sustained the fall. I think I told you so. Why should I change my mind because you offer one?'

Marcus gave him a peculiar smile. 'Partly because it is my duty, Senator, as senior magistrate, to honour the curia by introducing them to you. And partly because, with the help of Councillor Libertus here, I hope to lure Druscilla to the banquet too – or rather, to the entertainment afterwards – though, of course, I have not told her that you will be there.'

There was almost a gleam in the cold grey eyes at this. 'Splendid.' He rubbed together his jewel-encrusted hands. He glanced at me again. 'I obviously underestimate you, citizen. In that case, naturally, I'll be delighted to accept.'

'I presume that, once you are reunited with your bride, you will wish to start for Rome as soon as possible? You'll wish to take advantage of the feast, I'm sure – the finest food and drink the province can provide – but it is wise to be cautious of rich food when travelling.'

'You are quite right, of course. One would not choose too rich a diet immediately before a journey on the seas – at this time of year, especially. Rather, I think, I will presume upon your hospitality a little more and marry her at once. After the banquet, even, before the guests disperse – that should ensure sufficient witnesses.'

Marcus gaped at me. 'Surely that would be . . .?'

'Unusual? Indeed, but there is nothing to prevent it, under law, I think you'll find. I have a contract ready and for remarriage nothing more is legally required. Though – in order to make sure she does not escape again – I intend that it should be co-emptio. That means there must be bread available for us to share, and I would require you, in your role as guardian, to sell the girl to me in front of witnesses. Magistrates for preference, of patrician blood. I presume that – with the curia present – this could be arranged?'

Marcus looked less than delighted at the plan. 'Assuming

that Druscilla can be persuaded to agree. She must make the public promises. Without that, the contract will not stand in law. And she has shown determined unwillingness so far.'

'Give me five minutes with her,' the groom said silkily. 'She will be persuaded. Few women will refuse when there are daggers at their back.'

'You would threaten her with death? It would make the contract void.' Marcus's face suggested he was horrified.

Hortius smiled. 'I would not propose to do it personally, of course. But if she still declines to speak the words, I will have her declared a public enemy. Her husband was an acknowledged traitor to the Emperor, and she supported him. The penalty is death. And I would be within my rights, as Senator, to see it carried out.'

'She knows this?'

'Clearly – otherwise she could simply have refused to speak the words in Rome. But she has not escaped this wedding, as she hoped. Given the alternatives, I think she will choose me.'

Remembering the poison, I was not so sure, but no one was paying any heed to me. A pity, as I was anxious to hurry home at once – but I dared not interrupt, for fear of losing the offered ride and being forced to walk.

'But how would you propose to take her to your home – which is an important feature of the marriage ritual – seeing that you do not have one locally?' Marcus was asking.

'This flat will suffice as my temporary abode, and after that, of course, I will be taking her to Rome. But if I am to buy her from you, you must first agree, of course, to take her formally under your potestas.'

I could see Marcus looking horrified. His fears of offending the Empress were coming true. 'Perhaps we should invite Druscilla to discuss all this with us?'

'What for? She threw herself upon your mercy, I believe, and you are not acting against her family's wish. They have agreed the union, after all. They are in danger from her dead husband's traitorous actions, too – I think we can agree that they would simply be relieved.' He gave his thin-lipped smile. 'So we are settled upon that. And best we do it quickly, or it will be May, when marriage is officially ill-starred.'

'Not remarriage,' my patron said. 'A widow may—'

But Hortius cut him off impatiently. 'True, but we would not want to tempt the Fates. Make arrangements for somewhere for her to stay in town the night before – this citizen could lend his flat, perhaps, since I understand he has one locally, and obviously she cannot spend it here. That can be the bride's home, for the purposes, and he can hold the scales on which I place the coin.' I felt the full force of the reptilian smile this time – enough to notice that it did not reach his eyes.

Marcus was swift to protect me from the necessity. 'I fear that might not be convenient just now. Libertus has illness in the family – so such an arrangement would invite bad luck. There is a magistrate, however, who might be pleased to help. He has already offered to accommodate Druscilla Livia over-night and provide her with a female escort of patrician rank to attend the feast with her.'

Hortius bowed his head a thumb's-breath, scarcely more. 'Then I'm obliged to him. He can be scale-holder then. See that it is arranged.'

Marcus shot a secret look at me. (I, too, was wondering what Hortius would have said if he'd realized that the desig-nated holder of the wedding scales was the 'old fool' of whom he'd been so publicly contemptuous.) To the Senator, however, he turned a sober face. 'I will attend to it at once. And now, with your permission, Eminence, I fear that I must go. I have promised the duumvir that I will take him home. He has a family crisis and I've delayed him far too long. I only brought him here to let you know that he had got his slave, and acknowledges that proper compensation has been—'

Hortius turned his flinty eyes on me again. 'Then I hope that your new servant is better than your last.'

I needed all my years of training as a slave to hold my tongue at this, and merely murmur, 'I am contented with my choice. But with your permission, Worthiness, there is some-thing I would like to ask – on a different matter.'

Hortius summoned a thin smile. 'Of course. You have helped me with Druscilla, as I understand. How may I assist?'

'That crisis that His Excellence was speaking of. The truth is, Eminence, that I have lost my wife.'

'Then, Councillor, you have my sympathies, of course. What would you have me do? Find you another? Come man, do not look so shocked. The best cure for widowhood, as I know myself, is to acquire another wife as soon as possible. Someone young, for preference, who might bear you sons – you are not yet past fertility, I think. Or, you may have a candidate in mind? If there are any legal problems with the match, believe me, duumvir, I'll see they are undone.'

'Your pardon, Eminence,' I said, when he permitted me to speak. (It would have been insolent to interrupt.) 'You misunderstand. I mean that she is physically lost. She's disappeared and we don't know where she is.'

Hortius looked puzzled. 'Then how can I assist?'

'If I understand correctly, Eminence, you were riding yesterday – somewhere in the direction of my patron's country house – before you, regrettably, had your accident.'

I'd angered him by speaking of that indignity. 'And what of that?'

'Only that I wondered, Eminence, if you'd chanced to see a woman on the road. Unaccompanied and walking with a limp?'

He did not answer for a moment but frowned the more – as though reluctantly struggling to recall. 'An ancient hag in Celtic garments? I think I may have done. What moves you to enquire?' A strange expression flashed across his face. 'Don't tell me that she was yet another slave of yours?'

I was so appalled at his description of my precious Gwellia that I could not say a word.

Marcus did it for me, in a warning tone. 'Not his slave, Hortius. He is asking if you saw his wife.'

TWENTY

For a heartbeat Hortius seemed a little less than confident, but immediately he was himself again. 'Then it cannot be the person that I saw. This was no citizen. What Roman matron would be on foot, alone, on a dusty country road? With no attendant slave? In public, without a cloak or veil and with her foot wrapped up in filthy rags?' He waved a dismissive hand. 'The woman was just a Celtic peasant – and an aged one at that. Dressed in one of their frightful garments, too, made of some barbaric homespun plaid.' He did that thin-lipped smile again.

'Nonetheless, Eminence, that was indeed my wife,' I said, suppressing my rage at his insulting words and waiting for abject apology.

I should have known better. Hortius shook his head. 'Impossible. The woman was a slave, or had been one at least. I noticed there was scarring visible, on one shoulder where there had been a brand.'

I saw a look of panic cross my patron's face, and I knew why, of course. It is not illegal for a citizen to free and wed a slave, but emphasizing Gwellia's servile past might draw attention to my own – and it was Marcus who had proposed me, as a duumvir. What would the Provincial Governor say to that?

But I had more urgent matters on my mind. Hortius's description of my wife persuaded me that he had seen her on the road. He had insulted me – unpardonably – but if I offended him, he would be only too delighted to obstruct, and it was essential that I found out what he knew. So I managed, with an effort, not to show my rage.

'You saw her, obviously, Eminence. Do you remember where? Which way was she going – towards my patron's villa or away from it?'

The Senator allowed his face to take up an expression of incredulity. 'Merciful Jove, that really was your wife? My dear councillor – but how was I to guess? I assumed that she was someone's ancient dye-slave, or something of the sort, who had been turned out on the road, as being too old and too infirm to be of further use.'

This time it required all my years of training as a slave not to seize him by the shoulders and shake him till he squeaked. 'Then you were wrong in your assumption, Worthiness. That was indeed my wife. And my question was an urgent one.

Please be good enough to answer it.' My tone was studiously level, but I earned a warning look from Marcus.

He clearly felt the need to be the diplomat. 'Remember, duumvir,' he said, 'my houseguest is a stranger hereabouts. He cannot be familiar with the roads. It might be difficult for him to tell you exactly where he was.'

It was a reasonable point, as I acknowledged with a bow 'Though I'm sure the Senator could help us a little further, if he searched his memory.' I saw Hortius bridling – an obvious danger sign – so I softened this with a little flattery. 'He is clearly observant, as his description shows. Did he, for instance, happen to see a fallen tree beside the path? My servants say they left her sitting on a stump.'

It was patently risky to insist like this, and I braced myself for the inevitable wrath. But Hortius seemed to consider, briefly, then gave me a chilling little smile. 'Councillor, forgive me. I had a fearful fall – my memories of the incident are blurred.'

'But . . .' I was ready to begin, but he raised a hand to silence me.

'I saw the woman – that I do recall – but then my stupid horse reared up and threw me to the ground, and after that . . .' He gave an airy wave. 'I must have struck my head. I cannot really tell you any more.'

Could not or would not? It was impossible to say. Whatever I suspected, it could not be proved. By such means, I thought, do senators survive a succession of different emperors in Rome. The toad-like features were set in an expression of regret, and there was little I could do but bow acceptance and withdraw.

But as I stepped away, I glimpsed something in his eyes. They were mocking and triumphant. He was enjoying this. I do not often permit myself to hate, but I felt something very like it at that moment, looking at this spoiled, vindictive creature on the chair, whom riches, birth and power made unassailable.

This gave rise to a sudden, interesting thought. Hortius flaunted his patrician birth. Then where was the famed patrician pride? He was so ready to cite that accident – a humiliating lack of horsemanship, which any well-bred Roman would find shaming, normally. And which a moment earlier he'd been keen to minimize, himself!

Till now I'd only been concerned for Gwellia's whereabouts, but now I began to worry whether she'd been hurt – by that rearing horse, perhaps? Hortius was so evasive – so ready to claim his brain had been befogged – that I was suddenly suspicious that he might have things to hide. I could imagine him refusing to rein in for what he probably did imagine – at the time – to be a homeless peasant on the road. And Gwellia, with that poisoned foot, was in no state to move hurriedly aside.

'You say the horse reared up – what happened to her then?' A dreadful picture flitted through my head. 'She was not trampled underneath the hooves?'

Hortius held my eyes with his own stony ones. 'I'm quite sure she wasn't, Councillor – though, as I say, I have no clear recollection of events.'

'Then perhaps your escort might enlighten me?' I nodded towards the two attendant guards. Marcus was frowning and sending signals with his eyes, seeking to communicate that I should say no more, but if I was courting trouble I no longer cared.

Hortius did not even glance towards his men. 'They cannot help you. They were not with me at the time.'

'And the ones who were?'

'Are at the garrison today. I will send and ask them, natur-ally, if you require – it is the least I can offer, since I find you in distress.' The words were civil, but there was again that hint of mocking in his tone, especially when he added – with a smirk, 'But I doubt my men will have anything of conse-quence to say.'

Of course they wouldn't, I realized with a certainty that stung – not if they placed any value on their future lives. They would remember nothing – until they had instructions as to what they were to say, or (more disturbingly) what he wished them to forget. I was about to mutter that we would not trouble him, privately thinking we might call in and catch them unawares, but he was ahead of me.

'I'm sure they'd only tell you what I've already said.' He favoured me again with that reptilian smile. 'My men were naturally too concerned for me to pay attention to what – we thought – was simply an unwanted and discarded slave. But, if you think it will assist . . .' He clicked his fingers. 'You two, over by the wall.'

His pair of guard-slaves – who had been in earshot anyway – now came forward and stood before his chair.

'Hurry to the garrison. Ask the other members of my staff – especially the escort who were riding with me yesterday – if they have anything to say that might help this duumvir to locate his missing wife.' He paused, then added in measured tone, with careful emphasis on every word, 'It seems she was that peasant woman we encountered on the road, just before I had my fall – though I doubt that they'll be able to remember more than that. You understand?'

They murmured that they did.

'Good. If they have anything whatever to report, you are to send a message to His Excellence at once. To his country residence?' He glanced at Marcus who nodded his assent. 'To his villa then. The garrison will afford a courier – since I no longer have one – I am sure. Indeed, on second thoughts, tell them to send a message anyway – so there can be no doubt of their receiving this command. Is that instruction clear?'

'Perfectly, master,' said the larger of the men. He and his colleague saluted, bowed and left – and I saw the look that passed between them and their master as they went. So much for trying to interview the escort guards! Hortius had signalled that they were not to talk to me. Or, indeed, to anyone at all.

Hortius saw that I had realized this, but he seemed more gratified than otherwise. 'I am sorry that I cannot help you further, Councillor,' he said, in a tone which was not sorry in the least.

Was he hiding something or simply enjoying the power to torment? Marcus was making furious gestures at me to desist, but I was desperate. I flung myself upon my knees before the Senator.

'Worthiness, you know what it is to love,' I exclaimed. 'You've travelled to the farthest outpost of the Empire in pursuit of someone who was to be your bride. And,' I had an inspiration, 'I believe you lost a wife you loved, so much that you were famous for indulging her.'

Hortius merely looked stonily at me. 'And how, exactly, did you hear of that?'

Marcus was still anxious to play the peacemaker. 'Worthiness, your reputation as a loving husband had preceded you. Tertillius was talking of it, when you first arrived. Naturally Libertus has also heard of it – which is why he has been helping me to bring about a reunion with your second bride.'

Hortius simply went on gazing at me like a basilisk, so after an awkward moment my patron spoke again. 'It was the duumvir's suggestion that Druscilla might be lured to this banquet, and thus reunion with you.'

It was brave of Marcus to attempt to champion me like this – he could not afford to alienate his visitor – but Hortius refused to be impressed.

'But he did not choose to let me know at once that she was here, so I was obliged to learn that from the garrison next day. That is the counsel that you so admire?'

I could not let that pass without remark. I scrambled to my feet. 'But how could I know then that you had an interest in her presence, Worthiness? The lady did not mention you at any time – simply claimed kinship to the lady of the house. She asked me for discretion and I respected her request, so when I sent to Marcus – as I did at once – I told my slave to speak to no one else. And if Rastus had not paid for his obedience with his life, no doubt you would have heard the news before you did!'

This was specious, but Hortius Valens could not know that – and it clearly made him think. For the first time I saw a flicker of doubt across the adamantine stare. I pressed my small advantage. 'But I am not here to talk about my slave – whom you have in any case replaced – but my wife, who is irreplac—'

I was interrupted by a rapping at the door. Marcus looked at me in some surprise. 'I wonder who that is, at this morning hour?'

We did not have long to wonder. The doorkeeper was already

ushering in a purple-striper with a page. It proved to be Tertillius, accompanied by a pretty pageboy – possessed of all his teeth – that I had noticed him eyeing at the slave-market. Tertillius allowed this lad to divest him of his cloak then hobbled forward on his stick to shake arms with his host.

'Marcus, forgive my intrusion at this hour.' His reedy voice was feebler than before. 'I have just learned that Hortius had an accide—'

I saw the look of fury cross Hortius's face. 'Nothing of the—' It started as a roar, and I thought that he was going to order the old man from the room for insulting him, but Marcus intervened.

'This is Councillor Tertillius, whom I believe you've met. And you will meet again. He has kindly agreed to act as temporary host to a visitor of mine, a female relative of my wife's, and provide a chaperone, in order that she may be present at that feast that I propose.'

Hortius gave us a poisonous glance, but modified his tone dramatically. 'Tertillius, it is civil of you to enquire. The fall was not severe. Nothing that a little rest won't cure, though my memory of the incident is unfortunately blurred.' He extended one ringed hand towards his visitor.

Tertillius was flattered by this unexpected warmth. 'Worthiness, I have brought an unguent and a draught to soothe the pain. Do me the honour of accepting them . . .' He quavered over to bow and kiss the ring – then broke off in surprise when he caught sight of me. 'My dear Libertus – I did not see you there. You look distraught? Is all well with you?'

Hortius was every inch the great patrician, now. 'The Senator is unhappily alarmed about his wife. She is missing and it happens that I passed her on the road, before I had this little mishap with the horse.'

Tertillius turned his pale blue eyes on me. 'Gwellia, missing?' He turned to Hortius. 'Then we must help him all we can. Libertus is quite famously devoted to his wife.'

Hortius made an expansive gesture with his hand. 'Then we must hope that they will be reunited very soon. And as for helping, I only wish that there was more that I could do. If we had realized who it was, we might have paid her more attention at the time. But as it is, we must not keep him further from his search.' He gave that smile that did not reach his eyes. 'And Marcus too, since he intends to drive him home. Tertillius here can keep me company – if one of the slaves will bring a stool for him.'

Marcus looked surprised – as well he might – at Hortius giving orders to his household in this way, and also at his choice of company. Tertillius, though, seemed only too willing to pay court. He bowed – so low I thought that he would fall – then took the proffered seat and motioned to the pageboy to hand him the bag that he was carrying. From it he produced an elaborate ointment jar, and a fine bronze stoppered jug – which Hortius accepted, glanced at and set instantly aside.

I looked at Marcus, and he looked at me. 'Then with your permission, we will leave you, Eminence. The sooner we can join the search, the greater chance we have of finding Gwellia alive.'

Tertillius tore his eyes away from Hortius's face. 'Great Minerva, duumvir? You really fear for her? I assumed that there had merely been an argument. But if she's wandered in the forest and has lost her way . . . I know she gathers dye-stuff and if she met a wolf . . .? I hear they have been heard in the forest recently.' He was agitated now.

It fell to me to calm his panic – and my own. 'She was on the pathway, last time she was seen. Then Hortius had his accident and no one's seen her since. She had a foot that was poisoned by a nail, she can't have wandered very far with that. I was simply asking Hortius to tell me what he knew.'

'Then let me send a message to my house.' Tertillius was all concern at once. 'It happens that I have a manservant who's an expert horseman, too – he'll help to look for her.' He motioned to his page who hurried to his side. 'Go to the hiring stables at the southern gate and arrange for a horse to be waiting for him there. I will pay them when he returns the animal. Then take word to Glaber that he's to ride out and join the hunt.' His servant bobbed a bow and scurried off, and Tertillius turned to me. 'Pray Jove you find her soon. Everybody knows bad humours can ensue from poisoning. There could be fever and delirium.'

Hortius gave an exaggerated sigh. 'I only wish that I could do as much. But of course my escort do not know the area. Though rest assured, if anything unfortunate should somehow have occurred . . .'

I gasped in horror – was there something that he knew?

He quelled me with a glance. 'For instance if she stumbled into a ditch and hit her head – or was carried off by wolves – which Tertillius persuades me must be possible, since she was apparently alone and injured in the woods all night. Or even bears, Marcus tells me there are some hereabouts . . .'

I closed my eyes. I had been trying not to think of this, but it was true.

'Then, of course, I would be anxious to do anything I could,' the Senator went on, oblivious to my pain. 'But remember what I said. No wife is irreplaceable, whatever you may think – not even my first one, as you remarked yourself. There must be wealthy widows, even here, who would be glad of your protection.'

'Enough of these grim imaginings,' my patron said, seeing that this notion was causing me distress. 'Gwellia is more likely feverish and lost, and trying to shelter somewhere in the trees. The sooner we are searching, the sooner she'll be found.'

'By all means, Marcus, take your leave at once and take no thought for me,' his guest replied. 'When Tertillius has gone I will attempt to rest. All this excitement has quite wearied me. Though perhaps on second thoughts I will after all partake of a little of that fruit and bread and cheese.'

TWENTY-ONE

After a few instructions to Marcus's driver slave we were on our way, to my profound relief. After Hortius's pretence at sympathy, I wanted to send a rider as soon as possible with orders to the search party to look in every single ditch within a mile.

We collected Minimus, who had been squatting on the stairs, awaiting us, then my patron turned excitedly to me. 'I wanted a word with you where Hortius couldn't hear. I know you thought of calling at the garrison to interview his other guards, but there is no longer any point – he's ensured that they won't help. But I remembered something . . .' He paused and gave me a triumphant smile.

I was in no mood for playing games. 'Hortius and his men encountered a detachment from the army on the road, shortly after the famous accident?'

He looked a touch deflated. 'So it occurred to you as well? Mars knows what they were doing on a country road like that – foraging for firewood or something, I suppose – but if they were in the area, they may have seen her, too. And they know the whole vicinity. So they could tell us exactly where she was.'

'Supposing that we can discover who they were!' I said. 'There are always army parties going out on fatigues, either as punishment or requisitioning supplies. It could take hours to find the men involved, and that would mean unfortunate delay.'

'That's where I might be of use,' my patron said. 'The new commander did not start off very well with me – because of rumours from Imperial spies – but these days he seems anxious to atone. The army keeps records of everything it does. So – since the fort is on our way home anyway – perhaps we could call by and see if he can give me any information which would guide us in our search.'

I was touched that my patron should include himself – or propose this strategy at all. But I had an urgent proposal of my own. 'With your permission, Excellence – of course – I'd rather go to Tertillius's house, as fast as possible. He spoke of somebody called Glaber, but I'm sure he must be talking about Hortius's ex-slave, the one that he purchased in the slave-market today. He told us yesterday about the establishment he kept before, and there was no mention then of anyone likely to be skilful on a horse. And if that is Dasypyges, I want to speak to him. He was present when Hortius fell, I think you said. Blamed by his master for the accident, in fact?'

Marcus nodded thoughtfully. 'And if it's Hairy-buttocks (which I imagine that it is, and probably delighted to be given a new name!) he will feel no loyalty to his former master now, after having been cast off and destined for the mines. You think he will be able to identify where Gwellia was seen? I suppose he has ridden that way several times.'

'To my house as well as yours,' I pointed out. 'He should recognize the route. And perhaps he can also tell us – more importantly – exactly what occurred. Hortius talked about her "possibly" falling in the ditch – I think he knows she did. Dasypyges could tell us. But we must make haste to catch him, or he will have had Tertillius's message and gone to join the search – if in fact he does that. If I were his new master I would not have let him go alone.'

Marcus looked aghast. 'You think he might be tempted to escape? But that would be a capital offence.'

'I think it is a possibility. He will reason that Hortius's bodyguard might be there, and they would report his presence to their master, instantly. In which case he could find himself being repossessed and sent back to the mines. Hortius has influence enough, and is capable of petty cruelties like that.'

'So Dasypyges might feel that running away was worth the risk?'

'All the more reason to hurry to the house.' I was impatient now. 'There should be time to get there before the page arrives – he had to go to the hiring stables first. But a carrying-chair would get there faster than I could go on foot.' I nodded towards some litter-bearers loitering hopefully. 'I presume that chair is waiting for Tertillius. And I do not have the fee, in any case, I came out to buy a slave – or have bought for me – and did not bring a purse,' I added hopefully. Marcus could be generous when he chose.

'Leave it to me.' He sent his servants off to summon it, citing his name and rank so that it came at once. 'The bearer-boys can take you first,' he said. 'Tertillius won't be needing this for a little while. I'll leave a page of mine to tell him that it will return for him – and I can walk, for once.' That was gracious of him, I have never seen Marcus voluntarily go anywhere on foot. 'I will meet you at the south gate with the gig and meanwhile I'll call in at the garrison, in case the commander knows something that might help. But first . . .' He produced a purse and paid the litter-boys. 'The chair can take you to Tertillius's townhouse first, then wait to bring you to meet me at the gate.' He saw my doubtful look, and misinterpreted. 'You can repay me sometime when it's convenient.'

He moved away, accompanied by his remaining page, while Minimus helped me up into the chair. There wasn't room for him as well, of course, and he was left to hurry after me, and came panting up as the boys put down the litter and helped me out of it.

'Considering what I've just done to Tertillius,' I murmured to my slave, 'I only hope they stay and wait for me. I would have declined to pay until we reached the city walls – but Marcus paid the fare so probably they will. And here we are, I think.'

The entrance to Tertillius's house was rather a surprise – just a narrow alley between a row of shops – but there was a proper gate with a surly gatekeeper, who grumbled as he undid the locks and admitted us into the wider court beyond. He did not offer to escort me at the door, so Minimus ran ahead while I followed at the maddeningly slow pace demanded by my robes.

The courtyard was surprisingly agreeable, since it was hemmed in all round by other properties, but none of these had rear windows so it was not overlooked. It was a smart little courtyard, with bushes, statues and a pond – and a fine house beyond. I'd heard about this building – it had a history: originally built for another councillor who'd perished in a fire, it had enjoyed a reputation for bad luck for years, and stood unoccupied, until Tertillius had acquired it, at a famously low price. I had never visited before and I was impressed.

Not even Marcus lived in splendour such as this (though rumour says he was offered this property himself at the time, but declined it on the grounds of the expense. Tertillius is regarded as an ineffective fool, but he'd shown some vision here.) One thing was certain: as a place to bring Druscilla, this was excellent.

I was greeted by a stooped and aged steward in a dark green

Grecian robe, with long flared sleeves which emphasized his bony arms. 'Greetings, duumvir.' He creaked into the low bow appropriate to my rank. 'If you wish to see the master, I fear you come in vain. My mistress, however, may receive you. If you'd like to follow me?'

He led the way into a handsome atrium with richly painted walls, and furnished with vases and statues set on marble plinths. But there was also a wooden form, with cushions, where visitors might sit, and I was shown to that while the ancient steward led Minimus away to the servants' room elsewhere.

I did not have long to wait. I had scarcely time to notice the fine mosaic floor (a depiction of the seasons, and well-done – though not by me) before the old retainer hurried back again, accompanied by a woman of advancing years, whom he announced as 'the lady Fulvia'. She was accompanied by a pretty little maidservant in blue (one of the comely girl-slaves from the market, I realized, though now decorously clad).

'Citizen Libertus?' Fulvia was neither young nor handsome but her voice was musical.

Clearly this was Tertillius's sister – one might have guessed it from her features at a glance, though she was of middle height and plump where he was tall and thin. Her tunic and stola were of sober blue, adorned with sombre jet, and her hair was veiled – but, like Druscilla, she had not drawn the veil across her face. The effect, however, was quite different. Fulvia's skin was pale and parchment-like, as her brother's was, though there was no hint of his fragility. She had a pair of startlingly blue eyes, which were looking at me now with sharp intelligence as I returned her bow.

'Can I be of some assistance, Councillor?' She saw me hesitate, and immediately gestured to the steward to withdraw.

Clearly a lady of some character, I thought. Most dependant widows would have taken to their room and declined to meet visitors without the master there. (Especially male callers who turned up unannounced!) But this one had not only done so, she had now dismissed her male attendant, too.

I found myself in a dilemma now. I had not expected to be received like this.

How could I courteously request to see Dasypyges? (Or Glaber, as I must obviously call him now.) It is not usual – or polite – to call upon a servant rather than his master. But Gwellia's welfare was at stake and so I blundered on. 'I saw your brother at the market, earlier,' I said. 'I believe that he'd just bought himself a courier.'

Fulvia gave me a rather puzzled smile. 'A courier? I don't believe so, citizen. He did buy several slaves today, it's true. This girl, and another one for me – her counterpart is shopping for me as we speak – a pageboy for himself, and a steward – that is all. And not a day too soon, we have been honoured to be asked to accommodate a guest – a distant relative of the Empress, I believe. But not a courier, I think.'

I frowned. 'I saw a man he'd purchased – fairly young and strong and obviously shaved.'

'Ah, that would be the steward. Glaber is his name. Bought at my personal urging, I'm afraid, the present man – the one who let you in – is ailing and forgetful and will have to be retired. Though the replacement does not promise to be a great success. I shall be obliged to tell my brother so.'

'May I ask where he is now?' I was aware that sounded rude.

Fulvia assumed that I was talking about Tertillius himself. 'He did bring his purchases back here – I needed my attendant urgently, and the new steward is being fitted with a uniform and instructed in his duties at this moment – but he went out again. He intended to visit someone called Marcus Septimus – perhaps you know the man? I didn't meet him, though he called here yesterday – he's the one who asked us to have this guest, in fact. I understand he's the senior magistrate and playing host to a visiting senator from Rome.'

She paused, allowing me just sufficient time to say, 'I know him very well.'

'Tertillius managed somehow to fall out with him – the visitor, that is,' she went on, ruefully. 'Not a good idea because the man's related to the Provincial Governor. But Marcus mentioned that he'd had an accident, so I persuaded my brother to take him an offering of peace – some balm and soothing mixture that I brought here with me. It happens that I have

some skill with herbs. Tertillius was unwilling – feared he was
likely to be snubbed again – but in the end I talked him into
it. It's possible that you still might catch him at this Marcus
person's flat.'

'I know,' I said. 'I've seen him. I came from there myself.
My business here is with the manservant he bought. The one
that you call Glaber. I think I know the man. I recognized him
when I saw him at the auction, earlier.'

Fulvia looked doubtful. 'So he was a courier?' she said.
'That might explain the problems we have had. He hardly
seems to know what is required—' She broke off with a little
gesture of dismay. 'Though, of course, I do not mean to criticize my brother's choice.'

I was impatient, but I needed her to help. 'The fellow is
intelligent and no doubt he will learn.' I assayed a little smile.
'But it's as a courier I've come to see him now – if he has
not already left.'

'Left?' I saw by her expression that this was not the case.

'Your brother sent a message, by that new page of his,
giving instructions that Glaber – who is a splendid horseman,
by the way – should assist me in a search. I take it that the
order has not yet arrived?'

'Not to my knowledge certainly, but I will send and ask –
since, of course, if Tertillius sent you, that changes everything.
I was wondering if I should let you talk to this new slave or
not. I will have him sent for.' She turned to her maidservant.
'Fetch Glaber here at once.' Then, as the servant hurried to
obey, Fulvia leaned towards me, saying in an undertone, 'And
if you think to buy him back then, citizen, please do. I do not
think that he will suit this house at all.'

Any more than he would have suited mine, I thought. 'I
was not his owner.'

She shook her head. 'I wish I knew who was. I fear my
brother may have been misled, and purchased someone of bad
character.'

'Glaber . . .' (the name, which ironically means 'bald', did
not come easily to me) 'was unfairly blamed for things that
weren't his fault – but to my knowledge he was skilled at
what he did, and there was no suggestion of dishonesty.' I was

surprised to hear myself defending him. 'But you're dissatisfied?'

'He's has no notion of supervising staff – he simply shouts at them, and has no idea of anticipating wants. I had to send for him and warn him, quite severely too, that if he did not learn a little more humility, I would see that he was sent back to service in the mines – from which, I understand, my brother rescued him. Glaber's former master must have been remarkably displeased, surely, to have sentenced him to that?'

'His former master was easy to displease,' I said. 'Glaber was the servant of that visiting Senator.' I was straying onto dangerous territory here, and I hurried on, 'Which reminds me that my patron – the Marcus Septimus that you were speaking of – wishes to ask an additional favour of you. I know you have agreed to have Druscilla here.'

'And to accompany her to a civic feast, I understand – though for some reason she is not to know the guest of honour's name.'

'Exactly. Because he wants to marry her – and there is a proposal that it should happen then and there.' I explained Hortius's plan, including the idea that Tertillius might hold the wedding-scales.

'That is unorthodox!'

'But legal, and might save the lady's life.' I outlined how her husband had joined the rebel force. 'So not only her welfare is at stake but her family's too – the bridegroom had their blessing for the marriage long ago.'

'And she defied them?' Fulvia sounded outraged at the thought. 'Young women have no sense of duty nowadays.'

I took a risk. 'Her groom is confident that she'll accept him, when she is forced to face the facts. But it is essential that she does not know about it in advance. She is a wilful spirit – as she has proved by coming here, alone – and it would mean trouble for everyone – your brother most of all – if she should run away again. So your discretion is imperative.'

Fulvia said firmly, 'I can hold my tongue.'

I had seen little sign of this so far, but I bowed acknowledgement. 'You would oblige my patron, greatly, and Hortius as well.'

'I should be delighted to act as chaperone.' Fulvia seemed quite delighted by the prospect, now. 'And I am quite certain that Tertillius could be persuaded to play his part as well. Leave that to me—' She broke off as the maidservant appeared again. 'But here is the courier that you want to see. I will withdraw and let you talk to him. Until we meet again, then, Councillor.' She offered me a hand, and I bowed over it, then she and her serving-girl withdrew and left me alone with Glaber, as he now called himself.

More than his name had altered. If I met him on the street I would not have known him, I am sure. Now that he was hairless, and the eyebrows having lost something of their dye, he looked much older – perhaps the result of the uniform he wore. He was dressed exactly as the aged man had been (except that the long green robe did not quite reach the floor, or cover up his wrists). The borrowed drapes constrained his movement and gave him dignity, though he had lost his distinctive swagger anyway. There was also a brand-new slave-disc round his neck, saying in large letters, which I could read from here: 'Glaber, steward to Tertillius the magistrate – return this man if found'.

He was looking very anxious as he glided in, and the bow he gave me was unusually deep. 'Councillor Libertus.' He was flustered and alarmed. 'I am told you have come from my ex-master and want to speak to me?'

'I do,' I said, but before I could explain I found that he was on his knees and clutching at my cloak.

'Citizen, duumvir,' he said, not raising his spectacularly hairless head but talking to my feet. 'Do not send me back to him, I beg of you. The sale was quite legal – the commander told me so. It is true that Hortius intended to commit me to the mines, but what he did was send me to the garrison. And when the commandant realized it was me, he had the dealer called to quote a price for me.'

Of course, when Hortius first arrived in Glevum, he had slept there at the military inn – and Glaber, who had been with him, would have been recognized at once. "The commander had a high regard for your abilities?'

'Not exactly, duumvir.' He raised himself onto his knees and looked up at me. 'He simply realized that – having trained in Rome and being Greek – I might fetch a decent sum. One which he rather needed.'

'For himself?' I was surprised at that. The Legate was fond of luxury, but he was well rewarded and not known for gambling.

A shake of the shaved head. I could still see the marks where the knife had nicked the skin. 'He wanted it to settle an uncomfortable debt. There was a man harassing the garrison, it seems, demanding compensation for something Hortius did. The army would not pay it – it could not be justified. And Hortius had refused. This was a way of achieving settlement.'

'The brothel-keeper whose best girl was spoiled for further use?' I motioned him to rise.

'That news had reached you, Councillor? So there is a problem with the sale?' The slave looked unhappy but he did not rise. 'I was assured that it was binding – that I was someone else's now, and therefore beyond my former master's reach. But of course, you'd know, you are a magistrate.' He gave a sigh which almost melted my hostility. 'Has Hortius written to the Governor about that?'

I felt a shiver of anxiety, myself. 'My role as duumvir?'

He looked up at me as if I'd lost my wits. 'About my sale, Councillor. I knew he would be furious if he knew that I'd escaped his savage punishment and the commandant agreed. He told the slave-trader as much – so I was shaved and sold off as an indoor slave. I hoped that – being confined to someone's house – I might escape attention until Hortius had gone. But, since he sent you here, I gather he's found out.'

'Not as far as I'm aware,' I said. 'I did not tell him, and I doubt Tertillius will . . .' I saw the look of undisguised relief, and added, rather cruelly, 'So, since I'm sure you would prefer that it remains that way, I suggest that you tell me quickly what I want to know. Incidentally, he did not send me here.'

He goggled at me, scrambling to his feet. 'Anything within my power, duumvir.'

'Then listen carefully, and think before you speak. I have a problem, which I think that you can solve. Hortius will not help me – he claims he does not know, because he hit his head when he fell off his horse. An accident for which he blames you, I understand? Answer truly, did you deliberately choose a skittish mount?'

Glaber snorted. 'I certainly did not. It was a splendid animal – very well-behaved. If the man were not so violent it would have served him well, but he cut a switch and would insist on whipping it to urge it on, and the poor thing got more jumpy by the mile. Until at last, when something startled it, it reared up violently.'

'And threw him?'

'More that he slithered off. If you have some interest in the horse, I will take you to the stables where it lives and point it out. But I fear at present I do not have much time. Immediately after you had summoned me, I received a message from my new master's page that my presence is urgently required elsewhere. If Hortius does not want me, I should obey at once. Searching for a missing woman in the woods – the errant wife of some town councillor.' He sighed. 'I only hope that my ex-owner's men are not out looking too. They would betray me to Hortius at once.'

'I know you have instructions to join the hunt,' I said. 'I'm returning there myself. But the missing woman is not the caped and stola-ed Roman matron you suppose. They are looking for that peasant woman with the injured foot – the one your party encountered yesterday. Don't bother to deny it,' I added hastily, seeing that he was about to speak. 'Hortius has admitted that you saw her on the road. That is what I want to speak to you about.'

He was looking at me very doubtfully. 'I have told no one anything. Does Hortius claim I have?'

'Hortius does not even know that I am here. But what he said about her frightened me. I am her husband, as you may have guessed by now. She was already injured and I fear she may be hurt again.' I saw the troubled look that came into his eyes, but he said nothing, so I pressed again. 'Is it true, as I suspect, that she was frightened by the rearing horse and fell into a ditch?'

TWENTY-TWO

Glaber took a moment before he spoke at all. When he did it was in a troubled tone. 'You are quite sure, duumvir, that we are speaking of your wife? I know you have a roundhouse, and live in semi-Celtic style, but this woman was a . . . I took her to be . . .' He tailed off, embarrassed.

'Someone's ancient dye-slave, turned out from the house as of no further use?' I snapped. 'Hortius explained how little value you all placed on her. But that does not tell me what I want to know. She was frightened by the horses – that I understand but . . .' I realized that he was shaking his shaved head and stopped.

'Rather, citizen, it was the opposite.' He spoke as if he hardly dared to form the words.

I frowned at him. 'I do not understand.'

'It was not so much that she was frightened by the horses, as that she frightened them. She was walking slowly in the middle of the road. When we came round the corner we were travelling very fast – Hortius in the lead was almost galloping. She was alarmed – you are quite right in thinking that – and clearly unable to jump sharply to one side. She threw both hands into the air and screamed, thinking that the horse was going to trample her . . .'

'Hortius assured me that it hadn't!' I was shaking with both fear and rage. 'I shouldn't have believed him.'

'It did not touch her, citizen. It was too well trained. But she had startled it, and it jittered as it veered. It would have missed her, I am almost sure, but Hortius was pulling fiercely on the reins, cursing and lashing at the creature with his switch – so fiercely that it reared up on its hind legs, whinnying, and slid him off its back.' He met my eyes. 'It was an accident.'

That picture might have been amusing at any other time, but all my focus was upon my wife. 'What happened to the woman, that is my concern. If she was not trampled, she still fell into the ditch – that much I learned from Hortius, I think. What happened? She stepped backwards? Is that how she fell?'

'Hortius did not tell you?'

'He declines to say any more than that. Claims he hit his head and can't remember properly. What I want to know is how badly she was hurt and how far, for instance, she might possibly have crawled . . .' I tailed off, reading something in his eyes. 'What is it, Dasy– Glaber? Something I should know?'

'Perhaps!' He glanced around as though he were afraid of being overheard. No doubt he was accustomed to Hortius's spies.

'You may speak freely,' I assured him. 'I am no friend of your ex-master, and neither is this house. Although we are obliged to serve him when we can – which is why Tertillius has gone to see him now – we are not obliged to like it or to tell him anything.'

Gaber looked shaken. 'You do not know him, duumvir. If you cross him – in the slightest way – you should fear for life and liberty. As I am in a position to confirm. I have seen it too often from the other side.'

I said sourly, 'Yet you were proud to be his courier?'

'I was, although I blush to think so now. I thought he valued me – but in fact, of course, I was of no account to him. I was simply part of his show of power and wealth. I should have known him better – and been more afraid. I'd seen the way he treated those who angered him.'

'That being the way that things are done in Rome?'

I meant to be sarcastic, but Glaber said, 'You're right. He modelled himself on Commodus, I think. Not the more recent Emperor – he has no regard for him – but Commodus he served for very many years. He used to help him think of new, ingenious ways of causing suffering—'

'I know,' I interrupted. 'The rumours reached us here. But this does not help me. What about my wife?'

He gave that nervous look to either side again. 'You swear Hortius will not discover that I told you this?'

'Before the gods!' I said impatiently. 'My own as well as yours. Tell me quickly, or, I swear, I will inform him where you are. Though that's not what I prefer. All I want to do is find her – and we are wasting time.'

Glaber swallowed, so hard I saw the movement in his throat. 'Then, duumvir, I must make you understand that Hortius was furious at being thrown. Half-crazed with anger, as only he can be. He whipped the horse until it reared again, then . . . turned the switch on her. He was ranting and cursing . . .'

'You are telling me that Hortius struck my wife?' The words came slowly. I could taste the bile. If the Senator had been there at that moment, I declare, I would have slammed that toad-like face with both my fists. I found myself saying, 'I will see he pays for that.' Those words might cost me dearly, later, but I did not care.

Glaber was looking at me in alarm. 'Do not underestimate him, citizen. He can be dangerous.' He sounded almost human, suddenly. 'You might seek compensation, that he'd understand – dispensing money demonstrates his wealth.'

'And what price does one put upon a beating of one's wife? When you're a councillor and she's a citizen – and already injured, in particular? It was a savage beating, I've no doubt?'

The courier nodded dumbly.

I was by now so angry that I could hardly speak. 'And Hortius will claim, of course, that he did no such thing! Could not have done so, since the fall had hurt his head and he had to be brought home across his horse—' I broke off in disgust. 'I wondered at his readiness to admit to such a humiliating lack of horsemanship! You are going to tell me that he wasn't hurt at all?'

'Oh, he was hurt all right, but that was afterwards.' Glaber was babbling now, as traitors often do. 'After the woman fell he turned his anger on the horse again, brought his switch down on its back and broke the stick. This time it did not rear. It brought its back legs up instead and kicked him hard – so hard that sent him sprawling on the ground. I'd almost swear the creature knew what it was doing. Hortius was dazed and winded – and bruised so much he could not sit upon his mount – and of course he needed someone he could blame. This time it was me – thanks to the leader of his escort for the day. There was no love between us anyway – I was "indoor staff" and had more privileges than him. I heard him whisper to Hortius, then the two guards turned on me. I'm lucky that they didn't beat me to death as well . . .'

I took a step towards him, almost ready to seize him by the throat. 'As well?' I could hardly find the wits to frame the words.

Glaber tried to backtrack and disown his words. 'I can't be sure what happened to your wife – within a moment I was seized and bound and tied behind the tail of the offending horse. She wasn't moving when we left her, that is all I know. I did protest – I said that she might be someone's slave and the owner might be looking for her, and make trouble later on. I was hoping to divert attention from myself, but all it earned me was a gag around my mouth.'

I was not sure that I believed this last convenient element, but I said, 'So they left her, lying in a ditch?'

He shook his head. 'I can't be certain. I could not turn around. Hortius was by this time face-down on my horse, and moaning constantly. If he'd been well enough for us to move at any speed I would have been dragged to death – (which was what they planned, I think) – but as it was we met the army cart and the escort saw an opportunity. They told the driver that there'd been an accident – of my making, which was why they had me bound. Hortius wished to have me taken to the fort and handed to the commandant for consignment to the mines. But we'd just seen a body on the track – it seemed to be a woman, probably a slave – so perhaps they could collect that in the cart as well, and take us both back to the garrison. The soldiers did as they were ordered, they had very little choice.' He shuddered. 'It was a grim experience.'

I had no sympathy to spare for him. 'So my wife was taken to the garrison?' I gave him scant time to confirm this with a nod, before I added, 'Then there's no need to hunt. I wonder what they will have done with her.' The garrison had a hospital, of course, and the medical staff attending it were the best there were – but they rarely dealt with civilians at all, let alone women of no obvious rank. However, it was just possible the commandant would recognize her face, and if Gwellia was to make a recovery at all, her chances were much greater in his hands than anywhere. But speed was of the essence. 'So you need not leave these premises.'

'But Councillor . . .'

I waved his agitation hastily aside. 'I'll let Tertillius know there is no need to hunt. In the meantime, I must hurry to the fort. Please inform the lady Fulvia that I have gone and thank her for her hospitality and help.'

The ex-courier looked as if he might protest again and I said more firmly, 'Send my slave to me and say no more. That is an order, steward, coming from a guest. If you hope to prosper, see that you obey.'

Glaber sighed, but nodded, bowed and hurried off. A moment later Minimus arrived, accompanied by the aged manservant who showed us to the gate.

The litter was still waiting, and I climbed into it, urging the bearers to their fastest speed. They must have caught my tone of urgency, because they set off at a trot, weaving so expertly among the crowds that they left Minimus far behind.

My surprise was doubled, when I reached the fort, to find my patron standing at the gate awaiting me – alone, to the obvious consternation of the man on guard and the goggle-eyed interest of the passers-by. I thanked my bearers fulsomely, gave them the message for Tertillius and got down hurriedly. I was alarmed myself to find my patron standing unescorted in this way – especially in a public thoroughfare.

He clasped me warmly by both elbows. 'You heard?' he said, without preamble, looking at my face.

'She was brought here in a cart!' I broke free of his grasp. 'We have to find what they have done with her.'

He shook his head. I have never seen my patron look so troubled and upset. 'I have enquired. It is too late. There is no chance of that.'

I said, 'But—'

He interrupted. 'Libertus my old friend, do you know what cart it was?'

And suddenly the realization came to me.

The army death cart. I had seen it many times, and even had dealings with it once or twice. An army fatigue party drove around each day, picking up the corpses of unfortunates who'd died, unclaimed, on public roads – from accident, disease, starvation or old age.

This made sense of why the soldiers had been asked to pick the body up – and explained Glaber's shuddering at the thought of his ordeal. The cart would not be empty. There were always candidates, and the cadavers were tipped into the communal pit – along with any executed criminals – covered with earth and lime and left to rot. And my Gwellia was among them. I felt sick and there was a roaring in my ears.

'I knew that you would want to have her back for burial,' my patron said, 'but the army say that Hortius told them there'd been plague about – or rumours of it, which is true, of course – and if she was a victim she could yet pass it on. So today's consignment was covered with a thicker layer of lime, the pit was sealed with earth – and the law will not permit a disinterment now.'

TWENTY-THREE

I heard myself saying, 'We should call off the hunt,' without having the conscious intention of saying anything. (There are legends about warriors who refuse to die and, though carrying mortal wounds, continue with the fight until awareness strikes them and they fall. I seemed to be operating like that, now.)

'Old friend.' My patron's voice appeared to come from far away. 'You're shivering. You've had a fearful shock.'

I glanced down and realized he was right, though I was not aware of feeling cold. Perhaps it was anger – I knew that fury was bubbling somewhere deep within, ready to seize me, body, mind and soul. But for the moment, I was simply numb. I couldn't even feel the paving-stones beneath my sandal-soles – I might have been floating in the air.

I have only the haziest recollection of what happened next. I know that Marcus grasped me by one arm and – together with Minimus (who seemed to have arrived) – personally supported me into the fort. We must have been taken to the commander's private room – I recognized the massive furniture, the ranks of flickering oil-lights and the battle souvenirs – but I have no memory of getting there.

The commander was talking to Marcus, as though I was not there. 'Excellence!' He was obviously distraught, running a distracted hand through his scrupulously sculpted hair. 'I cannot apologize enough. I did not see the emptying of the cart myself – I was dealing with a slave that was brought in bonds to me. I will see the men responsible are punished, you can be sure of that.'

'But they were acting on your orders, I presume? I understand the woman was in Celtic dress, but she must have worn a wedding ring and they should have noticed that. Surely they're trained to look for signs of ownership – before they tip a body in the pit?'

'I taxed them with that very thing, but they swore there wasn't one. But you're right, they were my orders, in a general sense. It is standard practice to lime and seal the pit if there is any threat of plague – and they were told there was. But I very much regret that it is now too late.'

Behind me Minimus let out a wail of grief and disbelief. Obviously he had not heard the news before. 'My mistress? Thrown into the pit. And we cannot have the body. Oh, master!'

I had not realized that I had closed my eyes, but I opened them to find that he was kneeling at my side, pressing his lips to my still-shaking hand. I felt the wet warmth of tears.

His undisguised emotion roused me. 'Do not weep. The time of mourning is not yet.' Some other person seemed to be inhabiting my skin. I was struck through by grief and shock so much that I felt incapable of thought, but this second self was unnaturally calm – and suddenly certain of what had to happen next. 'We will go to the roundhouse – there are rites we can perform, to mourn her properly and say a last farewell.' My tongue and brain were functioning without my willing it. 'A message must be sent to Junio.'

'That has been done already.' That was the Legate's voice. 'I sent my fastest courier.'

'Then I should follow, there is much to do.' I tried to rise, but my legs refused to hold me and I almost fell.

'The duumvir is shaken. Bring a drink for him.'

Two orderlies rushed forward and I was helped back to my seat. A moment later someone was putting a cup of honeyed wine into my hand.

'I'll find him a room here, overnight,' I heard the Legate say, above my head again. 'The one that Hortius occupied is free.'

'I think he would prefer it if I took him home – though of course he's had a shock.' Marcus sounded doubtful. 'Unless you think it wiser that he should not travel yet?'

'We must think about his public dignity, as well. As duumvir he would hardly wish to be observed by the electorate in an unmanly state.'

I lacked the energy to challenge this tasteless quibbling. I did not care who saw me, or what they chose to think. I was not even weeping outwardly – I was too shocked to cry. I rather wished I could – though the Legate would no doubt have disapproved. A man of status may decently exhibit grief, but only as part of mourning rituals – and then generally more for a statesman or general than a wife. (Roman marriage is a businesslike affair and strong affection rarely enters into it; comfortable compliance and an heir are all a man expects. Whereas Gwellia is – had been – the other half of me.)

My patron was ready to apologize for me. 'He was a Celt before he was a Roman citizen. Their mourning customs are not the same as ours. But Celt or Roman – surely – any man would be concerned about the way her body went into the pit. Have you no anxiety yourself? Her unquiet spirit, lacking proper burial?' He sounded uneasy, as if my poor Gwellia might return to haunt him too.

The commander ran ringed fingers through his hair, again. 'Your Excellence is right. I should have thought of it. I will order that three doves be sacrificed at once as a propitiation to the gods. On my household altar. Soldier, see to it.' He motioned to the orderly behind my chair, who saluted smartly and hurried off to arrange the offering. The Legate turned to me, bending down, speaking slowly, as if I were a child. 'Three doves is all that I have available, but I am happy to do more – arrange for something public at the temple possibly? The prospect of a vengeful spirit is not a pleasant one.'

I took a sip of *mulsum*, and found my voice. 'You might arrange to have a prayer disc nailed up for her – on my behalf,' I said. 'And do not fear her ghost. You acted in accordance with the law. If there is vengeance, it will be visited on Hortius alone. This was his doing – even to the rumour that she had the plague – though I accept that he did not know it was my wife.'

Secretly, I was not even certain about that. Hortius knew I kept a Celtic roundhouse, close nearby, and must have heard that, when his courier came, my slaves and I were dressed in plaid and not in Roman robes. Besides, Gwellia would certainly have worn her ring to visit Julia, who had gifted it to us when we wed the second time – and I could guess where it had gone. Though, even if Hortius's escort had wrenched it from her hand, their master had contrived to warn them who she was, and no amount of searching would locate it now.

The Legate cut across my thoughts. 'You wish to make an accusation against the Senator?' He sounded as frightened as he was horrified. 'You'll make yourself a powerful enemy.'

Meaning that I did not stand a chance in court. Hortius had killed Gwellia – I was certain about that. But I had no proof that would convince a magistrate. I dared not mention the beating that Glaber had described. Hortius would deny it (supported by his escort, once again) and I could produce no corpse to show the injuries. And his word outweighed mine in any court of law. All I would do, if I ever tried to sue, would ensure the death of the former courier – he would be 'questioned' by the torturers, as required by law (on the grounds that slaves would either defend a beloved ex-master to the death, or deliberately lie to bring a hated owner down) until he said what the inquisitors required. Or died beneath the lash.

'I have no intention of arraigning anyone,' I said. 'My only claim is that Hortius had her picked up by the cart. I think your own soldiers will attest to that.'

'So he clearly knew that she was dead. Though not of plague, I think. He suggested to us that she fell and hit her head, and might therefore have ended in a ditch,' Marcus said. He was anxious to offer me support, but this was treading on dangerous ground – implying that Hortius had deliberately lied.

Which he had, of course, but I was not concerned with that. 'Once I had learned the nature of the cart, it was not difficult to guess the rest,' I said. 'I should have done so sooner, probably, especially as Hortius had already offered to find me a new wife.'

Marcus shot me an enquiring glance, but the Legate looked relieved. 'Compensation then! In front of witnesses?' he asked.

'Two of the most senior magistrates.' I was thinking much more clearly, though still in the grip of that unearthly calm. 'Thank you for the mulsum.' I put down the cup. 'I think I am revived enough to travel now, so with your permission, Commandant . . .'

'I can provide you with an army cart – an escort, if you like . . .'

'I will take my patron's offer of a ride back in his gig.' I rose, though I was still unsteady on my feet. 'If a mule could be provided for my slave to ride, I would be glad of that – my son has taken ours.' The Legate – still desperate to please – gave the order and I thanked him once again, then I turned to Marcus. 'So, if you are ready, Excellence? It must be well past noon by now and there is much to do.'

Marcus was frowning at me doubtfully. I thought for one moment he was about to demur – for my own safety, probably – but he caught my eye. 'I have my driver already waiting with the gig. You will be at your roundhouse in no time at all.'

That was not wholly accurate, of course – it was a long and jarring ride, though rendered more relaxed by not having a pageboy squatting at our feet. Marcus had decided that we two should ride alone, for my greater comfort, and the last I saw of my patron's serving-boy, he was riding with Minimus behind us on the army's mule.

The driver was the same slave as had taken us before – the one who'd saved my life – so I calculated that it was safe to talk, even supposing he could hear above the clattering of the wheels. I was about to do so when my patron spoke himself.

'You are strained and shocked, old friend,' he hollered, with a supportive frown. 'When you reach the roundhouse you must go and rest. I would ask you to the villa – but . . .' He broke off as we bounced across a set of larger ruts. 'Julia is in child-bed and we have Druscilla there. I wish that we did not. I fear it is her presence which has upset my wife, and caused her lassitude.'

I had forgotten Marcus's worries about his wife, with the tragedy of mine. 'I'd go to Junio, if anywhere,' I said. 'But thank you for the thought. And about Druscilla, I want to speak to you.'

He looked at me, between the judders of the cart. 'You will not wish to attend the banquet now, of course. We will find someone else to bring the ladies in. Even Hortius could not object to that.' He sighed. 'I wish Druscilla had never thrown herself upon us in this way – she has brought nothing but trouble to my house, and yours.'

I took a deep breath. 'But you have not formally accepted potestas, I think?' I gave him time to shake his head. 'Supposing she could be persuaded to come under mine? I cannot like the woman, she is spoiled and vain, but nobody deserves a fate like Hortius. I could spare her that – and am prepared to do so too, after what that monster did to Gwellia.'

Marcus stared at me as though I'd lost my wits. 'Defy the Senator by denying him his bride?'

'It would give me active pleasure to defy him, Excellence. I know something about him that you don't.' I told him the story that Glaber had told me. 'So Hortius did not merely know that she was dead, he killed her. And he would have known, from staying in the fortress recently, how the death cart dealt with even possible victims of the plague.'

'He meant her body to be buried in the pit, knowing that it would instantly be sealed? But why?'

'I think he saw her ring – which she would certainly have been wearing, by the way – and realized that she was no cast-off slave, but someone's wife. And given where she was, and what she was wearing, I think he realized who her husband was! So I suspect – although of course I cannot prove – that he panicked and told his men to wrest it from her hand, and leave her in the ditch in the hope that I would think she'd fallen among thieves. And then he saw the death cart, and the rest you know. If I had not spoken to Dasypyges – Glaber, as he has now been renamed – I might have gone on thinking she'd been dragged off by wolves. He was eager to suggest that possibility.'

It was the longest speech I'd managed since I heard the news, but now the words spilled out of me, like water from a dam – jolting cart or not.

Marcus was looking horrified. 'Old friend, I can't believe it. Can you trust the courier-slave? It is too horrible – to steal the ring as well.'

I shook my head. 'What does that matter, compared to all the rest? Gwellia and I were married, long ago, by hand-fasting and mutual dropping of pebbles in a stream – and that is something Hortius can never take away. But you can see why there's a pleasing vengeance in depriving him of his intended wife – as he succeeded in taking mine from me. Will you speak to Druscilla, and tell her what I am suggesting? Tertillius and his sister will have to know, of course.'

Marcus was frowning. 'There would be some risk to them. And much, much more to you. Libertus, my old friend, you are not thinking straight. You have no claim to family connection with the girl. And, without one, it would seem improper now – taking her into a household where there is no female chaperone. You have no wif—' He stopped, looking as if he wished he'd bitten off his tongue.

'I have never thought more clearly in my life,' I said. 'And your objections are not insurmountable. That could be managed at the feast if the lady Fulvia can be persuaded to assist. She is a lady of high lineage, and does have claims to know Druscilla's family. Any such arrangement would be a sham, of course – that must be understood. It can be legally undone once Hortius has gone.'

'Hortius would make your life a misery.'

'Hortius would have to find me first,' I muttered. 'There are ships in Glevum that would take me north, beyond the wall, where Roman jurisdiction does not run. There's one tomorrow, due to leave at dawn – I arranged a licence for the captain only recently. I could have my things aboard and leave at once. Besides, nothing Hortius could ever do could make me more wretched than I already am. And you need not be involved. Though I should need to attend your banquet, naturally.'

'You are quite sure of this? So soon after Gwellia . . .' He tailed off again.

'I know my wife. She would support me utterly. But make my apologies to Julia. I may not see her before I have to flee. And we must maintain the superstition that there is a curse, till the days of purification have elapsed. Perhaps there really is – I flouted it a day or two ago, and see what the Fates have done to me. Tell Hortius Valens that. We are not out of danger from him, yet!'

But I had to wait until the jolting stopped before I could explain exactly what I planned. The initial part of it, at least.

TWENTY-FOUR

When we had finished our earnest private talk, I looked up to realize that the gig had stopped outside my house – instead of proceeding to the villa, as before. A measure of my patron's sympathy, today. Junio, Tenuis and Kurso were standing by, politely at a distance, but ready at any time to assist me from the gig. I realized all three were dressed in sober clothes. My heart gave an uncomfortable lurch. They were in mourning, and I – as yet – was not.

My patron extended his own ringed hand to help me down. 'Farewell, old friend. I will leave you to your household and your grief. I will draw a contract up, and send a message if Druscilla will agree to sign. Meantime, let me know at once if there is anything at all that you require.'

'I hope she will agree,' I murmured. 'You haven't met her yet!' I paused in the act of scrambling to the ground. 'Excellence, there's one more thing, perhaps. I should be glad to have a cart. I shall have need of one – perhaps for quite a time – and I know that you have several working your estate.'

'But I thought you spoke of travelling by . . .?' He saw me
shake a warning head, and stopped. 'Ah, misdirection?' He
tapped a conspiratorial finger to his lips. 'Have one, with my
blessing. I'll have my servants bring one round this afternoon,
and you can have an ox to pull it if you wish?'

'Thank you, but I prefer to use my own. I am more
accustomed to his ways.'

'Very well. Take your time to do whatever you require. If
you need me, you know where I shall be. Otherwise, I will
see you at the feast. Until then, farewell.' He tapped the driver's
shoulder, and I watched him drive away.

With a sigh, I turned towards the gate, but I did not go
immediately inside. I stood for a long moment gazing at my
home, where I had been so happy and content. It did not seem
appropriate that it should look exactly as I'd left it – so lightly
and so very recently. Every part of it spoke of Gwellia.

There was the dye-house, in which she'd spent so many
hours of steamy industry; the kitchen garden, where she'd
waged a ceaseless war with weeds and pigs; even the ducks
and chickens reminded me of her – grumbling that they mobbed
her when she went to feed them scraps or pecked her when
she attempted to collect their eggs.

And most of all, there was the house itself, the centre of
her life. Our life, together. Smoke was still curling through
the chimney-space – making my heart stop, momentarily, as
though she might after all be there awaiting me. But of course
it was the slaves who'd kept the fire alight. Gwellia was absent,
and was never coming back. I was aware of an unmanly
pricking in my eyes.

'Father?' Junio was murmuring urgently. 'Don't go in just
yet, if you would rather not. There is nothing you can do here,
anyway. Come to us tonight. Cilla has cut extra reeds to
make a bed and is expecting you. Then perhaps tomorrow – if
we've all recovered at least a little from the shock – we'll
work out what to do.'

There was genuine emotion in his voice, as well, though
Gwellia was not his mother, naturally – or only in the sense
that she was my wife and I'd adopted him. In fact, when
she and I were first reunited, there'd been some jealousy,

Junio having been my only slave for years. (Gwellia and I were married when we were young and free, but the slavers who seized and dragged us off had sold us separately, so it was twenty years before I found – and formally remarried – her again.) But a genuine affection had since grown between the two, and Gwellia was devoted to Junio's little ones. Or 'had been devoted' I corrected mentally, and felt the tears again.

'This will get no easier for postponing it,' I said. 'And it is not true that there is nothing we can do. Kurso, run and ask Cilla to meet us in the house. We should perform a ritual for Gwellia. We do not have her body – and the burial that she had is of a dreadful kind. But we can honour her by making her a talisman – and pyre.'

Junio had been raised in Roman households till he came to me so he did not understand at once. 'A talisman? A pyre? Without the . . .' He choked upon the word. 'Without the person?'

'First a talisman to set her free, then a pyre to send her grave-goods after her,' I said. 'And celebrate her soul. An opportunity to praise her life in song – not simply to lament.'

'Then, better after dark, perhaps?' he asked respectfully.

'Better now, while the sun is making its journey down into the west – that is the direction of the islands of the dead. And the wind is taking the chimney-smoke that way. A good omen.' The old traditions rose unbidden to my tongue, and brought strange comfort with them. 'The sky gods will understand the sacrifice. The earth and fire gods too – with every mention of her name. But first the water gods. So, let us make a start.'

I began to walk, now with a firmer tread, through the three-fold palisade and up the path. Gwellia's ducks and chickens flocked around my feet, which almost broke my heart. 'Drive those into your enclosure, Junio.'

'I will tend them for you, naturally. But do you wish to wring the neck of one, for offering? And should we kill the pig?' (At a Roman funeral a pig is always sacrificed, and part of it is buried in the ground.)

'We are not performing that kind of ritual,' I said gently,

as we walked into the smoky interior of the dear, familiar house. 'Where Gwellia is sleeping, she has no need of propitiating blood. Only the talisman. I must be a Celt for this.' I took off my curial toga as I spoke and pulled on a homespun tunic and cloak my wife had made. 'Tenuis, pass me those willow-twigs that she laid by to make a basket with.'

'Can I assist you, Father?' That was Cilla, coming up behind me. The thought was kind but I resisted it.

'This is something that I must do myself.' I took some of the osiers and while the household watched in silence I wove and plaited them into the general semblance of a boat. Then from the bedding-pillows and her combs, I found four strands of her long silvering hair, which I reverently placed in the symbolic craft.

With violent hands I twisted another pair of twigs, this time into a rough figure of a man, to which I tied my heavy fishing-weight. I gave that to Kurso, while I took the boat and led the way towards the little stream that trickled from the spring. The others followed me. Nobody spoke a word.

Then very gently I leaned forward and set the wicker ship afloat, whispering the name of my beloved wife, and calling on the ancient gods of water, wood and wind to accompany her spirit to the afterlife. The little craft bobbed and lurched alarmingly, but suddenly – as though it were a sign – it set itself upright and bore its burden swiftly out of sight towards the sea.

When it was safely gone, I seized the image of the man. 'I name you Hortius Valens. May you be cursed,' I cried, then dropped it in the rapid stream and watched it sink.

I turned to see my family watching me. I had been speaking Celtic – which they did not understand – but the meaning of the ritual was clear.

'Hortius?' Junio ventured.

'He killed your mother, and ensured that she was thrown into the pit. I cannot prove it, and I dare not try. But this' – I gestured at the bubbling water at our feet – 'is cleansing. We have set her spirit free.' It was true, I did feel better for the simple rite. 'Now we must offer grave-goods, things that will serve her in the afterlife. Her shoes and some dye-stuffs and the finest homemade plaid that she possessed. Our homely hearth will be her offering pyre. Kurso, run ahead and collect things for the fire.'

'Should we add her distaff, Father, too?' Cilla murmured, as we walked back to the house.

I nodded. 'I should have thought of it. And anything else you think appropriate.' I watched, approving, as she unhooked the drying herbs and simples from the rack, and took them in to add them to the sacrifice.

'Kurso, fetch me oil, and Tenuis, bring some mead,' I said, but even as I spoke there was a noise outside and Minimus came in, dusty and apologetic and rather out of breath. An army mule is not the fastest mount.

'Master there is an ox-cart at the gate, the driver says you are expecting it. I've left him hitching—' He broke off and looked around, sensing that something sacred was afoot. 'This is for the mistress? Then I must do my part.'

He slipped off his cloak and went to help Kurso fill a little jug with oil, while Tenuis fetched my remaining stock of mead. Then, beckoning everyone around the fire again, I murmured a solemn invocation to the gods, and – each in turn – we placed onto the burning wood the tokens of my wife, while murmuring her name with love and urging her spirit to pass onward to the west.

I poured on oil and mead until the flames licked up, devouring the grave-goods with their crimson tongues. Then – with sudden passion, and not waiting for assistance from my slaves – I seized the bedding rake and pulled into the fire the reeds and straw, where we had lain together in such love and never would again. They crackled as they burned.

I felt a hand upon my shoulder. It was Cilla's and I covered it – in silence – with my own. 'Oh Father!' She broke down completely, and took me in her arms. It was not her custom and it undid me totally. For several moments I clung to her and sobbed. Then I found my voice and dignity again, and – using an old tune I heard my mother sing, and thought I had forgotten long ago – I began my elegy.

'Praise to the lady Gwellia, whose fingers never tired . . .' One by one my household took their cue from me, singing their love and admiration for my wife. Gwellia was honoured. No woman could ever have been offered more respect.

The fire was burning low by now and it was time to act. 'It's done,' I said. 'Cilla, take the loom, the table, and the stools and cooking pots – anything at all that might be of use to you. Equipment is expensive and you have young mouths to feed.'

My daughter-in-law looked doubtfully at me. 'But you will need them, Father. Not the loom perhaps – but—'

I shook my head. 'I shall not be coming here again. I could not bear it. There is nothing for me here – except yourselves, of course – but if I visit, it will be at your roundhouse now. I will take my clothes, my cloaks and tunics and perhaps my hunting knife. Otherwise my town apartment holds all that I require.'

'But Father, the apartment is only yours on loan. You will need things, afterwards. And you would be sorry to have nothing about you that was hers.'

I looked at Junio dully. 'You are right, of course. So, I will take the combs I carved for her. And perhaps, the potions that she made. There are things among them I may need . . . to help me sleep. I will see to that, myself. Meanwhile, Tenuis, put the other things out onto the cart and see they are secure.'

'And you'll want a cup and bowl and spoon for you, and one each for the slaves. And perhaps a cooking pot, and tinderbox.' Cilla was collecting items as I came in again. 'And the fur coverings and blankets from the bed . . .' She handed them to Minimus who trotted off to add them to the cart.

'Cilla,' I said. 'Please do as I require. Don't worry about me. Take away the things that you could use yourself. But do it speedily. The light is fading and I want to pull down the centre of the thatch, and put it on the pyre – along with anything remaining which it's possible to burn.'

'Father, you can't mean it!' Cilla's face was white. 'This roundhouse is your home!'

'From henceforward it is no one's home,' I said. 'I thought I had explained. I invite you to take anything you wish, but what has not been otherwise accounted for tonight, I'll offer on the pyre.'

'But—'

I held up an interrupting hand. 'I assure you, this is for the best. This is the way my tribe has always marked the passing of a chief. Besides, I am about to make a powerful enemy – and I would prefer to burn this down myself than have a bunch of ruffian soldiers come and fire the place. Take everything you can, and seal up the connecting gate between our properties. Clear out the grain-store, too. We'll leave them the dye-house and the slave-hut to destroy, otherwise they might turn their wrath on you.'

Cilla looked startled. 'What is it you propose?'

I shook my head. 'Better that you remain in ignorance of that. That way no one can suppose you were involved. That's one reason why I'm anxious to return to town tonight – I'll make sure that I'm seen. I have to wait for a signal from Marcus, first, that is all.'

'Your patron knows? So it's not illegal, whatever it might be!' Cilla looked relieved and began to gather up the stools. 'Then we shall take these, in memory of you. They will be awaiting your first visit. And, since you wish it, I will have the loom.' She gave instructions to the slaves to take it down, and carry it away, calling as they did so, 'Be very careful as you move those stones – don't let them swing and dangle or they will break the wool.' She turned to me again. 'You'll come and see the children once more, before you leave. I didn't bring them – they are too young to understand – but obviously they will want to say their own goodbyes . . .' She broke off with a sob and returned to taking down the cooking items from the shelf.

With all of us assisting, it did not take long to carry the remaining movables across to Junio's. There were too many items for his roundhouse, really, which made it very crammed, and the excited grandchildren began to talk of putting up another, larger one.

'Your grandfather could help me, when he next comes to stay,' my son replied. 'You are quite certain, Father, that you will not sleep here tonight?' He broke off as there was a tapping at the door, and little Freckle-face appeared, a message in his hand.

'Oh, thank Jupiter, I wondered where you were. There was not anyone next door.' He seemed to recall his mission, and added formally, 'For the citizen Libertus, from His Excellency.'

I put down, untouched, the bowl of soup which had been pressed on me, struggled to my feet and took the little twist of bark-paper. As I undid the scroll, and held it to the fading light, I read the scribbled words: *Not easy, but Druscilla has reluctantly agreed. Had to threaten. Quite a handful. Shall be glad to see her gone. Due with Tertillius tomorrow afternoon.*

'No answer, except thank him,' I said to Freckle-face, and watched him hurry off. I turned back to my little family. 'And now I must get back to the house before the embers die and do what I propose. The children can sleep on the new bed you made for me.' I ruffled their hair, as they shrieked and squabbled. 'I had not intended to be as late as this.'

'I will come with you,' Junio said. 'I'll bring a lighted torch, and extra oil to feed the flames.'

'I still have half a jugful,' I replied. But I was grateful for his company. I sent the slaves to tie the last things on the cart and re-hitch the ox. Then, while Junio's strong arms helped me pull down the thatch, I gave him a private, hasty outline of my plans.

He stopped in the act of thrusting a lighted torch into the pile. 'Father! You cannot! Not even to save that wretched woman from his grasp. Think of the consequences! Hortius has influence and powerful friends. They will hunt you down – and do not think your rank would save you from their wrath.'

I gave him a slow smile. 'As I said to Marcus, they would have to find me first. And as for living with the consequences – that need not be for long. I doubt that otherwise the lady would agree. This is for your mother; my mind is quite made up. So, will you make sure you are not present at the feast? Marcus may invite you – but much better not to go.'

He shook his slowly. 'Well – if you are determined . . .'

'Then it is agreed. Now, here come the slave-boys, put that brand into the thatch. They must not overhear.'

Reeds are quick to catch, but fairly slow to burn and we watched for a moment before I turned away. 'Minimus and

Kurso, come with me,' I said, allowing them to help me with my cloak. 'You're good with animals. You can take turns to lead the ox. Tenuis, you stay here with my son. He will be glad of an extra pair of hands. Won't you, Junio?' I gave his arm a squeeze. 'I'll send word when I can.'

'But master, when shall I . . .?' Tenuis began, but I waved his words away. Then before I, too, began to weep, I urged the ox forward and we lumbered off.

TWENTY-FIVE

I t was almost dusk before we reached the town and for the last few miles we were forced to crawl, part of a long line of carts all making for the gates – wheeled transport is only permitted in Glevum after dark. Already there was shouting and cursing up ahead as drivers prepared to make deliveries of things too inconvenient to be moved by day. Several of the wagons – happily for us – had lighted torches which helped illuminate the way.

We did not take our own cart into town – that would have left the problem of what to do with it – we left it at the hiring stables just outside the walls, where we often left the mule. My intention was also to leave Kurso there tonight to unhitch the ox and bed down on the cart. It is usual to leave a slave to 'guard the cargo' in this way, though on this occasion my only thought was speed – Kurso was too small and timid to be much use confronting thieves.

But when I went to pay the fee, the owner – far from charging extra, which I expected, since I had not booked ahead – insisted on summoning his son to guard the cart for me, while he himself produced a lighted torch and personally accompanied us into the town. He had heard about my tragedy, he said, and was anxious to assist.

Kurso – thus freed to help unload and carry things – was overcome with awe as we passed the sentry on watch, and went through the arch into the shadowed town. He pressed very close beside me, which I could understand. The streets were unfrequented (no unloading here); the dark and silence broken only by a shaft of light and burst of rowdy noise from the open doors of an occasional tavern or a hot-soup stall. I was glad of the illumination of the torch myself, as we came to my apartment block and climbed the unlit stairs.

We knocked on the door and waited – for some little time. We were not expected and the slaves had gone to bed (a practice I encourage when I am not there: it saves both heat and candles and they rise at dawn). I had to fairly batter before we heard the bolt go back. The door was opened half a finger-span and Ossius appeared, clutching a feeble taper in his hand.

He peered at us, obviously dazzled by our brighter light. 'Who are you at this time of night? The master isn't here.'

'He is now,' I said softly, and the slave leapt back with feverish apologies. He let us pass, then helped us to unload our parcels on the floor. I gave the stable-owner a substantial tip, and he hurried off before I changed my mind.

Ossius was apologizing still. 'Master, you were not expected! Nothing is prepared.' He kept darting startled glances at my Celtic plaid, as if unsure that it was really me.

Servus emerged, disturbed by all the noise, still in the undertunic in which he'd gone to bed. Then, seeing who it was, he brought out bread and cheese and a little jug of milk. Not a feast, but I was not hungry anyway. My roundhouse slaves tucked into it, though they were looking as weary as I felt.

I gestured to the bundles still littering the floor. 'This will keep till morning. Kurso can make a nest among the blankets here and I'll sleep with Minimus at my feet as usual.'

But I was wrong on both counts. I did not sleep – I was too full of anger, hurt and grief – but when morning came, I rose to find that everything was neatly put away, though I hadn't heard a sound. Neither had I any appetite, though I pretended to nibble a piece of oatcake which Servus – knowing my tastes – had gone out and bought for me. This morning it tasted like ashes on my tongue.

I was grateful that I'd set myself a lot of things to do. Empty hours would have stretched before me like the sea.

Visiting the temple was the first thing on my list. I'd resolved to make a Roman-style sacrifice for Gwellia, as well. Whatever happened next, I did not wish my fellow citizens to suppose that I'd shown her disrespect.

I had rescued several garments from the roundhouse yesterday, so leaving my other slaves to sponge and air my curial robes (which smelt of smoke and were dusty to the hems) I got Minimus to help me into mourning clothes – a dark-coloured toga and tunic – and set off with him for the Capitoline shrine.

I did not call a litter. I preferred to walk, despite my awkward robes, rather than have time to sit and think. I should have guessed that I would be approached by many previous customers and fellow councillors, who had heard the rumours and wished to sympathize. Cyrus and Decimus Valerius came hurrying across to offer their condolences and ask if the 'dreadful news' was true. I acknowledged that it was, adding that I was on my way to make memorial sacrifice, but that proper Celtic rites had already taken place. Given my audience, that should be around the town within the hour!

At the stalls beside the temple, I bought some incense and a pair of turtle doves, and arranged to have them offered at the shrine at my expense. Even the stallholder had heard about my wife – immediately suggesting a prayer-disc which I could have inscribed for her, together with a curse 'on whoever caused her death'. Minimus looked astonished that I did not purchase them. I told him that both these matters had been attended to – I had forgotten that he had not been there to see the talismans.

Our next task was to call on Tertillius again. My status in this household had obviously improved. This time, though we arrived on foot, we were greeted as honoured visitors. The gatekeeper went so far as to desert his post and escort us up to the inner door himself.

Glaber opened it. 'Councillor Libertus!' he exclaimed, bowing very low. 'You wish to see the master? I think he is still here. There is no meeting of the curia this morning – though you will no doubt be aware of that.'

'Of course!' I muttered, though not really in reply. I had

not given the council calendar a thought – but today was still
a council holiday, so I had not been missed. It meant, though,
that Tertillius was likely to be home. 'And I'd like a moment
with his sister, too, if that is possible.'

Glaber gave another bow. 'I'll go and see if they're available. If you would be good enough to wait.' He indicated the
cushioned bench again. 'And if your servant would like to
come with me, I'll see he has refreshments and that some are
sent to you.' Clearly the man was learning what his new role
entailed.

I had hardly touched my breakfast and I was not hungry
now, but I toyed a little with the cheese and dates, and sipped
the proffered wine, more as a way of passing time than
anything. My host outranked me, so I expected a delay, but
in fact it was not long before Tertillius appeared. He was
dressed for a day at home in a lime-green synthesis (that useful
combination of tunic and toga) and his greeting was equally
relaxed.

'Libertus, you are welcome to my house. I hope your
presence means that you have found your wife?' He had seized
me by my elbows and was warmly shaking both my arms,
before he registered the colour of my clothes. 'But, I see, your
costume . . .' He tailed off in dismay.

This social blundering unmanned me totally. I'd succeeded
in maintaining my composure up till now, by concentrating
fiercely on what I had to say and do, but suddenly I found hot
tears were in my eyes. 'Of course,' I managed, 'you won't
have heard the news. She is dead and in the plague pit.'

'Duumvir! Not Gwellia?' He was horrified. 'How, by all
the gods?'

'By command of your new friend the Senator!' I told him
the whole tale – without revealing who my informant was. If
I sounded bitter, I no longer cared.

Tertillius had a parchment skin in any case, but he'd grown
paler still. 'Hortius Valens is no friend of mine – nor ever was.
He has treated me in public with total disrespect. My courting
of him – as I thought you knew – was simply a desire not to
make a powerful enemy. And at my sister's urging. I regret it
now.' He squeezed my arms again. 'If I'd ever had a friendly

thought towards the man, what you have just told me would have eliminated it. I can't believe it. Can you challenge him in court?' But Tertillius, the expert on the law, was looking doubtful as he spoke. 'There might, at least, be reparation you can claim?'

'I lost my wife, Tertillius,' I said. I could taste the bitter bile upon my tongue. 'What could possibly compensate for that? The army-cart had taken her, as my informant said, but I could not even get permission to retrieve the corpse. There have been rumours of a plague, so everything was immediately limed and sealed. They've posted guard on it.' I broke off as I realized Glaber had come back, this time with the lady Fulvia at his heels. They'd clearly been listening to my last remarks and both were looking stricken – though for different reasons, I was sure.

'You poor man. Who was your witness? We will see this through the courts.' The woman came across to me and offered both veined hands in sympathy.

She seemed smaller and frailer than I had recalled, and for a moment I had doubts about involving her. But I steeled myself sufficiently to say, 'Not the courts, I think. For legal reasons that will not be possible. The testimony of a slave would bear no weight and calling him to testify would merely bring him grief.' I looked past her at the steward, and saw him close his eyes in gratitude. 'Suffice to say, it happened near my home, I know the slave concerned and I believe his tale.'

'But this is simply terrible!' Fulvia exclaimed. 'Is there nothing whatever we can do?'

I hesitated for a moment, even then, before I said, 'There might be something, though there would be a risk. Mostly to me, but to your household too. And it would disoblige the Senator, of course – greatly disoblige him – which I know you have been careful to avoid. Though I would try not to involve you publicly, of course.'

'I would be very glad to disoblige the monster – and I do not care how much,' Tertillius burst out. 'If it were not for my sister I would never have tried to lick his toga-hems. After the way that he insulted me . . .' He shot the lady a reproachful look. 'Public *indignitas*. Men have killed for less.'

'Brother, it was for your protection,' she replied. 'The man is well-connected, rich and powerful.' She caught my eye and paused. 'Power which he abuses, duumvir, I know. Permit us to try to make it up to you.'

As if anything under heaven could do that, I thought, but I said with courtesy, 'Nothing that you did caused my wife to die. Hortius is responsible, and Hortius alone. And Tertillius's flattery of him may assist me, now. This feast which Marcus is proposing was first your idea, I think?'

'Though Hortius declined when I first offered it. Another insult!' Tertillius complained.

His sister interrupted by holding up her hand. 'Steward, you may leave us. Go and wait outside, and close the door.' She waited a moment till the servant had complied, then turned to me again. 'Does this scheme of yours concern the feast? I've undertaken, at His Excellency's request, to go myself – at least to the entertainment afterwards – and to take Druscilla Livia with me. To reintroduce her to her bridegroom, I believe? Would you rather I did not?' She smiled, but did not wait for my reply. 'It would not be difficult to persuade me to decline. Or Druscilla either. She's expected here today. I am warned that if she discovers that Hortius will be there – or even that he's in Glevum – she will refuse to go.'

Tertillius snorted. 'Or run away again! I would, if I were to be forced to marry him.'

Fulvia ignored him. 'I will try to keep the secret, naturally – although in this house it might now be difficult, since you tell me that Glaber was once Hortius's slave. I'm surprised you've managed to keep her in ignorance thus far.'

I shook my head. 'Glaber would not betray us, or speak to Hortius at all – he is too afraid that he'll return him to the mines. But it does not matter, now, in any case. Druscilla already knows the Senator is here and will be at the feast.'

'And she still intends to come? I could withdraw the invitation, if you wish – perfectly properly,' Fulvia exclaimed. 'You mentioned that there have been rumours of a plague, so there'd be no disrespect, and it would be no hardship to forgo her company. She does not sound a very pleasant guest and I am not much drawn to banquets these days anyway.

Especially since – I now assume – you won't be there yourself?'

'On the contrary,' I said, 'It's important I attend. I do not like Druscilla, I confess. She is spoiled and vain. But even she deserves protection from a brute like Hortius. Marcus dare not thwart him, but I no longer care. I propose to bring her under my own potestas – I think I see how it could legally be done. I shall be happy to deprive that monster of his bride. He has robbed me of mine.'

Fulvia was frowning. 'But how? His Excellence would scarcely dare transfer his guardianship to you.'

I smiled. 'There is a way – and that, my friends, is where your help comes in.' I briefly outlined what I had in mind. 'There will have to be a binding contract,' I said finally. 'Tertillius, you understand the letter of the law. I need your guidance. Could it be achieved?'

The old man was clearly doubtful, but I'd appealed to his professional pride. 'A written form is surer,' he said, thoughtfully. 'That leaves no room for later argument – though a patrician's word, in front of witnesses, should be binding under law. If written, the wording must be very careful, though. The slightest error and it will not stand. Give me a few minutes to go and think this through and I'll try to draft you something satisfactory.' He clapped his hands for Glaber, who came hurrying in – so quickly that I suspected he'd been listening at the door. 'Escort me to my study, and bring me quills and ink. Fortunately I have some bark-paper prepared.' He turned to me again. 'It might be possible – if you can make him sign, and are prepared to live with the danger afterwards.'

He went out, leaving Fulvia alone with me again. To my relief, she was delighted with my scheme. 'Hortius deserves it, and what have I to lose? I should be very happy to assist you to avenge your loss! But if you will excuse me, duumvir? We are expecting Druscilla later on today – as I believe you know – and now there is a lot to be arranged.'

So, when I left a little later – with my document – it was all agreed.

TWENTY-SIX

'**M**aster?' Minimus ventured, when we came out onto the street. 'Why did the lady Fulvia ask the Fates to spin you luck?'

He looked so troubled that I told him everything, adding, 'Though you must not mention this to anyone. The fewer people who know what I intend, the safer it will be.'

'Not safe for you, master!' He was visibly upset. 'You could easily be killed. Hortius's escort are quite capable of that. And won't it put Tertillius and your patron into danger, too?'

'Not if I'm successful when I talk to Hortius, which I am about to do,' I said. 'Though he won't be pleased to see me, I am sure – especially as Marcus won't be there to speak for me.'

In fact, the Senator had other visitors. When I was shown in – with doubtful glances at my dark-coloured dress – it was to find Hortius ensconced again on my patron's favourite chair. He appeared to be holding some kind of audience – as though he owned the flat. Before him – perched uncomfortably on a pair of folding stools – were Cyrus and Decimus Valerius, the wealthy and loquacious brother councillors. Seeking favours, by the look of it – judging by the costly gifts displayed nearby, and their visible discomfiture as I was ushered in.

The room felt crowded, with Hortius's two guards on duty by the wall and two of my patron's pages flittering around with snacks and wine – though only Hortius was being served, it seemed. (Marcus would have been appalled at the discourtesy.) The visitors must have attendants, too – presumably crammed into the servants' room. I was glad that, once more, I'd left Minimus outside.

As I moved forward to present myself, one of the armed guards stepped out in front of me. 'Citizen Libertus! Your patron is not here.'

'Thank you, but it was the Senator that I came to see.' I

looked past him to Hortius and forced a little smile, though the effort raised my bile.

I need not have troubled. He was glowering fiercely and his expression did not change. 'Duumvir. We meet again. I'm busy, as you see.'

But Cyrus, the elder brother, had risen to his feet. 'Merely a matter of petitions to the Governor. Nothing that cannot wait. How can we help you? Does this concern your wife? Perhaps the Senator can intercede for you. Somebody must be responsible. What a dreadful thing – we were very shocked to hear.'

I saw Hortius blanch at this and I left caution at the door. 'It was the Senator who ordered it, in fact – as I am sure he's realized by this time. It was her dead body he had thrown into the pit – then limed and sealed, as though she had the plague.'

'It came to me later that it must have been.' He could hardly pretend otherwise, in this company. Both councillors were looking at him, horrified.

'Libertus, my dear fellow,' Decimus, the plumper one, was speaking now. 'Bad enough to hear that she had died – but for her to be . . .' He thought better of that sentence, and finished simply, 'What a tragedy!'

'I will offer compensation, naturally,' Hortius muttered, with another glower at me. 'Though, at this stage, there is nothing I can do to change the past.'

'Indeed,' I said. 'And that is what has brought me here today. You were kind enough to promise, yesterday, to help me offer for any bride I chose, should I ever find myself a widower. I said then I could never replace the wife I had, but just one day of loneliness has shown me otherwise.' I saw suspicion moving in his eyes, and added hastily, 'Tertillius has a sister, as I think you know?'

The toad face thawed a little. 'A widow of patrician birth and independent means! It could not be more perfect, if you have changed your mind, so soon.' His scowl was now replaced by a triumphant smile.

It almost shamed me but I managed to reply, 'Worthiness, I am not looking to replace Gwellia in my heart. Nothing in the Empire could possibly do that. But I have had time to consider overnight, and there are other reasons one might take a wife.'

Both brothers looked frankly scandalized by this, but Decimus murmured, 'Companionship, perhaps? The duumvir would not be the first to find himself bereft, and the future unsupportable alone. Several of the Emperors have wed again, in fact, no sooner than the funeral rites were safely done.' He didn't mention that some of the deaths had been no accident. 'A cultured lady can be a comfort in distress.' He was savouring this story, you could see.

'To say nothing of a handsome dowry, and connections with a well-born family?' The irony in Hortius's voice was unmistakable. 'I see no objection, once the rites have been performed.'

I nodded, unable to meet the disapproving eyes. 'I have fulfilled the Celtic funeral rituals,' I said, and saw Decimus nod, acknowledging that I'd mentioned it to him.

'Then, if the woman's willing – there is no cause to wait.' Hortius managed to sound almost gracious now. 'So, duumvir, what do you want of me? The lady is not without a dowry, I believe? If you have come simply to ask my blessing on the match, I give it willingly.'

I pretended to be looking at the floor. 'The thing is, Senator, that there might be a bar. I am – as you must know by now – of Celtic birth. A noble family – my father was the chieftain of our tribe – but I was betrayed, captured and sold to slavery. I am now a Roman citizen and councillor, but all the same, her brother may object . . .'

'Indeed.' Cyrus was anxious to exhibit what he knew. 'Tertillius is a stickler for tradition and the law. Rank and background are of high importance in his eyes.'

I seized the cue that he had given me. 'Exactly, Worthiness.' I forced myself to meet the granite eyes again. 'But if you would be prepared to urge him to the match – declaring that you favour it yourself, I think he could be persuaded to agree.' I glanced towards the listening councillors. 'Though, with your indulgence, gentlemen, I'd wish to be discreet and not have this matter discussed outside this room.'

'Of course not, duumvir!' Decimus replied, pretending that I had offered an affront, but I had the satisfaction of seeing them exchange a glance – which assured me that the news would be safely round the town by dusk.

I turned back to Hortius. 'Then, a private written letter, under seal, perhaps? I have taken the liberty of sketching something out – since you had pledged to help. Would you be good enough to read it through?' I produced the little roll of bark-paper, which Tertillius had so carefully prepared.

Hortius snatched it from me, and read the words aloud. 'From Hortius Lollius Valens, Senator, greetings . . . trust you are in health . . . et cetera, et cetera . . . I wish to have it known that I support the claim of the councillor and duumvir, Longinus Flavius Libertus, for your widowed sister's hand. Expedition of the union would be a favour done to me.' He scowled at me. 'The fortunate lady has a name, I suppose?'

'She does,' I answered, as nonchalantly as I could. 'Tertillius's sister is called Fulvia. But I am not certain of her patronym – her father died, and I think the mother married twice. Tertillius will know, of course. He could insert the details if you so instruct – there is sufficient space between the lines.'

Hortius's toad face looked suspicious still. 'This will go directly to Tertillius?' he enquired.

'Of course,' I told him blithely. 'You may send it there yourself – with your instructions – if you'd care to add your seal.'

He looked at me as though he hated me, and I returned his gaze.

'Come, Hortius,' Decimus exclaimed excitedly. 'Libertus has made a reasonable request – very reasonable, given what occurred. What could be more natural than to add your seal – and we two can be witnesses to that. It's fortunate we happened to be here.'

'Very fortunate,' I murmured, though I had hoped they might. If Tertillius had called yesterday, with gifts, it was almost certain that they would be the first to do the same, as soon as they heard of Hortius's accident. Asking him to petition the Governor against the tax, no doubt, and finding a good story – both at once.

Cyrus was gesturing to Marcus's slaves to bring a beeswax candle so we could melt some for the seal. So Hortius, who was visibly sporting a flamboyant signet ring, could summon no excuse.

'Very well,' he said abruptly. 'I'll put my seal on it. And you two can add your names, as witnesses. My own guard shall deliver it to Tertillius. You, duumvir, will not handle the document again.' He glared at me, as though he dared me to object.

I merely bowed and gave him a sweet smile. 'As the Senator desires. My thanks to all of you.' I watched as quills and a pot of bark-ink were produced, the names and seal were appended to the note, and Hortius's two guardsmen disappeared with it. 'And that, I think, concludes my business here. With your permission, gentlemen, I will now withdraw. My patron is holding a feast tomorrow night – in celebration of his recent fatherhood, and as a civic honour for the Senator. There are arrangements that I'm asked to oversee, since he is not in town, himself. I believe that both you gentlemen are invited too?'

The brothers were preening. 'We are bidden to the highest table. Perhaps we'll see you there?' Decimus seemed to think better of the question, suddenly. 'Though I presume that you . . .?' He let the sentence fail.

'I shall attend, for the later part of it, at least – though I have at present no appetite for feasts. Until then, gentlemen!' I bowed myself away.

I was glad to get outside to Minimus. Even the stale air on the landing – heavy with the usual smells of cooking-smoke, wet wool, damp shoes and sweat – was preferable to a room containing Hortius.

My slave was looking mournful and I saw his eyes were red. 'You have been crying?' I asked him as we went into the street. 'Tears for your mistress? That I understand.'

He shook his head. 'I'm frightened for you, master. For myself, as well. I have lost the mistress. If I should lose you too . . .' He broke off in despair.

'Minimus, I promise. You will not be left to starve. If I leave Glevum, you shall come with me, and – if anything unfortunate befalls – I have arranged with Junio that you revert to him. As soon as you are old enough, he'll see that you are manumitted and set free.'

'Master, I would rather be a slave and have you live . . .' He faltered. He was in danger of tears again, and so was I.

'Then I shall do my best to do so – for the moment, anyway, though we are none of us immortal,' I told him, with a heartiness I did not feel. 'I have things to do. First, I must call on the vintners and check the food and wine, then confirm the entertainment afterwards, and ensure that sufficient servants can be hired to help.' Minimus was already looking happier. 'When we have finished, we will go back to the flat – and take some pies and fruit with us, perhaps. Everybody will be hungry by that I time, I am sure – and afterwards I'll try to get some rest. Tomorrow will be a very busy day, so you can bring me some of Cilla's poppy juice.'

And that was more or less precisely what we did, though I delayed the sleeping draught, and – when the others were asleep – I had a private hunt among the items from the roundhouse, and took possession of another one of Gwellia's potion-pots. I kissed it, in memory of her, then slipped it into my leather drawstring pouch – where, when it was hanging from my tunic belt, it could not be seen under the curial toga, which I was wearing to the feast.

If my plans went desperately wrong, I was equipped for anything.

Reassured, I crept back to my room, stepped over the sleeping Minimus on the mat and climbed – for what might be the last time in my life – into that comfortable bed. There, I drank Cilla's potion to the dregs, put out my feeble taper and (thanks entirely to the poppy juice) fell – at last – to sleep.

TWENTY-SEVEN

I t was well past dawn by the time that I awoke, and all my slaves were already busy at self-appointed tasks: Minimus brushing down the hems of my previous day's attire; Kurso refilling oil-lamps and stoking braziers; while Ossius was energetic with a broom, proving his worth by sweeping floors as though the Emperor might call. Servus, I learned, was fetching water from the fountain in the street, and had promised to bring fresh bread and oatcakes back with him.

I startled Minimus by turning down my mourning clothes today. 'The time for that is past. I've done my grieving now, in public anyway. I'll wear my plain white toga and a Roman cloak and hood. Then, when we have eaten, you can find a carrying-chair for me, and I'll go down to the docks.' I saw the other slaves look sharply up at this, and I added quickly, 'There is a feast tonight and there are things I need to finalize.' I gave my head the tiniest of shakes, signalling Minimus to silence.

He understood. 'I'll go down now, master, and have a litter waiting in the street. I have had an apple, I need not wait for more.' He disappeared, and by the time that Servus had returned and I had eaten a mouthful of fresh bread (all the breakfast that I had stomach for) the chair was waiting, and my slave was standing by, ready to accompany me as usual.

But I surprised him. 'Run to Tertillius's house, as fast as possible,' I said. 'Ask him to send that letter to the garrison at once, and have it forwarded to Rome. Hortius's escort will not be watching for it now, if they ever were. Check that the address instructions are quite clear, to reach Druscilla's brother as fast as possible.'

Minimus was looking horrified at me. 'The letter was not for Tertillius at all? I heard the escort talking as they set off with it – where they were taking it, and what it said.' His mouth gaped further. 'Master, you are not thinking what I fear? You are not planning to marr—?'

'Minimus,' I interrupted, sternly, 'think twice before you speak. There are more ears in Glevum than in a field of wheat.' I glanced at the litter-bearers, who were staring at the floor, trying to pretend that they weren't listening avidly. 'My arrangements with the lady Fulvia are private ones. Kindly do not abuse my confidence. Now, I gave you an order, I believe?'

'Master. I am already on my way.' And before I was fairly in the litter, he was gone.

I had taken the precaution, when I left the roundhouse finally, of bringing some possessions with me in a bag, including my late household's stock of gold and silver coins, some of which I was carrying in an arm-purse now. I was glad of it – not merely to pay the carriers for my ride, but to seal the bargain with the captain of the ship, and arrange that he'd collect my baggage later in the day. I had no intention of returning to my flat, whatever happened at the feast tonight.

I am no lover of travelling by boat (days in an airless pirate hold, chained with a half-hundred other newly captured slaves, tossed in high seas and howling winds, had cured me of that), but as a means of swift escape, it was unmatchable. Once safely down the river – and no land-transport could match a well-trimmed boat that travelled with the tide – and on the open sea, one had escaped the Roman Empire and its laws and senators. Even in a different province one could disappear – in more comfort too – if one did not make oneself conspicuous. But I could not trust Druscilla to do that.

The bargain cost me less than I had feared – I had half-expected that, once he saw it was important, the man would raise the fee – but he was sympathetic to my plight, and I'd helped him with that licence previously, he said. That was comforting. I'd had some anxiety about my safety on the trip – a man with money and without armed guards, is too easy to lose overboard. (Though I vowed I'd keep a guard on my possessions, even so.)

My private business done, I picked a path across the heaps of ropes and chains towards the warehouses. The docks were busy at this hour of day and I had to dodge the slaves – some working the creaking wooden gantries, till their veins stood on their brows, others moving cargo the old-fashioned way, bent double under sacks (a task made still more difficult when, as now, the planks into the holds were wet and slippery).

I made my way to a wine-importer's repository. I knew the owner and the manager-slave, and made sure they noted my appearance there, by ordering a few amphorae of less expensive wine to be charged to Marcus. For the lower tables, I explained, where I myself would sit – which improved the quality of what they offered me. (The official of the vintners' guild might grumble, but they already had the sale of the Falernian, and – besides – the arrangement was not unusual.

As Tertillius had discovered, the guild always charged inflated prices for wine which they themselves supplied.)

A discreet visit to a pair of fellow councillors, arranging for the temporary loan of serving slaves (or hire, since a small consideration was involved) and my official business was completed for the day. There was nothing for it but to go back to my flat and write a farewell note to Junio and his family – if all went well, I'd leave instructions for it to be delivered after I was gone.

Then, after a few unwanted spoonsful of the stew my servants pressed on me, there was not much time to kill – as the expression goes. All the same, the afternoon hung heavy on my hands. I was nervous, there is no denying that.

At last, though, it was appropriate for me to leave – although not directly to the feast – the start of which would be a disorganized affair. Such occasions always are, since there can be no accurate set hour for diners to arrive: water or candle-clocks are not reliable, and many people do not own them anyway – so time is largely guesswork, especially when the sun cannot be seen.

Most guests would assemble shortly before dusk, but I was not scheduled to arrive till after dark. The vintners always tend to time their banquets late – possibly because the members of their guild are merchants with other business to pursue – and I was not due to go, accompanying the ladies, until the latter part when most of the heavy eating had been done.

The arrangement was that I should go to Tertillius's residence as the sun went down. He would go ahead, accompanied by his new page (who had been assigned the unenviable role of poison-taster to the guest-in-chief, should he request the services of one). Both my roundhouse slaves would go with them, Minimus to help with service and Kurso behind the scenes, assisting to put things on platters and bring them through from the separate – and well-appointed – kitchen at the rear. I and my two female charges (who would have a dainty snack) would await a messenger to tell us when it was convenient to come.

The vintners' hall was only minutes from Tertillius's house, even in a curial toga, which I had on by now, and – the evening being fine, if cold – it was proposed that we would walk. (It would, in any case, be hard to order a litter in advance – since we could not know the time, and they rarely ply for casual business after dark. After the feast, of course, it would be different – a free-for-all with carriers competing for a fare.)

We would be escorted by Glaber, carrying a club, against the possibility of harassment (though more from wine-bar revellers, than thieves) and Fulvia's two young maidservants could walk behind to hold the ladies' hems out of the gutters and the damp. Not ideal, of course, but for two dozen paces it seemed sensible. And so it was agreed.

Agreed by Tertillius, the lady Fulvia, and myself, that is. Druscilla was affronted and simply furious. 'Me? Walk? After dark and in a public street? I don't care how close this venue is, it's not acceptable. Why if this were Rome . . .'

'If this were Rome,' I said, as evenly as my irritation would allow, 'you would be married to Hortius by now. Or have been declared an enemy of state and exiled to a barren rock – if not killed outright. And your whole family with you.' She seemed about to make a hot response, then changed her mind and sulked, so I went on, 'I am attempting to save you from this fate – though, understand, I'm not doing this for you. It is entirely for my patron, to save him trouble with the Governor and perhaps the court.'

'But also because you loathe the Senator, I think?' Fulvia's musical voice put in, surprising me. She met my gaze and smiled. 'In which opinion you are not alone. My brother certainly agrees – hence his agreement to assist you in all this. And me, too, of course.'

She looked magnificent, this evening, quietly dignified in a floor-length tunic and stola of dark blue – one of the most expensive of all dyes – trimmed with jet and silver, with a veil to match. Druscilla, by agreement (and by contrast too), was dressed as though resigned to accepting Hortius. She wore a simple under-gown of yellow silk, under a flame-coloured stola and a veil to match: an outfit which – though hurriedly assembled in the last few hours – suggested marriage robes. There was nothing of the modest bride about Druscilla, though.

She wore the garments like a soldier's uniform, bold and ready to defy the enemy.

'Save me?' she muttered, in an ungrateful tone. 'I suppose I must agree. But I warn you, duumvir – or whatever title they choose to give you here – if you cheat me, I will kill myself – you know I have the means. In fact, if you betray me, just be careful I don't kill you as well.'

'Druscilla!' I lost patience. 'Learn to hold your tongue. I did not choose this, any more than you. I cannot think of any woman I have ever met, whom I would not prefer to take under my protection. I am simply trying to save your stupid life – at some danger to my own – and protect you from a monster who, not content with merely murdering my slave, went on to kill my wife and then condemn her to the plague-pit like a common thief. But one more complaint from you and I will change my mind and leave you to his mercies. Or the Emperor's. Or to that poison that you boast about – if you dare drink it, which I rather doubt.'

She looked at me with blazing fury in her eyes, as though I were the source of all her grief. She might have retorted something – I think she would have done, had not the old, retiring steward (clearly delighted at being reinstated to his post, if only for the evening) tottered in, declaring that the messenger had come and we were expected at the feast as soon as possible.

I was surprised at this. Roman banquets, especially civic ones, are sometimes twenty courses and rarely less than twelve – so I was astonished that the summons came so soon. It was almost certainly at Hortius's behest – Marcus as official host would never cut things short, especially where fine food and finer drink was being served but, as the guest of honour, Hortius Valens could ask for anything and – if achievable – it was improper to refuse. The courtesy was never usually invoked, but I could just imagine the toad-like Senator, sneering at the delicious food that had been expensively prepared, and deciding that all he wanted was Druscilla to be brought to him as soon as possible. In that case there would be a lot of unhappy magistrates – no one could go on eating if the chief guest did not.

However, if that was the case, there was some benefit for us. There was still a suspicion of lightness in the sky (though nonetheless Glaber carried a burning torch to illuminate our way) and there was, as yet, no frost to make the pavements slippery. In no time at all, we were at the vintners' hall.

I had been there once before, with Gwellia, to a civic banquet very much like this – though not as large, of course. It's an impressive place. Fronted by massive columns, it is just as grand within, with handsome frescoes painted on the walls, and window-spaces filled with strips of tortoiseshell, cut so finely that an amber light can pass. (Even now we could make out a glow, from the scores of lighted candles and oil-lamps within.) A perfect location to hold a public feast, especially as the kitchens are famous for their food – exotic dishes in interesting forms.

I remember what appeared to be a swan but proved to be a pastry mould filled with delicious little honey cakes – some such wonder would be produced tonight. The vintners' guild is the richest in the town, supported by people of serious influence: I hoped that they were not about to be insulted by their guest.

I need not have worried – about that at least. As we walked up the steps and through the vaulted entrance-way to be greeted by club-carrying attendants in the vestibule ('Citizen Libertus, ladies, we were expecting you! More slaves will be useful. Do the females dance?') there were raucous shouts and sounds of drunken laughter from within.

I glanced at Fulvia. This was a problem I had not foreseen. Banquets to which councillors do not invite their wives some-times do descend into a *comissatio* – a drinking party – in which the emphasis is not on food at all, but on wine, bawdy jokes and half-clad dancing girls. Not a place to bring two well-bred widows. I had envisaged a far more staid affair, with formal speeches, and worthy poetry or flutes between each course.

But before I had the chance to beat a swift retreat, the inner door flew open and Freckle-face appeared, dressed in a smart tunic – clearly not his own – in the dark red colour of the vintners' livery, with their insignia embroidered on the chest.

'Councillor Libertus!' he exclaimed at once. 'Thank Mars that you are here. I was sent to find you. Hortius asked for you.' He dropped his voice, lest he was overheard. 'My master says to warn you that he is jovial now, but he seems to have taken too much wine and may be unpredictable. He is waiting' – he gestured through the open door – 'and waving you inside.'

I glanced in and saw that he was right. The small stage holding the top three tables, was at the further end and those reclining round them were clearly visible – that was after all the purpose of the dais. Marcus, the official host, was naturally there (beckoning, but looking uncomfortable and strained) with Tertillius and other senior members of the curia, including the two Valerii that I'd seen yesterday. Hortius, lying at my patron's side, was propped up on one elbow dipping bread into a dish, flushed and dishevelled with his dining-wreath askew; there could be no doubt who had set the drunken tone.

He stuffed the titbit in his mouth and used his hand to raise his goblet high. 'Ah! The duumvir has joined us. And the ladies too.' He did not sound entirely sober. 'Tertillius move over, and make room – Druscilla Livia can sit here by me.'

This was a dilemma. It was not his place to reorganize the seats, and there were clearly places set aside for us at a trestle table just inside the door. Like the other tables crammed into the lower room, it was piled with food and crowded with other junior magistrates, who sat on simple stools; lesser guests were not permitted to recline.

So it was insulting to Tertillius to demote him in this way (beside me I heard my fellow diners gasp) and even if he moved reluctantly away, as he now did, there was no room on his one couch for all three of us. Meantime a hundred eyes had turned to stare, some of my colleagues raising goblets at our predicament, or gesturing towards the place reserved for me. The drunken roars had hushed to muffled whispers now.

Lentigines was plucking at my arm. 'Shall I escort you up? And whom should I announce?' He meant that he did not know Fulvia's name.

'Don't worry,' I told him. 'I will announce myself.'

That was not necessary, either, as it proved. As I moved forward to approach my host, Hortius banged his cup against the tabletop. 'Libertus and Tertillius's sister, Fulvia, I believe. The banquet welcomes you. And Druscilla Livia, I say again, come here and lie by me. I sent for you especially. I am tired of stuffy speeches, we have too much of that in Rome, and I took a fancy to have you at my side.' There was no mistaking it, the ringing tones were marred by an inebriated slur. 'Come, my little tigress, what are you waiting for? Gentlemen, this is the lady I was speaking of. One of you servants, bring her here to me.' He quaffed whatever was remaining in the cup.

Druscilla nudged my side, her face set in a scowl, but I could see a genuine terror in her eyes. 'So, Citizen Duumvir, now what am I to do? I warn you . . .'

'Hush,' I told her. 'It will be all right. The more you look reluctant, the more convinced he'll be. But first I must persuade him to repeat his words to me – here, in public, where everyone can hear. For the moment, do as he requires.'

There was no option really. Two burly slaves appeared, also dressed in the vintners' uniform, and looked ready to take her by the arm. Druscilla flashed a look at me that would have curdled milk. Then suddenly she shrugged off the would-be guiding hands, threw back her orange veil defiantly and made her way between the cheering diners towards the Senator.

He half-moved over and pulled her to him with a smile, but I saw the hand that grasped her upper arm made her wince. Marcus, on his other side, made rueful signs at me. This was his banquet, and he had lost control to Hortius, who was clearly very drunk. (This in itself was an insult to polite society. Bawdy jokes and ribald songs may be acceptable – at all-male drinking-parties, anyway – but no well-bred Roman lets himself become incapable, especially when he is the guest-in-chief.) But Hortius was manifestly on the way to that, and even now he was calling for more wine.

'Dispense with the poison-taster. Druscilla can perform the service, from now on,' he said thickly, while the plates and goblets were hastily exchanged. (The hearers roared as though it were a joke, but I wondered if he too had noticed what I'd seen: a tiny stealthy movement of her hand – as though to withdraw something from beneath her stola-folds.) He did extend his refilled cup for her to sip, as more of the best

Falernian was poured out in hers, there to be diluted with warmed water to her taste – a refinement only practised at the most exclusive feasts. (Generally they are pre-mixed and the water will be cold.)

Druscilla made a face and signalled for the slave to add more water still, and that was the moment when I saw who was attending her. All servers wore the wine-red tunic of the vintners' uniform but now I realized it was Minimus who held the water jug – and little Kurso who'd refilled it and brought new platters in.

But when I glanced at the slave dispensing wine, and saw that it was Glaber, I almost swayed and fell – genuinely shocked at how Hortius would react if he realized who it was. The ex-courier was white with fright himself, but clearly he'd been directed there by the establishment – presumably delighted by the arrival of what seemed a senior slave – and as a servant, had no choice but to obey.

Of course, he did look very different now and someone had found him a vintner's uniform, so he was not conspicuous. His head and limbs had been recently rescraped, but his beard had started to regrow, giving his face a very different look. The steward's gliding walk had replaced the swagger too. But still, as he moved behind his former owner with the jug of wine, I saw him hold his breath – as I was holding mine.

Hortius did not so much as glance at him – or, indeed, at any of the slaves. He was wholly occupied in ensuring that Drusilla's tunic sleeve was trapped under the arm that he lay propped upon, making it impossible for her to move away, or – since it was her right arm and she was propped herself – easily to help herself to food. He amused himself by selecting titbits from the choice in front of him and feeding them to her.

It looked affectionate, until one saw her face – and realized that he was deliberately choosing things she did not like. I recalled the tales of how indulgent he had been towards the former wife – had that, perhaps, been something similar?

I expected violent protest from Druscilla Livia. It was not like her to suffer this without complaint – but, as she cast another anguished look at me, I realized that not only the fabric had been trapped but Hortius was leaning deliberately on her arm, pinning the skin against the table-edge. He must already be causing her some degree of pain, but the toad-like smile that he bestowed on her was clearly a warning that this was no accident, and he could and would increase it tenfold if she breathed a word. Druscilla was to pay for having fled from Rome.

But I could not help her until I'd made my move and forced the Senator to publicly renew his promises. And if I did not do so quickly, I might lose my chance – if he was incoherent or incapable through drink, there would be legal questions about validity. So, with thumping heart, I ushered Fulvia towards the rostrum steps, bowed and began the little speech I had prepared.

I had got as far as: 'Your Pardons, Excellence and Worthiness. I have a petiti—' when Hortius intervened. His blurring diction made my spirits sink.

'Of course. I'd not forgotten. But first let's eat and drink. You and your party have only just arrived.' Clearly he was still capable of thought – his cowing of Druscilla demonstrated that. (Unless the instinct for cruelty ran so deep in him that he didn't need to think – which seemed improbable, even for a monster such as this.) So was this drunken mumbling merely a pretence? To ensure that any verbal contract with me would not stand? Certainly he was capable of that.

But he seemed strangely clumsy, as he raised his cup again. 'So sit down, duumvir, and enjoy the feast. The next course is dormice, I believe?'

Marcus, beside him, gave me a helpless little shrug. He would have permitted me to speak, but the guest of honour had made his wishes clear, so once again there was little the host could do. (At least, politely, and Marcus would not stoop to the rudeness of his guest.) I bowed, and gave an inward sigh, but even as I began to shepherd Fulvia towards the humble seats which were reserved for us, someone shouted, 'Duumvir!'

I looked around. The Valerii were getting to their feet, inviting us to take their places on the dais. I looked at my patron, who signalled his assent, so there was nothing for it but to climb up to the couch.

As we passed the brothers on the steps, Decimus leaned over and murmured in my ear, 'If those are Roman manners, give me Glevum any day. You're welcome to the seat. I knew he was unpleasant, but the man's a drunken pig. Sweating and swaying from the moment he arrived.'

So, I thought – as we settled on the dining-couch and more fresh platters and goblets were produced – Hortius's behaviour was not an act exclusively for me! In fact, now I was reclining close to him and could see him more plainly in the candle-light, it did not seem to be an act at all. The hand that held the wine cup was so unsteady now that it scattered droplets on his toga as he raised it to his lips, and his attempt to lift a honeyed dormouse from the plate resulted in it falling to the floor.

But he seemed oblivious, holding his goblet out to have it filled again – like some plebian unaccustomed to a feast. His eyes were visibly glazing over, too, and I no longer feared that he would notice who was serving him. Another half an hour and he would be asleep. Which meant one thing, of course. If I still hoped to do what I had planned, I had to do it now – however improper it might be to persist.

Then I had an inspiration – or I thought I had. 'Senator,' I murmured, as he took a slurping sip, 'that accident you had. Perhaps it has affected you more than you suppose.'

He turned his body half around to glare at me – causing Druscilla to give a stifled gasp. 'What are you suggesting, Councillor?' It came out as 'srugestin canshular'. Behind him, I saw Marcus stiffening.

'That blow,' I said. 'It may have bruised your brain. There are drops of perspiration on your brow.' The other diners at the table were staring at him now; I could see them wondering if this might be true. 'And it is not usual with you, I think, to spill your wine?'

He looked at the wine stains on his front with a bewildered air – as if he could not understand why they were there, but he could still be angry. 'Dumva, jadar to crishise?' (which I took to mean, 'Duumvir, you dare to criticize?') He looked around as if to call his escort-guards, but they were not in evidence.

'On the contrary, Worthiness,' I said. 'I am concerned for you. I know how far you've travelled to bring this night about. You would not wish to find yourself unable, after all – entirely on account of that injury, of course – to complete what you had planned? Would it not be wise to move directly to exchanging promises?' I was speaking calmly, but my heart was thumping hard. If Hortius refused I was taking dreadful risks – for Druscilla and my patron as well as for myself. 'Feasting can come afterwards, if you are so inclined.'

Hortius was staring at me stupidly. He seemed to be considering my words. After a moment he took a gulp of wine. 'May have misjdged, c'ncillor,' he said, even more indistinctly than before. 'Y'right. I'm not f'ling altogether well. May be a . . . relaspse. Le's do as you s'ggest.' He rapped his goblet on the wooden board again, and rose – scarlet-faced and swaying – as reluctant silence fell.

Druscilla snatched her arm away and cradled it. I thought that she would speak – she turned to me with indignation in her eyes – but Hortius was already talking to the crowd.

'Citiz'ns of Glevum. Thiz joyful night f'me. I am re . . . nited with Drusc'llivia. But . . . not not quite myshelf. Duumvir's sugg'shion . . . marry shtraitaway. Better move few treshels out way.' He sketched a broad sweep with his goblet hand, splashing a lot of droplets on the way.

'Duumvir . . .?' Druscilla's despairing whisper was so shrill I feared that they would hear it at the back, but I was already on my feet.

'Hortius, Senator, Worthiness . . .' I spluttered. 'There was the little matter of my own union first.'

Hortius gave a triumphant, tipsy leer. 'N'a minute, pavemen'-maker. Portant bushnuuss first. Bring Drushilla n' the shcales, an' I w'll buy my bride.' He had to catch his balance suddenly, and it was getting difficult to recognize the words, but the meaning was disastrously clear. If he persisted in this wedding, then everything was lost, and I had failed.

I was reminded of this sharply as Druscilla gave a screech and pummelled at me violently with both her fists. Glaber came forward to restrain her, and discreetly fill her cup.

'You promised!' she broke down in noisy tears, burying her head in both her arms.

I looked to see what Hortius had made of this – and, what, if anything could still be done. But he seemed unaware of anything.

'Ma bri'e,' he said again, waving his goblet at Druscilla, who sat up, sniffling and half-paralysed by fright, 'Call on all a' deities . . .' He raised the cup in drunken tribute to the gods. A lot of wine tipped out onto the floor. 'Libashion,' he declared, before he raised the remainder to his lips.

For a long moment he stood and smiled and swayed. Then he crumpled suddenly, dropped the cup and fell face-down into a dish of peppered leeks.

TWENTY-EIGHT

An embarrassed silence. Everybody stopped as though Jove had descended and turned them all to stone: servants holding platters, diners holding forks, people in the act of putting food into their mouths. For several moments there was no sound at all – then someone gave a snigger, hastily suppressed.

As if that were a signal, or the breaking of a spell, suddenly everything began at once. Druscilla, beside me, gave a sobbing breath and I saw that she was shaking – most likely with relief. Marcus seemed to have found his old authority and began to struggle to his feet, ready to address the audience, while Glaber and one of the vintners' men moved forward to move Hortius from the plate of food, and Kurso brought napkins and clean water to sponge off the sticky sauce.

Marcus noticed, and turned to nod at them. 'When you've finished, help him to his feet and take him home. He will clearly need a litter.' He looked across at me. 'That did not go as we intended, I'm afraid, though at least Druscilla has a short reprieve. Though I'm not sure how we could manage this again – after this evening, we could not hold another feast.

Hortius is going to be a laughing-stock. I only wish I did not have to take him home.' He sighed. 'And you will have to alter your travel plans, I fear. I am rather sorry that your plan did not succeed – it only leaves the problem for another day – but I could not guess that this disgrace was possible. Hortius seemed quite normal when we left the flat.'

I raised an eyebrow. 'Decimus seemed to think that he was drunk when he arrived.'

'Not until we got here and he began to drink. I've never seen a man more affected by his wine – not even you, Libertus, and you don't drink it much. Odd, because he has drunk a great deal more than this several times lately – and at my expense – with no apparent effect on him at all.'

'Excellence.' Decimus – inquisitive as ever – had edged up to the dais and now discreetly cleared his throat. 'Your guests are expecting a word from you, I think.'

Marcus made a rueful face at me, then turned to the assembled company – many of whom were now excitedly whispering behind their hands. (A drunken senator, unconscious in the leeks? This was a piece of gossip beyond imagining.) 'Fellow councillors, this is unfortunate – but, as perhaps you've heard, Hortius Valens has been unwell for several days. He sustained a riding accident in which he hit his head. We should perhaps be flattered . . .'

But I was no longer listening. I had turned to glance at Hortius again – and there was something wrong. The slaves had dropped him back onto the tabletop and seemed to be uncertain what to do. Glaber looked at me and shook his head. 'I don't think he's breathing,' he mouthed – exaggerating to be sure I caught the words.

Druscilla had drawn herself away, disgustedly, as far as possible from her would-be groom, so when I signalled that we should changes places on the couch, she was only too anxious to comply. However, I realized that she was trembling violently. I paused to check that this was merely with relief, but as I moved away I felt Fulvia pluck my sleeve-edge on the other side. But there was now some urgency, I felt, so I murmured, 'In a moment!' – just as Hortius had.

I sat down beside him on his couch and lifted up the

toad-like head. It felt extremely heavy and there was no muffled groan. Nor could I feel the faintest movement of his chest, and the hand I raised flopped back, inanimate. I picked up a silver spoon and held it to the slightly-blueing lips. Glaber was right. No mist of breath at all. My detested enemy was dead.

Marcus was still busy making his address, but Decimus had been watching me throughout, and now he gently touched my patron on the arm. 'The duumvir wants urgent words with you.'

My patron, impatient at the interruption, turned irascibly to me, but when I murmured what I'd found his whole demeanour changed – though he clearly had difficulty in believing me.

'He can't be! Are you certain? But he was in perfect health a little while ago – I can't believe that drink has caused a sudden death like that.' He had omitted to speak softly, and the word was overheard. There was an instant flutter in the crowd. Marcus looked at me.

'Better that you send them home, I think,' I said. 'Make a brief announcement and then let them go. Only the people on the dais should remain – and perhaps Tertillius. And Decimus and Cyrus, since they left it halfway through. Oh, and I think the undertakers should perhaps be called. The ones who handle patrician funerals.'

'With instructions to take the body to the garrison, perhaps?' Marcus seemed eager to prevent his apartment being turned into a place of death. 'They have a military hospital and mortuary, where he can wait and be prepared for a civic funeral. Since he's a relative of the Governor, Chief Commander of all the legions in Britannia, that would seem more fitting.'

I agreed, and Marcus turned back to announce the news – causing a general pandemonium. Several diners were already on their feet, rubbing spit onto their ears to ward off the bad luck, and so determined to rush away that they jostled one another at the door. Others, less superstitious, did the opposite, cramming forwards to get a better look, while still others seemed reluctant to leave the food behind and unashamedly began to stuff as much as possible into their mouths, and dining-napkins, too. There was a lot of frenzied conversation in an undertone.

Under the hubbub Decimus came to look more closely at the corpse. 'You don't think this death is natural, do you? I can tell. Some kind of poison? It looks like that to me. I once witnessed something of the kind before.'

I have wondered many times if, without his intervention, I might have been content to let my patron go on thinking that Hortius had simply drunk himself to death, or had a seizure or something of the kind. It would have made what followed a great deal easier. But if one man had suspicions, others would as well – especially if Hortius was carried to the garrison. Army doctors are very well-informed.

'I'm afraid I think it is a poisoning,' I answered cautiously – and sensed, rather than saw, the consternation that it caused among the people round about.

Marcus had not been listening to our exchange, but now he abandoned attempts to organize – in any case the vintners' slaves had taken charge, reuniting owners with their cloaks and slaves, and sending out for lighted torches and any litters that might be available. My patron bent and looked at Hortius – though not as though the loss of his guest would break his heart. When he spoke, his tone was one of conventional respect. 'Libertus, I've ordered those you specified to stay. People to accompany the corpse – call on his spirit and close his eyes, perhaps – until the undertakers come. I presume that's what you meant?'

'People who might have killed him,' I returned – dropping my voice as much as possible. 'You said yourself you can't believe that wine had caused his death. And nor can I. Or Decimus.' Marcus was gawping at me, and I added urgently, 'There is no need to tell the crowd that it's unnatural death – just let them go for now. There will be sufficient rumour as it is.'

'There can't be many people who could have managed it.' Decimus was irritatingly persistent, though he was quite right. 'No one on His Excellency's left could possibly have poisoned anything that Hortius ate or drank – not without stretching over in front of everyone, or else endangering the entire company.'

That was also self-evidently true, and I was glad of the

excuse. 'You are quite right,' I told him, 'so we need not detain them any more.' The councillors who had been seated on that side now hastily retired – though sufficiently excited by events, to make me think the cause of death would not be secret long. 'Now,' I said to Glaber and the slave assisting him, 'if you have finished washing Hortius's face, you can fetch a door to carry him, and lie him down on one of the vacated couches over there. Close his eyes and give him a little dignity, until the funeral guild arrive to do things properly.'

I turned back to the ladies. Cyrus Valerius and Tertillius had joined us by this time, and I gestured them to sit with us – nobody was still reclining now. Decimus rushed over to tell them everything, and I had to clap my hands to make them look at me.

'If Hortius was poisoned at this feast,' I said at last, 'and it looks as if he was, then it was done by one of us. Though I understand that he was showing symptoms shortly after he arrived, so it might have been something . . .'

I broke off as I saw my patron's face. 'Are you suggesting that I gave him some slow poison before we left the flat?'

Of course, that was the logical conclusion from my words, and I hastened to correct them, as quickly as I could. 'Of course not, Excellence. But did he, by any chance, take something of his own – something that might have been tampered with elsewhere?'

I was addressing Marcus, but Fulvia answered me. 'I might have known that you would find me out. But it could not possibly have killed him, yet.'

All heads swivelled round together, like soldiers at a drill. My own included – till I worked out what she meant! 'There was poison in that ointment that you sent to soothe his wounds? Or in the reviving draught you sent to him?'

Fulvia found the courage to give a little smile. 'In the potion only, and in very small amounts. Believe me, Councillor. I know about these things. I meant to kill him – he deserved it after the way he treated poor Tertillius, insulting our whole ancient family while knowing there could be no recourse in law – but it could not have happened yet. Not unless he'd drunk the whole bottleful at once.'

I looked at Marcus, but he shook his head. 'He did take one extra dose of it before we left the flat. Said he was feeling flatulent, and hoped that it would help. Otherwise he took it as he was advised – a little in the morning. He seemed to think it had improved his health.'

'And so it might have done,' the lady said. 'It contains *arsenicum*. Some people swear that in tiny doses it does make them strong. This was, however, a little more than that. Enough to make him feel progressively unwell – in ways which might persuade him to return to Rome, but not dissuade him from travelling at all – then weaken him enough to make him slowly die. And I made sure it tasted pleasant, too, so that he was encouraged to go on taking it.'

'It would have killed him?' Tertillius was shocked.

She gave him her lovely smile. 'But very slowly – so that no one could suspect that anything in Glevum had a part in it. Certainly not my potion – which by then he would have been taking for a moon or so at least – even claiming that it actually improved his health. Though the flatulence you speak of may be a first effect.'

'And now it has killed him?' Cyrus made the words sound ominous.

She shook her head. 'I say again that it could not have done! Indeed, I was slightly worried that the dose was not enough – one hears that it is possible to take it every day, in very small amounts, and by degrees become immune to it, like the famed old King of Pontus – who afterwards tried to commit suicide and failed!'

Marcus was frowning. 'But since Hortius took a double dose today . . .?'

'It might have weakened him,' she said, with dignity. 'Upset his digestion – but no more than that. It's possible it made his stomach more susceptible to wine. But it could not have been fatal to him unless he drained the bottle at one draught – and then he would have dropped dead instantly. Which he obviously did not. So I say it did not kill him – though it would have in the end.' She gave a long, deep sigh. 'But all the same, no doubt I'll be accused, and – since he was after all a senator – sent to a rocky island where I'll slowly starve. All for a man that no one loved alive. But no matter what you choose to do with me, there's one thing I want clear. Whatever happened, it is my fault alone. Tertillius had no part in it at all.'

'Although he might have guessed?' I looked at Tertillius, who was staring dumbly at us, as though – like my poor Rastus – he had lost his tongue.

'This is what you were proposing to put into the wine that you wanted me to give to Hortius?' He sounded truly shocked. 'You said it was something that would enhance the taste.' He shook a disbelieving head. 'I could have murdered Marcus and the duumvir with that – to say nothing of possibly drinking it myself!'

I had been thinking something similar and I saw Marcus pale.

But Fulvia was dismissive. 'It would not have harmed you greatly, I did not have enough, diluted in a whole amphora as it would have been. But I had decided against that anyway. Wine was very likely to be shared and I wanted something only Hortius would take. So when he had his accident, I saw my chance at once. So' – she looked around defiantly – 'aren't you going to accuse me of the crime? Marcus has a slave-cell where I can be put, until you can bring me to the court! Since you can hardly put me in our own!'

There was silence, until Cyrus said, 'That must be your decision, Excellence.' He turned to Marcus, who I knew was listening to all this, though he appeared to be absorbed in overseeing the cleansing of leek sauce from Hortius.

'Perhaps we should consult the duumvir,' my patron sighed. 'He has helped me with such things before. What do you say, pavement-maker? You are good at seeing patterns and how pieces fit.'

'But you cannot ask Libertus to be neutral in this case.' Cyrus was emphatic. 'He was going to marry Fulvia, tonight – I have that on the best authority. Far too soon to be respectable. But he won't condemn her, will he? She is a formidable lady, who would bring a dowry too. Though, duumvir, if you still decide to marry Fulvia, be very careful what you eat and drink.'

'Don't be silly,' Decimus declared. 'He was only going to

do it so he had a wife, whose family had connections with Druscilla's long ago, and so she could apply to his house for potestas. He wanted to impede the marriage between her and Hortius.' He turned to me. 'Well, duumvir, did I not deduce aright? I realized yesterday, at His Excellence's flat, that you were planning that . . .' He looked at Cyrus and let the sentence die.

'You're quite wrong, both of you.' I looked him in the eye. 'It was never my intention to marry Fulvia. I had Hortius's promise, formally acknowledged in front of you, in fact, that he would provide me with any bride I chose. I was going to claim Druscilla Livia, of course!' I heard both brothers gasp in unbelief and saw them look at her, as if she might protest at the brazenness of this. I added, quickly, 'With her agreement, naturally. I was to marry her in the quickest manner possible. She had a marriage contract Marcus wrote for her – which I just had to countersign, then a simple exchange of public vows. Afterwards I'd planned to take her somewhere safe and let her go again.'

'And what about her family in Rome? Would they not hunt you down, anywhere you settled within the Empire?'

'Hortius signed a letter, and you witnessed it, requesting her brother to approve the match.'

Decimus still seemed to find this difficult to understand. 'Her brother? But it went to Tertillius – Hortius sent it, and I witnessed that.'

'To Tertillius, who – by agreement – sent it on to Rome. A written document, not easy to disprove, whatever Hortius said when he returned. But fortunately it does not matter now – and I have no need to take another wife. I have no wish to marry anyone – though of the two, I would certainly prefer the lady Fulvia. Indeed, I had intended to take a poisoned draught with me, and drink it once Druscilla was safe ashore in far Hibernium.' I glimpsed my patron's face. 'Excellence, I did not mention that before – I knew you would dissuade me, if you could, but my intention was to follow Gwellia, leaving Druscilla free to wed again – to someone of her choice. Which she now is, of course.'

'As you always promised, duumvir!' Druscilla raised a tear-stained face – smeared with eye-kohl which had trickled down her cheeks. 'I don't know how you managed it. I should have trusted you. I thought I was going to have to—'

It was my turn to catch a startled breath. 'Are you accusing me? I seem to remember that it was you who said you'd poison him – and had the phial of aconite to do it with?' I intended merely to tease her and rebuke, but I saw the look that crossed her face, and a dreadful possibility occurred to me. 'You were not foolish enough to bring that to the feast?'

'I was going to drink it, if I was betrayed. I very nearly did. But when I realized that Hortius was dead I gave the phial to Glaber and asked him to throw it out.'

TWENTY-NINE

I turned to Glaber who, having, with assistance, moved the corpse – was now engaged in smoothing down the wine-bespattered clothes. The undertakers had not yet arrived. (Not surprising, since both stretcher-bearer slaves and the women who would wash and purify the corpse, had very likely needed to be roused from sleep. Only a celebrity like Hortius – or Marcus Septimus – could guarantee attendance at so late an hour.) Glaber looked at me.

'And did you?' I enquired. 'Throw it all away?'

'I did as I was told.' Glaber straightened up and met my gaze, and sighed. 'Councillors, I will not disguise the truth. The duumvir already knows it, anyway. If that poison had come into my hands while my ex-owner here was still alive, I would cheerfully have put it in his wine and – if suspicion fell on me – have drunk the rest myself. He was not a . . .' He stopped. He had already said too much. Criticizing a previous master – however horrible – can earn a slave a flog-ging, if not something worse. Especially if the former master was a man of influence.

'He was not . . . what?' my patron challenged him.

'A kindly man to his inferiors, when roused – as I think the duumvir Libertus will agree,' Glaber said, with a defiant glance at me. 'Little slave-boys in particular.'

Everyone turned their gaze on me again, but I refused to be deflected onto Rastus now. 'So what did you do with it? The poison phial?' I said. 'If you threw it out unused we should find it on the midden pile, outside. Which, of course, would prove your innocence – and that of Druscilla, incidentally, too. One the slaves perhaps, could light a torch and look?'

Minimus and Kurso, who had been standing at the rear, seemed ready to comply but Marcus signalled that they should remain. 'One of the vintner's men should go,' he said. 'They will know exactly where to look, and if it's there they'll find it in no time at all.'

Glaber looked uneasy, for the first time since his former owner's death. 'The phial will be there and I'm sure it could be found,' he blurted. 'But it will not be proof of anything. At the lady's bidding, I tipped the contents out.'

'Druscilla?' I said sharply.

She flounced and turned her braided head from me. 'I suppose I panicked,' she said sullenly. 'I did not want it said that I had poisoned him – if it was shown that I had brought a draught of aconite, I would have been accused. Just when I might finally have been truly free of him!' She gave me another of her ferocious scowls. 'And if you had not startled me, by asking me outright, no one would have guessed that I'd brought the phial with me. Or that I had such a thing at all. Nobody but you, that is, of course!'

'So why give it to Glaber? It was safe with you – and you could have produced it, full. No suspicion could have fallen on you then – even if I had confronted you!'

'Because he asked for it,' she murmured, with a murderous look at him.

'So, he knew you had it? And had brought it here?'

'I told him earlier.' She leaned back with a sigh. 'It was supposed to be a sort of second shield for me. I spoke to him this morning in Tertillius's house. My maidservant reported that the gossip in the servants' hall was that Glaber had belonged to Hortius once, and that he hated him. I was very worried that your plan would fail – which, if Hortius had not mercifully died, it surely would have done!' She dared to flounce at me.

'Go on.' I sounded dangerous.

Druscilla felt it, too. 'So I called for him and asked him, since he was promised to help out here tonight, whether he would volunteer to serve the wine, and so contrive to poison Hortius for me if anything went wrong. If he refused, I told him, I would bring it anyway and drink the stuff myself.'

'You signalled to Glaber that you had the phial?' I prompted, remembering the gesture I had seen.

'I don't know how you realized that!' she said.

'The evidence of my eyes,' I muttered, although I closed them now, trying to recall a moment after Hortius's death when Glaber had approached her – which he briefly had. There might have been a chance for the phial to be exchanged – though there were many, easier opportunities to do so earlier.

Marcus was frowning doubtfully at me. 'So Libertus, what would you propose we do? We have two people who might have poisoned him, but they both deny it and we have no proof. But I would like this solved. This is not the first unnatural death of a visitor from the capital. I would not care to have it reach the Governor – or even worse, the Emperor himself – that Glevum is dangerous for guests who come from Rome.'

'I suppose, unless the guilty person is produced and charged, there will be endless investigations from the authorities?' Cyrus sounded panicked at the thought.

'Precisely. There will be rumours otherwise. Even claims that there was poison in the wine that I supplied. Or that Tertillius was responsible, since he first ordered it.'

Everyone was now accusing everybody else, in their anxiety to move suspicion from themselves.

'Well, I did not kill him,' Druscilla said again. 'It could have been either of those other councillors. They were reclining next to him when we arrived. And giggling with the poison-taster too – I noticed it when Hortius first had me brought up here. And there's another thing. How could I have possibly foreseen that he was going to have me next to him throughout? I was expecting to sit with Fulvia and the duumvir, until I was called upon to make my vows.'

This was self-evidently true, and Marcus looked at me. But Glaber was speaking – uninvited, too.

'And with your permission, Excellence,' he said, although he did not wait for it before he spoke again, 'the same applies to me. I could not get the poison if she was not up here on the dais – which I did not expect. I did not expect, in fact, to be up here myself – I almost fainted when they assigned me here, so close to Hortius. The plan was only that she would call on me, if the other plan had failed, and she had been forced to marry Hortius – when she would be naturally seated next to him. I was to bring the jug for libation afterwards, and then – while Hortius was busy with invocations to the gods – she would slip the phial to me and I would add the poison to his final – and fatal – cup of wine. But I did none of this, of course. Someone else had killed him, before the need aro—'

He was interrupted by the reappearance of the vintner's slave, who came to stand in front of Marcus with a bow.

'Well,' my patron said, 'did you locate the phial?'

The boy was almost trembling with fear. 'Not one phial, Excellence, but two.' There was a general gasp as he handed them across.

My patron held them up for everyone to see. 'Both of them empty – though different in style.'

Almost by instinct, I touched the purse that dangled from my belt, where I had put my own phial earlier. But, of course, it was no longer there.

Marcus had now put both containers down. He turned to look at me. 'Perhaps Druscilla has been telling us the truth?'

'Of course, I have,' that lady said, with heat. 'The smaller one is mine. The other must belong to someone else. Not that I blame anyone for killing Hortius. He was the most unpleasant person I have ever met – it is a wonder someone did not do it long ago.'

Fulvia placed a warning hand upon her arm. Well-bred women don't express opinions of this kind, especially in a public place and in the company of men – and most of all if she might be accused of killing the person criticized! Druscilla shrugged off the gesture, though it was kindly meant, and for a moment, it gave me cause to think. If Druscilla were a man,

I realized, she might command respect. She had many Roman virtues, including being articulate, fearless, and prepared to die to save herself from a dishonourable fate.

Her next words, though, dispelled my sympathy. 'It could be anyone who killed him. Even feeble old Tertillius. His whole family had a public grievance, after all – and Fulvia admits she thought of poisoning the wine.'

Tertillius was so shocked by this ingratitude that he seemed ready to explode, like a fireship set alight – perhaps because Druscilla had a point. Clearly his household had the knowledge – and the wherewithal – to have poisoned Hortius. And he had been sitting closest to him until we came in.

But Tertillius had an accusation of his own. 'You could say the same of Decimus and Cyrus!' he declared. 'I hear that Hortius insulted them as well – Decimus was telling me about it earlier. Got tired of giving them an audience and sent them both away – refused to take their petition to the Governor, too, when he'd accepted brib— gifts.'

'Or Libertus,' Decimus was anxious that I did not escape. 'He had more cause than any of the rest of us. And he has poison, he just told us so. To "follow Gwellia" I believe he said. He might well have brought some here tonight.'

It was my turn to be shocked, especially as Marcus did not leap to my defence. But before I could find anything to say we were interrupted by a tapping at the outer door, which proved to be the arrival of the undertaker's team. There were at least a dozen, accompanied by the priest of Mercury (bleary-eyed and clearly unimpressed at not having been invited to the feast himself). He'd come, he said, at the vintners' particular request to purify the room, after the removal of the corpse, in order that it could be used again as soon as possible.

There was a lot to do, of course, if the corpse was to be moved and readied for a formal lying-out in state, so that visitors might come and pay respects. And there were elements of ritual that had not been performed, like the threefold calling of Hortius by name, lest his spirit should still be lingering nearby and wish to be invited back. Marcus was prevailed on to perform this hastily.

'The rest we can leave to the undertakers, now, I think,' he said, with evident relief that the incantation had not invoked the ghost. 'They can arrange for mourners to keep up the lament, and take the body to the garrison. You have warned the commandant that it's expected, I suppose?' The supervisor assured him that this had been done, and Marcus turned back to the company. 'Then, perhaps, we should disperse, for now at any rate. There is not a great deal more that we can do, tonight – and our presence will only be a hindrance here. Druscilla will, after all, have to sleep at Tertillius's house again – I will send for her tomorrow. From my villa she can go back to Rome as soon as she desires – unless she wishes to attend the funeral?' He gave me a curious glance. 'Provided, of course, that the duumvir agrees. No doubt he will want to question everyone again?'

I sketched a little bow. 'As your Excellence commands.'

'In that case,' he said, 'I will see you all tomorrow, at my apartment. Shortly before noon would be convenient. Failure to present yourself will be interpreted as an admission of your guilt. Libertus can interrogate you, one by one, and consider all the evidence. It is essential that the murderer is identified, but the duumvir is clever. I've never known him fail. In the meantime, we will take our leave – although Libertus, there's one detail I must discuss with you. I presume that you will return, now, to your flat? Perhaps we could arrange to have some torches lit, and you could walk part-way with me?'

THIRTY

It took a little while for our slaves to find our cloaks and organize the lights. The Valerii brothers were the first to leave, with only the briefest of goodbyes. There was a marked unwillingness to meet each other's gaze – as if we might see the night's events still mirrored there. There is a theory that a murderer will carry such a reflection in his eyes – but I did not see one. I had not expected to.

Tertillius found the litter that he had contracted for, put the ladies in it, and had them borne away, while he and all his slaves – of either sex – walked on behind. That left me and Marcus – and our attendants – in the street alone.

Marcus sent the boys ahead to light the way, then took me by the arm.

'Libertus, my old friend . . .' he said, and stopped, confused.

'You want to tell me something?' I enquired, though this was evident. 'Something about the death of Hortius? Something that might identify the murderer?'

I felt his fingers tighten on my elbow. 'The thing is, my old friend, I saw that second phial. It is identical to one your servant brought to us, containing the strengthening potion for my wife. One of a series that your Gwellia made, I think. And when I saw your face I knew you recognized it, too.'

I felt emotion rising in my throat. 'I do not deny it. It was mine.'

'Libertus . . .' He was very urgent now. 'I have every sympathy. If Hortius had killed Julia, I would have murdered him, I think. But I cannot protect you. There is too much else at stake. And I can't ignore it, as I would like to do. Even if you claim you're baffled – which I'm sure is what you planned, since you would not accuse the innocent – the town will be hounded by Imperial spies and people suspected who were not involved – perhaps including me. Fulvia and Tertillius might well be forced to flee, because of the potion she prepared for Hortius, and Druscilla and Glaber could be arraigned and brought to trial – simply to satisfy the Emperor that something has been done.'

I said nothing, and he pressed the point again. 'There is no proof they did not poison Hortius. She admits she brought a phial of aconite. Decimus and Cyrus will see that story spreads. And I cannot sanction persecution for what they did not do. All that I can do is to delay the search for you. That is why I set tomorrow's gathering for midday. You have already booked a passage on a ship. You were going to take Druscilla – take the trip yourself. By the time we are meeting you will be far away. Let your non-appearance be admission of your guilt. People in Glevum will forgive, and understand – and there will be something to report to Severus.'

I made no answer. I could find no words to speak.

'You are a citizen, a councillor,' he said. 'For you the legal punishment would be exile, anyway. If you remain, I cannot answer for where you might be sent – this way you go to a place you choose yourself, because it is beyond the reach of Roman law. This is no different from what you planned to do. The only changes are those I must applaud; you have not been compelled to have Druscilla as your wife, even for an instant; and – having used the poison to dispose of Hortius – you can no longer kill yourself with it.' He sighed. 'You have done the world a service, duumvir,' he said. 'It is unjust that you should be obliged to flee. But promise me you'll do so?'

I found my voice. 'I suppose I must.'

'Then do so with my blessing, and know this, my friend. I shall miss you very much. Remember you with great affection and respect.'

'Then look after Junio,' I said, more gruffly than I meant. 'See that he does not suffer from his links with me.'

'That much I can promise you,' he replied.

'I fear Hortius's escort. If they called on him . . .'

'Libertus, they were bodyguards, but they were also slaves. His possessions, like his jewels and gold. I'll have them put into a transport and returned to Rome. With the garrison to guard them until that moment comes – though the commandant does not have a high opinion of them, I believe, which may affect their comfort in his care. And here, I think, we've reached the crossroads where our paths diverge. But there can be no unusual farewells. It is important that the servants do not notice anything, *Salve atque vale*, my old friend.'

He grasped both my elbows and squeezed them warmly, once. Then he was gone without another word.

I was never to set eyes on him again.

Hello. My name is Junio. You may have heard of me. I promised my father that I would finish this account.

I saw him briefly at a roadside inn, perhaps a half a moon after he disappeared. I took the ox-cart as he had asked me to, in a smuggled message that he sent.

I did not actually see him come ashore, though it must have been amusing. There is a mooring post not very far away, where ships can sometimes be held against the tide, and a little jetty where locals bring food and furs to trade. But the river is tidal, and the tide was wrong. He had to wade ashore, with water to his thighs. The captain could not bring the vessel closer in. Crewmen carried the baggage and the slaves.

When I saw him he had got his clothing dry. He was dressed in plaid again – a tunic over trews – and he'd disposed of his Roman togas anyway. Dropped them in the river wrapped round a heavy stone, just where the mud was thickest, which is very thick indeed. He took me to the spot, but there was nothing to be seen.

He wanted news of how his flight had been received in town. I told him most of it. There was sympathy, of course. People said he had been crazed with grief. Decimus and Cyrus were telling everyone that they'd known he'd done it all along, and Decimus had even accused him at the time.

Druscilla had decided that she might prefer to stay, and Marcus had been hard put to make her change her mind. Tertillius had proposed that a fountain be installed, once the immediate commotion had died down, 'in tribute to a former duumvir' – no names to be inscribed. (At his expense, but it was rumoured to be the lady Fulvia's idea.) My father was amused, though he was clearly touched as well.

I asked why he had not gone to Hibernia, after all. The ship was going there, he had money in his purse – quite a lot of money – and Hibernia was safe. Anywhere in the Empire he would be at risk, now that a sentence of exile was declared. Anyone who harboured him would be at risk themselves.

'Not here among the Salurians,' he said. 'They've never

*forgotten their King Caractacus, and how he refused to bow
to Rome. There are still rebels here. Pleased to help a man
who had killed a senator. Besides, only an idiot would
choose to stay within the Empire if he could escape. Everyone
knows that. Therefore they will not be looking for me here.
They think I've travelled north. I shall go the other way. The
Roman's have another frontier there – and I was born
the other side of it. There will be members of my family still
alive – I had much younger cousins. They will be
chieftains now. If I arrive there safely, I will let you know.'*

'And if you're found?' I said.

'Who will be looking for an aged Celtic peasant in a cart?
Only Marcus, in a moon or so, when it occurs to him. If he
asks you, you can tell him what you know. He will not betray
me, I am sure of that. Best not to confide in Cilla and the
children though. The loss of them, and you, is the hardest
thing to bear. But now it is getting time for me to move.'

'But, Father,' I protested. 'It is a long journey. It might take
many moons. I know that you have money, but how will you
survive?'

'I could make mosaics, if I'm far away from here. I used to
be quite good at that.' He tried to smile but failed. 'And I have
Kurso and Minimus with me – I could not leave them
behind. They have served me and Gwellia faithfully. Even this
moment they have loaded up the cart, and as you say, it is
not safe to stay. Take care of the workshop. Think of me
sometimes.'

My heart was breaking. So, I think, was his. 'Father,' I said,
'you cannot go like this. You have to tell me first. You didn't
murder Hortius – I know you far too well. You wouldn't do
that. I don't believe you did.'

He looked at me slowly. 'Naturally not.'

'But you know who did?'

'Of course. And that is why I knew I had to leave. And that,
dear Junio, is all that I can say.' He turned away and climbed
onto the cart.

It was Minimus who came sidling up to me. 'Surely you
understand it, master Junio?'

I stared at him. 'He's protecting someone, I can see. It can't *be me, I wasn't there at all. Does he think that Marcus murdered Hortius?'*

The slave-boy shook his head. 'On the contrary, he knows that Kurso did. Although I helped, of course. I spotted that the master had put the poison in his purse so we took it from him while helping him to dress – we hoped to save his life. We knew that he was planning to drink it later on. But then Kurso had a plan. He loved the mistress very much indeed – and the master even more. So when he was instructed to assist with bringing platters and refilling jugs he saw his chance. He put it in the water jug that I was carrying, and I poured it into Hortius's goblet and mixed it in the wine. He was very drunk in any case, and I let him knock the pitcher down, so that it spilt and no one else could ask for any more. Kurso brought a new jug and I carried on. We threw the phial away. A few moments later Hortius was dead. If Druscilla had not had a phial of poison too, it is unlikely anybody would have looked for it. But as it was . . .' He paused. 'We volunteered to go and search ourselves – we would not have brought our phial back in, of course – but we were overruled.'

'And your master knew what you had done?'

'I think he worked it out. But imagine what would happen to a slave, if it was discovered. The punishment would be excruciating death. And the master knew that too. And now he is waiting for me – he will be displeased. Give my regards to Tenuis – but please, do not explain. He would wish he was with us, even more – which I can understand.' His voice broke, and there was a little pause before he said, 'Your father has sacrificed his whole life here in Glevum, to protect his slaves. Was there ever a better master in the world?'

And perhaps there wasn't, I thought, as I watched them draw away. An aged Celtic peasant and pair of cheeky slaves, in an oxcart, like a thousand others on the road.

I watched them out of sight and then set off myself, aiming for the nearest marketplace, where perhaps I could find a passing cart to take me home. A long walk. Even when there was not a mist before your eyes.